M000309148

Europe

1997

HOSTELLING INTERNATIONAL

Hostelling International is the brand name of the International Youth Hostel Federation, the organization that represents over sixty member Associations, worldwide.

Look for the blue triangle symbol for budget accommodation you can trust.

The information in this Guide has been supplied by the national Associations of each country represented. Every effort has been made to ensure that it is correct and Hostelling International can accept no responsibility for any inaccuracies or for changes subsequent to publication.

© Hostelling International 1996

ISBN 0 901496 48 0

CONTENTS

Page/Seite/Página

Introduction, Travel Checklist (English) 3
Introduction, Quelques Conseils (Français) 12
Einführung, Reise-Checkliste (Deutsch) 20
Introducción, Lista de Viaje (Español) 30
Africa, America, Asia and Pacific addresses 38
Embassy addresses 40

HOSTEL INFORMATION

Page/Seite/Página

Austria 45
Belgium 59
Croatia 71
Cyprus 81
Czech Republic 91
Denmark 99
Egypt 117
England & Wales 125
Finland 157
France 183
Germany 209
Greece 275
Hungary 283
Iceland 295
Ireland (Northern) 303
Ireland (Republic of) 313
Israel 325
Italy 337
Liechtenstein ☞ Switzerland
Luxembourg 351
Netherlands 359
Norway 373
Poland 391
Portugal 407

Page/Seite/Página

Scotland 419
Slovenia 435
Spain 439
Sweden 459
Switzerland 491
Yugoslavia (Federal Republic of) .. 505

Associate Organizations/
   Accredited Agents 515
Associate Organization Addresses . 516
Accredited Agent Addresses 517
Estonia 518
Lithuania 519
Macedonia (former Yugoslav
   Republic of) 519
Malta 520
Russia 520

Other Organizations

International Student Travel
Confederation (ISTC) 522
Federation of International Youth
Travel Organisations (FIYTO) 523

INTRODUCTION

A good night's sleep in friendly surroundings at an affordable price.

This Guide offers you more choice of reliable, budget accommodation than any other.

Choose from around 5,000 hostels in over 60 countries, providing more than 31 million overnight stays a year. This Guide alone gives you details of around 2,000 throughout Africa, the Americas, Asia and the Pacific.

And you can book virtually everywhere in advance. For the key locations - the peak tourist centres around the world - you can now reserve your accommodation up to six months ahead with one phone call by using IBN, our computerized International Booking Network. IBN already covers over 300 destinations, including London, Paris, Rome, Amsterdam, Brussels, Tokyo, New York, Washington, Los Angeles, Melbourne, Sydney, Toronto, Vancouver and Auckland, and more are being added every month.

Wherever you travel, Hostelling International offers you the company of like-minded people, a friendly welcome and affordable accommodation all over the world.

It means that on five continents, you can be sure of a good night's sleep in friendly surroundings at an affordable price - as little as US$6.00 a night in Bali for example - and there are many more savings as well.

Best of all, of course, you know what to expect.

No age limit

Despite their name, Youth Hostels are open to people of virtually all ages (with a few exceptions due to local legislation). Anyone under 14 should be with an adult and some hostels offer family rooms. Under fives can sometimes be accommodated by special arrangement. Most hostels accept group bookings too.

How you can stay at Youth Hostels - and travel cheaper

To stay at Youth Hostels anywhere in the world - and to qualify for special concessions including lower cost travel - all you have to do is become a member of the Youth Hostel Association in the country where you live. If you do not have a membership card you can purchase a Hostelling International Card or buy individual 'welcome' stamps when you spend a night in a hostel.

You can obtain your membership card from the YHA of the country where you live or a Hostelling International Card at any hostel outside your own country.

Most hostels offer a comprehensive range of local discounts to members and you can take advantage of the major travel savings listed at the end of each national section in this Guide.

INTRODUCTION

The facilities you enjoy

Large city hostels are likely to be open 24 hours a day. Smaller hostels, in the countryside, may have shorter opening hours and most hostels are open all year round. Each Guide entry will tell you if the hostel is closed at any time.

You are normally able to check-in (or out) between 0700hrs and 1000hrs and 1700hrs and 2230hrs at all hostels. The entries in the Guide will show you any variations. Remember, you can use the computerized advance booking system (IBN) to guarantee you a bed whatever time you arrive.

Sleeping accommodation (usually in bunk beds) will range from rooms sleeping two to four people up to rooms with 20 bunks, though these are becoming much rarer. Bedding is provided but you do need to bring or hire your sheets and pillowcases or a sheet sleeping bag in some hostels.

Many hostels have self-catering facilities and most provide meals, the individual entries will tell you what is available.

Local customs and practices obviously vary around the world, so check the introductory section for each country as well as the entry for each hostel.

You will find all the various facilities and prices are shown alongside each listing in this Guide so that you will know what is available before you arrive.

Book ahead through IBN

Whether you want to plan a full tour or just be sure of a place to rest your head on the first night, our computerized *international booking network* (IBN) offers you a simple and cheap advance booking solution for more than 300 key locations throughout the world for a small fee.

Using IBN means you can pay for reservations in the local currency of where you make the booking, avoiding bank or exchange charges - and secure your accommodation in advance.

You can reserve accommodation from all the hostels shown with the IBN symbol in this Guide (see entires in blue print), call in to or contact any of the IBN booking centres listed in this Guide.

CREDIT CARD BOOKINGS

Australia	02 9261 1111
England	0171 836 1036
New Zealand	09 379 4224
Northern Ireland	01232 324733
Republic of Ireland	01 301766
Scotland	0141 332 3004
USA	0202 783 6161

Credit card bookings are standard for telephone reservations made to any of these IBN centres.

Other ways to book

Of course, you *can* turn up at a hostel without a reservation but it is best to book ahead. Families who want the use of a family room and groups should *always* book in advance.

You can also book ahead by fax or by letter enclosing an international postal reply coupon (available from most Post Offices) and a self-addressed envelope.

One thing to remember, if you book *without paying a deposit*, you need to arrive at the hostel and claim your reservation by 1800hrs, unless a different time is agreed.

However you book, you will be welcome in the world of international youth hostelling, meeting new people, making new friends from all over the world, exchanging ideas and broadening your experience of other cultures.

We know you will enjoy it. You will certainly be able to afford it. And we look forward to meeting you.

Assured Standards

Hostelling International recognizes that consistent quality and service is important to budget travellers. That is why we are introducing our new Assured Standards Scheme, to ensure that in these important areas, you can rely on a consistent level of services and facilities wherever you stay in our hostels.

By 1999 all our hostels will offer the basic assurance of standards - and many will continue to offer a much higher standard.

Warm welcome with comfort, cleanliness, security and privacy

Hostel Associations in some 14 countries already offer these assured standards, the remainder are working towards joining the scheme as soon as possible. Standards will be monitored by Hostelling International and you, the user. If you are dissatisfied, let us know and we assure you that we will investigate and, where necessary, ensure the appropriate action is taken. There are comment forms within this guide to help you contact us.

For many people the essence of hostelling is remote, unusual locations and very special buildings. We must admit it is hard to apply the same standards in the middle of a rain forest or in a remote shepherds hut! So we do make some exceptions for small hostels and those with simple facilities, you may find limited staffing and shorter opening hours (especially inside the Arctic circle!). This type of hostel is clearly indicated in the detailed entries. However, the Assured Standards apply at these hostels in all other respects.

Sometimes we 'borrow' accommodation from other organizations, to make sure you can find a bed for the night where there are no Hostelling International hostels, you will find this type of hostel listed at the back of each country and they may not all meet our standards

What do Assured Standards at hostels mean to you?

Welcome

Hostels are open to everyone, irrespective of age, sex, culture, race or religion. If you do not already have the advantage of being a member, you will be able to take out full or short term membership at the hostel.

You will be able to reserve a bed in advance, for as long as it is available and receive a prompt answer to any enquiries. Hostels will keep to at least the core opening times quoted on page 4, and if not open 24 hours, stay open long enough for you to enjoy the social life the area has to offer! If the hostel is closed for a period during the day, you will have access to shelter, a WC and storage, for your luggage.

INTRODUCTION

Above all, welcoming you will be a priority for the hostel staff and they will be committed to providing the support and information you need to get the most out of your stay.

Comfort

You can expect a good, comfortable night's sleep, sufficient showers, WCs and washing facilities plus a good supply of hot water!

Where it is not included in the overnight charge, freshly laundered bed linen will be available for hire if you need it.

Although meals are generally available, where only self catering is provided, you will normally be able to buy basic food supplies in the hostel or close by. We provide food storage, preparation and cooking and washing up areas for you to use.

Cleanliness

Wherever you travel you can expect the highest standards of cleanliness and hygiene from Hostelling International.

Security

Hostel staff will make every endeavour to ensure your personal security, and the security of your possessions during your stay. They will give you advice about the neighbourhood too. In many locations you can use a locker with a key for your luggage and valuables.

Privacy

Although you may find yourself sharing a room with other hostellers of the same sex, (unless you have reserved a private or family room) the Assured Standards Scheme promises privacy when you need it - especially in showers, washing areas and toilets - and always between the sexes.

Environmental Charter

In addition to these Assured Standards, hostels will also adhere to the IYHF Charter, which lays down the criteria for the consumption and conservation of resources, waste disposal and recycling, nature conservation and the provision of environmental education.

Assured Standards in this guide are offered by Australia, New Zealand and the United States of America.

Read on for your Travel Check-list

INTRODUCTION

Travel Check-List

You already know some of this, but, on the basis that the experienced traveller leaves nothing to chance, we thought you would appreciate these instant reminders to run through before every trip *and* while you are away.

1 **Money**

- Use travellers' cheques or credit cards for maximum peace of mind. Note the numbers and keep them separately.

- Carry the minimum amount of actual cash.

- Spread your cash, travellers' cheques, credit cards, passport, tickets and YHA card around your person and your luggage so that if you *do* get robbed or lose some luggage you don't lose everything.

- *REMEMBER,* in an increasing number of countries you will need a Personal Identification Number (PIN) to be able to use some credit cards in both Youth Hostels and other places.

- If the worst comes to the worst, or if you simply run out of cash, there are services like Western Union who can help you get money from home in minutes (see page 9).

2 **Passports, Visas**

- Check that your passport will not expire before you return. Some countries require your passport to be valid for 6 months after your arrival.

- **Check what individual documents you might need for different countries and apply well ahead of time - several weeks' notice might be required, especially in the summer.**

3 **Insurance**

- Take out travel insurance. Your Youth Hostel Association's Travel Section or travel agent will advise you.

4 **Health**

- Remember, medical treatment can be costly in many countries and you should insure for it. Also, some countries have reciprocal arrangements on medical costs, so check with your local Health Authority/Social Services/ Welfare Office and obtain the necessary forms before you set off.

- Vaccinations are required for some of the countries listed in this Guide. Check with your doctor 6-8 weeks before you travel because some vaccinations take time to become effective.

Got a cash crisis? Don't panic. With Western Union, money is transferred to you in minutes. Easy-peasy. Phone someone at home who can deposit the money you need at their nearest Western Union office. Minutes later you can collect the cash wherever you are.

WESTERN UNION | MONEY TRANSFER™

The fastest way to send money worldwide.

Austria 0660 8066* Canada 1800 235 0000 France Consult Minitel Germany (069) 2648 201 Greece (01) 927 1010
Ireland 1800 395 395* Italy 1670 16840,* 01670 13839 Netherlands 06 0566* Russia 095 119 8250 Spain 900 633 633*
Sweden 020 741 742* Switzerland 0512 22 3358 UK 0800 833 833* USA 1800 325 6000 *Toll free telephone

5 Theft

- If you have any belongings stolen while you are in a Youth Hostel, notify the hostel manager *immediately*. If your belongings are not recovered, get the hostel manager to confirm the details on headed paper and to stamp, date and sign it. Notify the police and obtain a typed report from them. Many insurance companies will not pay out unless they have this support for your claim.

6 Telephoning from abroad

- When you phone another country you need to dial the International Code + Country Code + Area Code + Number.

For example, if you were dialing from Hong Kong to Paris you would dial:

001	+	33	+	1	+	the
International		Country		Area		number
code		code		code		you
				Paris		want

You will find the relevant International Code in each Association entry in this Guide, plus the Country Code and some of the main Area Codes for that country.

Remember, when you are dialing *internationally* you may need to omit the '0' or '9' at the start of the area code. Remember, too, that you might have to wait up to a minute for the connection to be made, **AND** ringing and engaged tones vary from country to country.

7 Time Zones

- If you have ever had a 04.00hrs phone call from someone abroad, you will know the importance of remembering time differences between countries.

The basic rule is 1 hour for every 15° of longitude. The further west you are, the earlier it is, the further east you are the later it is.

This chart shows the approximate times round the world compared with Greenwich Mean Time.

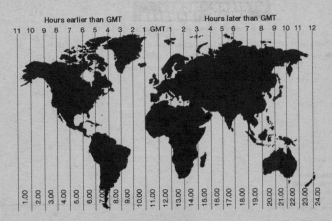

INTRODUCTION

Une bonne nuit de sommeil dans un milieu accueillant à des prix abordables.

Ce guide vous offre un plus grand choix d'hébergements fiables et économiques que n'importe quel autre guide.

Faites votre choix parmi les quelques 5 000 auberges réparties dans plus de 60 pays qui vous proposent plus de 31 millions de nuitées par an. Ce guide-ci vous renseignera sur environ 2 500 auberges en Europe.

Vous pouvez également réserver pratiquement partout à l'avance. Pour les destinations-clés - les centres touristiques les plus visités dans le monde - il vous est possible maintenant de réserver votre hébergement jusqu'à six mois à l'avance avec un seul coup de téléphone en utilisant l'IBN (International Booking Network), notre réseau international de réservation. IBN couvre déjà plus de 300 destinations dont Londres, Paris, Rome, Amsterdam, Bruxelles, Tokyo, New York, Washington, Los Angeles, Melbourne, Sydney, Toronto, Vancouver et Auckland et d'autres destinations viennent s'ajouter à la liste tous les mois.

Où que vous voyagiez, Hostelling International vous offre la compagnie de gens qui partagent vos goûts, un accueil chaleureux et un hébergement à un prix raisonnable partout dans le monde.

Cela veut dire que sur les 5 continents, vous pouvez être sûr que vous passerez une bonne nuit de sommeil dans un milieu accueillant à un prix abordable - à partir de 8.00 $US à Athènes, par exemple - tout en profitant de nombreuses remises et économies de toutes sortes.

Et bien sûr et surtout, vous savez à quoi vous attendre.

Pour les jeunes de tous les âges!

Malgré leur nom, la plupart des auberges de jeunesse accueillent les voyageurs de tous les âges (à part quelques exceptions dûes à la legislation locale). Les moins de 14 ans doivent être accompagnés d'un adulte et de nombreuses auberges sont équipées de chambres familiales. Les moins de 5 ans peuvent parfois être hébergés par arrangement spécial. La plupart des auberges acceptent aussi les réservations de groupes.

INTRODUCTION

Comment séjourner dans une auberge de jeunesse - et voyager à prix réduit

Pour séjourner dans des auberges partout dans le monde - et avoir droit à des concessions spéciales, y compris des voyages à prix réduits - il vous suffit de devenir membre de l'Association des Auberges de Jeunesse du pays où vous habitez. Si vous ne possédez pas de carte d'adhérent, vous pouvez vous procurer une carte Hostelling International ou bien acheter des 'Timbres de Bienvenue' quand vous passez une nuit dans une auberge de jeunesse.

Vous pouvez obtenir votre carte d'adhérent à l'Association des Auberges de Jeunesse de votre pays de résidence et la carte Hostelling International à n'importe quelle auberge en dehors de votre propre pays.

De nombreuses auberges offrent aux adhérents toute une gamme de réductions régionales, et vous pourrez profiter d'offres spéciales pour vos voyages. Vous les trouverez dans les sections consacrées aux divers pays mentionnés dans ce Guide.

Les services qui vous sont offerts

Les grandes auberges situées dans les grands centres sont ouvertes 24 heures sur 24, alors que d'autres, plus petites et situées à la campagne, pourront être ouvertes moins longtemps. La plupart d'entres elles sont ouvertes toute l'année. Vous trouverez dans ce guide les dates d'ouverture de chaque auberge.

En principe, vous devriez pouvoir arriver entre 7h et 10h, et 17h et 22h30 dans toutes les auberges. Toute exception à cette règle sera indiquée dans le paragraphe consacré à chaque auberge. N'oubliez pas que vous pouvez utiliser le système informatisé de réservations à l'avance, IBN, pour être sûr d'avoir un lit quelle que soit votre heure d'arrivée.

Les types d'hébergement varient et peuvent comprendre des chambres à un ou deux lits superposés ou des dortoirs de 20 lits, entre autres, mais ces derniers sont en voie de disparition. La literie est en principe fournie, mais il vous faudra apporter ou louer des draps et des taies d'oreiller ou un sac de couchage-drap.

Beaucoup d'auberges sont équipées de cuisines pour les voyageurs et bon nombre d'entre elles servent également des repas. Ce guide vous indiquera ce qui est disponible dans chaque auberge.

Les coutumes et usages locaux varient bien entendu de par le monde; il est donc bon de consulter l'introduction sur chaque pays ainsi que les renseignements concernant chaque auberge.

Les services offerts et les prix sont indiqués dans l'introduction de chaque pays ou dans les paragraphes concernant chaque auberge pour que vous sachiez toujours à quoi vous attendre avant votre arrivée.

INTRODUCTION

Réservez à l'avance avec IBN

Que vous vouliez organiser un circuit complet ou simplement vous assurer d'un endroit où reposer votre tête la première nuit, notre Réseau informatisé International de Réservation (IBN) vous offre une solution simple et économique pour réserver à l'avance et à peu de frais dans plus de 300 sites-clés répartis à travers le monde.

IBN, c'est d'abord la possibilité de régler vos réservations dans la devise du pays où vous vous trouvez au moment de la réservation et donc d'éviter les commissions bancaires et de perdre sur le change. C'est aussi un moyen de vous garantir un hébergement à l'avance.

Vous pouvez réserver des nuitées dans toutes les auberges marquées du symbole IBN (cf paragraphes en bleu clair), vous présenter ou contacter n'importe lequel des centres de réservation mentionnés dans ce guide.

Autres méthodes de réservation

Bien sûr, vous *pouvez* arriver à l'auberge sans réservation mais il est préférable de réserver à l'avance. Les familles qui souhaitent séjourner dans une chambre familiale et les groupes doivent *toujours* réserver à l'avance.

Vous pouvez également réserver par lettre, en joignant un coupon-réponse international (que vous trouverez dans les bureaux de poste) ainsi qu'une enveloppe à vos nom et adresse.

N'oubliez pas cependant que si vous réservez *sans verser d'arrhes* vous devrez arriver à l'auberge et confirmer votre réservation avant 18h, à moins de vous être arrangé avec l'auberge pour arriver à une heure différente.

Quelle que soit votre méthode de réservation, vous serez le bienvenu dans le monde des auberges de jeunesse internationales; vous rencontrerez des gens, vous vous ferez de nouveaux amis des quatre coins du monde avec lesquels vous échangerez vos idées, élargissant ainsi votre expérience d'autres cultures.

Nous savons que vous vous plairez chez nous, et que vous pourrez certainement vous le permettre. Nous serons très heureux de vous rencontrer.

INTRODUCTION

Normes Garanties

Hostelling International reconnaît qu'une qualité et un service constants importent beaucoup aux gens qui voyagent sur un petit budget. C'est pour cette raison que nous introduisons un nouveau Plan pour la Garantie des Normes en auberges pour faire en sorte que, dans ces importants domaines, vous puissiez compter sur un niveau constant de qualité dans les prestations et installations de chacune de nos auberges.

D'ici à 1999, **toutes** nos auberges offriront une garantie de normes minimales même si beaucoup d'entre elles continueront d'offrir des normes bien supérieures.

Accueil chaleureux dans le confort, la propreté, la sécurité et l'intimité

Les Associations d'auberges de jeunesse de quelques 14 pays offrent déjà ces normes minimales tandis que les autres s'efforceront de s'y conformer le plus vite possible. Ces normes seront contrôlées par Hostelling International et par vous, les utilisateurs. Si vous n'êtes pas satisfaits, faites-le nous savoir et nous vous promettons que nous examinerons le problème en question et si le cas l'exige, nous nous engageons à prendre les mesures appropriées. Ce guide contient des formulaires spéciaux pour vous aider à nous contacter à ce sujet.

Pour beaucoup de gens, ce qui caractérise l'ajisme ce sont des endroits perdus, isolés et inhabituels et des bâtiments très spéciaux. Nous devons admettre qu'il nous est difficile d'appliquer les mêmes normes au milieu de la forêt tropicale ou dans une cabane de berger isolée! C'est pourquoi, nous avons fait une exception de quelques petites auberges plus simplement équipées où le personnel ainsi que les périodes d'ouverture peuvent être limités (surtout dans le cercle Artique!). Toutes les auberges appartenant à cette catégorie sont clairement indiquées dans ce guide. Cependant, tous les autres aspects des Normes Garanties s'appliquent également à ces auberges.

Parfois il nous arrive d'"emprunter' les hébergements d'autres organisations pour que vous puissiez trouver un lit pour la nuit là où il n'y a pas d'auberge Hostelling International. Vous trouverez la liste de ce type d'auberge au dos de chaque pays et il se peut qu'elles ne se conforment pas toutes à nos normes.

Que signifient les Normes Garanties pour vous?

Accueil

Les auberges sont ouvertes à tous quels que soient votre age, sexe, culture, race ou religion. Si vous n'avez pas déjà l'avantage d'être membre, vous aurez la possibilité de prendre une adhésion complète ou partielle à l'auberge.

INTRODUCTION

Vous aurez la possibilité de réserver un lit à l'avance - à partir du moment où il est disponible - et de recevoir une réponse rapide à toutes vos questions. Les auberges respecteront au moins les heures d'ouverture minimales indiquées à la page 13, et si elles ne sont pas ouvertes 24 heures sur 24, resteront ouvertes suffisamment longtemps pour que vous puissiez sortir et profiter des animations que la région a à vous offrir! Si l'auberge est fermée pendant un certain temps dans la journée, vous aurez accès à un abri, à des toilettes et à un endroit où garder vos bagages.

Mais surtout, vous accueillir sera la priorité du personnel de l'auberge et il s'engagera à vous fournir l'aide et l'information dont vous aurez besoin pour tirer un maximum de votre séjour.

Confort

Vous pouvez compter passer une bonne nuit de sommeil confortablement et trouver un nombre suffisant de douches et de sanitaires ainsi qu'une bonne réserve d'eau chaude!

Là où ce n'est pas compris dans le prix de la nuitée, il vous sera possible de louer des draps frais et blanchis, si vous en avez besoin.

Bien qu'elles servent en général des repas, certaines auberges peuvent n'être aménagées que d'une cuisine individuelle. Dans ces cas-là, vous devriez être en mesure d'acheter des denrées de base, soit à l'auberge, soit à proximité. Nous mettons à votre disposition un endroit de stockage des denrées, une surface de préparation et de cuisson et un évier pour la vaisselle.

Propreté

Où que vous alliez, vous êtes en droit d'attendre des auberges et de leur personnel un haut degré de propreté et d'hygiène.

Sécurité

Le personnel des auberges fera tout son possible pour garantir votre sécurité personnelle et celles de vos biens pendant votre séjour. Dans de nombreuses auberges, des consignes qui ferment à clé seront à votre disposition pour y déposer bagages et objets de valeur.

Intimité, vie privée

Même si vous vous trouvez dans la même chambre que d'autres ajistes de même sexe, (à moins d'avoir réservé une chambre privée ou familiale), le Plan pour la Garantie des Normes vous promet votre intimité là où vous en avez besoin - spécialement dans les douches, salles de bain et toilettes - et dans tous les cas, entre les sexes.

INTRODUCTION

Charte de l'environnement

Outre ces Normes Garanties, les auberges s'engagent à adhérer à la Charte de l'IYHF qui dicte les critères de consommation et de préservation des ressources, de destruction des ordures ménagères et de recyclage, de défense de l'environnement et prévoit également que les auberges devront jouer un rôle dans l'éducation écologique.

Les Normes Garanties dans ce guide vous sont offertes par L'Autriche, La Belgique, Le Danemark, L'Angleterre et Le Pays de Galles, Israël, Les Pays Bas, L'Irlande du Nord, L'Ecosse, La Suède et La Suisse.

Voir les conseils de voyage ci-après.

INTRODUCTION

Quelques Conseils

Vous ne serez pas sans ignorer certains de ces conseils, mais étant donné que le voyageur expérimenté ne laisse rien au hasard, nous avons pensé que vous trouveriez ces quelques détails utiles avant votre départ *et* pendant votre voyage.

1 Argent

- Pour plus de sûreté, utilisez des chèques de voyage ou des cartes de crédit. Prenez note des numéros et gardez-les séparément.

- Gardez sur vous le minimum d'argent liquide.

- Répartissez votre argent, vos chèques de voyage, vos cartes de crédit, votre passeport, vos billets et votre carte YHA en plusieurs endroits sur votre personne et dans vos bagages de façon à ce que, si vous *êtes* agressé ou si vous perdez des bagages, vous ne perdiez pas tout.

- N'oubliez pas que dans de plus en plus de pays, il vous faudra un Numéro Personnel d'Identification (PINCODE) pour vous permettre d'utiliser certaines cartes de crédit dans les auberges de jeunesse et ailleurs.

- Si le pire devait vous arriver ou si vous êtes tout simplement à court d'argent, il existe des services comme Western Union qui pourront vous aider à tranférer de l'argent depuis chez vous en quelques minutes (voir page 9).

2 Passeports, visas

- Assurez-vous que votre passeport n'expirera pas avant votre retour. Certains pays exigent que les passeports soient valides 6 mois après l'arrivée des voyageurs.

- Renseignez-vous sur les documents dont vous aurez besoin pour divers pays et faites-en la demande le plus tôt possible - il faudra peut-être vous y prendre plusieurs semaines à l'avance, surtout en été.

3 Assurance

- Souscrivez à une police d'assurance. Le service voyages de votre Association des auberges de jeunesse ou votre agent de voyage vous conseilleront.

4 Soins médicaux

- Souvenez-vous que les soins médicaux peuvent revenir cher dans beaucoup de pays; il est donc prudent de vous assurer. D'autre part, certains pays ont conclu des accords réciproques en ce qui concerne les frais médicaux; vérifiez auprès de votre bureau de sécurité sociale et procurez-vous les formulaires nécessaires avant votre départ.

- Des vaccinations sont requises pour certains des pays indiqués dans ce guide. Parlez-en à votre médecin 6 à 8 semaines avant votre départ, certains vaccins ne devenant efficaces qu'au bout d'un certain temps.

INTRODUCTION

5 Vols

- Si vous constatez que certaines de vos affaires ont été volées pendant un séjour dans une auberge, informez-en le gérant *immédiatement*. Si elles ne sont pas retrouvées, faites confirmer les détails par le gérant sur papier à en-tête, avec date, signature et cachet. Avertissez la police et obtenez d'elle un rapport dactylographié. De nombreuses compagnies d'assurance refuseront de payer si vous ne pouvez leur soumettre cette preuve avec votre revendication.

6 Pour téléphoner de l'étranger

- Lorsque vous téléphonez dans un autre pays, il vous faudra composer l'indicatif international suivi de l'indicatif du pays et de l'indicatif régional avant le numéro que vous appelez.

Par exemple, pour téléphoner de Hong Kong à Paris, vous composerez les:

001	+	33	+	1	+	le
Indicatif		Indicatif		Indicatif		numéro
International		du Pays		de		que vous
				Paris		voulez

Vous trouverez l'indicatif international approprié dans les renseignements sur chaque Association, plus l'indicatif du pays et certains des indicatifs régionaux principaux de ce pays.

N'oubliez pas, lorsque vous téléphonez *à l'étranger,* qu'il vous faudra peut-être omettre le '0' ou le '9' au début de l'indicatif régional. N'oubliez pas non plus que vous aurez peut-être à attendre jusqu'à une minute avant d'obtenir votre communication, **ET** que les sonneries et les tonalités occupé varient de pays en pays.

7 Fuseaux horaires

- Si quelqu'un vous a déjà appelé au téléphone de l'étranger à 4h du matin, vous saurez combien il importe de se souvenir des différences horaires entre les pays.

En règle générale, on compte une heure pour 15° de longitude. Plus vous êtes à l'ouest, plus il est tôt, plus vous êtes à l'est, plus il est tard.

Cette carte indique les heures approximatives dans le monde par rapport à l'heure de Greenwich.

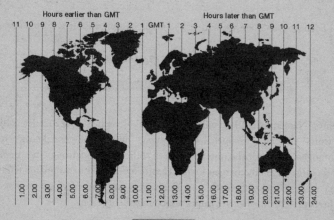

EINFÜHRUNG

Eine ruhige Übernachtung in angenehmer Umgebung zu einem vernünftigen Preis.

Dieser Jugendherbergsführer bietet Ihnen mehr Auswahl an verläßlichen, Ihrem Budget angemessenen Übernachtungsmöglichkeiten als irgendein anderer Reiseführer.

Wählen Sie aus ungefähr 5,000 Jugendherbergen in über 60 Ländern mit mehr als 31 Millionen Übernachtungen jährlich. Allein dieser Jugendherbergsführer bietet Ihnen Einzelheiten über mehr als 2,500 Jugendherbergen in ganz Europa.

Und sie können buchstäblich überall im voraus buchen. An den Hauptstandorten - in den Hauptzentren des Tourismus in der ganzen Welt - können Sie jetzt Ihre Übernachtungen über IBN, unser computergesteurtes internationales Buchungsnetz, sechs Monate im voraus mit einem Telefonanruf reservieren. IBN erfaßt bereits mehr als 300 Zielorte wie London, Paris, Rom, Amsterdam, München, Brüssel, Tokio und New York, Washington, Los Angeles, Melbourne, Sydney, Toronto, Vancouver und Auckland, und jeden Monat kommen weitere dazu.

Wohin auch immer Sie reisen, Hostelling International bietet Ihnen die Gesellschaft gleichgesinnter Menschen, eine freundliche Aufnahme und preiswerte Unterkünfte auf der ganzen Welt.

Sie können also sicher sein einen gesunden Nachtschlaf in freundlicher Umgebung zu günstigen Preisen - so günstig wie etwa US$8.00 pro Nacht beispielsweise in Athen in fünf Kontinenten zu finden, und es gibt darüber hinaus eine Menge weiterer Einsparungen.

Und das Schönste vor allem ist natürlich, daß Sie wissen, was Sie erwarten können.

Keine Altersbegrenzung

Trotz ihres Namens sind Jugendherbergen für Menschen nahezu aller Altersstufen offen (mit einigen wenigen Ausnahmen aufgrund gesetzlicher regionaler Bestimmungen). Jugendliche unter 14 Jahren sollten in Begleitung eines Erwachsenen sein, und einige Jugendherbergen bieten Familienräume. Unterkunft für Kinder unter 5 Jahren steht manchmal durch eine Sonderregelung zur Verfügung. Die meisten Jugendherbergen nehmen auch Gruppenbuchungen entgegen.

EINFÜHRUNG

Wie Sie sich in Jugendherbergen aufhalten - und billiger reisen können

Um in einer Jugendherberge an irgendeinem Ort der Welt zu übernachten und um Vergünstigungen zu erhalten, so daß Sie billig reisen können, müssen Sie nur Mitglied des Jugendherbergsverbandes in dem Land, in dem Sie wohnen, werden. Wenn Sie keine Mitgliedskarte haben, können Sie eine internationale Jugendherbergskarte erwerben oder einzelne Willkommen-Marken für die Übernachtungen kaufen, die Sie in einer Jugendherberge verbringen.

Ihre Mitgliedskarte können Sie vom Jugendherbergsverband des Landes, in dem Sie wohnen, erhalten oder eine Karte des internationalen Jugendherbergsverbandes in jeder Jugendherberge außerhalb Ihres Landes erwerben.

Die meisten Jugendherbergen bieten Mitgliedern eine große Auswahl von örtlichen Vergünstigungen, und Sie können die meisten der wichtigsten Reisevergünstigungen in Anspruch nehmen, die am Ende jedes Abschnittes über einzelne Länder in diesem Herbergsführer aufgelistet sind.

Einrichtungen, die Sie erfreuen

Jugendherbergen in großen Städten sind oft 24 Stunden täglich geöffnet. Kleinere Jugendherbergen auf dem Lande haben kürzere Öffnungszeiten, und die meisten Jugendherbergen haben das ganze Jahr über geöffnet. In jeder Eintragung des Jugendherbergsführers finden Sie einen Hinweis, ob die Jugendherberge irgendwann im Laufe des Jahres geschlossen ist.

Normalerweise können Sie sich in allen Jugendherbergen zwischen 07.00 Uhr und 10.00 Uhr und 17.00 Uhr und 22.30 Uhr an- oder abmelden. Abweichungen davon sind im Jugendherbergsführer jeweils angemerkt. Denken Sie daran, daß Sie das computergestützte Vorausbuchungssystem (IBN) benutzen können, damit für jeden beliebigen Zeitpunkt Ihrer Ankunft ein Bett für Sie reserviert ist.

Schlafgelegenheiten (im allgemeinen Etagenbetten) gibt es in Schlafräumen für 2-4 Jugendherbergsgäste und in Räumen mit bis 20 Etagenbetten, obgleich dies immer seltener wird. Decken und Kissen stehen zur Verfügung, aber Sie müssen Ihre eigene Bettwäsche und Kissenbezüge mitbringen oder mieten. Lakenschlafsäcke können in einigen Jugendherbergen benutzt werden.

Viele Jugendherbergen haben Selbstversorgungseinrichtungen, und in den meisten erhalten Sie Mahlzeiten. In den Angaben zu den einzelnen Herbergen erfahren Sie, was angeboten wird.

Landessitten und Verhaltensweisen sind selbstverständlich überall auf der Welt unterschiedlich. Informieren Sie sich also in dem Vorwort zu jedem Land sowie in den Angaben zu jeder Jugendherberge über Einzelheiten.

In diesem Jugendherbergsführer werden die Ausstattung und die Preise aller Jugendherbergen aufgeführt, so daß Sie vor Ankunft wissen, was die Jugendherberge bietet.

EINFÜHRUNG

Vorausbuchung durch IBN

Unabhängig davon, ob Sie die ganze Reiseroute planen oder nur sicher sein möchten, daß Sie in der ersten Nacht einen Platz finden, ein Dach über dem Kopf haben, unser computergestütztes *internationales Buchungsnetz* (IBN) bietet Ihnen eine einfache und kostengünstige Lösung für Vorausbuchungen in mehr als 300 der wichtigsten Standorte auf der ganzen Welt für nur eine kleine Gebühr.

Wenn Sie IBN benutzen, bedeutet dies, daß Sie für Ihre Reservierung in der Währung des Landes bezahlen können, von dem aus Sie Ihre Buchung vornehmen und auf diese Weise Bank- oder Umtauschgebühren sparen - und natürlich Ihre Unterbringung im voraus sichern.

Sie können Reservierungen aus allen Jugendherbergen, die in diesem Jugendherbergsführer mit dem IBN-Symbol und blauem Druck gekennzeichnet sind, vornehmen oder ein IBN-Buchungszentrum anrufen oder kontaktieren.

Sonstige Möglichkeit zur Buchung

Natürlich *können* Sie bei einer Jugendherberge ohne eine Reservierung erscheinen, aber es ist besser, im voraus zu buchen. Familien, die einen Familienraum haben möchten sowie Gruppen sollten *immer* im voraus buchen.

Sie können auch per Fax oder brieflich im voraus buchen, wenn Sie einen internationalen Postantwortcoupon (erhältlich in den meisten Postämtern) und einen Rückumschlag mit Ihrer Anschrift beifügen.

Wenn Sie eine Buchung vornehmen, *ohne eine Anzahlung zu leisten* sollten Sie daran denken, daß Sie, wenn keine andere Zeit abgesprochen wurde, in der Jugendherberge bis 18.00 Uhr ankommen müssen, um Ihre Reservierung zu beanspruchen.

Wie Sie auch immer buchen, Sie sind in der Welt des internationalen Jugendherbergswesens willkommen, treffen neue Menschen, finden neue Freunde auf der ganzen Welt, tauschen Ihre Gedanken aus und erweitern Ihre Erfahrungen mit anderen Kulturen.

Wir sind überzeugt, daß Ihnen das Freude macht. Sie werden sich das ganz bestimmt leisten können und wir freuen uns auf Ihren Besuch.

Zugesicherte Standards

Hostelling International weiß, daß budget reisender Wert auf eine gleichbleibende Qualität und gleichbleibenden Service legen. Aus diesem Grunde haben wir unser neues Programm zur Gewährleistung eines hohen Qualitätsstandards eingeführt. Damit wollen wir sichern, daß Sie sich in diesem wichtigen Bereich auf ein konstantes Niveau von Dienstleistungen und Einrichtungen verlassen können, wo immer Sie sich in unseren Jugendherbergen aufhalten.

Bis 1999 werden **alle** unsere Jugendherbergen auf den Mindeststandard gebracht - und viele werden einen ein wesentlich höheren Standard aufweisen.

Herzlicher Empfang mit Komfort, Sauberkeit, Sicherheit und Privatesphäre

Die Verbände der Jugendherbergen in ca. 14 Ländern bieten bereits diesen zugesicherten Standard; die übrigen arbeiten daran, diesen Anforderungen sobald als möglich zu entsprechen. Die Standards werden durch den Verband der Internationalen Jugendherbergen überprüft, außerdem durch Sie, die Gäste. Wenn Sie enttäuscht sind, lassen Sie uns das wissen, und wir sichern Ihnen zu, daß wir den Fall überprüfen und ggf. notwendige Maßnahmen ergreifen. In diesem Reiseführer befinden sich Formblätter, mit denen Sie mit uns Kontakt aufnehmen können.

Für viele Menschen sind Jugendherbergen abseits gelegene, ungewöhnliche Standorte und sehr eigene Gebäude. Wir müssen zugeben, daß es schwierig ist, dieselben Standards mitten im Regenwald oder in einer abseits gelegenen Schäferhütte zu gewährleisten! So machen wir einige Ausnahmen für kleine Herbergen und solche mit einfacher Ausstattung; Sie werden dort weniger Personal und kürzere Öffnungszeiten finden (insbesondere innerhalb des Polarkreises). Diese Art von Herbergen wird bei den betreffenden Einträgen deutlich ausgewiesen. In allen anderen Fragen jedoch treffen die zugesicherten Standards auf diese Herbergen genauso zu.

Mitunter leihen wir uns Unterkünfte von anderen Organisationen aus, um sicher zu sein, daß Sie eine Übernachtung finden, wenn keine internationalen Jugendherbergen unseres Verbandes zur Verfügung stehen. Diese Herbergen finden Sie am Ende jedes Kapitels zu dem betreffenden Land. Hier können Abweichungen von einigen unserer Standards auftreten.

EINFÜHRUNG

Was können Sie bei zugesicherten Standards von Jugendherbergen erwarten?

Empfang

Jugendherbergen stehen jedem offen, unabhängig von Alter, Geschlecht, Kultur, Rasse oder Religion. Falls Sie noch nicht die Vorteile eines Mitglieds in Anspruch nehmen, können Sie trotzdem für eine Kurzzeit oder regulär die Mitgliedschaft im Jugendherbergsverband erwerben.

Sie können vorab eine Übernachtung buchen, sofern diese verfügbar ist und erhalten unverzüglich Antwort auf alle Anfragen. Die Jugendherbergen sind zumindest zu den auf S.4 angegebenen Kernöffnungszeiten geöffnet. Falls sie nicht 24 Stunden durchgehend geöffnet sind, bleiben die Herbergen doch solange offen, daß Sie das gesellschaftliche Leben in dem betreffenden Ort kennenlernen können! Falls die Jugendherberge für eine bestimmte Zeit des Tages geschlossen ist, haben Sie doch Zugang zur Unterkunft, zur Toilette und zu einem Abstellraum für Ihr Gepäck.

Kurz, ein herzlicher Empfang für Sie ist die vornehmste Aufgabe für das Personal der Jugendherberge. Das Personal wird sich alle Mühe geben, um Ihnen die gewünschte Unterstützung und die Informationen zu geben, mit denen Sie den größten Nutzen aus Ihrem Aufenthalt ziehen.

Komfort

Sie können eine gute, komfortable Übernachtung und ausreichende Wasch- und Duschgelegenheiten sowie Toilette und heißes Wasser erwarten!

Wenn frische Bettwäsche nicht in der Übernachtungsgebühr enthalten ist, ist sie gegen eine geringe Gebühr bei Bedarf erhältlich.

Obwohl Mahlzeiten angeboten werden, auch wenn nur Selbstversorgung vorgesehen ist, können Sie Grundnahrungsmittel zumeist in der Jugendherberge oder in der Nähe käuflich erwerben. Wir bieten Ihnen Aufbewahrungsmöglichkeiten für Nahrungsmittel, Kochgelegenheiten zur Essenszubereitung sowie Spüleinrichtungen.

Sauberkeit

Einerlei, wohin Sie reisen, können Sie die höchsten Standards bei Sauberkeit und Hygiene von Hostelling International erwarten.

Sicherheit

Das Personal der Jugendherbergen wird jede Anstrengung unternehmen, um während Ihres Aufenthaltes Ihre persönliche Sicherheit sowie die Sicherheit Ihres Besitzes zu gewährleisten. Man wird Ihnen Ratschläge zur Umgebung geben und in vielen Standorten können Sie Schließfächer für Ihr Gepäck und Ihre Wertsachen benutzen.

EINFÜHRUNG

Privatsphäre

Obwohl Sie sich in der Regel ein Zimmer gemeinsam mit anderen Gästen gleichen Geschlechtes teilen (sofern Sie nicht ein Einzel- oder Familienzimmer gebucht haben), garantieren die zugesicherten Standards doch eine Privatsphäre für Sie, wenn Sie das möchten, insbesondere in Duschen, Waschräumen und Toiletten - und auf jeden Fall zwischen den Geschlechtern.

Umweltcharta

Zusätzlich zu diesen zugesicherten Standards befolgen die Jugendherbergen auch die Umweltvorgaben des IYHF, die die Kriterien für den Verbrauch und die Bewahrung von Ressourcen, Müllbeseitigung, Recycling, Schutz der Umwelt und Erziehung zum Umweltschutz festlegen.

Die zugesicherten Standards in diesem Reiseführer werden für folgende Länder angeboten: Österreich, Belgien, Dänemark, England und Wales, Israel, die Niederlande, Nordirland, Schottland, Schweden und die Schweiz.

Lesen Sie weiter zum Thema Reisecheckliste

EINFÜHRUNG

Reise-Checkliste

Einige der Faktoren, auf die wir nachstehend eingehen wollen, sind Ihnen sicher schon bekannt. Erfahrene Reisende überlassen jedoch nichts dem Zufall. Deshalb sind Sie uns sicher dankbar, wenn wir nachstehend noch einmal alles kurz aufführen, woran Sie vor jeder Reise, *und* während Sie sich unterwegs befinden, immer denken sollten.

1   Geld

- Wer beruhigt reisen will, sollte Reiseschecks oder Kreditkarten benutzen. Notieren Sie sich die Nummern, und bewahren Sie diesen Zettel getrennt auf.

- Nehmen Sie möglichst wenig Bargeld mit.

- Verteilen Sie Ihr Geld, Ihre Reiseschecks, Ihre Kreditkarten, Ihren Reisepaß, Tickets und Ihren Jugendherbergsausweis über verschiedene Stellen an Ihrer Person oder in Ihrem Gepäck, damit Sie nicht alles verlieren, wenn Sie *doch einmal* bestohlen werden oder Gepäck verlieren.

  Vergessen Sie nicht, daß Sie in mehreren Ländern eine Personalausweisnummer brauchen, bevor Sie eine Kreditkarte in Jugendherbergen, gleichfalls anderen Standorten benutzen können.

- Wenn all Striche reissen, oder wenn man einfach kein Geld mehr hat, gibt es Dienste wie Western Union die Ihnen helfen können um Geld vom Zuhause in wenigen Minuten zu bekommen (Siehe Seite 9).

2   Pässe, Visa

- Vergewissern Sie sich, daß Ihr Reisepaß nicht schon vor Ihrer Rückkehr abläuft. In einigen Ländern wird verlangt, daß Ihr Reisepaß nach Ihrer Ankunft noch weitere 6 Monate gültig ist.

- Erkundigen Sie sich, was für Dokumente Sie für verschiedene Länder benötigen, und beantragen Sie diese rechtzeitig - besonders im Sommer muß das manchmal schon mehrere Wochen im voraus gemacht werden.

3   Versicherung

- Schließen Sie eine Reiseversicherung ab. Die Reisesektion Ihres Jugendherbergsverbands oder ein Reisebüro berät Sie gerne. (Siehe auch unter 'Diebstahl')

EINFÜHRUNG

4 Gesundheit

- Denken Sie daran, daß ärztliche Behandlung in vielen Ländern sehr teuer sein kann. Sie sollten sich daher dagegen versichern. Einige Länder haben aber auch mit anderen Ländern reziproke Vereinbarungen über die Kosten einer ärztlichen Behandlung. Erkundigen Sie sich bei der Geschäftsstelle Ihrer Krankenkasse und beschaffen Sie sich vor Antritt Ihrer Reise die notwendigen Formulare.

- Für einige der in diesem Führer aufgeführten Länder sind Impfungen vorgeschrieben. Erkundigen Sie sich 6-8 Wochen vor Antritt Ihrer Reise bei Ihrem Arzt, weil es einige Zeit dauern kann, bis die Impfungen wirksam werden.

5 Diebstahl

- Wenn Ihnen während Ihres Aufenthaltes in einer Jugendherberge etwas gestohlen wird, verständigen Sie *sofort* die Jugendherbergsverwaltung. Wenn Sie Ihr Eigentum nicht mehr zurückbekommen, lassen Sie sich vom Jugendherbergsverwalter die Einzelheiten auf einem Briefbogen der Jugendherberge bestätigen, der vom Jugendherbergsverwalter abzustempeln, zu datieren und zu unterzeichnen ist. Verständigen Sie die Polizei und lassen Sie sich von ihr einen maschinengeschriebenen Bericht ausstellen. Viele Versicherungsgesellschaften zahlen nur, wenn Ihr Anspruch auf diese Weise bestätigt wird.

6 Telefonieren aus dem Ausland

- Wenn Sie aus einem anderen Land anrufen, müssen Sie die internationale Kennzahl + die Landeskennzahl + die Ortsnetzkennzahl + die Nummer wählen.

Wenn Sie zum Beispiel aus Hongkong in Paris anrufen wollen, wählen Sie:

001	+	33	+	1	+	die
Internationale		Landes-		Ort		gewünschte
Kennzahl		Kennzahl		Kennzahl		Nummer
				Paris		

- Die internationale Kennzahl sowie die Landeskennzahl und einige der wichtigsten Ortsnetzkennzahlen für das betreffende Land finden Sie unter den Angaben für den jeweiligen Verband in diesem Führer.

- Denken Sie daran, daß Sie, wenn Sie eine *ausländische Nummer* wählen, vielleicht die '0' oder '9' zu Beginn der Ortsnetzkennzahl weglassen müssen. Berücksichtigen Sie auch, daß Sie oft bis zu einer Minute warten müssen, bis die Verbindung zustande kommt, **UND** daß sich das Frei- und das Besetztzeichen in jedem Land wieder anders anhören.

EINFÜHRUNG

7 Zeitzonen

- Wenn Sie schon einmal durch ein Auslandsgespräch um 04.00 Uhr geweckt wurden, wissen Sie, wie wichtig es ist, daß man beim Telefonieren die Zeitunterschiede zwischen den einzelnen Ländern berücksichtigt.

- Die Grundregel lautet: 1 Stunde für jeweils 15 Längengrade. Je weiter westlich Sie sich befinden, desto früher ist es; je weiter östlich Sie sich befinden, desto später ist es.

- Aus dieser Tabelle gehen die ungefähren Zeiten an verschiedenen Orten der Welt im Vergleich zur Mittleren Greenwicher Zeit hervor.

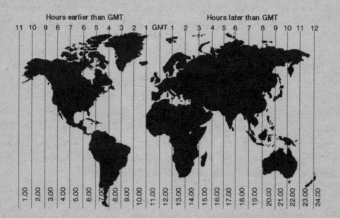

INTRODUCCION

Pase una buena noche en un ambiente acogedor, a un precio asequible.

Las guías de Hostelling International le ofrecen un surtido de lugares fiables y económicos donde alojarse más amplio que ninguna otra guía.

Elija entre un total de más o menos 5.000 albergues juveniles, repartidos por más de 60 países, los cuales ofrecen más de 31 millones de pernoctaciones anuales. En esta guía encontrará información sobre aproximadamente 2.500 albergues distribuidos por toda Europa.

Además, puede reservar por adelantado en casi todas partes del mundo. En los emplazamientos claves - los principales centros turísticos del mundo - ahora le es posible efectuar una reserva con hasta 6 meses de antelación, mediante una simple llamada telefónica, gracias a IBN (International Booking Network) - nuestra Red Internacional de Reservas por computadora. IBN cubre actualmente más de 300 puntos de destino, tales como Londres, París, Roma, Amsterdam, Bruselas, Tokio, Nueva York, Washington, Los Angeles, Melbourne, Sydney, Toronto, Vancouver y Auckland, y todos los meses añadimos alguno más a nuestra lista.

Adondequiera que viaje, Hostelling International le ofrece la compañía de personas de ideas afines, un recibimiento cordial y alojamiento a un precio asequible, en todas partes del mundo.

Esto quiere decir que, en los 5 continentes, Ud. tiene la garantía de pasar una buena noche en un ambiente acogedor a un precio asequible - por ejemplo, a partir de tan sólo 8,00 $USA por noche en Atenas - además de beneficiarse de otros muchos descuentos y ahorros.

Pero, sin lugar a dudas, la mayor ventaja es que Ud. sabe con qué se va a encontrar.

¡Para jóvenes de todas las edades!

A pesar de su nombre, los albergues juveniles están abiertos a personas de todas las edades (salvo algunas excepciones debidas a la legislación local). Los menores de 14 años deben ir acompañados de un adulto y algunos albergues disponen de habitaciones familiares. A veces se admiten a menores de 5 años si se acuerda de antemano. La mayoría de los albergues aceptan también reservas para grupos.

INTRODUCCION

Cómo hospedarse en un albergue juvenil - y viajar más económicamente

Para alojarse en un albergue en cualquier parte del mundo - y beneficiarse de descuentos especiales, incluyendo viajes más económicos - Ud. no tiene más que hacerse socio de la Asociación de Albergues Juveniles de su país. Si no tiene el carné de socio, puede comprar un Sello de Bienvenida (Welcome Stamp) en el albergue donde vaya a pasar la noche.

La mayoría de los albergues ofrecen un amplio surtido de descuentos locales a sus socios. Al final de cada sección nacional de esta Guía, encontrará una lista de los grandes ahorros que le ofrece cada país a la hora de viajar y de los cuales puede sacar provecho.

Prestaciones ofrecidas

Los albergues más importantes ubicados en las grandes ciudades están generalmente abiertos las 24 horas del día, mientras que los más pequeños, situados en el campo, a veces tienen un horario reducido, y la mayoría de ellos están abiertos todo el año. Bajo cada albergue listado en esta Guía encontrará las fechas en que está abierto.

En la mayoría de los albergues, Ud. puede registrarse a su llegada o salida entre las 7.00 h. y las 10.00 h. y entre las 17.00 h. y las 22.30 h. En la información relativa a cada albergue encontrará las excepciones. Recuerde que puede servirse del sistema informático de reservas por adelantado IBN para asegurarse una cama, llegue a la hora que llegue al albergue.

Las habitaciones en los albergues son de varios tipos, a partir de 2 a 4 camas (normalmente literas), hasta dormitorios para 20 personas, aunque éstos son cada vez menos frecuentes. El albergue le proporcionará mantas o un edredón y una almohada, pero Ud. tendrá que alquilar el resto de la ropa de cama o traerse sus proprias sábanas, fundas o saco de dormir sábana en algunos albergues.

Muchos albergues tienen cocinas para huéspedes y la mayoría de ellos sirven comidas (bajo cada albergue se indican los servicios ofrecidos).

Como es sabido, los usos y costumbres locales cambian de un sitio a otro. Por lo tanto, es recomendable leer la introducción general de cada país, además de la información sobre cada albergue en particular.

Observará que todos los precios y diversas prestaciones están indicados en la información relativa a cada albergue en esta Guía, para que Ud. sepa de antemano qué le van a ofrecer.

INTRODUCCION

Reserve por adelantado mediante IBN

Ya sea que Ud. quiera organizar toda una gira o simplemente asegurarse una cama para la primera noche, nuestra *red internacional de reservas informatizada* (IBN) le ofrece una forma fácil y económica de reservar por adelantado en más de 300 emplazamientos claves repartidos por todo el mundo, por una módica suma.

IBN le permite abonar sus reservas en la moneda del país donde realice las mismas, ahorrándose así las comisiones bancarias y posibles pérdidas al cambiar divisas - además de asegurarse alojamiento con anticipación.

Ud. puede reservar su alojamiento en todos los albergues que lleven las siglas IBN en esta Guía (véase la información impresa en color azul). Visite o póngase en contacto con cualquiera de los centros de reservas IBN enumerados en la misma.

Formas alternativas de reserva

Por supuesto, Ud. *puede* llegar al albergue sin reservar antes, pero es preferible reservar por adelantado. Las familias que deseen una habitación familiar y los grupos deberían *siempre* reservar con anticipación.

También puede reservar por adelantado por fax o por correo, adjuntando un cupón internacional de respuesta pagada, que encontrará en la mayoría de las oficinas de correos, más un sobre con su nombre y dirección.

Tenga en cuenta que, si hace una reserva *sin pagar un depósito*, deberá llegar al albergue y solicitar su habitación antes de las 18 h., a menos que haya acordado otra hora de antemano con el albergue.

Sea cual sea su forma de reservar, Ud. será bienvenido al mundo de los albergues juveniles internacionales, donde conocerá a gente de todo el mundo, hará nuevas amistades, podrá intercambiar ideas y así ampliar sus conocimientos de otras culturas.

Estamos convencidos de que disfrutará de la experiencia y de que no le saldrá cara. Esperamos tener el agrado de su visita.

INTRODUCCION

Normas Garantizadas

Hostelling International es consciente de la importancia de un nivel constante de calidad y servicio para los viajeros con un presupuesto reducido.

Para 1999, **todos** nuestros albergues estarán en condiciones de garantizar unas normas básicas - y un gran número de ellos seguirá ofreciendo normas aún superiores.

Un recibimiento cordial, junto con comodidad, higiene, seguridad e intimidad

Las Asociaciones de Albergues Juveniles de unos 14 países ya ofrecen este Plan de Normas Garantizadas y el resto se están preparando para adherirse al Plan lo antes posible. Las normas estarán controladas por Hostelling International y por Ud., el usuario. Si Ud. no está satisfecho, díganoslo y le prometemos que haremos averiguaciones y que tomaremos las medidas oportunas cuando el caso lo requiera. Encontrará una tarjeta de comentarios en esta guía para ayudarle a contactar con nosotros.

Para muchas personas, la base del alberguismo está en lugares aislados y poco corrientes y en edificios muy especiales. Tenemos que admitir que es difícil mantener las mismas normas en el medio de la selva tropical o en una remota cabaña de pastor. Por este motivo, hemos hecho una excepción en algunos albergues más pequeños o con instalaciones más sencillas, donde podrá encontrarse con un número de empleados y un horario de apertura limitados (¡especialmente dentro del círculo polar ártico!). Este tipo de albergue está indicado claramente en las listas de esta Guía. No obstante, las Normas Garantizadas son válidas también en estos albergues en todo lo demás.

A veces "pedimos prestado" alojamiento a otras organizaciones, con el fin de que Ud. pueda conseguir una cama en lugares donde no haya albergues de Hostelling International. Encontrará este tipo de albergue al final de las listas de cada país, pero no todos satisfacen nuestras normas.

¿Qué significan las Normas Garantizadas para Ud.?

Recibimiento

Los albergues están abiertos a todos, sin distinción de edad, sexo, cultura, raza ni religión. Si Ud. no tiene aún la ventaja de ser socio, podrá hacerse socio de pleno derecho o a corto plazo en el albergue.

INTRODUCCION

Siempre que haya disponibilidad, podrá reservar su cama por adelantado para el tiempo que Ud. desee y recibirá una respuesta inmediata a sus consultas. Los albergues estarán abiertos por lo menos durante el horario básico indicado en la página 31 y los que no estén abiertos las 24 horas del día, ¡sin duda tendrán un horario que le permita disfrutar de las diversiones que le ofrezca el lugar! Aunque el albergue esté cerrado durante parte del día, Ud. tendrá acceso a un lugar donde refugiarse, a los servicios y a un sitio donde dejar su equipaje.

Sobre todo, la prioridad del personal del albergue será acogerle a Ud. y éste hará todo lo posible por ayudarle y darle la información que Ud. requiera para aprovechar su estancia al máximo.

Comodidad

Puede contar con una buena y confortable noche de descanso, con suficientes duchas, servicios y baños y, además, ¡puede estar seguro de que habrá suficiente agua caliente!

En los casos en que no estén incluidas en el precio de la pernoctación, será posible alquilar sábanas y fundas recién lavadas.

Aunque normalmente los albergues sirven comidas, en los que sólo haya cocinas para huéspedes será posible generalmente comprar alimentos básicos en el albergue mismo o en sus inmediaciones. Pondremos a su disposición un lugar donde guardar los alimentos, encimeras para la preparación de comidas, una cocina para guisar y una pila para fregar la vajilla.

Limpieza

Adondequiera que viaje, Hostelling International le garantiza las más rigurosas normas de limpieza e higiene.

Seguridad

El personal del albergue hará todo lo posible por garantizar tanto su seguridad personal como la de sus bienes durante su estancia. También le harán las advertencias oportunas con respecto al barrio. Muchos albergues tienen armarios que cierran con llave, donde podrá depositar su equipaje y objetos de valor.

Intimidad/vida privada

Aunque puede darse que tenga que compartir una habitación con otros albeguistas del mismo sexo (a menos que haya reservado una habitación individual o familiar), el Plan de Normas Garantizadas respeta su intimidad donde es necesario - especialmente en las duchas, baños y servicios - y, en cualquier caso, entre los sexos.

INTRODUCCION

Carta Medioambiental

Además de estas Normas Garantizadas, los albergues se comprometen a adherir a la Carta Medioambiental de la IYHF, la cual establece los criterios para el consumo y conservación de los recursos, la eliminación de residuos, reciclaje y conservación del medio ambiente, así como la provisión de educación medioambiental.

Los países de esta Guía que le ofrecen las Normas Garantizadas son Austria, Bélgica, Dinamarca, Inglaterra y Gales, Israel, los Países Bajos, Irlanda del Norte, Escocia, Suecia y Suiza.

Véase a continuación la lista de recomendaciones para antes del viaje

INTRODUCCION

Prepárese para el viaje

Aunque Ud. ya sabrá algunas de estas cosas, pues el viajero experimentado no deja nada al azar, hemos pensado que le podría ser útil esta lista de recomendaciones para refrescarle la memoria antes de salir de viaje y durante el mismo.

1 Dinero

- Para más seguridad, utilice cheques de viajero o tarjetas de crédito. Anote los números correspondientes y guárdelos por separado.

- Lleve lo indispensable en efectivo.

- Distribuya su dinero, cheques de viajero, tarjetas de crédito, pasaporte, billetes y carné de alberguista por su persona y equipaje, de forma que, *si* le roban o si pierde parte de su equipaje, no pierda todo.

- RECUERDE que en cada vez más países se requiere un Número Personal de Identificación (PIN) para poder utilizar ciertas tarjetas de crédito, tanto en los albergues juveniles como en otros lugares.

- En el peor de los casos, o si simplemente se queda sin dinero, existen servicios como Western Union que pueden ayudarle a conseguir dinero desde su país en unos minutos (véase la página 9).

2 Pasaportes, visados

- Compruebe que su pasaporte no vaya a caducar antes de su regreso. En algunos países, le exigirán que a su pasaporte le queden 6 meses de validez después de su llegada.

- **Averigüe qué documentos necesita para distintos países y solicítelos con tiempo - en algunos casos, serán necesarias varias semanas de anticipación, sobre todo en verano.**

3 Seguros

- Hágase un seguro de viaje. En la Sección de Viajes de su Asociación de Albergues Juveniles o en su agencia de viajes podrán asesorarle.

4 Sanidad

- Recuerde que, en muchos países, los tratamientos médicos pueden resultar caros, por lo que debería hacerse un seguro. Por otra parte, algunos países tienen acuerdos mutuos en materia de gastos médicos; diríjase a sus oficinas locales de la Dirección de Sanidad, Seguridad Social o Asistencia Social y consiga los formularios correspondientes antes de salir de viaje.

- Es necesario vacunarse para algunos de los países de esta Guía. Consulte a su médico 6-8 semanas antes de viajar, ya que algunas vacunas tardan en surtir efecto.

INTRODUCCION

5 Robos

- Si le roban durante su estancia en un Albergue Juvenil, comuníqueselo al director del albergue *inmediatamente*. Si no consigue recuperar sus pertenencias, pida al director del albergue que confirme los datos en papel con membrete y que le ponga sello, fecha y firma. Informe a la policía del suceso y solicite un informe escrito a máquina. Muchas compañías de seguros se negarán a pagar si no presenta estos documentos como prueba junto con la reclamación.

6 Cómo llamar por teléfono desde el extranjero

- Para llamar por teléfono a otro país, Ud. debe marcar el código internacional, seguido del código nacional y del prefijo regional y, finalmente, el número de teléfono del abonado.

Por ejemplo, para llamar a París desde Hong Kong, tendrá que marcar:

001	+	33	+	1	+	el
Código		Código		Prefijo		número
Internacional		del País		Regional		de teléfono
				de París		deseado

Encontrará el código internacional, así como el código nacional y algunos de los prefijos regionales principales, en la información relativa a cada país.

Cuando haga una llamada *internacional*, recuerde que posiblemente no deba marcar ni el "0" ni el "9" del prefijo regional. Recuerde también que a veces tardará hasta 1 minuto en obtener la conexión y que las señales de llamada y de ocupado varían de un país a otro.

7 Husos horarios

Si alguna vez le ha despertado una llamada telefónica del extranjero a las 4 h. de la mañana, sabrá lo importante que es recordar las diferencias horarias entre países.

Por regla general, se cuenta una hora por cada 15° de longitud. Cuanto más se dirija hacia el oeste, más temprano será y cuanto más vaya hacia el este, más tarde será.

En el siguiente mapa se indican las horas aproximadas en todo el mundo a partir de la hora del meridiano de Greenwich (GMT).

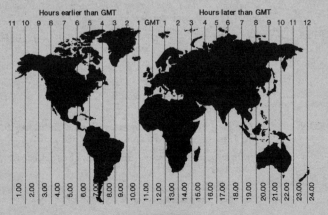

INTRODUCTION

Africa, Americas, Asia, Pacific

Youth Hostels outside of Europe are listed in the Hostelling International Guide - Africa, Americas, Asia and the Pacific. The addresses of the full member Associations are given below:

Les Auberges de jeunesse en dehors de l'Europe figurent dans le Hostelling International Guide - Afrique, Amériques, Asie et le Pacifique. Les adresses des Associations membres à part entière sont données ci-dessous:

Die Jugendherbergen ausserhalb von Europa werden im Hostelling International Guide - Afrika, Amerika, Asien und de Pazifik, aufgeführt. Die Adressen der vollberechtigten Mitgliedsverbände sind unten angegeben:

Los Albergues Juveniles fuera de Europa se incluyen en la Hostelling International Guide - Africa, América, Asia y el Pacífico. A continuación se encuentran las direcciones de las Asociaciones miembros de pleno derecho:

ALGERIA: *Fédération Algérienne des Auberges de Jeunesse*, 213 Rue Hassiba Ben Bouali, BP 15 El-Annasser, 16015 Alger. ☎ (2) 670321.

ARGENTINA: *Asociación Argentina de Albergues de la Juventud*, Talcahuano 214-200 "6", 1013 - Capital Federal, Buenos Aires. ☎ 476-2537, 1001.

AUSTRALIA: *Australian Youth Hostels Association, Inc*, Level 3, 10 Mallett St, Camperdown, 2050 New South Wales. ☎ (2) 9565 1699.

BAHRAIN: *Bahrain Youth Hostels Society*, PO Box 2455, H No. 1105 R No. 4225 Block 342, Manama. ☎ (973) 727170.

BRAZIL: *Federação Brasileira dos Albergues de Juventude*, R.da Assembléia No. 10 S/1211, Centro- Rio de Janeiro. CEP: 20011-000. ☎ (21) 531-1129.

CANADA: *Hostelling International - Canada*, 400-205 Catherine St, Ottawa, Ontario K2P 1C3. ☎ (613) 237-7884.

CHILE: *Asociación Chilena de Albergues Turísticos Juveniles*, Avda Providencia 2594, Of 420, Santiago. ☎ 2333220.

COSTA RICA: *Red Costarricense de Albergues Juveniles*, PO Box 1355-1002 P E, Ave Central, Calles 29 y 31, San José. ☎ 2348186.

ECUADOR: *Asociación Ecuatoriana de Albergues*, Pinto 325 y Reina Victoria, Quito. ☎ (2) 543995.

EGYPT: *Egyptian Youth Hostels Association*, 1 El-Ibrahimy St, Garden City, Cairo. ☎ (2) 3561448.

HONG KONG: *Hong Kong Youth Hostels Association*, Room 225, Block 19, Shek Kip Mei Estate, Kowloon, Hong Kong. ☎ 27881638.

INDIA: *Youth Hostels Association of India*, 5 Nyaya Marg, Chanakyapuri, New Delhi 110 021. ☎ (11) 3011969.

ISRAEL: *Israel Youth Hostels Association*, Binyanei Hauma, 1 Shazar St, PO Box 6001, Jerusalem 91060. ☎ (2) 6558400.

INTRODUCTION

JAPAN: *Japan Youth Hostels Inc*, Suidobashi Nishiguchi Kaikan 5F, 2-20-7 Misaki-cho, Chiyoda-ku, Tokyo 101. ✆ (3) 3288-1417.

KENYA: *Kenya Youth Hostels Association*, PO Box 48661, Ralph Bunche Road, Nairobi. ✆ (2) 721765.

S. KOREA: *Korea Youth Hostels Association*, Rm 408, Hyndai Jaeil Bldg, 80 Juksun Dong, Jongro-Ku, Seoul 110-052. ✆ (2) 7253031.

LIBYA: *Libyan Youth Hostel Association*, 69 Amr Ben Al-Aas Street, PO Box 8886, Tripoli, Al-Jamahiriya. ✆ (21) 4445171.

MALAYSIA: *Malaysian Youth Hostels Association*, KL International Youth Hostel, 21 Jalan Kg. Attap, 50460 Kuala Lumpur. ✆ (3) 2736870/71.

MOROCCO: *Fédération Royale Marocaine des Auberges*, BP 15998, Parc de la Ligue Arabe, Casa Principale, Casablanca 21000. ✆ (2) 470952.

NEW ZEALAND: *Youth Hostels Association of New Zealand Inc*, PO Box 436, 173 Gloucester St, Christchurch 1. ✆ (3) 3799970.

PAKISTAN: *Pakistan Youth Hostels Association*, Shaheed-e-Millat Rd, Aabpara, Sector G-6/4, Islamabad. ✆ (51) 826899.

PERU: *Asociación Peruana de Albergues Turisticos Juveniles*, Avda Casimiro Ulloa 328, San Antonio, Miraflores, Lima 18. ✆ (1) 2423068.

PHILIPPINES: *Youth & Student Hostel Foundation of the Philippines*, 4227-9 Tomas Claudio St, Baclaran, Parañaque 1700, Metro Manila. ✆ (2) 8320680.

QATAR: *Qatar Youth Hostels Association*, PO Box 2511, Doha. ✆ 867180, 863968.

SAUDI ARABIA: *Saudi Arabian Youth Hostels Association*, PO Box 2359, Riyadh 11451. ✆ (1) 4055552, 4051478.

SOUTH AFRICA: *Hostels Association of South Africa*, 101 Boston House, Strand St, Cape Town 8001. ✆ (21) 4191853.

SUDAN: *Sudanese Youth Hostels Association*, PO Box 1705, House 66, Street No 47 Khartoum East, Khartoum. ✆ (11) 222087.

THAILAND: *Thai Youth Hostels Association*, 25/14 Phitsanulok Road, Dusit, Bangkok 10300. ✆ (2) 628-7413-5.

TUNISIA: *Association Tunisienne des Auberges de Jeunesse*, 10 Rue Ali Bach Hamba, BP 320, 1015 Tunis. ✆ (1) 353277.

UNITED ARAB EMIRATES: *United Arab Emirates Youth Hostel Association*, Al Qussais Road, Near Al Ahli Club, PO Box 19536, Dubai. ✆ (4) 665078.

USA: *American Youth Hostels, Inc*, 733 15th Street N.W, Suite 840, Washington DC 20005. ✆ (202) 783-6161.

URUGUAY: *Asociación de Alberguistas del Uruguay*, Pablo de María 1583/008, PC 11200, PO Box 10680, Montevideo. ✆ (2) 404245.

INTRODUCTION

Embassies

If you have difficulties abroad - for example if you lose your passport or your money - you have various options. You can go to the local police, or alternatively your country's embassy or consulate - if your country does not have diplomatic relations with the country you are visiting, another national embassy will be acting on behalf of your country. The addresses of some of the embassies in the most visited countries - based on statistics submitted to the International Youth Hostel Federation - are given below. Also check locally as there may be representatives in other cities not listed here especially in the larger countries:

Si par hasard vous rencontrez des problèmes à l'étranger, si vous perdez votre passeport ou votre argent par exemple, plusieurs solutions se présentent à vous. Vous pouvez aller soit au commissariat, soit à l'ambassade ou au consulat de votre pays. Si votre pays n'a pas de relations diplomatiques avec le pays que vous visitez, une autre embassade (agissant au nom de votre pays) pourra régler votre problème. Veuillez trouver ci-dessous la liste des embassades des pays les plus visités, d'après des statistiques soumises à la Fédération Internationale des Auberges de Jeunesse. Cette liste n'est pas exhaustive, aussi nous vous conseillons de vérifier sur place, particulièrement dans les grands pays:

Wenn Sie sich in Schwierigkeiten im Ausland befinden - z.B. Sie verlieren Ihren Paß oder Ihr Geld - haben Sie verschiedene Möglichkeiten. Sie können zur Polizei oder zur Botschaft Ihres Landes gehen. Wenn Ihr Land keine diplomatische Beziehungen mit dem Land das Sie besuchen hat, wird eine andere nationale Botschaft sich im Auftrag von Ihrem Land fungieren. Die Adressen von einigen Botschaften in den meist besuchten Ländern (den zum Internationalen Jugendherbergsverband eingereichenen Statistiken nach) werden unten angegeben. Erkundigen Sie sich auch am Ort, da es könnte Vertretern in anderen Städten sein, besonders in größeren Ländern, die hier nicht angegeben sind:

Si se encuentra en apuros en el extranjero - por ejemplo, si pierde su pasaporte o su dinero - tiene varias opciones. Puede ir a la policía, o bien a la embajada o consulado de su país. Si su país no tiene relaciones diplomáticas con el país que está visitando, habrá otra embajada nacional que represente a su país. A continuación encontrará una lista de algunas de las embajadas de los países más visitados, según las estadísticas suministradas a la Federación Internacional de Albergues Juveniles. Además, recomendamos que efectúe las averiguaciones pertinentes in situ, ya que es posible que existan representantes en otras ciudades que no hayamos mencionado, especialmente en los países más grandes:

AUSTRIA

France:	Technikerstrasse 2, 1040 Vienna. ☎ 1/5054747.
Germany:	Metternichgasse 3, 1030 Vienna. ☎ 1/71554-0.
Great Britain:	Jauresgasse 12, 1030 Vienna. ☎ 1/7131575.
Hungary:	Bankgasse 4-6, 1010 Vienna. ☎ 1/5332631.
Italy:	Rennweg 27, 1030 Vienna. ☎ 1/7125121.
USA:	Boltzmanngasse 16, 1090 Vienna. ☎ 1/31339.

INTRODUCTION

BELGIUM

France: Rue Ducale-Hertogstraat, 65-1000 Brussels. ✆ 2/5488711.
Germany: Av de Tervueren-Tervurenlaan, 190-1150 Brussels. ✆ 2/7741911.
Great Britain: Rue d'Arlon-Aarlenstraat, 85-1040 Brussels. ✆ 2/2876211.
Netherlands: Av Herrmann Debrouxlaan 48, 1160 Brussels. ✆ 2/6791711.

DENMARK

Belgium: Øster Alle 7, 2100 Copenhagen Ø. ✆ 3526-0388 **FAX** 3543-0102.
Czech Republic: Ryvangs allé 14, 2100 Copenhagen Ø. ✆ 3929-1598, 3929-1888
                         FAX 3929-0930.
Finland: Skt. Annæ Plads 24, 1250 Copenhagen K. ✆ 3313-4214
                         FAX 3332-4710.
France: Kongens Nytorv 4, 1050 Copenhagen K (F4). ✆ 3315-5122
                         FAX 3393-9752.
Germany: Stockholmsgade 57, 2100 Copenhagen Ø. ✆ 3526-1622
                         FAX 3526-7105.
Great Britain: Kastelsvej 36-40, 2100 Copenhagen Ø. ✆ 3526-4600
                         FAX 3138-1012.
Italy: Engskiftevej 4, 2100 Copenhagen Ø. ✆ 3118-3444
                         FAX 3927-0106.
Netherlands: Toldbodgade 33, 1253 Copenhagen K. ✆ 3315-6293
                         FAX 3314-0350.
Norway: Trondhjems Plads 4, 2100 Copenhagen Ø. ✆ 3138-8985
                         FAX 3138-0915.
Poland: Richelieus Allé 10, 2900 Hellerup. ✆ 3162-7244
                         FAX 3162-7120.
Sweden: Skt Annæplads 15A, 1250 Copenhagen K ✆ 3314-2242
                         FAX 3332-9035.
USA: Dag Hammerskjolds Allé 24, 2100 Copenhagen Ø. ✆ 3142-3144
                         FAX 3543-0223.

FINLAND

Denmark: Centralgatan 1A, 00100 Helsingfors. ✆ (09) 171511
                         FAX (09) 62202810.
Estonia: Itäinen Puistotie 10, 00140 Helsinki. ✆ (09) 6220260
                         FAX (09) 62202610.
                         Consulate (visas):
                         Kasarminkatu 28 A 1, ✆ (09) 6220288 **FAX** (09) 62202850.
France: Itäinen Puistotie 13, 00140 Helsinki. ✆ (09) 171521
                         FAX (09) 174440.
Germany: Krogiuksentie 4, 00340 Helsinki. ✆ (09) 4582355.
                         FAX (09) 4582283.
Great Britain: Itäinen Puistotie 17, 00140 Helsinki. ✆ (09) 22865100
                         FAX (09) 22865262.
Italy: Itäinen Puistotie 4 A 1, 00140 Helsinki. ✆ (09) 175144
                         FAX (09) 175976.

INTRODUCTION

FINLAND (continued)

Latvia: Armfeldintie 10, 00150 Helsinki. ☎ (09) 4764720.
visas: ☎ (09) 47647222, 47647233.

Lithuania: Rauhankatu 13A, 00170 Helsinki. ☎ (09) 608210
FAX (09) 608220.

Norway: Rehbinderintie 17, 00150 Helsinki. ☎ (09) 171234
FAX (09) 657807.

Russia: Vuorimiehenkatu 6, 00140 Helsinki. ☎ (09) 661449.
Open: 09.30-12.00hrs (visas)

Sweden: Norra esplanaden 7B, 00170 Helsingfors. ☎ (09) 651255.
FAX (09) 655285.

Switzerland: Uudenmaankatu 16 A, 00120 Helsinki. ☎ (09) 649422
FAX (09) 649040.

USA: Itäinen Puistotie 14 B, 00140 Helsinki. ☎ (09) 171931
FAX (09) 174681.

FRANCE

Australia: 4, rue Jean Rey, 75015 Paris. ☎ (1) 40593300.
Austria: 6, Rue Fabut, 75007 Paris. ☎ (1) 45559566.
Belgium: 9, rue Tilsitt, 75017 Paris. ☎ (1) 44093939.
Canada: 35, ave Montaigne, 75008 Paris. ☎ (1) 44432900.
Germany: 13, Av Franklin-D. Roosevelt, 75008 Paris. ☎ (1) 53834500.
Great Britain: 35, Fbg. St. Honore, 75008 Paris. ☎ (1) 44513100.
Italy: 51, Rue Varenne, 75007 Paris. ☎ (1) 49540300.
Netherlands: 7, rue Eblé, 75007 Paris. ☎ (1) 40623300.
Switzerland: 142, rue de Grenelle, 75007 Paris. ☎ (1) 49556700.
USA: 2, rue St Florentin, 75001 Paris. ☎ (1) 42961488.

GERMANY

Australia: Godesberger Allee 105-107, 53175 Bonn (Bad Godesberg).
☎ 0228/81030.

Belgium: Kaiser-Friedrich-Strasse 7, 53113 Bonn. ☎ 0228/212001.

Canada: Friedrich-Wilhelm-Str 18, 53113 Bonn. ☎ 0228/9680.

Denmark: Pfälzer Strasse 14, 53111 Bonn. ☎ 0228/729910.

Finland: Friesdorfer Strasse 1, 53173 Bonn (Bad Godesberg).
☎ 0228/382980.

France: An der Marienkapelle 3, 53179 Bonn (Bad Godesberg).
☎ 0228/362031.

Great Britain: Friedrich-Ebert-Allee 77, 53113 Bonn. ☎ 0228/91670.

Italy: Karl-Finkelnburg-Strasse 51, 53173 Bonn (Bad Godesberg).
☎ 0228/8220.

Japan: Godesberger Allee 102-104, 53175 Bonn (Bad Godesberg).
☎ 0228/81910.

Netherlands: Straßchensweg 10, 53113 Bonn. ☎ 0228/53050.

Sweden: Heussallee 2-10, 53113 Bonn. ☎ 0228/260020.

Switzerland: Gotenstrasse 156, 53175 Bonn (Bad Godesberg). ☎ 0228/810080.

USA: Deichmanns Aue 29, 53170 Bonn (Bad Godesberg). ☎ 0228/3391.

INTRODUCTION

GREAT BRITAIN

Australia: Australia House, The Strand, London WC2B 4LA.
    ☎ (171) 3794334.
Canada: 38 Grosvenor St, London W1X 0AA. ☎ (171) 2586600.
France: 58 Knightsbridge, London SW1X 7JT. ☎ (171) 2011000.
Germany: 23 Belgrave Square, London SW1X 8PZ. ☎ (171) 2355033.
Netherlands: 38 Hyde Park Gate, London SW7 5DP. ☎ (171) 5845040.
New Zealand: New Zealand House, 80 Haymarket, London SW1Y 4TQ.
    ☎ (171) 9308422.
USA: 24 Grosvenor Square, London W1A 1AE. ☎ (171) 4999000.

HUNGARY

Australia: 1126 Budapest, Királyhágó tér 8/9. ☎ 201-8899 **FAX** 201-9792.
Belgium: 1015 Budapest, Toldy F. u. 13. ☎ 201-1571.
France: 1062 Budapest, Lendvay u 27. ☎ 132-4980.
Germany: 1143 Budapest, Stefánia ut 101-103. ☎ 251-8999 **FAX** 160-1903.
Great Britain: 1051 Budapest, Harmincad u 6. ☎ 266-3004, 2888.
Italy: 1143 Budapest, Stefánia ut 95. ☎ 268-1080.
Japan: 1125 Budapest. Zalai út 7. ☎ 275-1275.
Russia: 1062 Budapest, Bajza u. 35. ☎ 131-8985.
Ukraina: 1125 Budapest, Nógrádi u. 8. ☎ 155-2443
USA: 1054 Budapest, Szabadság tér 12. ☎ 267-4400.

IRELAND

Australia: 2nd Floor, Fitzwilton House, Wilton Terrace, Dublin 2.
    ☎ (1) 6761517 **FAX** (1) 6685266.
France: 36 Ailesbury Road, Dublin 4. ☎ (1) 2694777 **FAX** (1) 2830178.
Germany: 31 Trimleston Ave, Booterstown, Blackrock, Co Dublin.
    ☎ (1) 2693011 **FAX** (1) 2693946.
Great Britain: 29 Merrion Road, Dublin 4. ☎ (1) 2695211 **FAX** (1) 2053885.
Italy: 63/65 Northumberland Road, Ballsbridge, Dublin 4.
    ☎ (1) 6601744 **FAX** (1) 6682759.
USA: 42 Elgin Road, Ballsbridge, Dublin 4. ☎ (1) 6688777
    FAX (1) 6689946.

ITALY

Australia: Via Alessandria 215, Rome. ☎ (6) 852721 **FAX** (6) 85272300.
Canada: Via G.B. de Rossi 27, Rome. ☎ (6) 445981 **FAX** (6) 44598750.
France: Piazza Farnese 67, Rome. ☎ (6) 686011, 6896421
    FAX (6) 6860125.
Germany: Via Po 25C, Rome. ☎ (6) 884741 **FAX** (6) 8547956.
Great Britain: Via XX Settembre 80, Rome. ☎ (6) 4825441 **FAX** (6) 48903073.
Spain: Via Campo Marzio 34, Rome. ☎ (6) 6871401, 68300587
    FAX (6) 6871198.
Switzerland: Via B.Oriani 61, Rome. ☎ (6) 844801 **FAX** (6) 8088510.
USA: Via Vittorio Veneto 119A, Rome. ☎ (6) 46741 **FAX** (6) 4882672.

INTRODUCTION

LUXEMBOURG

Belgium:	4 rue des Girondins, L-1626 Luxembourg. ☎ 442746.
Germany:	20-22 avenue Emile Reuter, L-2420 Luxembourg. ☎ 453445.
Netherlands:	5 rue C.M. Spoo, L-2546 Luxembourg. ☎ 406036.

NETHERLANDS

Belgium:	Lange Vyverberg 12, 2513 AC The Hague. ☎ (70) 3644910.
France:	Smidsplein 1, 2514 BT The Hague. ☎ (70) 3560606.
Germany:	Groot Hertoginnelaan 18-20, 2517 EG The Hague. ☎ (70) 3420600.
Great Britain:	Lange Voorhout 10, 2514 ED The Hague. ☎ (70) 3645800.
USA:	Lange Voorhout 102, 2514 EJ The Hague. ☎ (70) 3109209.

NORWAY

Denmark:	Olav Kyrres gt 7, 0273 Oslo 2. ☎ 22441846.
Germany:	Oscars Gate 45, 0258 Oslo 2. ☎ 22552010.
Great Britain:	Ths Heftyes gt 8, 0264 Oslo 2. ☎ 22552400.
Sweden:	Nobels Gate 16, 0268 Oslo 2. ☎ (22) 443815.

SPAIN

France:	Salustiano Olazaga 9, 28001 Madrid. ☎ 4355560.
Germany:	Fortuny 8, 28010 Madrid. ☎ 3199100.

SWEDEN

Denmark:	Jakobs Torg 1, Box 1638, 111 86 Stockholm. ☎ (8) 231860.
Finland:	Regeringsg 20, Box 7423, 103 91 Stockholm. ☎ (8) 6766700.
Germany:	Skarpögatan 9, 115 27 Stockholm. ☎ (8) 6701500.
Norway:	Strandvägen 113, Box 27829, 115 93 Stockholm. ☎ (8) 6656340.

SWITZERLAND

Australia:	Alpenstrasse 29, 3006 Bern. ☎ (31) 3510143.
Canada:	Kirchenfeldstrasse 88, 3006 Bern. ☎ (31) 3526381.
France:	Schosshaldenstrasse 46, 3006 Bern. ☎ (31) 3512424.
Germany:	Willadingweg 78+83, 3000 Bern 16. ☎ (31) 3594111.
Great Britain:	Thunstrasse 50, 3000 Bern 15. ☎ (31) 3525021.
USA:	Jubiläumstrasse 93, 3001 Bern. ☎ (31) 3517011.

AUSTRIA
AUTRICHE
ÖSTERREICH
AUSTRIA

ASSURED STANDARD

(1) Österreichischer
Jugendherbergsverband,
1010 Wien, Schottenring 28,
Austria.

☎ (43) (1) 5335353
FAX (43) (1) 5350861

Office Hours:
Monday-Thursday,
09.00-17.00hrs
Friday 09.00-15.00hrs

Travel Service, GmbH:
Österreichischer
Jugendherbergsverband, 1010
Wien, Gonzagag 22, Austria.

☎ (43) (1) 5321660
FAX (43) (1) 5350861

(2) Österreichisches
Jugendherbergswerk, 1010
Wien, Helferstorferstrasse 4,
Austria.

☎ (43) (1) 5331833
FAX (43) (1) 5331833 Ext 81

Office hours:
Monday-Friday, 09.30-18.00hrs

Travel Section: Supertramp,
1010 Wien,
Helferstorferstrasse 4, Austria

☎ (43) (1) 5335137
FAX (43) (1) 5331833 Ext 85

IBN Booking Centres for outward bookings
- **Graz (ÖJHV)**, Idlhofgasse 74, A 8020 Graz.
  ☎ (43) (316) 9083 **FAX** (43) (316) 9083-88
- **Klagenfurt (ÖJHV)**, Neckheimgasse 6,
  A-9020 Klagenfurt.
  ☎ (43) (463) 230020 **FAX** (43) (463) 230020-20
- **Vienna-Central (ÖJHW)**, *via National Office above*
- **Vienna-IBN Austria (ÖJHV)**, *via Vienna Region,
  National Office above*

Capital:	Vienna
Language:	German
Currency:	AS (Schilling)
Population:	8,025,000
Size:	83,849 sq km

AUSTRIA

AUSTRIA

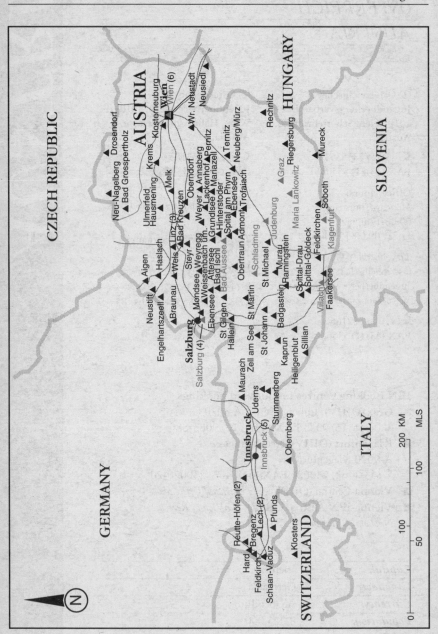

ENGLISH

AUSTRIAN HOSTELS

Youth Hostels in Austria are controlled by two Associations which operate independently, ÖJHV and ÖJHW. Both Associations are participating in Hostelling International's new Assured Standards Scheme see page six for details. Many hostels have facilities for ski-ing, see individual entries for details.

Hostels are generally open 07.00-22.00hrs (07.00-24.00hrs in cities). Few have self-catering facilities and where they do exist you may be charged for use, but most serve meals.

Expect to pay in the region of 100-190 AS including breakfast and linen hire, unless otherwise stated.

HEALTH

In case of an accident or emergency which requires a stay in hospital full payment has to be made for treatment and medication received. Also general practioners' fees have to be paid in full. It is therefore advisable to take out private insurance before travelling.

BANKING HOURS

Generally 08.00-12.30 and 13.30-15.00hrs on Monday, Tuesday, Wednesday and Friday; 08.00-12.30 and 13.30-17.30hrs on Thursday. All banks are closed Saturday and Sunday.

The exchange counters at airports and main railway stations are usually open from the first to last plane or train, ie 08.00-22.00hrs every day.

POST OFFICES

Post offices are open Monday to Friday 08.00-12.00 and 14.00-18.00hrs. (Monetary transactions only up to 17.00hrs).

SHOPPING HOURS

Weekdays 08.00-18.30hrs and Saturday 08.00-13.00hrs, except the first Saturday of every month when they remain open until 17.00hrs. Many shops close for two hours at midday.

Refund on Value-Added Tax: Ask for leaflet "Tax-Free Shopping".

TRAVEL

Rail

Rail travel in Austria is extremely developed. Special offers are available via the Austrian Federal Railways (information at main railway stations).

Bus

Developed regional network.

Driving

It is advisable to have an international driving licence; third party insurance is obligatory. The wearing of seat-belts is compulsory and children under 12 are not allowed in front seats. Dipped headlights must be used at all times. Tolls are payable on a number of mountain roads and road tunnels.

All major international car-hire firms have offices in Austria.

TELEPHONE INFORMATION

International Code	Country Code	Main City Area Codes
00	43	Salzburg 662
		Vienna . . . . 1 or 9

FRANÇAIS

AUBERGES DE JEUNESSE AUTRICHIENNES

Les auberges de jeunesse autrichiennes sont administrées par deux Associations indépendantes l'une de l'autre, l'ÖJHV et l'ÖJHW. De nombreuses auberges sont équipées pour le ski, se reporter à la liste des auberges pour plus de détails. Toutes les auberges participent au nouveau Plan Hostelling International pour la Garantie des Normes en auberges - voir page 15 pour plus de détails.

Les auberges sont en général ouvertes de 7h à 22h (de 7h à 24h dans les grandes villes). Quelques-unes seulement sont équipées d'une cuisine pour les touristes et dans ce cas, il pourra vous être demandé une contribution financière, mais la plupart servent des repas.

Une nuit, petit déjeuner et location de draps compris (sauf indication contraire), coûte entre 100 et 190 SCH environ.

SOINS MEDICAUX

En cas d'accident ou d'urgence nécessitant une hospitalisation, le patient sera tenu d'acquitter la totalité des frais relatifs aux soins et médicaments reçus, ainsi que les honoraires des médecins généralistes. Il vous est par conséquent recommandé de souscrire à une police d'assurances avant votre départ.

HEURES D'OUVERTURE DES BANQUES

En général, les banques sont ouvertes de 8h à 12h30 et de 13h30 à 15h les lundi, mardi, mercredi et vendredi. Le jeudi, elles ouvrent de 8h à 12h30 et de 13h30 à 17h30. Toutes les banques sont fermées le samedi et le dimanche.

Les bureaux de change situés dans les aéroports et les gares principales sont d'habitude ouverts entre les heures de départ ou d'arrivée du premier et du dernier avion ou train, c'est-à-dire de 8h à 22h tous les jours.

BUREAUX DE POSTE

Les bureaux de poste sont ouverts du lundi au vendredi de 8h à 12h et de 14h à 18h. (Les transactions monétaires sont possibles jusqu'à 17h seulement).

HEURES D'OUVERTURE DES MAGASINS

En semaine, les magasins sont ouverts de 8h à 18h30 et le samedi, de 8h à 13h, sauf le premier samedi du mois, lorsqu'ils restent ouverts jusqu'à 17h. De nombreux magasins ferment entre midi et deux heures.

Remboursement de la TVA: procurez-vous le dépliant "Les achats hors-taxes".

DEPLACEMENTS

Trains
Les services ferroviaires sont très développés en Autriche. Des offres spéciales sont disponibles auprès des Chemins de fer fédéraux autrichiens (renseignements dans les gares principales).

Autobus
Réseau régional développé.

Automobiles
Un permis de conduire international est conseillé et l'assurance au tiers est obligatoire. Le port des ceintures de sécurité est également obligatoire et il est interdit aux enfants de moins de 12 ans de voyager à l'avant de la voiture. Les codes doivent être utilisés en permanence. Un certain nombre de routes de montagne et de tunnels routiers sont à péage.

Toutes les grandes agences internationales de location de voitures possèdent des bureaux en Autriche.

TELEPHONE

Indicatif International	Indicatif du Pays	Indicatifs régionaux des Villes principales
00	43	Salzbourg 662
		Vienne . . . . 1 ou 9

DEUTSCH

ÖSTERREICHISCHE JUGENDHERBERGEN

Für Jugendherbergen gibt es in Österreich zwei unabhängige Verbände, den ÖJHV und das ÖJHW. Viele Jugendherbergen bieten Möglichkeiten zum Skilaufen - siehe jeweilige Angaben. Alle Jugendherbergen sind an dem 'Plan garantierter Standards' beteiligt (siehe Seite 24 für Einzelheiten).

Die Herbergen sind im allgemeinen von 07.00-22.00 Uhr (in Städten von 07.00-24.00 Uhr) geöffnet. Wenige Jugendherbergen haben Selbstversorgungsmöglichkeiten und einige berechnen dafür. In den meisten Jugendherbergen sind Mahlzeiten erhältlich.

Es ist mit einem Preis von 100-190 S, einschließlich Frühstück und Miete von Bettwäsche, zu rechnen (sofern nicht anders angegeben).

GESUNDHEIT

Bei Unfällen oder dringenden Krankheitsfällen, die einen Krankenhausaufenthalt erfordern, muß für die empfangene Behandlung und Arzneimittel voll bezahlt werden. Auch Arztrechnungen müssen voll bezahlt werden. Es empfiehlt sich daher, vor Antritt der Reise eine Privatversicherung abzuschließen.

GESCHÄFTSSTUNDEN DER BANKEN

Im allgemeinen montags, dienstags, mittwochs und freitags 08.00-12.30 und 13.30-15.00 Uhr; donnerstags 08.00-12.30 und 13.30-17.30 Uhr. Samstags und sonntags sind alle Banken geschlossen.

Die Devisenschalter auf Flughäfen und großen Bahnhöfen sind im allgemeinen vom ersten bis zum letzten Flugzeug bzw. Zug, d.h. täglich von 08.00-22.00 Uhr geöffnet.

POSTÄMTER

Postämter sind montags bis freitags von 08.00-12.00 und von 14.00-18.00 Uhr geöffnet (Geldgeschäfte nur bis 17.00 Uhr).

LADENÖFFNUNGSZEITEN

Werktags 08.00-18.30 Uhr und samstags 08.00-13.00 Uhr, außer am ersten Samstag jedes Monats, wenn sie bis 17.00 Uhr geöffnet sind. Viele Geschäfte sind um die Mittagszeit zwei Stunden geschlossen.

Mehrwertsteuer-Rückerstattung: Lassen Sie sich den Prospekt "Steuerfreies Einkaufen" geben.

REISEN

Eisenbahn
Der Eisenbahnverkehr ist in Österreich außerordentlich gut ausgebaut. Über die Österreichischen Bundesbahnen sind Sonderangebote erhältlich (Auskunft auf den größeren Bahnhöfen).

Busse
Gut ausgebautes regionales Netz.

Autofahren

Es ist ratsam, sich einen internationalen Führerschein zu beschaffen. Haftpflichtversicherung ist Pflicht. Das Tragen von Sicherheitsgurten ist obligatorisch, und Kinder unter 12 dürfen sich nicht auf den vorderen Sitzen befinden. Man muß immer mit Abblendlicht fahren. Bei Benutzung mehrerer Bergstraßen und Straßentunnels ist eine Maut zahlbar.

Alle großen internationalen Mietwagen-Unternehmen haben Niederlassungen in Österreich.

FERNSPRECHINFORMATIONEN

Internationale Kennzahl	Landes- Kennzahl	größere Städte - Ortsnetzkennzahlen
00	43	Salzburg 662
		Wien . . . . 1 oder 9

ESPAÑOL

ALBERGUES DE JUVENTUD AUSTRIACOS

Los Albergues de Juventud austriacos están controlados por dos asociaciones que operan de forma independiente, ÖJHV y ÖJHW. Las dos Asociaciones participan en el nuevo Plan de Hostelling International de Normas Garantizadas (ver la página 33 para más información). Muchos albergues disponen de medios para esquiar, véase datos concretos de cada uno.

Por lo general los albergues están abiertos de 07.00 a 22.00 horas (de 07.00 a 24.00 horas en las ciudades). Pocos disponen de cocina donde los huéspedes se preparan la comida y en caso de tenerla a veces cobran por su uso, pero la mayoría sirven comidas.

Los precios de los albergues oscilan entre 100 y 190 chelines incluyendo desayuno y alquiler de ropa de cama, a no ser que se indique lo contrario.

SANIDAD

En caso de accidente o urgencia que requiera ser ingresado en el hospital, se deberá abonar todo el tratamiento y medicamentos recibidos. También hay que pagar por completo los honorarios de los médicos generales. Por consiguiente, se aconseja suscribir un seguro privado antes de viajar.

HORARIO DE BANCOS

Por lo general, de 08.00 a 12.30 y de 13.30 a 15.00 horas los lunes, martes, miércoles y viernes; de 08.00 a 12.30 y de 13.30 a 17.30 horas los jueves. Todos los bancos cierran los sábados y domingos.

Los mostradores de cambio de divisas en los aeropuertos y principales estaciones ferroviarias suelen estar abiertos desde el primer avión o tren hasta el último, es decir, de 08.00 a 22.00 horas cada día.

CASAS DE CORREO

Las casas de correo abren de lunes a viernes de 08.00 a 12.00 y de 14.00 a 18.00 horas. (Transacciones monetarias sólo hasta las 17.00 horas).

HORARIO COMERCIAL

Días entre semana de 08.00 a 18.30 horas y sábados de 08.00 a 13.00 horas excepto el primer sábado de cada mes, cuando los establecimientos permanecen abiertos hasta las 17.00 horas. Muchas tiendas cierran durante dos horas a mediodía.

Reembolso del Impuesto sobre el Valor Añadido: solicite el folleto "Tax-Free Shopping" (compras sin impuestos).

DESPLAZAMIENTOS

Tren
El sistema ferroviario de Austria está muy desarrollado. Existen ofertas especiales a través de los Ferrocarriles Federales de Austria (información en las principales estaciones).

Autobús
Red regional desarrollada.

Coche
Se aconseja estar en posesión de un permiso de conducir internacional; el seguro contra terceros es obligatorio. También es obligatorio llevar cinturones de seguridad y los niños menores de 12 años no pueden viajar en el asiento delantero. En todo momento se deben utilizar las luces cortas. En algunas carreteras de montaña y túneles se paga peaje.

Todas las grandes compañías de alquiler de vehículos tienen oficinas en Austria.

INFORMACION TELEFONICA

Código Internacional	Código Nacional	Indicativo de área de las Ciudades principales
00	43	Salzburgo 662
		Viena . . . . 1 o 9

DISCOUNTS AND CONCESSIONS

Your Hostelling International membership entitles you to a wide range of discounts in Austria, including reduced admissions to sports facilities and attractions near hostels, reduced ski passes in many areas and cheap travel deals from Supertramp, the travel section of ÖJHW.

Hostels in this country may also display this symbol.

Les auberges de ce pays pourront également afficher ce symbole.

Jugendherbergen in diesem Land können auch dieses Symbol zeigen.

Es posible que los albergues de este país exhiban además este símbolo.

Admont (2) ▲ 8911 Admont-Schloss Röthelstein, Aigen 32 Steiermark. (Alt 800m) ☎ (3613) 2432 **FAX** (3613) 279583 **Open:** 27.12-30.10 **Shut:** 13.00-17.00hrs ⊕ 118 ⊖ 135-255AS ᴮᴮⁱⁿᶜ ▯◦▯ ♦♦♦ 🏠 ⬛ 🅿 ⚲ ᵀᵂ Admont ⓡ (☎ (3613) 2432, (316) 824481)

Aigen (2) ▲ 4160 Aigen im Mühlkreis, Adalbert-Stifter-Landesjugendherberge, Oberösterreich. ☎ (7281) 6283 **FAX** (7281) 62834 **Open:** 1.1-31.8; 23.9-31.12 ⊕ 80 ⊖ 100AS ᴮᴮⁱⁿᶜ ▯◦▯ ⓡ (4160 Aigen, Berghäust 32, ☎(7281) 6283 **FAX** (7281) 6283-4

Annaberg (2) ▲ 3222 Annaberg, Annarotte 77, Niederösterreich. (Alt 973m) ☎ YH (2728) 8496 **FAX** (2728) 8442 ⊕ 116 ▯◦▯ ♦♦♦ ⬛ 🅿 ⚲ ⓡ

(1.5-30.8; ÖJHW, 1070 Wien, Mariahilferstr 24 ☎ (1) 5237158, 5237167 **FAX** (1) 5237158 Ext 22)

Bad Aussee (1) ▲ [IBN] A-8990 Bad Aussee, Jugendherbergsstr 148, Steiermark.(Alt 659m) ☎ (3622) 52238 **FAX** (3622) 52238 Ext 88 **Open:** 07.00-09.00hrs, 17.00-22.00hrs ⚑ 145 ● 160-220AS BB|inc ⁙⁙ 2km 500m

Badgastein (2) ▲ 5640 Badgastein, Ederplatz 2, Salzburg. (Alt 1083m) ☎ (6434) 2080 **FAX** (6434) 50688 **Open:** 08.00-10.00hrs, 18.00-22.00hrs ⚑ 180

Bad Großpertholz (2) ▲ 3972 Bad Großpertholz, Bad Großpertholz 177, Niederösterreich. ☎ 2857, 2965 **Open:** 15.4-31.10 ⚑ 52 BB|inc Gmünd,change at Schmalspurbahn to Steinbach- Bad Großpertholz 2km (ÖJHW,Landesjugendherbergswerk Niederösterreich, 1070 Wien, Mariahilfer Straße 24. ☎ (1) 5237158 or 67, **FAX** (1) 5237158 Ext 22)

Bad Ischl (1) ▲ YGH 4820 Bad Ischl, Am Rechensteg 5, Oberösterreich. ☎ (6132) 26577 **FAX** (6132) 26577 Ext 75 **Open:** 1.1-10.12; 28-31.12 ⚑ 122 ● 140AS BB|inc 700m

Bad Kreuzen (2) △ 4362 Bad Kreuzen, Neuaigen 14, Burg. ☎ (7266) 6686, 6255 **Open:** 1.4-30.9 ⚑ 45 (B)

Braunau (1) ▲ 5280 Braunau am Inn, Osternbergerstr 57, Oberösterreich. ☎ (7722) 81638 **FAX** (7722) 81638, 313614 **Open:** 7.1-22.12 ⚑ 48 ● 165AS BB|inc

Bregenz (1) △ 6900 Bregenz, Belruptstrasse 16a, Vorarlberg. ☎ (5574) 42867 **FAX** (5574) 42867 Ext

4 **Open:** 1.4-30.9 ⚑ 155 ● 121AS BB|inc

Drosendorf (2) ▲ 2095 Drosendorf, an der Thaya, Badstrasse 25. ☎ YH (2915) 2257 **Open:** 1.4-15.10 ⚑ 51 (ÖJHW, 1070 Wien, Mariahilferstrasse 24 ☎ (1) 5237158, 5237167 **FAX** (1) 5237158 Ext 22)

Ebensee (2) ▲ 4802 Ebensee-Rindbach, Rindbachstrasse 15, Oberösterreich. (Alt 440m) ☎ (6133) 6698 **FAX** (6133) 669885 **Open:** 1.4-30.10 **Shut:** some weekends ☎ in advance ⚑ 80 BB|inc (4020 Linz, Kapuzinerstr 14 ☎ (732) 782720 **FAX** (732) 7817894)

Engelhartszell (2) ▲ Bike Hostel, 4090 Engelhartszell 68. ☎ (7717) 8115 **FAX** (7717) 8115 **Open:** 1.5-31.10 ⚑ 38 (on request) Engelhartszell Linz/Passau ap YH (4020 Linz, Kapuzinerstrasse 14 ☎ (732) 782720 **FAX** (732) 7817894)

Feldkirch (2) ▲ 6805 Feldkirch-Levis, Reichstrasse 111, Vorarlberg. (Alt 458m) ☎ (5522) 73181 **FAX** (5522) 79399 ⚑ 80 BB|inc (B D) 2km 2

Feldkirchen (1) ▲ 9560 Kärnten, Briefelsdorf 7, Am Maltschachersee. ☎ (4277) 2644 **Open:** 08.00-18.00hrs, 23.4-15.10 ⚑ 38 BB|inc

Graz (1) ▲ [2SW] [IBN] [CC] A-8020 Graz, Idlhofgasse 74, Steiermark. (Alt 368m) ☎ (316) 914876 **FAX** (316) 914876 ext 88 **Open:** 07.00-22.00hrs ⚑ 136 ● 200-240AS BB|inc ✈ 7km Radweg 500m 50m (1.5-30.8)

Grundlsee (1) ▲ A-8993 Grundlsee, Wienern- Gössl 149. (Alt 723m) ☎ (3622) 8629 **FAX** (3622) 8629 Ext 4 **Open:** 1.5-31.10 ⚑ 60 ● 160-180AS

BBinc ⑩ ♦♦♦ ⌖ 🅿 ⚓ 🚆 7km 🚐
500m Ⓡ (1.5-30.8)

Hallein (1) ▲ A-5400 Hallein, Schloss
Wispach-Esterhazy, Salzburg. ☎ (6245)
80397 **FAX** (6245) 80397 Ext 3 **Open:**
07.00-22.00hrs, 1.4-30.9 ⌁ 112 ●
160AS BBinc ⑩ ⌖ 🅿 🚆 1km 🚐
700m

Hard (1) △ 6971 Hard, Allmendstr 73,
Vorarlberg (15km from Bregenz). ☎
(5574) 65947 **Open:** 1.4-31.12 ⌁ 22
● 110AS Ⓡ

Haslach (2) △ 4170 Haslach an der
Mühl, Sternwaldstrasse 7,
Oberösterreich. ☎ (7289) 71153 ⌁ 45
📱 Ⓡ (4170 Haslach, Postfach 53)

Heiligenblut (1) ▲ 9844 Heiligenblut,
Hof 36, Kärnten. (Alt 1301m) ☎ (4824)
2259 **FAX** (4824) 2259 **Open:**
26.12-1.9 ⌁ 84 ● 160AS BBinc ⑩ ♦♦♦
🅿

Hinterstoder (2) ▲ 4573 Hinterstoder,
Mitterstoder 137, Oberösterreich. (Alt
585m) ☎ (7564) 5227 **FAX** (7564)
522711 **Shut:** some weekends ☎ in
advance ⌁ 96 ⑩ ♦♦♦ ⊞ 🅿 ⚲ 🚲 Ⓡ
(4020 Linz, Kapuzinerstr 14 ☎ (732)
782720 **FAX** (732) 7817894)

INNSBRUCK (5 Hostels)

Innsbruck (2) - **Reichenauerstrasse** ▲
2NE IBN 6020 Innsbruck,
Reichenauerstrasse 147, Tirol. (Alt
574m) ☎ (512) 346179, 346180 **FAX**
(512) 346179 Ext 12 Open:
07.00-10.00hrs, 17.00-23.00hrs,
1.1-22.12; 27-31.12 ⌁ 178 ⑩(B) 📱
♦♦♦ 🅿 ⚲ ✈ Innsbruck Kranebitten
5km 🚐 R 2 stops / change to O

Innsbruck (2) - Studentenheim ▲ 2NE
6020 Innsbruck, Reichenauerstrasse
147. (Alt 574m) ☎ (512) 346179,
346180 **FAX** (512) 346179 Ext 12
Open: 07.00-10.00hrs, 17.00-23.00hrs,
5.7-31.8 ⌁ 96 BBinc 🅿 ✈ Innsbruck

Kranebitten 5km 🚐 R 2 stops/change
to O

Innsbruck (2) - Rennweg ▲ 2NE 6020
Innsbruck, Rennweg 17b, Tirol. (Alt
574m) ☎ (512) 585814 **FAX** (512)
585814-4 **Open:** 1.7-31.8 ⌁ 75 ⑩
(Grps only) ⚲ ✈ Innsbruck
Kranebitten 5km 🚐 4 or C stop
Handelsakademie

Innsbruck (1) - Volkshaus ▲ 6020
Innsbruck, Volkshaus, Radetzkystr 47.
(Alt 574m) ☎ (512) 395882 **FAX** (512)
395882/4 ⌁ 52 ● 155-170AS BBinc
⚲ ✈ Innsbruck Kranebitten 5km

**Innsbruck (1) - St Nikolaus +
Glockenhaus** △ 3W 6020
Innsbruck, Tirol, St.Nikolaus, Innstr
95. ☎ (512) 286515 **FAX** (512) 286515
Ext 14 ⌁ 100 ● 100AS ⑩ 🚆 5km

Judenburg (1) ▲ IBN YGH
Judenburg, Kaserngasse 22, A-8750
Judenburg. (Alt 735m) ☎ (3572) 87355
FAX (3572) 87355-88 Open:
07.00-09.00hrs, 17.00-22.00hrs ⌁ 80
● 195-270AS BBinc ⑩ ♦♦♦ ♿ ⌖ 📷 🅿
🚲 ⚓ 🚆 Judenburg 2km 🚐 500m
Ⓡ

Kaprun (1) ▲ A- 5710 Kaprun,
Nikolaus Gassnerstrasse 448, Salzburg.
(Alt 911m) ☎ (6547) 8507 **FAX** (6547)
7522 Ext 3 **Open:** 07.00-22.00hrs ⌁
150 ● 170-230AS BBinc ⑩ ♦♦♦ 🅿 ⚲
🚆 Zell am See 6km

KLAGENFURT (2 Hostels)

Klagenfurt (1) - **YGH** ▲ IBN A-9020
Klagenfurt, Universitätsviertel,
Neckheimg. 6. ☎ (463) 230020 FAX
(463) 230020 Ext 20 Open:
07.00-10.00hrs, 17.00-22.00hrs ⌁
146 ● 180-185AS BBinc ⑩ ♦♦♦ ♿ 📷 🅿
✈ 4km ⛴ 2.5km 🚆 3km 🚐 10,
11, 12 100m Ⓡ (1.5-15.7)

Klagenfurt (2) - Kolping ▲ 9020
Klagenfurt, Kolping Jugendgästehaus,

Enzenbergstrasse 26, Kärnten. ℓ (463) 56965 **FAX** (463) 5696532 **Open:** 10.7-10.9 ⊠ 200 🍽(B) ⚱

Klosterneuburg (2) ▲ 3400 Klosterneuburg-Gugging, Hüttersteig 8, Niederösterreich. ℓ (2243) 83501 **Open:** 1.5-15.9 ⊠ 65 🍽 ☞

Krems (1) ▲ 3500 Krems an der Donau, Ringstrasse 77, Niederösterreich. ℓ YH (2732) 83452 **Open:** 07.00-09.30hrs, 17.00-20.00hrs, 1.4-31.10 ⊠ 52 ⊖ 160AS 🅱inc 🍽 Ⓡ (1060 Wien, Gumpendorferstr 63 ℓ (1) 5864145 **FAX** (1) 5864145 Ext 3)

Lackenhof (2) ▲ 3295 Lackenhof am Ötscher, Niederösterreich. (Alt 810m) ℓ YH (7480) 251 **FAX** (7480) 338 ⊠ 137 🍽 👪 🚃 ⊼ 🚴 Ⓡ (ÖJHW, 1070 Wien, Mariahilferstr 24 ℓ (1) 5237158, 5237167 **FAX** (1) 5237158 Ex 22)

Lech (1) ▲ 6764 Vorarlberg, Arlberger Taxizentrale, Lech 428. (Alt 1444m) ℓ (5583) 2501 **FAX** (5583) 32586 **Open:** 15.6-15.10 ⊠ 45 ⊖ 180AS 🅱inc ☞ 👪 🔲

Lech- Stubenbach (2) ▲ Jugendheim Lech- Stubenbach, A- 6764 Lech am Arlberg, Stubenbach 244. ℓ (5583) 2419 **FAX** (5583) 24194 **Open:** 07.00-10.00hrs, 17.00-20.00hrs, 15.12-23.4; 1.7-20.9 ⊠ 64 ⊖ 70-280AS 🍽(B D) 👪 ⊼ ⚱ 🚌 Langen am Arlberg 🚐 Langen am Arlberg-Lech am Arlberg Ⓡ (Wi)

LINZ (3 Hostels)

Linz (1) - **Stanglhofweg** ▲ 4020 Linz, Stanglhofweg 3, Oberösterreich: (near the stadium, 1km to centre) ℓ (732) 664434 **FAX** (732) 602164 **Open:** 7.1-20.12 ⊠ 170 ⊖ 158AS 🅱inc 🍽 👪 🔲 ✈ 20km 🚌 2km 🚐 17, 45, 1922, 300m; 27, 30m 🚃 1.5km ap Tennisplatz

Linz (1) - **Blütenstr** ▲ Landesjugendherberge Linz im Lentia 2000, 4040 Linz, Blütenstr 23. ℓ (732) 737078 **FAX** (732) 737078-15 ⊠ 106 ⊖ 125-175AS 🅱inc 🍽

Linz (2) - **Kapuzinerstr** ▲ 4020 Linz, Kapuzinerstr 14. ℓ (732) 782720 **FAX** (732) 7817894 ⊠ 36 ☞ 👪 🔲

Maria Lankowitz (1) ▲ 〔IBN〕 A 8591 Maria Lankowitz, Am See 2, Styria. (Alt 500m) ℓ (3144) 71700 **FAX** (3144) 71700 Ext 88 **Open:** 07.00-09.00hrs, 17.00-22.00hrs, 1.1-31.10; 25-31.12 ⊠ 126 ⊖ 195-230AS 🅱inc 🍽 👪 ♿ 🔲 ⊼ 🚴 ⚱ 🚂 1km 🚐 🚃 300m

Mariazell (1) ▲ A- 8630 Mariazell, Fischer v. Erlachweg 2, Steiermark. (Alt 868m) ℓ (3882) 2669 **FAX** (3882) 2669 Ext 88 **Open:** 07.00-09.00hrs, 17.00-22.00hrs ⊠ 130 ⊖ 135-195AS 🅱inc 🍽 👪 ⊼ 🚂 2.5km 🚐 500m Ⓡ (1.5-30.8)

Maurach am Achensee (1) △ 〔CC〕 Dr Stumpf Jugendherberge, 6212 Maurach am Achensee. (Tirol) (Alt 950m) ℓ (5243) 5239 **FAX** (5243) 5239 ⊠ 200 Su, 70 Wi ⊖ 160AS 🅱inc 🍽(B D) 👪 🚃 🔲 ⊼ 🚴 ⚱ ✈ Innsbruck 40km 🚂 Jenbach 10km 🚐 Achenseelinie 7km ap Maurach

Melk (2) ▲ 3390 Melk an der Donau, Abt-Karl-Strasse 42, Niederösterreich. ℓ YH (2752) 2681 **FAX** (2752) 4257 **Open:** 15.3-31.10 ⊠ 104 🍽 👪 🚃 🔲 Ⓡ (ÖJHW, 1070 Wien, Mariahilferstr 24 ℓ (523) 7158, (523) 7167 **FAX** (1) 5237158 Ext 22).

Mondsee (1) ▲ 5310 Mondsee, Krankenhausstrasse 9, Oberösterreich. ℓ (6232) 2418 **FAX** (6232) 2418 Ext 75 **Open:** 15.1-14.12 ⊠ 80 ⊖ 140AS 🅱inc 🍽 👪 🔲 ⚱

Murau (2) ▲ 8850 Murau, St. Leonhardsplatz 4 Steiermark. (Alt

832m) ☎ (3532) 2395 **FAX** (3532) 2395 **Open:** 27.12-30.10 **Shut:** 13.00-17.00hrs ⊟ 130 ● 115-230AS ᴮᴮinc ⦿ ⋔⬥ ⛗ ⬚ P ⟐ ℝ (☎ (316) 824481, (3532) 2395)

Mureck (2) △ 8480 Mureck, Austraße, Steiermark. ☎ (3472) 2164/2 **FAX** (3472) 21056 **Open:** 07.00-19.00hrs ⊟ 70

Neuberg (1) ▲ 8692 Neuberg an der Mürz, Kaplanweg 8, Steiermark. (Alt 781m) ☎ (3857) 8495 **FAX** (3857) 8495-4 ⊟ 50 ● 125-150AS ᴮᴮinc ⦿ ⛟ 300m ⛍ 300m

Neu- Nagelberg (1) ▲ 3871 Neu-Nagelberg 114. ☎ (2859) 476 **Open:** 10.1-23.12 ⊟ 39 ● 120 AS ᴮᴮinc ⦿ ℝ (1060 Wien, Gumpendorferstr 63 ☎ (1) 5864145 **FAX** (1) 58641453)

Neusiedl (1) ⚇ 7100 Neusiedl am See, Herbergsgasse 1, Burgenland. ☎ (2167) 2252 **FAX** (2167) 2252 **Open:** 1.3-30.11 ⊟ 86 ᴮᴮinc ⦿ ⋔ ⬚ ♣ ▲ ℝ

Neustift (2) ▲ 4143 Neustift im Mühlkreis 71, Rannahof, Oberösterreich. ☎ (7284) 8196 ⊟ 100 ⦿ ⋔ ⬚ P

Obernberg (2) ▲ Jugendheim am Brenner, Obernberg 49, 6156 Obernberg. (Alt 1400m) ☎ (5274) 87475 **FAX** (5274) 87475 **Open:** (Grps only) **Shut:** 16.4-31.5; 1.10-26.12 ⊟ 85 ᴮᴮinc ⦿ P ⟐

Oberndorf (2) △ 3281 Oberndorf an der Melk, Unterhub 5, Rauschhof, Niederösterreich. ☎ (7483) 267 ⊟ 60 ⦿

Obertraun (2) ▲ 4831 Obertraun, Winkl 26, Oberösterreich. (Alt 511m) ☎ (6131) 360 **FAX** (6131) 3604 **Shut:** some weekends ☎ in advance ⊟ 160 ⦿ ⋔ ⬚ P ⟐ ♣ ℝ (4020 Linz,

Kapuzinerstr 14 ☎ (732) 782720 **FAX** (732) 7817894)

Pernitz (2) △ 2763 Pernitz, Hauptstr 47, Niederösterreich. ☎ (2632) 72373 **Open:** 1.4-31.10 ⊟ 42 ☀

Pfunds (1) ▲ JGH Dangl, A- 6542 Pfunds 347, Tirol. ☎ (5474) 5244 **FAX** (5474) 5244-4 **Open:** 08.00-23.00hrs ⊟ 50 ● 160-190AS ᴮᴮinc ⦿ ☀ ⋔ ⬓ ✈ Munich A⛍ Innsbruck ⛟ Landeck 30km ⛍ Landeck- Pfunds ℝ ● may also be rented as self-catering accomodation (house)

Ramingstein (1) ▲ Burg Finstergrün, 5591 Ramingstein, Wald 65 ☎ (06475) 228 **Open:** (Grps only) 1.5-31.10 ⊟ 160 ● 140AS ᴮᴮinc ⦿ ⛗ ⬚ P

Rechnitz (1) ▲ Burgenland, 7471 Rechnitz, Hochstrasse 1 ☎ (03363) 245 **Open:** (Grps only) ⊟ 58 ● 74AS ᴮᴮinc ⦿

Reutte (2) △ 6600 Reutte, Prof Dengel-Strasse 20, Tirol. ☎ (5672) 72310, 72309 **Open:** 1.7-25.8 ⊟ 28 ☀

Reutte- Höfen (1) ▲ 6600 Reutte, Jugendgästehaus am Graben 1, Tirol. ☎ (5672) 62644 **FAX** (5672) 65904 **Open:** 18.12-2.11 ⊟ 50 ● 140-160AS ᴮᴮinc ⦿ ⋔ ⟐ ℝ (**FAX** (5672) 65904)

Riegersburg (2) △ 8333 Riegersburg 3, im Cillitor, Steiermark. ☎ (3153) 8217 **FAX** (3153) 824481/6 **Open:** 1.5-31.10 **Shut:** 13.00-17.00hrs ⊟ 48 ● 115-135AS ᴮᴮinc ⦿ ⛗ ▲

SALZBURG (4 Hostels)

Salzburg (1) - **Jugendgastehaus** (*see town plan on next page*) ⚇ ⸢1 SW⸣ ⸢IBN⸣ ⸢CC⸣ A-5020 Salzburg Nonntal, Josef-Preis Allee 18. ☎ (662) 8426700 **FAX** (662) 841101 **Open:** 07.00-24.00hrs ⊟ 390 ● 160-265AS ᴮᴮinc ⦿ ☀ ⋔ ⬥ ⬓ P ♣ ✈ Salzburg 4km ⛍ 5, 51 ap Justizgebaude

SALZBURG - Jugendgastehaus

Salzburg (2) - Aigner Strasse ▲ 2NW
5026 Salzburg, Aigner Strasse 34. ✆
(662) 623248 **FAX** (662) 623248 Ext
13　　**Open:**　　07.00-09.00hrs,
17.00-24.00hrs, 1.7-31.8 ⇿ 120 ⛄
⭢ ✈ Salzburg 🚐 49

Salzburg (2) - Eduard-Heinrich-Haus
△ 3SW IBN CC Eduard-Heinrich-
Haus, 5020 Salzburg -Josefiau, Eduard-
Heinrich- Str 2. ✆ (662) 625976 FAX
(662) 627980 Open: 07.00-09.00hrs,
17.00-24.00hrs ⇿ 150 ⛄ ⭢ ⬚ P ✈
Salzburg 🚐 51, 95 R (⭢)

Salzburg (2) - Haunspergstrasse ⛰
2SE 5020 Salzburg, Haunspergstrasse
27. ✆ (662) 875030 **FAX** (662) 883477
Open:　　　　　07.00-14.00hrs,
17.00-2400hrs, 1.7-26.8 ⇿ 105 ⛄(B)
⭢ ⬚ ✈ Salzburg

Schladming (1) ⛰ IBN 8970
Schladming, Coburgstrasse 253,
Steiermark. (Alt 749m) ✆ (3687) 24531
FAX (3687) 24531 Ext 88 Open:
07.00-09.00hrs, 17.00-22.00hrs ⇿
198 ⊖ 170-260AS BBinc ⛄ ⭢ P ⛷
🚂 2km 🚐 200m R (24.12-31.3)

Sillian (2) △ 9920 Sillian-Arnbach 37,
Tirol. (Alt 1100m) ✆ (4842) 6321
Open: 1.5-31.10 ⇿ 37 ⛴

Soboth (2) ▲ 8554 Soboth, Steiermark.
(Alt 1065m) ✆ (3460) 207 **Open:**
1.5-31.10 **Shut:** 13.00-17.00hrs ⇿ 56
⊖ 115-235AS BBinc ⛄ ⚒ P ⛵ R
(✆ (3460) 207, (316) 824481)

Spital am Pyhrn (2) ▲ 'Lindenhof',
4582　Spital　am　Pyhrn　77,
Oberösterreich. ✆ (7563) 214 ⇿ 140
⛄ ⭢ P

Spittal (1) ▲ 9800 Spittal an der Drau,
Stadiongelände, zur Seilbahn 2 neben
Goldecktalstation, Kärnten. ✆ (4762)
3252 **FAX** (4762) 3252 Ext 4 **Open:**
08.00-22.00hrs ⇿ 67 ⊖ 130AS ⛄ P

Spittal/Goldeck (2) ▲ 9800
Spittal/Goldeck, Kärnten. (Alt 1650m)
✆ (4762) 2701 **Open:** 26.12-31.3;
28.6-20.9 ⇿ 45 ⛄ ⭢ ⛷ (access by
cable- railway only) R (1.4-27.6;
21.9-25.12 Supertramp, 1010 Wien,
Helferstorferstrasse 4 ✆ (222) 5335137)

Steyr (1) ▲ 4400 Steyr, Josef
Hafnerstrasse 14, Oberösterreich. ✆
(7252) 45580 **FAX** (7252) 45580
Open: 9.1-22.12 ⇿ 45 ⊖ 69-83AS
BBinc ⛄ ⛴

Stummerberg (2) △ 6272
Kaltenbach/Stumm,　　Zillertal,
Stummerberg 68, Tirol. ✆ (5283) 3577
⇿ 40 ⛄ ⛴

St Gilgen (1) ⛰ YGH, 5340 St Gilgen,
Mondseerstraße 7-11, Salzburg. (Alt
646m) ✆ (6227) 365 **FAX** (6227) 365
Ext 75 **Open:** 08.00-09.00hrs,
17.00-1900hrs, 27.1-20.12 ⇿ 128 ⊖
140-265AS BBinc ⛄ ⭢ P ⛵ 🚐
500m

St Johann im Pongau (1) ⛰ 5600 St
Johann im Pongau, JH Weitenmoos,
Salzburg. (Alt 900m) ✆ (6412) 6222
FAX (6412) 6222 Ext 4 **Open:**
07.00-22.00hrs, 2.12-14.10 ⇿ 130 ⊖
180-230AS BBinc ⛄ ⭢ P ⛷

St Martin am Tennengebirge (1) ⚠
4SE JH Sonnrain, A-5522 St Martin
Nr 100, Salzburg. (Alt 1080m) ☎
(6463) 7318 **FAX** (6463) 7318 Ext 3
Open: 07.00-22.00hrs, 1.1-17.4;
11.5-30.9; 16-31.12 ⊠ 126 ⊜
160-230AS BBinc ⚙ ⛄ P ⚓

St Michael im Lungau (1) ⚠ 4SE A-
5582 Herbergsgasse 348, Salzburg. (Alt
1075m) ☎ (6477) 630 **FAX** (6477) 630
Ext 3 **Open:** 07.00-2200hrs, 1.1-17.4;
11.5-30.9; 16-31.12 ⊠ 188 ⊜
160-230AS BBinc ⚙ ⛄ ⛄ P ⚓

Ternitz (1) △ 2630 Ternitz, Straße des
12, Februar 38. ☎ (2630) 38483 **FAX**
(2630) 38483 **Open:** 1-31.1;
15.2-14.10; 15.11-31.12 ⊠ 28 ⊜
120AS BBinc ⚙

Trofaiach (1) △ A- 8793 Trofaiach,
Rebenburgg 2, Steiermark. (Alt 600m)
☎ (3847) 22603 **FAX** (3847) 22604
Open: (Grps only) ⊠ 41 ⊜ 120AS ⚙
⛁ P R

Uderns (1) ⚠ 6271 Uderns, Finsing 63,
YGH 'Finsingerhof'. ☎ (5288) 2010
FAX (5288) 2866 ⊠ 89 ⊜ 160AS BBinc
⚙ ⛄ P ⛄ 350m R

Ulmerfeld- Hausmening (1) ▲ 3363
Ulmerfeld- Hausmening Burgweg 1
Schloss, Niederösterreich. ☎ (7475)
4080 **Open:** 07.00-10.00hrs,
17.00-20.00hrs, 10.1-23.12 ⊠ 62 ⊜
160AS BBinc ⚙ ⛄ ⛁ ⛁ ⛄ Amstetten
14km, Ulmerfeld- Hausmening 3km
⛄ 14km R (ÖJHV-LG-NÖ, 1060
Wien, Gumpendorferstr 63 ☎(1)
5864145 **FAX**(1) 5864145 Ext 3)

Vienna/Vienne/Viena ☞ **Wien**

Villach (1) ⚠ IBN 9500 Villach, St
Martin, Dinzlweg 34, Kärnten. ☎
(4242) 56368 **FAX** (4242) 56368-20
(between 18.00-11.00hrs only) ⊠ 144
⊜ 160AS BBinc ⚙ P ⚙

Weissenbach am Attersee (1) ▲ Franz
von Schönthanallee 42, 4854
Weissenbach, Oberösterreich. ☎ (7663)
220 **FAX** (7663) 220 Ext 4 **Open:**
1.5-31.8 ⊠ 172 ⊜ 106AS ⚙ P ⚓
⛄ 150m

Wels (1) ▲ 4600 Wels, Dragonerstr. 22.
☎ (7242) 67284 **FAX** YH (7242)
51521 **Open:** 7.1-23.12 ⊠ 50 ⊜
105AS BBinc P ⛄ 3km

Weyer (2) ⚠ 3335 Weyer, Mühlein 56,
Oberösterreich. ☎ (7447) 284 **FAX**
(7447) 2844 **Shut:** some weekends ☎ in
advance ⊠ 136 ⚙ ⛄ ⛄ ⛁ P ⚓ R
(4020 Linz, Kapuzinerstr 14 ☎ (732)
782720 **FAX** (732) 7817894)

Weyregg (2) ⚠ 4852 Weyregg 3. ☎
(7664) 2780 **FAX** (7664) 27804 **Open:**
1.5-31.10 ⊠ 42 ⚙ ⛄ ⛁ P ⚓ R
(ÖJHW, 4020 Linz, Kapuzinerstr 14 ☎
(732) 782720 **FAX** (732) 7817894)

WIEN (6 Hostels)
(*see town plan on next page*)

Wien (1) - Brigittenau ⚠ 4NW IBN
1200 Wien, Friedrich Engelsplatz 24.
☎ (1) 33282940, 3300598 **FAX** (1)
3308379 **Open:** 07.00-01.00hrs ⊠
334 ⊜ 160-190AS BBinc ⚙ ⛄ ⛁ ⛁ ⛄
P ⛟ ⚓ ✈ Schwechdt 20km A⛄
Western Station, then U6 ⚓
Reichsbrücke 2.5km ⛄ W 6km, S
7km, Floridsdorfer Brücke 100m ⛄
11A, 5A ap Friedrich Engelsplatz ⛄
N, 31, 32 ap Friedrich Engelsplatz U
U6 Handelskai 500m R (Grps)

Wien (2) - Myrthengasse/Neustiftgasse
⚠ 2W IBN 1070 Wien,
Myrthengasse 7, Neustiftgasse 85. ☎(1)
52363160, 52394290 **FAX** (1)
5235849 **Open:** 07.00-01.00hrs ⊠
241 ⚙ ⛄ ⛁ ⛁ ⛄ ✈ 20km A⛄ to
Westbahnhof ⚓ 5km ⛄ W 1.2km,
S 3km ⛄ 13A, 48A ⛄ 46 R (Grps)

Wien (2) - Jugendherberge Lechnerstrasse △ ⬛3SE 1030 Wien, Lechnerstrasse 12. 📞 (1) 7131494 **Open:** 1.3-30.11 ⊠ 53 ✈ 15km 🚢 3km 🚂 W 5km, S 4km 🚃 18 1km ⬛U U3 Kardinal Nagl Platz 500m

Wien (1) - Hostel Ruthensteiner ▲ ⬛5W Ruthensteiner JH, 1150 Wien, Robert Hamerling 24. 📞 (1) 8934202, 8932796 **FAX** (1) 8932796 **Open:** 24hrs ⊠ 77 (no Grps) ⊖ 129-239AS ⭤(B) 🚹 ♦♦♦ 🚲 ✈ 20km A🚃 to Westbahnhof 🚢 6km 🚂 W 0.2km, S 3.2km 🚃 18 ⬛U 3, 6 Westbahnhof 200m

Wien (1) - Jugendgästehaus der Stadt Wien ▲ ⬛10W 1130 Wien, Hütteldorf, Schlossberggasse 8. 📞 (1) 8771501, 8770263 **FAX** (1) 8770263 Ext 2 **Open:** 07.00-24.00hrs ⊠ 270 ⊖ 153AS ⬛BBinc 🍴 ⬛ ⬛P ✈ 25km A🚃 to Westbahnhof 🚂 W 6km, S 7km, Hütteldorf 500m 🚃 52B ⬛U U4 Hütteldorf-Hocking 500m ⬛R (Grps)

Wien (1) - Schloßherberge am Wilhelminenberg ▲ ⬛10W 1160 Wien, Savoyenstrasse 2. 📞 (1) 4858503700 **FAX** (1) 4858503702 **Open:** 07.00-24.00hrs ⊠ 164 ⊖ 220AS ⬛BBinc 🍴 ♦♦♦ ⬛ ⬛P ✈ 40km A🚃 Air Terminal-Hilton 🚢 Reichstrücke 15km 🚂 S 13km, W 10km 🚃 46B, 146B ⬛U U6 Thaliastrasse/ Josefstädterstrasse ⬛R (♦♦♦)

Wiener Neustadt (1) ▲ 2700 Wiener Neustadt, Europahaus, Promenade 1, Niederösterreich. (50km SE of Wien) 📞 (2622) 29695 **Open:** 07.00-10.00hrs, 17.00-20.00hrs, 1.7-31.8 ⊠ 36 ⊖ 160AS ⬛BBinc ♦♦♦ ⬛R (1060 Wien, Gumpendorferstr 63 📞 (1) 5864145 **FAX** (1) 5864145 Ext 3)

Zell am See (2) ▲ 5700 Zell am See, Haus der Jugend, Seespitzstrasse 13, Salzburg. (Alt 800m) 📞 (6542) 57185 **FAX** (6542) 71854 **Open:** 1.12-31.10 ⊠ 102 🍴 ♦♦♦ 🛒 ⬛P 🏊

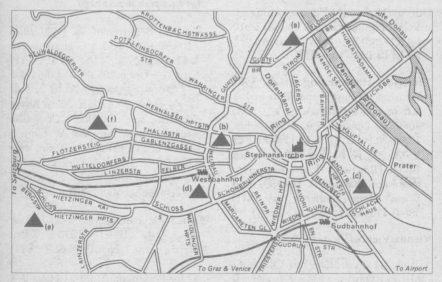

VIENNA - (a) Jugendgastehaus, (b) Myrthengasse, (c) Lechnerstrasse, (d) Ruthensteiner, (e) Stadt Wien, (f) Wilhelminenberg

BELGIUM
BELGIQUE
BELGIEN
BELGICA

ASSURED STANDARD

(1) Vlaamse Jeugdherbergcentrale, Van Stralenstraat 40, B-2060 Antwerpen, Belgium.

☎ (32) (3) 2327218
FAX (32) (3) 2318126

Office Hours:
Monday-Friday 09.00-18.00hrs, From Easter to 30.9 also Saturday 09.00-13.00hrs.

Travel Section: c/o Vlaamse Jeugdherbergcentrale, Van Stralenstraat 40, B-2060 Antwerpen, Belgium.

☎ (32) (3) 2327218
FAX (32) (3) 2318126

(2) Les Auberges de Jeunesse, Rue Van Oost 52, B-1030, Bruxelles, Belgium.

☎ (32) (2) 2153100
FAX (32) (2) 2428356

Office Hours:
Monday-Friday, 09.00-12.00hrs and 13.00-17.00hrs

Travel Section:
c/o Les Auberges de Jeunesse, Rue Van Oost 52, B-1030 Bruxelles, Belgium.

☎ (32) (2) 2153100
FAX (32) (2) 2428356

IBN Booking Centres for outward bookings
■ **Antwerp**, *via National Office (1) above.*
■ **Brussels**-Rue Van Oost, *via National Office (2) above.*

Capital:	Brussels
Language:	Dutch, French, German
Currency:	BEF (Belgian franc)
Population:	10,000,100
Size:	30,515 sq km

BELGIUM

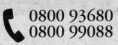

BELGIAN HOSTELS

The 'Vlaamse Jeugdherbergcentrale', hostels marked (1), runs hostels in the northern region. 'Les Auberges de Jeunesse' (LAJ) hostels marked (2), operate in the southern part of the country. Both Associations have hostels in the capital-city of Brussels.

Hostels are open 08.00-23.00hrs and in Brussels 07.00-01.00hrs. Some hostels close during the day between 10.00 and 16.00hrs or during the winter for one night a week, so check individual entries carefully.

Expect to pay 310-660BF per night including breakfast plus bedlinen hire if required. Half price for children under 9 and free for under 3's travelling with their family. Most hostels have family rooms which you should book in advance.

All Belgian Youth Hostels have inter-hostel Fax Reservation Service available named BELGOFAX.

PASSPORTS AND VISAS

An identity card is sufficient for nationals of EC countries. In any other case, please contact Belgian Embassy or Consulate in your country of residence.

HEALTH

If you are an EC national get an E111 form DSS for emergency treatment during a short stay in Belgium. Other nationals should obtain private health insurance before travelling.

There are no specific vaccinations required.

BANKING HOURS

Banks are open Monday to Friday, 09.00-16.00hrs.

POST OFFICES

Post Offices are open Monday to Friday, 09.00-17.00hrs.

SHOPPING HOURS

Shops are normally open 09.00-18.00hrs, Monday to Saturday.

TRAVEL

Rail
Rail travel is extremely good especially with a Benelux Tourrail Pass. The "Go-Pass" for young people up to 26 years and the "Multipass" for small groups offer cheap tickets.

Bus
Brussels has a metro system, buses and trams. All larger cities have good local buses. There is also a national bus company for longer distances.

Ferry
Ferry services are available from Oostende to Ramsgate and Zeebrugge to Hull.

Driving
Driving is on the right-hand side. Speed limits range from 50-120kmph. There is a good highway network.

PUBLIC HOLIDAYS

New Year, 1 January; Easter, 30/31 March; Labour Day, 1 May; Ascension, 8 May; Pentecost, 18/19 May; Flemish Community Day, 11 July; National Holiday, 21 July; Assumption, 15 August; French Community Day, 27 September; All Saints Day, 1 November; Armistice, 11 November; Christmas, 25 December.

TELEPHONE INFORMATION

International Code	Country Code	Main City Area Codes	
00	32	Antwerpen	3
		Bruges	50
		Brussels	2
		Gent	9
		Liège	4
		Namur	81
		Tournai	69

FRANÇAIS

AUBERGES DE JEUNESSE BELGES

La 'Vlaamse Jeugdherbergcentrale', auberges indiquées (1), gère les auberges situées dans la région du nord. 'Les Auberges de Jeunesse', auberges indiquées (2), gère celles qui se trouvent dans la partie sud. Les deux associations possèdent des auberges dans la capitale, Bruxelles.

Les auberges sont ouvertes de 8h à 23h et, à Bruxelles, de 7h à 1h. Certaines auberges ferment dans la journée entre 10h et 16h ou, en hiver, pendant une nuit par semaine. Nous vous conseillons de consulter la liste avec soin.

Une nuit avec petit déjeûner coûte de 310 à 660 FB, plus location de draps, éventuellement. Les enfants de moins de 9 ans paient demi-tarif et les enfants de moins de 3 ans s'ils voyagent en famille ne paient pas. La plupart des auberges peuvent offrir des chambres familiales qui doivent être réservées à l'avance.

Toutes les auberges belges mettent à votre disposition BELGOFAX, notre service de réservation par fax inter-auberges.

PASSEPORTS ET VISAS

Une carte d'identité suffit pour les citoyens des pays de la Communauté Européenne. Dans tous les autres cas, veuillez contacter l'Ambassade ou le Consulat de Belgique dans votre propre pays.

SOINS MEDICAUX

Si vous habitez dans un pays de la Communauté Européenne, il vous suffit d'obtenir un formulaire E111 DSS pour le cas où un traitement d'urgence serait requis au cours d'un bref séjour en Belgique. Il est conseillé aux citoyens d'autres pays de souscrire à une police d'assurance maladie avant d'entreprendre leur voyage.

Aucune vaccination spéciale n'est requise.

HEURES D'OUVERTURE DES BANQUES

Les banques sont ouvertes du lundi au vendredi, de 9h à 16h.

BUREAUX DE POSTE

Les bureaux de poste sont ouverts du lundi au vendredi, de 9h à 17h.

HEURES D'OUVERTURE DES MAGASINS

Les magasins sont en général ouverts de 9h à 18h, du lundi au samedi.

DEPLACEMENTS

Trains

Les déplacements en train sont excellents, surtout si vous avez une carte Bénélux Tourrail. Les cartes "Go-Pass" pour les jeunes jusqu'à 26 ans et "Multipass" pour les petits groupes permettent d'obtenir des billets à bas prix.

Autobus

Bruxelles possède un réseau de métro, de bus et de trams. Toutes les grandes villes ont un bon service d'autobus. Il existe également une compagnie d'autobus nationale pour les longs parcours.

Ferry-boats

Les traversées s'effectuent d'Ostende à Ramsgate et de Zeebrugge à Hull.

Automobiles

La conduite est à droite. Les limitations de vitesse vont de 50 à 120km/h. Le réseau autoroutier est très développé.

JOURS FERIES

Nouvel an, 1er janvier; Pâques, 30/31 mars; Fête du travail, 1 mai; Ascension, 8 mai; Pentecôte, 18/19 mai; Fête de la Communauté flamande, 11 juillet; Fête nationale, 21 juillet; Assomption, 15 août; Fête de la Communauté française, 27 septembre; Toussaint, 1er novembre; Armistice, 11 novembre; Noël, 25 décembre.

TELEPHONE

Indicatif International	Indicatif du Pays	Indicatifs régionaux des Villes principales	
00	32	Anvers	3
		Bruges	50
		Bruxelles	2
		Gand	9
		Liège	4
		Namur	81
		Tournai	69

DEUTSCH

BELGISCHE JUGENDHERBERGEN

Die 'Vlaamse Jeugdherbergcentrale', mit (1) gekennzeichnete Herbergen, betreibt Herbergen in der nördlichen Region. 'Les Auberges de Jeunesse', mit (2) gekennzeichnete Herbergen, sind im südlichen Landesteil tätig. Beide Verbände haben Herbergen in der Hauptstadt, Brüssel.

Die Herbergen sind von 08.00-23.00 Uhr und in Brüssel von 7.00-01.00 Uhr geöffnet. Einige Herbergen schließen während des Tages zwischen 10.00 und 16.00 Uhr oder im Winter für eine Nacht pro Woche. Die jeweiligen Angaben sind daher genau zu prüfen.

Es ist mit einem Preis von 310-660 bfr pro Nacht plus Frühstück und bei Bedarf einer Gebühr für die Miete von Bettwäsche zu rechnen. Für Kinder unter 9 gilt der halbe Preis, und kostenloss für Kinder unter 3, wenn sie mit ihrer Familie reisen. Die meisten Herbergen haben Familienzimmer, die vorbestellt werden sollten.

In allen belgischen Jugendherbergen steht ein Fax-Reservierungsdienst zur Verfügung (d.h. BELGOFAX).

PÄSSE UND VISA

Für Staatsangehörige der EG-Länder genügt eine Kennkarte. Andere Personen wenden sich bitte an die Belgische Botschaft oder das Belgische Konsulat in dem Land, in dem sie ihren Wohnsitz haben.

GESUNDHEIT

Staatsangehörige eines EG-Landes sollten sich für dringende ärztliche Behandlung während eines kurzen Aufenthaltes in Belgien das Formular E111 DSS besorgen. Staatsangehörige anderer Länder sollten vor Antritt ihrer Reise eine private Krankenversicherung abschließen.

Es werden keine speziellen Impfungen verlangt.

GESCHÄFTSSTUNDEN DER BANKEN

Die Banken sind montags bis freitags von 09.00-16.00 Uhr geöffnet.

POSTÄMTER

Postämter sind montags bis freitags von 09.00-17.00 Uhr geöffnet.

LADENÖFFNUNGSZEITEN

Die Geschäfte sind im allgemeinen montags bis samstags von 09.00-18.00 Uhr geöffnet.

REISEN

Eisenbahn
Der Eisenbahnverkehr ist außerordentlich gut, besonders mit einem Benelux Tourrail Pass. Der "Go-Pass" für junge Leute bis zu 26 Jahren und der "Multipass" für kleine Gruppen ermöglichen preisgünstiges Eisenbahnfahren.

Busse
Brüssel hat ein U-Bahn-Netz, Busse und Straßenbahnen. Alle größeren Städte haben gute Nahverkehrsbusse. Es gibt auch ein überregionales Bus-Unternehmen für längere Strecken.

Fähren
Von Ostende nach Ramsgate und von Seebrügge nach Hull gibt es einen Fährenverkehr.

Autofahren
Es herrscht Rechtsverkehr. Das Tempolimit reicht von 50-120 km/Stunde. Es gibt ein gutes Straßennetz.

FEIERTAGE

Neujahr, 1. Januar; Ostern, 30./31. März; Tag der Arbeit, 1. Mai; Himmelfahrt, 8. Mai; Pfingsten 18./19. Mai; Flämischer Gemeinschaftstag, 11. Juli; Nationalfeiertag, 21. Juli; Mariä Himmelfahrt, 15. August; Französischer Gemeinschaftstag, 27. September; Allerheiligen, 1. November; Tag des Waffenstillstands, 11. November; Weihnachten, 25. Dezember

FERNSPRECHINFORMATIONEN

Internationale Kennzahl	Landes- Kennzahl	größere Städte - Ortsnetzkennzahlen	
00	32	Antwerpen	3
		Brügge	50
		Brüssel	2
		Gent	9
		Liège	4
		Namur	81
		Tournai	69

ESPAÑOL

ALBERGUES DE JUVENTUD BELGAS

La 'Vlaamse Jeugdherbergcentrale', albergues marcados (1), se ocupa de los establecimientos de la región norte. 'Les Auberges de Jeunesse' (LAJ), albergues marcados (2), operan en la parte sur del país. Ambas asociaciones tienen albergues en la capital Bruselas.

Los albergues están abiertos de 08.00 a 23.00 horas y en Bruselas de 07.00 a 01.00 horas. Algunos cierran durante el día entre las 10.00 y las 16.00 horas o, en invierno, durante una noche a la semana, por lo que se recomienda leer detenidamente los datos de cada uno.

Se suele pagar entre 310 y 660 BF por noche incluyendo el desayuno, más el alquiler de ropa de cama en caso de requerirse. Los niños menores de 9 años pagan mitad de precio y la estancia es gratuita para menores de 3 años acompañados por su familia. La mayoría de los albergues dispone de habitaciones familiares que hay que reservar con antelación.

Todos los albergues juveniles belgas ofrecen un servicio de reservas por medio de fax que se llama BELGOFAX.

PASAPORTES Y VISADOS

Un carné de identidad basta para los ciudadanos de países de la CE. En cualquier otro caso, se ruega ponerse en contacto con la Embajada o Consulado Belga de su país de residencia.

SANIDAD

Si es ciudadano de la CE, solicite un formulario E111 en el Departamento de Seguridad Social para tratamiento de urgencia durante una corta estancia en Bélgica. Se recomienda a los ciudadanos de otros países suscribir un seguro privado de salud antes de viajar.

No se requiere ninguna vacuna en particular.

HORARIO DE BANCOS

Los bancos abren de lunes a viernes, de 09.00 a 16.00 horas.

CASAS DE CORREO

Las casas de correo abren de lunes a viernes de 09.00 a 17.00 horas.

HORARIO COMERCIAL

Las tiendas suelen abrir de 09.00 a 18.00 horas, de lunes a sábado.

DESPLAZAMIENTOS

Tren
El servicio ferroviario es muy bueno, especialmente con un Benelux Tourrail Pass. El "Go-Pass" para jóvenes de hasta 26 años y el "Multipass" para grupos pequeños ofrecen billetes baratos.

Autobús
Bruselas cuenta con una red de metro, autobuses y tranvías. Todas las grandes ciudades tienen un buen sistema de autobuses. También existe una compañía nacional de autobuses para distancias más largas.

Ferry
Existen servicios de ferry entre Ostende y Ramsgate y entre Zeebrugge y Hull.

Coche
Conducción por la derecha. Los límites de velocidad van desde 50 a 120 k/h. Buena red de autopistas.

DIAS FESTIVOS

Año Nuevo, 1 enero; Pascua, 30/31 marzo; Día del Trabajo, 1 mayo; Día de la Ascensión, 8 mayo; Pentecostés, 18/19 mayo; Día de la Comunidad Flamenca, 11 julio; Día Nacional, 21 julio; Asunción, 15 agosto; Día de la Comunidad Francesa, 27 septiembre; Día de Todos los Santos, 1 noviembre; Día del Armisticio, 11 noviembre; Navidad, 25 diciembre.

INFORMACION TELEFONICA

Código Internacional	Código Nacional	Indicativo de área de las Ciudades principales	
00	32	Amberes	3
		Brujas	50
		Bruselas	2
		Gent	9
		Liège	4
		Namur	81
		Tournai	69

DISCOUNTS AND CONCESSIONS

Use your membership to save on admission charges and boat hire near hostels, as well as cheap rail travel to most European destinations.

Local discounts for tourist activities around Youth Hostels.

Eurolines: 10% discount

Hostels in this country may also display this symbol.

Les auberges de ce pays pourront également afficher ce symbole.

Jugendherbergen in diesem Land können auch dieses Symbol zeigen.

Es posible que los albergues de este país exhiban además este símbolo.

Antwerpen (1) (*see town plan on next page*) ▲ 4S IBN CC 2020 Antwerpen, Eric Sasselaan 2. ☎ (3) 2380273 FAX (3) 2481932 ⊠ 122 ● 375 BEF BB inc ⑩ ☞ ♦♦♦ ♿ ⓞ P ✈ Deurne-Antwerp 5km ⛟ Antwerp Central 5km ⛟ 27 Central Station, 25 Groenplaats (direction Bouwcentrum) 100m U 2 Central station, direction Hoboken U Bouwcentrum 100m

Bokrijk/Genk (1)   ▲   3600 Bokrijk/Genk, Boekrakelaan 30. ☎ (89) 356220 **FAX** (89) 303980 **Open:** 1.3-31.10 ⊠ 116 ● 375 BEF BB inc ⑩ ☞ ♦♦♦ ♿ P ⛟ Bokrijk 6km ⛟ 46 Hasselt-Genk 4km

Bouillon (2) ▲ CC Chemin du Christ 16, 6830 Bouillon. ☎ (61) 468137 **FAX** (61) 467818 **Open:** 1-5.1; 7.2-31.12 ⊠ 136 ● 375 BEF BB inc ⑩ ☞ ♦♦♦ ⓞ P ⛟ Libramont 40km ⛟ 8 Libramont- Bouillon 600m Ⓡ (7.2-27.3; 1.11-31.12)

BRUGGE (2 Hostels)

Brugge (1) - **Europa** ⛺ [2 SE] (IBN) -CC-
8310 Brugge 4/Assebroek, Baron
Ruzettelaan 143. 📞 (50) 352679 **FAX**
(50) 353732 🛏 208 ● 375-470 BEF
[BB]inc ❌ 👫 ♿ 🅿 ⛴ Zeebrugge 10km
🚃 Brugge 1.5km 🚌 2 100m

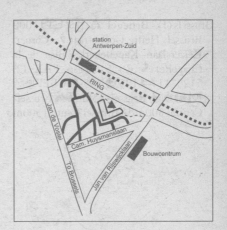

ANTWERPEN

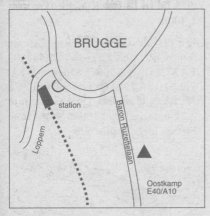

BRUGGE - Europa

Brugge - **Brugge/Dudzele**
"Herdersbrug" (1) ▲ 8380
Dudzele/Brugge, Louis Coiseaukaai 46.
📞 (50) 599321 **FAX** (50) 599349 🛏
86 ● 380 BEF [BB]inc ❌ 👫 🅿 🚌
Brugge 6km 🚌 788 Brugge/Knokke
500m

BRUSSELS (3 Hostels)

Brussels (2) - '**Jean Nihon**' ⛺ (IBN) -CC-
4 Rue de l'Eléphant, 1080 Bruxelles. 📞
(2) 4103858 **FAX** (2) 4103905 **Open:**
17.1-30.12 🛏 152 ● 395-660 BEF
[BB]inc ❌ 👫 ♿ 🅿 ✈ Brussels 15km
🚃 Brussels Central 2km Ⓤ Comte de
Flandre 500m

BRUSSELS - Jean Nihon

Brussels (2) - **Jacques Brel** ⛺ [1 NE] (IBN)
-CC- Rue de la Sablonnière 30, 1000
Bruxelles. 📞 (2) 2180187 **FAX** (2)
2172005 **Open:** 1.1-12.12 🛏 138 ●
395-660 BEF [BB]inc ❌ 👫 ♿ 🅾 ✈
Brussels 15km 🚃 Gare Bruxelles
Nord 1km Ⓤ Madou 200m

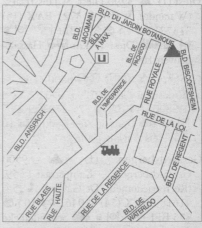

BRUSSELS - Jacques Brel

Brussels (1) - **Bruegel** ⚠ 1S CC 1000 Brussel, Heilig Geeststraat 2. (Corner: Keizerslaan- Kapellekerk/Eglise de la Chapelle) ✆ (2) 5110436 **FAX** (2) 5120711 ⚑ 125 ● 395-660 BEF BB inc ⦂⦂ ⛆ ✈ Brussels 15km 🚆 Brussel-Central 300m Ⓤ Brussel-Central 300m

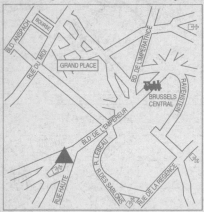

BRUSSELS - Bruegel

Champlon (2) ▲ CC Rue de la Gendarmerie 6, Barrière de Champlon, 6971 Champlon. ✆ (84) 455294 **FAX** (84) 455294 **Open:** 1-5.1; 7.2-31.12 ⚑ 72 ● 375 BEF BB inc ⦂⦂ ⛆ 🖥 🏭 Ⓟ ⚓ 🚲 ♨ 🚆 Marloie 20km 🚌 1 Blue Marche-Bastogne 100m Ⓡ (7.2-27.3; 1.11-31.12)

Diest (1) ▲ 3290 Diest, St Jansstraat 2 (Warande). ✆ (13) 313721 **FAX** (13) 313721 ⚑ 74 ● 375 BEF BB inc ⦂⦂ ⛆ ⦂⦂ 🎡 🚆 Diest 1.5km 🚌 Hasselt-Leuven 100m

Gent (1) ⚠ IBN CC 9000 Gent, St Widostraat 11. ✆ (9) 2337050 **FAX** (9) 2338001 ⚑ 103 ● 375-470 BEF BB inc ⦂⦂ ⦂⦂ 🚆 Gent St Pieters 3km 🚋 10 St Pieters Station 400m

Geraardsbergen (1) ▲ 9500 Geraardsbergen, Kampstraat 59. (Recreatiedomein 'De Gavers'). ✆ (54) 416189 **FAX** (54) 419461 ⚑ 104 ● 375 BEF BB inc ⦂⦂ ⛆ 🚆 Schendelbeke 1.5km

Huizingen (1) ▲ 1654 Huizingen, Prov Domein. ✆ (2) 3830026 **FAX** (2) 3830026 ⚑ 60 ⛆ ⦂⦂ 🚆 Huizingen 1km, Halle 10km Ⓡ (30.9-15.3)

Kortrijk (1) ▲ 8500 Kortrijk, Passionistenlaan 1A. ✆ (56) 201442 **FAX** (56) 204663 ⚑ 96 ● 375 BEF BB inc ⦂⦂ ⦂⦂ Ⓟ 🚆 Kortrijk 1km 🚌 1 300m

Liège (2) ⚠ IBN CC Rue Georges Simenon 2, 4020 Liège. ✆ (4) 3445689 **FAX** (4) 3445687 **Open:** 1-5.1; 7.2-31.12 ⚑ 204 ● 395-660 BEF BB inc ⦂⦂ ⦂⦂ ⛆ 🖥 🏭 🚆 Liège Guillemins 3.2km, Liège Palais 1.4km 🚌 4 from Station Liège Guillemins

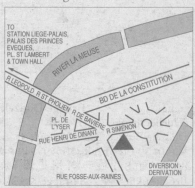

LIÈGE

GENT

Maldegem (1) ▲ 9990 Maldegem, Gentsesteenweg 124. ✆ (50) 713121

FAX (50) 719070 ⚑ 65 ⬤ 375 BEF BB|inc ⵔⵔ ✆ ⵜⵜⵜ ♿ 🅿 ⵙⵙ Eeklo 10km ⵙⵙⵙ 58A Gent-Brugge 100m

Malmédy (2) ▲ 1N CC 4960 Malmédy, Bévercé 8a. ✆ (80) 338386 **FAX** (80) 770504 **Open:** 1.1-30.8; 22.9-6.12; 15-31.12 ⚑ 178 ⬤ 375 BEF BB|inc ⵔⵔ ✆ ⵜⵜⵜ ♿ ▢ 🅿 ⵙⵙ Verviers 30km ⵙⵙⵙ Malmedy- Xhoffrais 30m R (1.1-27.3; 15.11-31.12)

Namur (2) ▲ IBN CC 5000 Namur, Rue Félicien Rops, 8 La Plante. ✆ (81) 223688 FAX (81) 224412 Open: 1-5.1; 7.2-31.12 ⚑ 96 ⬤ 375 BEF BB|inc ⵔⵔ ✆ ⵜⵜⵜ ♿ ▢ ⵝ ♠ ⵙⵙ Namur 3km ⵙⵙⵙ 3, 4 300m R (16.11-3.1)

Nijlen (1) ▲ 2560 Nijlen, Wijngaardberg 42. ✆ (3) 4110733 **FAX** (3) 4110725 ⚑ 64 ⬤ 375 BEF BB|inc ⵔⵔ ✆ ⵜⵜⵜ ⵙⵙ Nijlen 1km ⵙⵙⵙ Lier-Herentals 1km

Oostduinkerke (1) ▲ 8670 Oostduinkerke, Dorpstraat 19. ✆ (58) 512649 **FAX** (58) 522880 **Open:** 1.3-15.11 ⚑ 106 ⬤ 375 BEF BB|inc ⵔⵔ ✆ ⵜⵜⵜ ⵙⵙ Koksijde 7km ⵙⵙⵙ 768 Oostende- De Panne, 774 (Veurne-Oostduinkerke) 100m ⵝⵝ Oostende-De Panne 2km

Oostende (1) ▲ 8400 Oostende, Langestraat 82. ✆ (59) 805297 **FAX** (59) 809274 ⚑ 108 ⬤ 465-660 BEF BB|inc ⵔⵔ ✆ ⵜⵜⵜ ✈ Oostende 5km ⛴ Oostende 1km ⵙⵙ Oostende 1.5km

St- Vith (1) ▲ 4780 St Vith, Rodterstrasse 13A. ✆ (80) 229331 **FAX** (80) 229332 ⚑ 85 ⬤ 375 BEF BB|inc ⵔⵔ ✆ ⵜⵜⵜ ♿ 🅿 ⵗ ⵙⵙ Vielsalm 20, Gouvy 20km ⵙⵙⵙ 401 Vielsalm-St Vith 50m ap 48B Gouvy-St Vith

Tienen (1) ▲ 3300 Tienen, Kabbeekvest 93. ✆ (16) 822206 **FAX** (16) 822796 ⚑ 24 ⬤ 375 BEF BB|inc

ⵔⵔ ✆ ⵜⵜⵜ ⵙⵙ Tienen 1km ⵙⵙⵙ Tienen-Diest, Tienen- St Truiden 50m R 16.9-14.6 Grps only

Tilff (2) ▲ 4130 Tilff, Esplanade de L'abeille 9 ✆ (4) 3882100 **FAX** (4) 3882100 **Open:** (Grps only 7.2-31.12) ⚑ 65 ⵔⵔ ✆ ⵜⵜⵜ 🅿 ⵙⵙ Tilff 600m ⵙⵙⵙ 377 Liège-Tilff 300m R (7.2-31.12 Auberge Liège ✆ (4) 3445689 FAX (4) 3445687)

Tongeren (1) ▲ 3700 Tongeren, St Ursulastraat 1. ✆ (12) 391370 **FAX** (12) 391348 ⚑ 78 ⬤ 375-440 BEF BB|inc ⵔⵔ ⵜⵜⵜ ♠ ⵙⵙ Tongeren 1km

Tournai (2) ▲ CC 7500 Tournai, Rue Saint-Martin 64. ✆ (69) 216136 **FAX** (69) 216140 **Open:** 1-5.1; 7.2-31.12 ⚑ 100 ⬤ 375 BEF BB|inc ⵔⵔ ✆ ⵜⵜⵜ ♿ ⵕⵕ ⵙⵙ Tournai 1.5km ⵙⵙⵙ 0 50m R (7.2-27.3; 1.11-31.12)

Vleteren (1) ▲ 8640 Vleteren, Veurnestraat 4. ✆ (57) 400901 **FAX** (57) 401371 ⚑ 65 ⬤ 375 BEF BB|inc ⵔⵔ 🅿 ⵙⵙ Ieper 15km ⵙⵙⵙ Ieper-Veurne 200m

Voeren (1) ▲ 3790 St Martens Voeren, Comberg 29B. ✆ (4) 3811110 **FAX** (4) 3811313 **Open:** 1.3-9.11 ⚑ 80 ⬤ 375 BEF BB|inc ⵔⵔ ⵜⵜⵜ ⵙⵙ Visé 15km ⵙⵙⵙ 39C Montsen 500m

Westerlo (1) ▲ 2260 Westerlo, Papendreef 1. ✆ (14) 547938 **FAX** (14) 547938 ⚑ 82 ⬤ 375 BEF BB|inc ⵔⵔ ✆ ⵜⵜⵜ 🅿 ♠ ⵙⵙ Geel 12km, Herentals 15km ⵙⵙⵙ 307 Geel Station, 54 Herentals Station 300m

Zoersel (1) ▲ 2980 Zoersel, Gagelhoflaan 18. ✆ (3) 3851642 **FAX** (3) 3851642 **Open:** 1.6-30.9 + weekends + school holidays ⚑ 54 ⬤ 215 BEF BB|inc ⵔⵔ ✆ ⵕⵕ 🅿 ⵙⵙ Lier 16km ⵙⵙⵙ Antwerpen-Zoersel 200m

CROATIA (HRVATSKA)
CROATIE
KROATIEN
CROACIA

Hrvatski ferijalni i hostelski savez/Croatian Youth
Hostel Association, Savska cesta 5/1
10000 Zagreb, Croatia.

Office hours: Monday 08.00-18.00hrs;
                 Tuesday-Friday 08.00-16.00hrs.

☎ (385) (1) 411847
FAX (385) (1) 411738

Travel Section: Dežmanova 9,
10000 Zagreb, Croatia

Office hours: Monday 08.00-18.00hrs;
                 Tuesday-Friday 08.00-16.00hrs.

☎ (385) (1) 278239, 435781
FAX (385) (1) 426201

IBN Booking Centre for outward booking:
■ **Zagreb**, *via Travel Section above.*

Capital:	Zagreb
Language:	Croatian
Currency:	Kuna (Kn)
Population:	4,784,265
Size:	56,538 sq km.

CROATIA

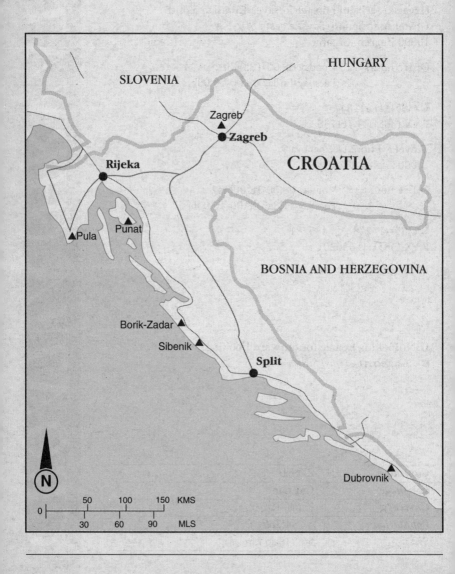

CROATIAN HOSTELS

Croatian Youth Hostels are situated in famous historical cities and areas with many interesting monuments, museums and galleries. Information about events, festivals, popular attractions, recreation, sports and other facilities for hostellers is available at Youth Hostels.

Hostels are generally open 08.00-23.00hrs. As Zagreb and Pula are the only hostels open all year, check individual entries carefully for opening dates. Expect to pay in the region of 12-25 DEM per night including visitors tax.

PASSPORTS AND VISAS

An Entrance Visa is necessary for citizens of all African and Latin American countries (except Chile), Asian and Pacific countries, USA, Canada, Luxembourg, Belgium, Netherlands, Albania, Greece and all countries of the former Soviet Union. Visas can be issued in Croatian Embassies, Consulates or at Croatian border offices.

HEALTH

Vaccinations are not required.

Reciprocal agreements on health care exist between Croatia and certain countries, entitling visitors to treatment on the same basis as Croatians. Enquire about obtaining a certificate before you travel. Other visitors are required to pay for treatment, but charges are very moderate in most cases.

BANKING HOURS

Monday-Friday 08.00-19.00hrs; Saturday 08.00-12.00hrs.

POST OFFICES

Monday-Friday 07.00-20.00hrs; Saturday 07.00-13.00hrs.

SHOPPING HOURS

Monday-Friday 08.00-20.00hrs; Saturday 08.00-13.00hrs.

TRAVEL

Air
Croatia Airlines run internal services linking major cities. The best air connections are via Zagreb.

Rail
Rail travel is good.

Bus
Coach services connect all towns. There are good bus services in the main towns.

Ferry
Coastal ferry routes link certain islands along the Adriatic Coast.

Driving
All towns are connected with good roads. Car hire is available in bigger towns.

Road assistance is organized by HAK (Croatian Auto-Club) and it operates on major roads and in towns by dialing 987. Drivers should have valid documents for themselves and the vehicle, as well as a green or blue insurance card.

PUBLIC HOLIDAYS

New Year, 1 January; Easter Monday, 31 March; International Labour Day, 1 May; Day of Croatian Statehood, 30 May; Day of Antifascist Fight, 22 June; Memorial Day, 5 August; Assumption, 15 August; Christmas, 25 December.

TELEPHONE INFORMATION

International Code	Country Code	Main City Area Codes	
99	385	Zagreb	1
		Dubrovnik	20
		Zadar	23

FRANÇAIS

AUBERGES DE JEUNESSE CROATES

Les auberges de jeunesse croates sont situées dans des villes célèbres d'importance historique et dans des lieux où se trouvent des monuments intéressants, des musées et des galeries d'art. Les auberges vous renseigneront sur les événements, festivals, attractions populaires, loisirs, sports et autres services à l'intention des voyageurs utilisant les auberges.

Les auberges sont en général ouvertes de 8h à 23h. Les auberges de Zagreb et de Pula sont les seules à être ouvertes toute l'année; il est donc prudent de consulter la liste avec soin pour les dates d'ouverture des auberges. Une nuit vous coûtera entre 12-25 DEM, taxe de séjour comprise.

PASSEPORTS ET VISAS

Un visa d'entrée est nécessaire pour les citoyens de tous les pays africains et latino-américains (sauf le Chili), les pays d'Asie et du Pacifique, les Etats-Unis, le Canada, le Luxembourg, la Belgique, les Pays-Bas, l'Albanie, la Grèce et tous les pays de l'ancienne Union Soviétique. Les visas peuvent être obtenus dans les Ambassades et Consulats croates ou dans les bureaux douaniers croates.

SOINS MEDICAUX

Aucune vaccination n'est requise.

Des accords médicaux réciproques ont été passés entre la Croatie et certains pays, permettant aux citoyens de ces pays de bénéficier des mêmes soins que ceux prodigués aux Croates. Renseignez-vous sur l'obtention d'un certificat avant votre départ. Les autres visiteurs devront payer tous frais médicaux encourus, mais ces derniers sont minimes dans la plupart des cas.

HEURES D'OUVERTURE DES BANQUES

Les banques sont ouvertes de 8h à 19h, du lundi au vendredi, et de 8h à 12h le samedi.

BUREAUX DE POSTE

Les bureaux de poste sont ouverts du lundi au vendredi, de 7h à 20h et le samedi de 7h à 13h.

HEURES D'OUVERTURE DES MAGASINS

Les magasins sont ouverts de 8h à 20h du lundi au vendredi et de 8h à 13h le samedi.

DEPLACEMENTS

Avions
Croatia Airlines relient les villes principales par des vols intérieurs. Les meilleures correspondances aériennes passent par Zagreb.

Trains
Le service ferroviaire est bon.

Autobus
Les villes sont reliées par des services de cars. De bons services d'autobus desservent les villes principales.

Ferry-boats
Des services côtiers relient certaines îles le long de la côte adriatique.

Automobiles
Toutes les villes sont reliées par de bonnes routes. Il est possible de louer des voitures dans les grandes villes.

L'automobile-club croate, HAK, organise les dépannages sur les routes principales et dans les villes; appelez le 987. Les conducteurs doivent être munis de documents valides, pour eux-mêmes et pour leur véhicule, ainsi qu'une carte verte ou bleue (pour l'assurance).

JOURS FERIES

Nouvel an, 1er janvier; Lundi de Pâques, 31 mars; Fête internationale du travail, 1er mai; Fête de l'Etat croate, 30 mai; Fête de la lutte antifasciste, 22 juin; Jour en mémoire des morts au champ d'honneur, 5 août; Assomption, 15 août; Noël, 25 décembre.

TELEPHONE

Indicatif International	Indicatif du Pays	Indicatifs régionaux Villes principales	
99	385	Zagreb	1
		Dubrovnik	20
		Zadar	23

DEUTSCH

KROATISCHE JUGENDHERBERGEN

Die kroatischen Jugendherbergen liegen in berühmten historischen Städten und Gegenden, wo es viele interessante Denkmäler, Museen und Galerien gibt. Die Jugendherbergen erteilen Auskunft über Veranstaltungen, Feste, beliebte Sehenswürdigkeiten, Unterhaltungs- und Sportmöglichkeiten sowie andere Einrichtungen, die in Jugendherbergen zur Verfügung stehen.

Die Herbergen sind im allgemeinen von 08.00-23.00 Uhr geöffnet. Da es nur in Zagreb und Pula eine ganzjährig geöffnete Herberge gibt, sind die in den einzelnen Einträgen stehenden Öffnungstermine genau zu beachten. Es ist mit einem Preis von 12-25 DEM pro Nacht einschließlich Gästesteuer zu rechnen.

PÄSSE UND VISA

Staatsbürger aus allen afrikanischen und lateinamerikanischen Ländern (außer Chile) sowie aus allen asiatischen und pazifischen Ländern, den USA, Kanada, Luxemburg, Belgien, den Niederlanden, Albanien, Griechenland und allen Ländern der ehemaligen Sowjetunion benötigen ein Einreisevisum. Visa werden in Botschaften und Konsulaten Kroatiens und an den kroatischen Grenzstellen ausgestellt.

GESUNDHEIT

Es sind keine Impfungen erforderlich.

Zwischen Kroatien und gewissen Ländern bestehen reziproke Verträge über die Gesundheitspflege, die ausländischen Reisenden Anspruch auf die gleiche Behandlung wie Kroatiern gewähren. Erkundigen Sie sich vor Ihrer Abreise, wie Sie sich eine entsprechende Bescheinigung beschaffen können. Reisende aus Ländern, mit denen kein solcher Vertrag geschlossen wurde, müssen für ihre Behandlung selbst bezahlen, aber in den meisten Fällen sind die Kosten nicht sehr hoch.

GESCHÄFTSSTUNDEN DER BANKEN

Montags-freitags 08.00-19.00 Uhr, samstags 08.00-12.00 Uhr.

POSTÄMTER

Montags-freitags 07.00-20.00 Uhr, samstags 08.00-13.00 Uhr.

LADENÖFFNUNGSZEITEN

Montags-freitags 08.00-20.00 Uhr, samstags 08.00-13.00 Uhr.

REISEN

Flugverkehr
Croatia Airlines bietet einen Inlandsverkehr zwischen größeren Städten. Die besten Flugverbindungen führen über Zagreb.

Eisenbahn
Die Eisenbahnverbindungen sind gut.

Busse
Zwischen allen Städten gibt es Busverbindungen. In den größeren Städten wird ein guter Busverkehr geboten.

Fähren
Küstenfähren verkehren zwischen gewissen Inseln an der adriatischen Küste.

Autofahren
Alle Städte verbindet ein gutes Straßennetz. In größeren Städten können Autos gemietet werden.

HAK (der kroatische Automobil-Club) bietet auf Hauptverkehrsstraßen und in Städten einen Pannendienst, der über die Nr 987 gerufen werden kann. Der Fahrer muß im Besitz gültiger Papiere für sich und das Fahrzeug sein und eine grüne oder blaue Versicherungskarte vorweisen können.

FEIERTAGE

Neujahr. 1. Januar; Ostermontag, 31. März; Internationaler Tag der Arbeit, 1. Mai; Tag der kroatischen Staatsgründung, 30. Mai; Tag des antifaschistischen Kampfes, 22. Juni; Gedenktag 5. August; Mariä Himmelfahrt, 15. August; Weihnachten, 25. Dezember.

FERNSPRECHINFORMATIONEN

Internationale Kennzahl	Landes- Kennzahl	größere Städte - Ortsnetzkennzahlen	
99	385	Zagreb	1
		Dubrovnik	20
		Zadar	23

ESPAÑOL

ALBERGUES DE JUVENTUD CROATAS

Los albergues de juventud croatas están situados en ciudades y áreas de fama histórica con numerosos monumentos, museos y galerías. En los albergues se puede conseguir información sobre actos, festivales, atracciones populares, recreación e instalaciones deportivas y de otro tipo para alberguistas.

Los albergues suelen abrir de 08.00 a 23.00 horas. Dado que los albergues de Zagreb y Pula son los únicos abiertos todo el año, se recomienda leer atentamente los datos de todos los demás en cuanto a fechas de apertura. Se paga alrededor de 12-25 DEM por noche incluyendo impuesto de visitantes.

PASAPORTES Y VISADOS

Todos los visitantes de países africanos y latinoamericanos (excepto Chile), asiáticos y del Pacífico, EE.UU., Canadá, Luxemburgo, Bélgica, Países Bajos, Albania, Grecia y todos los países de la antigua Unión Soviética precisan visado de entrada. Los visados pueden obtenerse en las embajadas y consulados croatas y en oficinas fronterizas de Croacia.

SANIDAD

No se requieren vacunas.

Existen acuerdos mutuos de atención sanitaria entre Croacia y algunos países, que dan derechos a los visitantes a recibir el mismo tratamiento que los croatas. Infórmese sobre la necesidad de obtener un certificado antes de partir de viaje. Los demás visitantes deben pagar el tratamiento, pero los costes suelen ser moderados.

HORARIO DE BANCOS

De lunes a viernes de 08.00 a 19.00 horas. Sábados de 08.00 a 12.00 horas.

CASAS DE CORREO

De lunes a viernes de 07.00 a 20.00 horas. Sábados de 07.00 a 13.00 horas.

HORARIO COMERCIAL

De lunes a viernes de 08.00 a 20.00 horas. Sábados de 08.00 a 13.00 horas.

DESPLAZAMIENTOS

Avión
Croatia Airlines ofrece servicios internos entre las principales ciudades. Las mejores conexiones aéreas son vía Zagreb.

Tren
Croacia cuenta con una buena red ferroviaria.

Autobús
Hay servicios de autocar que conectan todas las ciudades y buenos servicios urbanos en las ciudades principales.

Ferry
Las rutas costeras de ferry enlazan determinadas islas de la costa Adriática.

Coche
Todas las ciudades están conectadas por buenas carreteras. En las más importantes se pueden alquilar coches.

La asistencia en carretera está organizada por HAK (Automóvil Club de Croacia) y se puede obtener en las principales carreteras y poblaciones marcando el 987. Los conductores deberán poseer documentos válidos de sí mismos y del vehículo, además de una carta verde o azul de seguro.

DIAS FESTIVOS

Año Nuevo, 1 enero; Lunes de Pascua, 31 marzo; Día Internacional del Trabajo, 1 mayo; Día del Estado Croata, 30 mayo; Día de la Lucha Antifascista, 22 junio; Día de los Caídos, 5 agosto; Asunción, 15 agosto; Navidad, 25 diciembre.

INFORMACION TELEFONICA

Código Internacional	Código Nacional	Indicativo de área de las Ciudades principales
99	38	Zagreb 1
		Dubrovnik 20
		Zadar 23

Hostels in this country may also display this symbol.

Les auberges de ce pays pourront également afficher ce symbole.

Jugendherbergen in diesem Land können auch dieses Symbol zeigen.

Es posible que los albergues de este país exhiban además este símbolo.

Borik-Zadar   YH Borik, Obala Kneza Trpimira 76, 23 000 Zadar. 📞 (23) 331145 **FAX** (23) 331190 **Open:** 08.00-23.00hrs, 15.4-15.10 🛏 330 ⊖ 14 DEM [BB]inc ⟨O⟩ ⊞ 🅿 ⚫ ✈ Zemunik 10km A🚌 4km ⛴ Zadar 4km 🚎 Zadar 4km 🚋 Line "Borik" 4km **Ⓡ** (15 days in advance)

Dubrovnik   Bana Jelačića 15-17, 20000 Dubrovnik. 📞 (20) 412592 **FAX** (20) 412592 **Open:** 08.00-24.00hrs, 15.4-15.10 🛏 80 ⊖ 15 DEM [BB]inc ⚫ 👫 ✈ Dubrovnik 10km A🚌 500m ⛴ Gruž-Dubrovnik 1km 🚎 Ploče 85km **Ⓡ** (15 days in advance)

Pula   Zaljev Valsaline 4, 52 000 Pula. 📞 (52) 34211 **FAX** (52) 212394 **Open:** 07.00-23.00hrs 🛏 145 ⊖ 16 DEM

[BB]inc ⟨O⟩ 👫 ✈ Pula 5km A🚌 4km ⛴ Pula 4.5km 🚎 Pula 4.5km 🚋 2 or 4 4km ap City Centre **Ⓡ** (15 days in advance)

DUBROVNIK

Punat, Island KRK   YH Punat 51 521 Punat, Otok KRK. ☎ (51) 854037 **FAX** (1) 434962 **Open:** 08.00-23.00hrs, 10.6-30.9 🛏 125 ⊜ 16 DEM 🍽 👪 🚻 ① ✈ KRK 3km 🚌 ap Rijeka ⑱ (10 days in advance: Omladinski Turistički Centar, Pentrinjska 77, 10 000 Zagreb, Croatia)

Šubićevac-Šibenik   YH Šubićevac, Put Luguša 1, 22 000 Šibenik. ☎ (22) 26410 **FAX** (22) 26410 **Open:** 08.00-23.00hrs, 1.5-15.10 🛏 40 ⊜ 12 DEM 👪 🅿 ⛴ Šibenik 2km ⑱ (10 days in advance)

Zadar ☞ Borik-Zadar

Zagreb   Petrinjska 77, 10 000 Zagreb. ☎ (1) 434964 **FAX** (1) 434962 **Open:** 08.00-23.00hrs 🛏 210 ⊜ 15 DEM 👪 🅿 ✈ Pleso-Zagreb 10km A 🚌 500m 🚋 Glavni Kolodvor-Zagreb 150m 🚋 13 ap Ban Jelačič Square 500m ⑱ (20 days in advance)

ZAGREB

CYPRUS
CHYPRE
ZYPERN
CHIPRE

CYPRUS

Cyprus Youth Hostel Association,
34 Th Theodotou Street,
PO Box 1328, Nicosia, Cyprus.

☎ (357) (2) 442027
FAX (357) (2) 442896

Office Hours: Monday-Friday, 08.30-12.30hrs
and 15.00-17.30hrs
(1.5-1.10, Monday-Friday, 08.30-12.30hrs
and 16.00-18.30hrs)

Capital:	Nicosia
Language:	Greek
Currency:	C£ (Cyprus pound)
Population:	700,000
Size:	9,251 sq km

CYPRUS

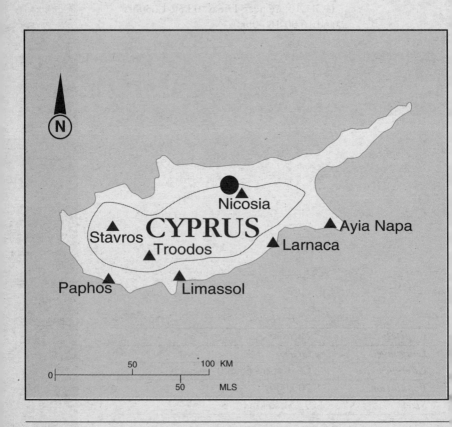

ENGLISH

CYPRUS HOSTELS

Six hostels, each offering unique locations, and all with family rooms.

All hostels are open 24 hours and with the exception of Stavros all have self-catering facilities. Expect to pay C£3.50-C£6.00, plus sheet hire if needed at C£1.00.

PASSPORTS AND VISAS

Visitors from most countries need only a valid passport for visits of up to three months, but it is advisable to check visa requirements before travelling.

HEALTH

There are no vaccination requirements to enter Cyprus.

BANKING HOURS

Banks are open Monday to Friday 08.15-12.30hrs. Centrally located Banks provide an "afternoon tourist service" on weekdays except for Tuesday afternoons.

POST OFFICES

Post Offices are open Monday to Friday 07.30-13.30hrs and Thursday 15.00-18.00hrs.

Additional to the above the District Post Offices in Nicosia, Larnaca, Limassol and Paphos, the Branch Post Office of Eleftheria Square in Nicosia, the City Central Post Office in Limassol and the Post Office in Paralimni are also open Monday, Tuesday and Thursday for the following hours: October-April, 15.30-17.30hrs and May-September, 16.00-18.00hrs. They are also open Saturdays, all year 09.00-11.00hrs.

All Post Offices are closed on Sundays and Public Holidays.

SHOPPING HOURS

During the winter period (1 October-30 April) shops are open Monday, Tuesday, Thursday, Friday 08.00-13.00hrs and 14.30-17.30hrs. On Wednesday and Saturday they are only open 08.00-13.00hrs.

In summer (1 May-30 September) they are open Monday, Tuesday, Thursday, Friday 08.00-13.00hrs and 16.00-19.00hrs. Wednesday and Saturday are the same as for winter.

TRAVEL

Travel is very easy along the main highways between larger cities. Smaller roads in mountainous areas are more difficult. There is very little public transport after 19.00hrs. Taxis are cheap and easy to find.

Rail
There is no rail network in Cyprus.

Bus
Transurban buses: Various bus companies link all major towns with daily routes at specified intervals.
Rural buses: Almost all villages are connected to the nearest town by local buses. Bus operation is limited to once or twice a day. Regional bus companies, formed recently, will provide more routes.
Urban buses: Operate frequently during the day and in certain tourist areas during the summer their routes are extended till midnight.

Driving

Fairly good surfaced roads complying with international traffic requirements link the towns and villages. Four lane motorways connect the capital, Nicosia, with the coastal towns of Limassol and Larnaca. Minor and forest roads are still largely unsurfaced but in good to fair condition.

Visitors can drive in Cyprus as long as they are in possession of either a valid international driving licence, or their national driving licence, provided this is valid for the class of vehicle they wish to drive. A six month Temporary Driving Licence is available to visitors at a cost of C£3.00.

Self drive car rental firms have offices in all towns, and at Larnaca International Airport, with English speaking personnel. Daily rates vary from C£13.00, for a small car to C£23.00 for larger cars.

TELEPHONE INFORMATION

International Code	Country Code	Main City Area Codes	
00	357	Nicosia	2
		Larnaca	4
		Limassol	5
		Ayia Napa	3
		Paphos	6

FRANÇAIS

AUBERGES DE JEUNESSE CYPRIOTES

Il y a six auberges à Chypre, chacune occupant un site unique. Elles offrent toutes des chambres familiales.

Toutes les auberges sont ouvertes 24h sur 24 et, à l'exception de celle de Stavros, disposent de cuisines pour les touristes. Le prix d'une nuit se situe entre 3.50 et 6 livres cypriotes, plus location de draps le cas échéant (1 livre cypriote).

PASSEPORTS ET VISAS

Un passeport en règle est requis pour la plupart des visiteurs pour un séjour de trois mois maximum, mais il est préférable de s'assurer avant le départ qu'un visa n'est pas nécessaire.

SOINS MEDICAUX

Aucune vaccination n'est requise pour Chypre.

HEURES D'OUVERTURE DES BANQUES

Les banques sont ouvertes du lundi au vendredi de 8h15 à 12h30. Les banques situées dans les centres offrent un "service pour touristes l'après-midi" tous les jours sauf le mardi.

BUREAUX DE POSTE

Les bureaux de poste sont ouverts du lundi au vendredi de 7h30 à 13h30 et le jeudi de 15h à 18h.

En outre, les bureaux de poste régionaux de Nicosie, Lárnaka, Limassol et Paphos, le bureau de poste local situé sur la Place Eleftheria à Nicosie, le bureau de poste central de Limassol et celui de Paralimni sont également ouverts les lundi, mardi et jeudi aux heures suivantes: d'octobre à avril, de 15h30 à 17h30 et de mai à septembre, de 16h à 18h. Ils sont aussi ouverts le samedi, toute l'année, de 9h à 11h.

Tous les bureaux de poste sont fermés le dimanche et les jours fériés.

HEURES D'OUVERTURE DES MAGASINS

En hiver (du 1er octobre au 30 avril), les magasins sont ouverts les lundi, mardi, jeudi et vendredi de 8h à 13h et de 14h30 à 17h30. Le mercredi et le samedi, ils ne sont ouverts qu'entre 8h et 13h.

En été (du 1er mai au 30 septembre), ils sont ouverts les lundi, mardi, jeudi et vendredi de 8h à 13h et de 16h à 19h. Le mercredi et le samedi, les horaires sont les mêmes qu'en hiver.

DEPLACEMENTS

Il est très facile de se déplacer sur les routes principales reliant les grandes villes. Les petites routes desservant les régions montagneuses sont plus difficiles.

Les transports publics sont très réduits après 19h. Les taxis sont bon marché et faciles à trouver.

Trains
Il n'y a pas de chemin de fer à Chypre.

Autobus
Autobus interurbains: Diverses compagnies d'autobus relient toutes les villes principales au moyen de trajets journaliers à intervalles spécifiés.
Autobus ruraux: Presque tous les villages sont reliés à la ville la plus proche par des autobus locaux qui toutefois ne passent qu'une ou deux fois par jour. Les compagnies d'autobus régionales, qui existent depuis peu de temps, offriront davantage d'itinéraires.
Autobus urbains: Ils sont fréquents pendant la journée et, dans certaines régions touristiques, ils continuent à fonctionner jusqu'à minuit en été.

Automobiles
D'assez bonnes routes conformes aux exigences internationales de la circulation relient villes et villages. Des autoroutes à quatre voies relient la capitale, Nicosie, aux villes côtières de Limassol et Lárnaka. Les petites routes et les routes forestières sont en grande partie non goudronnées mais sont dans un état allant de bon à assez bon.

Les visiteurs ont le droit de conduire à Chypre à condition d'être munis d'un permis de conduire international en règle ou de leur permis de conduire national pourvu qu'il soit valable pour la catégorie de véhicule qu'ils souhaitent conduire. Il est possible de se procurer un permis de conduire valable six mois moyennant 3 livres cypriotes.

Les agences de location de voitures possèdent des bureaux dans toutes les villes ainsi qu'à l'aéroport international de Lárnaka, qui dispose de personnel parlant anglais. Les tarifs journaliers vont de 13 livres cypriotes pour une petite voiture à 23 livres cypriotes pour les voitures plus importantes.

TELEPHONE

Indicatif International	Indicatif du Pays	Indicatifs régionaux des Villes principales	
00	357	Nicosie	2
		Lárnaka	4
		Limassol	5
		Ayia Napa	3
		Paphos	6

DEUTSCH

ZYPRIOTISCHE JUGENDHERBERGEN

Sechs Jugendherbergen, wovon jede einmalig gelegen ist; alle mit Familienräumen.

Alle Herbergen sind 24 Stunden am Tag geöffnet und, außer der Herberge in Stavros, haben alle Einrichtungen für Selbstversorger. Es ist mit einem Preis von Z£3,50-Z£6,00 plus, bei Bedarf, Lakenmiete (Z£1,00) zu rechnen.

PÄSSE UND VISA

Für einen Aufenthalt bis zu drei Monaten brauchen Besucher aus den meisten Ländern nur einen gültigen Reisepaß. Es empfiehlt sich jedoch, sich vor Antritt der Reise nach den Visumsvorschriften zu erkundigen.

GESUNDHEIT

Die Einreise nach Zypern unterliegt keinen Impfvorschriften.

GESCHÄFTSSTUNDEN DER BANKEN

Die Banken sind montags bis freitags von 08.15-12.30 Uhr geöffnet. Zentral gelegene Banken bieten werktags, außer am Dienstagnachmittag, einen "Nachmittagsservice für Touristen".

POSTÄMTER

Postämter sind montags bis freitags von 07.30-13.30 Uhr und donnerstags von 15.00-18.00 Uhr geöffnet.

Abgesehen davon sind die Bezirks-Postämter in Nikosia, Larnaka, Limassol und Paphos, die Postfiliale auf dem Eleftheria Square in Nikosia, das Postamt im Stadtzentrum von Limassol und das Postamt in Paralimni auch montags, dienstags und donnerstags zu folgenden Zeiten geöffnet: Oktober-April 15.30-17.30 Uhr und Mai-September 16.00-18.00 Uhr. Sie sind auch samstags ganzjährig von 09.00-11.00 Uhr geöffnet.

Alle Postämter sind sonn- und feiertags geschlossen.

LADENÖFFNUNGSZEITEN

Im Winter (1. Oktober-30. April) sind die Geschäfte montags, dienstags, donnerstags und freitags von 08.00-13.00 Uhr und von 14.30-17.30 Uhr geöffnet. Mittwochs und samstags sind sie nur von 08.00-13.00 Uhr geöffnet.

Im Sommer (1. Mai-30. September) sind sie montags, dienstags, donnerstags und freitags von 08.00-13.00 Uhr und von 16.00-19.00 Uhr geöffnet. Die Öffnungszeiten für mittwochs und samstags sind gleich wie im Winter.

REISEN

Auf den Hauptverkehrsstraßen zwischen den größeren Städten ist das Reisen sehr einfach. Kleinere Straßen im Gebirge sind schwieriger. Nach 19.00 Uhr gibt es kaum noch öffentliche Verkehrsmittel. Taxis sind billig und leicht zu finden.

Eisenbahn
In Zypern gibt es kein Eisenbahnnetz.

Busse

Transurbaner Busverkehr: Verschiedene Busunternehmen bieten zu bestimmten Zeiten einen täglichen Verkehr zwischen allen größeren Städten.

Busverkehr auf dem Land: Nahverkehrsbusse verkehren zwischen fast allen Dörfern und der nächsten Stadt. Die Busse fahren nur ein- oder zweimal am Tag. Vor kurzem gegründete regionale Busunternehmen werden auf weiteren Strecken verkehren.

Städtische Busse: Während des Tages wird ein häufiger Verkehr geboten, und in gewissen Fremdenverkehrsgebieten fahren die Busse im Sommer bis Mitternacht.

Autofahren

Ziemlich gute Straßen, für die die internationalen Verkehrsvorschriften gelten, verbinden die Städte und Dörfer. Vierspurige Autobahnen verbinden die Hauptstadt, Nikosia, mit den Küstenstädten Limassol und Larnaka. Neben- und Waldstraßen sind oft noch unbefestigt, aber in gutem bis annehmbarem Zustand.

Besucher können in Zypern autofahren, sofern sie im Besitz eines gültigen internationalen Führerscheines oder eines in ihrem Land ausgestellten Führerscheines sind, der für ihre Fahrzeugklasse gilt. Gegen Bezahlung einer Gebühr von Z£3,00 wird für Besucher ein vorübergehender Führerschein ausgestellt, der sechs Monate gültig ist.

Mietwagen-Unternehmen haben Niederlassungen in allen Städten und auf dem Internationalen Flughafen von Larnaka. Das Personal spricht Englisch. Die Tagessätze liegen zwischen Z£13,00 für einen Kleinwagen und Z£23,00 für größere Fahrzeuge.

FERNSPRECHINFORMATIONEN

Internationale Kennzahl	Landes-Kennzahl	größere Städte - Ortsnetzkennzahlen	
00	357	Nikosia	2
		Larnaka	4
		Limassol	5
		Ayia Napa	3
		Paphos	6

ESPAÑOL

ALBERGUES DE JUVENTUD CHIPRIOTAS

Seis albergues, todos en emplazamientos excepcionales y con habitaciones familiares.

Todos los albergues están abiertos las 24 horas del día y todos tienen cocina para los huéspedes, excepto el de Stavros. Suelen costar C£3,50-C£6,00 libras chipriotas, además del alquiler de la ropa de cama (C£1,00), si la necesita.

PASAPORTES Y VISADOS

Los visitantes de la mayoría de los países sólo necesitan un pasaporte válido para visitas de hasta tres meses de duración, pero recomendamos que averigüe si necesita visado antes de viajar.

SANIDAD

No se requiere ninguna vacuna en particular.

HORARIO DE BANCOS

Los bancos abren de lunes a viernes, de 08.15 a 12.30 horas. Los bancos más céntricos ofrecen además un "servicio turístico de tarde" los días laborales, excepto el martes por la tarde.

CASAS DE CORREO

Las casas de correo abren de lunes a viernes de 07.30 a 13.30 horas y el jueves de 15.00 a 18.00 horas.

Además del horario ya indicado, las casas de correo de distrito de Nicosía, Larnaca, Limassol y Paphos, la sucursal de correos de la Plaza Eleftheria de Nicosía, la Casa Central de Correos de la Ciudad de Limassol y la Oficina de Correos de Paralimni también abren el lunes, martes y jueves con el siguiente horario: de octubre a abril, de 15.30 a 17.30 horas y de mayo a septiembre, de 16.00 a 18.00 horas. También abren los sábados de 09.00 a 11.00 horas durante todo el año.

Las casas de correo están todas cerradas los domingos y festivos.

HORARIO COMERCIAL

En la temporada de invierno (del 1 de octubre al 30 de abril), las tiendas están abiertas los lunes, martes, jueves y viernes de 08.00 a 13.00 horas y de 14.30 a 17.30 horas. Los miércoles y sábados sólo abren de 08.00 a 13.00 horas.

En verano (del 1 de mayo al 30 de septiembre) abren los lunes, martes, jueves y viernes de 08.00 a 13.00 horas y de 16.00 a 19.00 horas. Los miércoles y sábados el horario es el mismo que en invierno.

DESPLAZAMIENTOS

Las comunicaciones viales son muy buenas por las carreteras principales entre las ciudades más grandes. Las carreteras pequeñas en zonas montañosas resultan más difíciles. Existen muy pocos servicios de transporte público después de las 19.00 horas, pero los taxis son baratos y fáciles de encontrar.

Tren
No existe red ferroviaria en Chipre.

Autobús
Autobuses interurbanos: Varias compañías de autobuses enlazan las principales ciudades con servicios diarios y un horario fijo.

Autobuses rurales: Casi todos los pueblos están conectados con la ciudad más cercana por medio de autobuses locales. Los autobuses operan de forma limitada una o dos veces al día. Las compañías regionales de autobuses, formadas recientemente, prestarán un servicio más amplio.

Autobuses urbanos: Operan con frecuencia durante el día y, en algunas zonas turísticas, en verano, el servicio se extiende hasta la medianoche.

Coche
Carreteras bastante buenas, que cumplen con los requisitos internacionales de tráfico, enlazan las ciudades y los pueblos. Autopistas de cuatro carriles conectan la capital, Nicosía, con las ciudades costeras de Limassol y Larnaca. Las carreteras secundarias y forestales, en su mayoría, todavía no se han asfaltado, pero están en condiciones aceptables.

Los visitantes pueden conducir en Chipre si tienen un permiso de conducir internacional o su permiso nacional, siempre que sea válido para el tipo de vehículo que deseen conducir. Los visitantes pueden obtener un Permiso de Conducir Provisional con validez de seis meses, al precio de C£3,00.

Las compañías de alquiler de coches sin conductor tienen oficinas en todas las ciudades y en el aeropuerto internacional de Larnaca, con personal que habla inglés. Las tarifas diarias oscilan entre C£13,00 para un coche pequeño y C£23,00 para uno más grande.

INFORMACION TELEFONICA

Código Internacional	Código Nacional	Indicativo de área de las Ciudades principales
00	357	

Nicosía 2
Larnaca 4
Limassol 5
Ayia Napa 3
Paphos 6

DISCOUNTS AND CONCESSIONS

Louis National Tours (excursions in Cyprus): 15% discount.
Louis Cruise Lines (Cruises to Israel, Egypt and the Greek Islands): 10% discount on fares only (excluding taxes).
Those interested have to contact the following LOUIS TOURIST offices:
Louis/Limassol, 65 Georgios A St, Potamos Germasogias. ☏ (05) 327343 **FAX** (05) 327318.
Louis/Larnaca, 94 Arch. Makarios Ave. ☏ (04) 657664 **FAX** (04) 657603.
Louis/Paphos, Posidonos Ave, La Piazza Complex. ☏ (06) 246245 **FAX** (06) 246220.
Louis/Ayia Napa, 18B Arch. Makarios Ave. ☏ (03) 721560 **FAX** (03) 722319.

Hostels in this country may also display this symbol.

Les auberges de ce pays pourront également afficher ce symbole.

Jugendherbergen in diesem Land können auch dieses Symbol zeigen.

Es posible que los albergues de este país exhiban además este símbolo.

Ayia Napa ⎚CC⎚ 23 Dionysios Solomos St, Ayia Napa. ☏ (3) 723433 **FAX** (2) 442896 **Open:** 24hrs, 1.3-30.11 ⇋ 80 ⊖ C£5.00 ☌ ⍾⍾ 🗓 ⛪ 🅿 ⚲ ⚓ ✈ Larnaca 40km 🚌 Eman ⓡ (Cyprus YHA)

Larnaca 27 Nicolaou Rossou St, Larnaca: near Ayios Lazaros church. ☏ (4) 621188 **FAX** (2) 442896 ⇋ 70 ⊖ C£3.50 ☌ ⍾⍾ 🏠 ⛪ 🅿 ✈ Larnaca 3km A🚌 Ayios Lazaros Church 50m ⛴ Larnaca 3km 🚌 50m

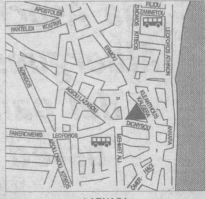

LARNACA

Nicosia 2SW 5 Hadjidakis St, Off Them. Dervis St, Nicosia. ☎ (2) 444808 **FAX** (2) 442896 ⊷ 50 ● C£4.00 ☞ ⅲ ⅏ ⅊ ✈ Larnaca 50km A⟐ Solomos Square 400m ⛴ Limassol 80km ⟐ 500m **R** (Cyprus YHA)

Paphos 37 Eleftherios Venizelos Ave, Paphos. ☎ (6) 232588 **FAX** (2) 442896 ⊷ 22 ● C£4.00 ⅉ ☞ ⅲ ⅊ ✈ Paphos ⟐ 100m **R** (Cyprus YHA)

Stavros Government Rest House (Ministry of Agriculture, Forestry Dept), Forest Centre, Stavros, Psoka. ☎ (6) 722338 ⊷ 14 ● C£6.00 ⅉ ⅲ ⅏ ⅊ ✈ Paphos 100km A⟐ Larnaca Airport 150km **R** (Cyprus YHA)

Troodos Ex- Olympus Hotel, Mount Troodos. ☎ (5) 422400 **FAX** (2) 442896

Open: 1.4 ⊷ 22 ● C£4.00 ⅉ ☞ ⅲ ⅏ ⅊ ⅊ ✈ Larnaca 120km ⛴ Limassol 50km ⟐ to Kakopectia OR Platres **R** (Cyprus YHA)

NICOSIA

CZECH REPUBLIC
LA REPUBLIQUE TCHEQUE
DIE TSCHECHISCHE REPUBLIK
LA REPUBLICA CHECA

KMC Club of Young Travellers (Secretariat),
Karolíny Světlé 30, 11000 Praha 1,
Czech Republic.

☏ (42) (2) 24230633, 90001518
FAX (42) (2) 24230633, 8550013

Office Hours: Monday-Friday, 08.00-16.30hrs

Travel Section: KMC-Travel Service,
Karolíny Světlé 30, 11000 Praha 1, Czech Republic.

☏ (42) (2) 24230633
FAX (42) (2) 24230633, 8550013

IBN Booking Centre for outward bookings
■ **Prague-KMC,** *via National Office above.*
   ☏ (42) (2) 24230633

Capital:	Prague (Czech Republic)
Language:	Czech
Currency:	Kč (Czech Republic)
Population:	10,500,000
Size:	78,864 sq km

CZECH REPUBLIC

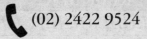

WESTERN UNION | MONEY TRANSFER®
The fastest way to send money worldwide.℠

(02) 2422 9524

Money
from home
in minutes
See Page 9

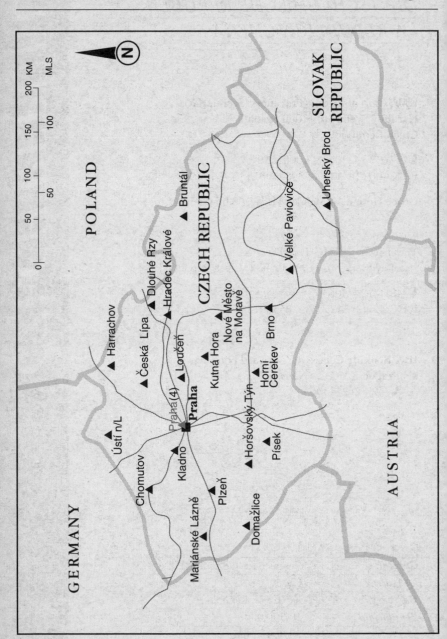

ENGLISH

CZECH HOSTELS

Take time to visit this rapidly changing country and make sure you see the countryside as well as the big cities. With three hostels in Prague and a network of 27 hostels in total, Youth Hostels are the best way to see them.

In Prague and other big cities hostels are open 24hrs, elsewhere they are open 06.00-22.00hrs, although dormitories are closed 09.00-17.00hrs, except for shelter in bad weather.

Expect to pay in the region of Kč 150-500, including sheet hire. All bookings should be made through the national office.

PASSPORTS AND VISAS

Visitors from most European countries and the USA generally do not require visas. When necessary visas can be obtained at Czech missions before arrival.

HEALTH

Visitors to the Czech Republic should take out private insurance before they travel.

BANKING HOURS

Banks are open 08.00-17.00hrs Monday - Friday.

POST OFFICES

Normal opening hours are 08.00-19.00hrs Monday - Friday. In Prague the main post office offers 24-hour service.

SHOPPING HOURS

09.00-19.00hrs Monday - Friday; 09.00-15.00hrs Saturday.

TRAVEL

Air
The national airline CSA offers some discounts.

Rail
Rail travel is cheap and Inter-Rail cards are valid.

Bus
The CSAD bus company offers a fast service but it is more expensive than rail travel.

TELEPHONE INFORMATION

International Code	Country Code	Main City Area Codes
00	42	Prague 2

FRANÇAIS

AUBERGES DE JEUNESSE TCHEQUES

Prenez le temps de visiter ce pays en pleine transformation, et faites en sorte d'explorer la campagne autant que les grandes villes. Avec 3 auberges à Prague et un réseau qui compte 27 auberges au total, les auberges de jeunesse représentent la meilleure façon de découvrir ce pays.

A Prague et dans d'autres grandes villes, les auberges sont ouvertes 24 heures sur 24. Ailleurs, elles sont ouvertes de 6h à 22h, bien que les dortoirs soient fermés entre 9h et 17h, à part un abri en cas de mauvais temps.

Une nuit vous coûtera entre 150 et 500 Kč, location de draps comprise. Toute réservation doit être faite en passant par le bureau national.

PASSEPORTS ET VISAS

En principe, les visiteurs en provenance de la plupart des pays européens et des Etats-Unis n'ont pas besoin de visa. Le cas échéant, vous pouvez obtenir un visa dans une mission tchèque avant votre arrivée.

SOINS MEDICAUX

Il est conseillé aux voyageurs se rendant en République Tchèque de souscrire à une police d'assurance avant leur voyage.

HEURES D'OUVERTURE DES BANQUES

Les banques sont ouvertes de 8h à 17h du lundi au vendredi.

BUREAUX DE POSTE

Les bureaux de poste sont normalement ouverts de 8h à 19h, du lundi au vendredi. A Prague, la poste principale est ouverte 24 heures sur 24.

HEURES D'OUVERTURE DES MAGASINS

Les magasins sont ouverts de 9h à 19h du lundi au vendredi, et de 9h à 15h le samedi.

DEPLACEMENTS

Avions
La ligne aérienne nationale CSA offre certaines réductions.

Trains
Le train est bon marché et les cartes Inter-Rail sont valides.

Autobus
La compagnie d'autobus CSAD assure un service rapide mais plus cher que le train.

TELEPHONE

Indicatif International	Indicatif du Pays	Indicatifs régionaux Villes principales
00	42	Prague 2

DEUTSCH

TSCHECHISCHE JUGENDHERBERGEN

Lassen Sie sich Zeit, um dieses Land zu besuchen, in dem viele Änderungen stattfinden. Dabei sollten Sie nicht nur die großen Städte besuchen, sondern auch aufs Land hinaus fahren. Da es in Prag drei Herbergen gibt und das ganze Netz aus 27 Herbergen besteht, bietet Ihnen diese Art des Reisens die beste Möglichkeit, alles genau zu besichtigen.

In Prag und anderen großen Städten sind die Herbergen 24 Stunden geöffnet. An anderen Orten sind sie von 06.00-22.00 Uhr geöffnet, aber die Schlafräume sind von 09.00-17.00 Uhr geschlossen, es sei denn bei schlechtem Wetter, wo sie als Unterstand dienen.

Es ist mit einem Preis von ca Kč 150-500 zu rechnen, in dem eine Gebühr für die Miete von Laken bereits enthalten ist. Alle Buchungen sind über die Landesgeschäftsstelle vorzunehmen.

PÄSSE UND VISA

Reisende aus den meisten europäischen Ländern und den USA brauchen im allgemeinen kein Visum. Bei Bedarf kann man sich vor der Ankunft in einer tschechischen Mission ein Visum besorgen.

GESUNDHEIT

Wer in die Tschechische Republik reist, sollte vor Antritt der Reise eine private Versicherung abschließen.

GESCHÄFTSSTUNDEN DER BANKEN

Banken sind montags-freitags von 08.00-17.00 Uhr geöffnet.

POSTÄMTER

Die normalen Öffnungszeiten sind montags bis freitags von 08.00-19.00 Uhr. In Prag bietet die Hauptpost einen 24-Stunden-Service.

LADENÖFFNUNGSZEITEN

Montags-freitags von 09.00-19.00 Uhr, samstags von 09.00-15.00 Uhr.

REISEN

Flugverkehr
Die staatliche Fluggesellschaft CSA bietet gewisse Ermäßigungen.

Eisenbahn
Das Eisenbahnfahren ist billig, und es gelten auch Inter-Rail-Karten.

Busse
Das Busunternehmen CSAD bietet einen schnellen Busverkehr. Die Busse sind aber teurer als die Eisenbahn.

FERNSPRECHINFORMATIONEN

Internationale Kennzahl	Landes-Kennzahl	größere Städte Ortsnetzkennzahlen
00	42	Prag 2

ESPAÑOL

ALBERGUES DE JUVENTUD DE KMC

Tómese tiempo para visitar este país que tanto está cambiando y asegúrese de ver tanto el campo como las grandes ciudades. Con tres albergues en Praga y una red de 27 albergues en total, la forma ideal de conocer el país es alojándose en albergues juveniles.

En Praga y otras grandes ciudades, los albergues están abiertos las 24 horas del día. En el resto del territorio abren de 06.00 a 22.00 horas, si bien los dormitorios están cerrados entre las 09.00 y las 17.00 horas, excepto como refugio en caso de hacer mal tiempo.

Se paga alrededor de 150-500 Kč incluyendo el alquiler de ropa de cama. Todas las reservas deben hacerse a través de la oficina nacional.

PASAPORTES Y VISADOS

Por lo general, los visitantes de la mayoría de los países europeos y de los Estados Unidos no necesitan visado. De ser necesario, éste puede obtenerse en las misiones checas antes de llegar al país.

SANIDAD

Se recomienda a los visitantes de la República Checa que se hagan un seguro privado antes de viajar.

HORARIO DE BANCOS

Los bancos abren de 08.00 a 17.00 de lunes a viernes.

CASAS DE CORREO

El horario normal es de 08.00 a 19.00 horas de lunes a viernes. En Praga, la casa de correos principal abre las 24 horas del día.

HORARIO COMERCIAL

De 09.00 a 19.00 horas de lunes a viernes. Sábados de 09.00 a 15.00 horas.

DESPLAZAMIENTOS

Avión
La compañía aérea nacional CSA ofrece algún descuento.

Tren
Viajar en tren resulta barato y se aceptan las tarjetas de Inter-Rail.

Autobús
La compañía de autobuses CSAD ofrece un servicio rápido, si bien es más caro que viajar en tren.

INFORMACION TELEFONICA

Código Internacional	Código Nacional	Indicativo de área de las Ciudades principales
00	42	Praga 2

Hostels in this country may also display this symbol.

Les auberges de ce pays pourront également afficher ce symbole.

Jugendherbergen in diesem Land können auch dieses Symbol zeigen.

Es posible que los albergues de este país exhiban además este símbolo.

Brno Lomená 48, 61700 Brno-Komárov
📞 (5) 43321335, 43216232 ✉ 150
BB inc 🍴 � ⛪ 🅿 ⛵ 🚌 Brno 🚃
40, 49, 63 10min ap Komárov 🚋 12,
22 10min ap End Stop ®

Bruntál - Hotel Slezan Revoluční 20,
79201 Bruntál 📞 (646) 711907 **FAX**
(646) 711913 **Open:** 24 hrs ✉ 161 🍴
♦♦♦ ♿ ⛪ 🅿 🏊 ⛵ 🚌 300m 🚃 300m

Česká Lípa Vila Adéla, Česká Lípa,
47001 Česká Lípa, Děčínská 1414. 📞
(425) 52786, 52831 ✉ 26 ♂ ♦♦♦ 🚃
1 Slovanka ®

Chomutov [1.5 SW] Hostel Energetik Na
Průhoně 4800, 43 011 Chomutov 📞
(396) 27516 or 27545 **FAX** (396)
21572 **Shut:** 1-30.8 ✉ 64 🍴 ♦♦♦ 🅿
🚌 Chomutov 🚃 4, 9 1.5km ap "Na
Kadaňské" ®

Dlouhé Rzy v Orlických Horách
Rekreační zařízení Astra. ☎(443)95051
Shut: 6.12-1.1 ⊠ 160 ⦿ ⚄ ⚿ ⓟ ⚒
⚓ ⛟ Nové Město nad Metují 5km
⛟ Nový Hrádek - Dlouhé Rzy 300m

Domažlice Domov mládeže Obchodní
akademie, 34401 Domažlice, Boženy
Němcové 116. ☎ (189) 2386 **Open:**
06.00-10.00hrs, 17.00-23.00hrs ⊠ 96
⦿ ♂ ⚄ ⛟ Domažlice 1km ⛟ 1km
Ⓡ

Harrachov Hotel Ludmila, Na
Hřebenkách 381, 51246 Harrachov. ☎
(432) 529156 **FAX** (432) 529156 ⊠
108 ⦿ ⚄ ⛪ ⓟ ⚒ ⚓ ⛟ Harrachov
1.5km

Horšovský Týn Domov mládeže SZŠ,
34601 Horšovský Týn, Nádražní ulice
43. ☎ (188) 2319, 2432 **Open:**
06.00-10.00hrs, 17.00-23.00hrs,
1.7-31.8 ⊠ 45 ⦿ ♂ ⚄ ⛟ Horšovský
Týn 1.5km Ⓡ

Hříběcí.u Horní Cerekve Ubytovna
Domu Dětí a Mládeže, 39403 Horní
Cerekev. ☎ (366) 26411 **FAX** (366)
26411 ⊠ 38 ⦿ ⚄ ⓟ ⚓ ⛟ Horní
Cerekev 2km

Hradec Králové Hotel Garni, Na Kotli
1147, 50296 Hradec Králové. ☎ (49)
27181 **FAX** (49) 25644 ⊠ 67 ⦿ ⚄
⛪ ⓟ ⚓ ⛟ Hradec Králové 5km ⛟
9, 20, 25, 26, 27, 28 100m ⛖ 1, 2, 7
100m

Kladno Domov mládeže SOU Poldi
Kladno, 27201 Kladno 2, ul 5, května
1870. ☎ (312) 3252 **FAX** (312) 5665
Open: 06.00-10.00hrs,
17.00-23.00hrs ⊠ 80 ⦿ ⚄ ⛟
Kladno 1km ⛟ 1km Ⓡ

Kutná Hora Domov dětí a mládeže,
28401 Kutná Hora, Kremnická 32. ☎
(327) 2089 **Open:** 06.00-10.00hrs,
17.00-23.00hrs ⊠ 28 ♂ ⚄ ⛟ Kutná
Hora ⛟ Kutná Hora 1km Ⓡ

Louceň Zámek, ubytovna, 28937
Louceň. ☎ (325) 92227 **FAX** (325)
92381 ⊠ 70 BB INC ⦿ ⚄ ⚿ ⛪ ⓟ ⚓
⛟ Louceň u Nymburka, 10min Ⓡ

Mariánské Lázně Hotel Krakonos,
35334 Mariánské Lázně. ☎ (165)
622624 **FAX** (165) 622383 ⊠ 250 ⦿
⛟ 5km ⛟ 12 ap End Stop Ⓡ

Nové Město na Moravě Hotelová
ubytovna DUO, 59231 Nové Město na
Moravě, Masarykova 1493, ☎ (616)
916245 **Open:** 24hrs ⊠ 150 ⦿ ♂ ⚄
⛟ Nové Město na Moravě, 10min Ⓡ

Písek Domov mládeže, 38701 Písek,
Budějovická 1664. ☎ (362) 214983
Open: 06.00-10.00hrs,
17.00-23.00hrs, 5.7-25.8 ⊠ 400 ⦿
♂ ⛟ Písek 500m ⛟ Písek Ⓡ

Plzeň 3W Hostel SOU č.4 Vejprnická 56,
31802 Plzeň ☎ (19) 286412 **FAX** (19)
280607 ⊠ 80 ⦿ except Jul/Aug ⚄
ⓟ ⛟ Plzeň 3km ⛖ 2 3km
ap Internáty Ⓡ

PRAHA (4 Hostels)

Praha - **CKM Juniorhotel** Žitná 12, 121
05 Praha 2. ☎ 292984 **FAX** (2)
24223911 ⊠ 50 Ⓡ

PRAHA - CKM Juniorhotel

Praha - Hotel Beta IBN Roškotova
1225/I, 14700 Praha 4 - Krč. ☎ (2)

61262158 **FAX** (2) 61261202 Open:
24hrs � 250 BB inc 📺 ⛄👫♿🏛 🅿 ✈
Praha-Ruzyně 20km A🚌 119 to U
Line A 🚃 Praha-Hlavní nádraží 9km
🚌 124,205 from U Line C-
Budějovická 50m ap U Statku U C-
Budějovická **R**

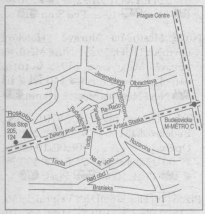

PRAHA -Hotel Beta

Praha - Hostel Bráník SOU Vrbova
1233, 14000 Praha 4-Bráník. ☎ (2)
4021682 **FAX** (2) 4021682 � 170 📺
👫♿🏛 🅿 ⛵ ✈ Praha-Ruzyně 20km
A🚌 119 to U Line A 🚃 Praha-Hlaví
nádraží 12km 🚌 198, 196 100m
ap Vrbova/Ke Smrčině/ U Line B -
Smíchovské nádraží

Praha - Hotel Standart Vodní Stavby,
17000 Praha 7 - Holešovice, Přístavní
2. ☎ (2) 875258 or 875674 **FAX** (2)
806752 Open: 24hrs � 150 📺 👫 🚃
Praha - Holešovice 🚋 1, 3, 12, 14, 25

5min ap Dělnická U C/Vltavská or
Nádraží 10min **R**

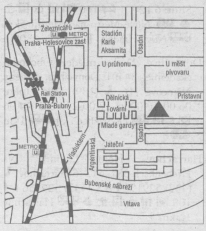

PRAHA - Hotel Standart

Uherský Brod Domov mládeže SOU,
68801 Uherský Brod, Větrná 1370. ☎
(633) 633190 **FAX** (633) 634127
Open: 06.00-10.00hrs,
17.00-23.00hrs � 78 ♂ 👫 🚃
Uherský Brod 500m 🚌 Uherský Brod
500m **R**

Ústí n/L Ubytovna Junior, 40000 Ústí
n/L, Kosmonautù 571/1. ☎ (47) 62215
Open: 24hrs � 15 📺 👫 🚃 Ústí n/L
1km 🚌 54, 56, 5 or 11 **R**

Velké Pavlovice Ubytovna TJ Slavoj,
69106 Velké Pavlovice, Hodonínská 2.
☎ (626) 922465 **Open:**
06.00-10.00hrs, 17.00-23.00hrs � 60
📺 👫 🚃 Velké Pavlovice 500m 🚌
Velké Pavlovice **R**

DENMARK
DANEMARK
DÄNEMARK
DINAMARCA

ASSURED STANDARD

Hostelling International - Denmark,
Vesterbrogade 39, DK-1620 Copenhagen V,
Denmark.

☎ (45) 31 313612
FAX (45) 31 313626

Office Hours: Monday-Thursday 09.00-16.00hrs and
Friday 09.00-15.00hrs.

Travel Section: Central reservation for
incoming groups: Hostelling International-Denmark,
Vesterbrogade 39, DK-1620
Copenhagen V, Denmark.

☎ (45) 31 313612
FAX (45) 31 313626

IBN Booking Centre for outward bookings
■ **Copenhagen,** *via National Office above.*

Capital:	Copenhagen
Language:	Danish
Currency:	kr (1 Krone = 100 øre)
Population:	5,170,000
Size:	43,069 sq km

DENMARK

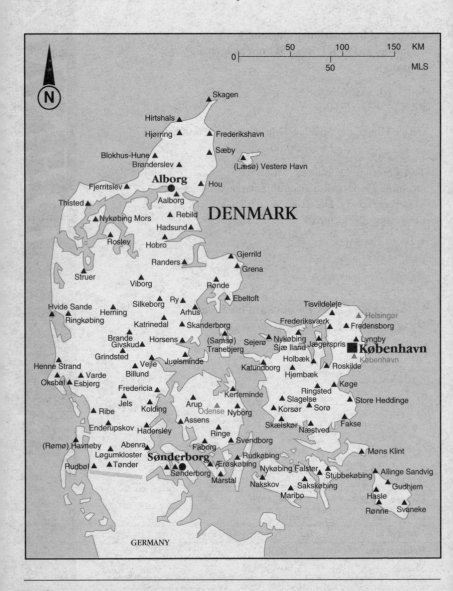

ENGLISH

DANISH HOSTELS

Youth Hostels in Denmark have excellent facilities for families.

Most Danish hostels are open 08.00-12.00hrs and 16.00-21.00hrs, but some are open 24hrs. See under each individual hostel. There is access to common areas the whole day. If you are not able to claim your bed by 17.00hrs, you must warn the hostel in advance. Reservations are essential from 1.9-15.5 (individuals), 1.1-31.12 (groups). Most Danish hostels accept group bookings. Contact national office or directly to hostel.

Danish hostels have prices for private rooms and prices for beds in sharing rooms/dormitory. The price for a private room fluctuates between DKK 120-540 for 2-6 persons per night. The maximum price for a bed per night is DKK 85. No charge for children under 2 years. Notify the hostel on reservation. All hostels except København Bellahøj, have self-catering facilities with pots and pans, but you need to provide your own cutlery and crockery. Many hostels also provide meals at reasonable prices.

From 1997 Hostelling International Denmark has introduced a national star rating classification system where the hostels are awarded from one to five stars. The stars are given according to the standard of 33 different parameters including building standards, sleeping/bathing/common facilities as well as basic service elements - just to name a few. Five stars of course being the highest classification. The star ratings will be displayed in the hostels and in the Danish 1997 catalogue.

Hostelling International Denmark is in the process of introducing environmental approved hostels. This is done in co-operation with the official body called The Green Key. So far The Green Key has been awarded to only one hostel - Kalundborg - but more are on the way. Look out for The Green Key Flag which indicate an environmental friendly hostel.

PASSPORTS AND VISAS

Please contact Danish Embassy or Consulate in your country of residence.

BANKING HOURS

Business Hours: Monday-Friday 09.30-16.00hrs, Thursday 09.30-18.00hrs. Many branches at airports, harbours and railway stations are open longer hours for exchange of currency. The hours may have slight local variations. The red cash dispensers "Kontanten" accept Visa Euro, Master and Cirrus cards for drawing Danish currency. "Kontanten" dispensers are always open. Please note that Danish banks may refuse to exchange large foreign bank notes.

POST OFFICES

Normally weekdays 09.00/10.00-17.00/17.30hrs and Saturday 09.00-12.00hrs. All post offices are closed on Sunday.

SHOPPING HOURS

In general shops are open Monday-Friday 09.00-17.30hrs and Saturday 09.00-13.00hrs. However supermarkets and department stores often stay open until 19.00hrs on weekdays and until 17.00hrs on Saturdays. Bakers are usually open on Sundays. In the cities and on large petrol stations there may be kiosks that are open 24hrs a day.

TRAVEL

Air

Copenhagen Airport is the hub of the domestic routes. Domestic airports are usually located so that they serve several towns. The flight times are minimal. There are numerous discounted domestic air fares, including the so called "green departures" as well as child, youth and group reductions.

Rail

Intercity services are the cornerstone of the DSB network and they link most towns in Denmark. On the principal routes there are regular services every hour. These trains also go on the Nyborg-Korsør Great Belt ferries. Seats must be reserved on these trains. When the Great Belt crossing forms part of the journey, seat reservations are compulsory.

An electrified metropolitan S-Train railway network connects Copenhagen city centre with the outskirts at intervals of 10-20. minutes. Tickets can be bought at all stations and must be time-stamped and nicked in the automatic machines on the platform before boarding the train. Return tickets to and from stations outside the central traffic area must be stamped again before returning. Passengers without valid stamped tickets run the risk of being fined. S-Trains run from 05.00 on weekdays and 06.00 on Sundays until around 00.30hrs.

A number of international trains link up with the internal services to form a very comprehensive rail network.

Bus/Coach

Many local bus connections. Further information at the railway stations. Tickets can be bought from the bus driver, please always have money or tickets ready on boarding by the front entrance and tell the driver where you want to go.

Ferry

Surrounded by water and with nowhere more than 55km from the sea, Denmark is a country of many inhabited islands. These are linked by an extensive network of ferry routes. Most of the routes are well established and carry passengers, cars and/or trains. There are just over 90 different ferry services sailing out of Danish harbours.

All vessels are part of the country's integrated transport system and are punctual and reliable.

Driving

Your driving licence must clearly indicate that it applies to a vehicle of the type being used. A green card is not compulsory but recommended. A warning triangle is obligatory as is the wearing of seat belts. Dipped headlights are compulsory 24 hours a day. Right hand drive cars must have black adhesive triangles often supplied by ferry companies or car shops.

PUBLIC HOLIDAYS

New Year, 1 January; Easter, 27-31 March; Great Prayer Day, 25 April; Ascension Day, 8 May; Whit Sunday/Monday, 18/19 May; Constitution Day, 5 June; Christmas, 24 noon/25/26 December.

TELEPHONE INFORMATION

International Code	Country Code	Main City Area Codes
00	45	Copenhagen 31

FRANÇAIS

AUBERGES DE JEUNESSE DANOISES

Les auberges de jeunesse au Danemark sont très bien équipées pour les familles.

La plupart des auberges danoises ouvrent de 8h à 12h et de 16h à 21h, mais quelques-unes restent ouvertes 24h/24 (cf. les renseignements donnés pour chaque auberge). L'accès aux salles communes est possible toute la journée. S'il vous est impossible de prendre possession de votre lit à 17h au plus tard, vous êtes prié d'informer l'auberge à l'avance. Il est essentiel de réserver entre 1/9 et 15/5 (pour les individus) et entre 1/1 et 31/12 (pour les groupes). La plupart des auberges danoises acceptent les réservations de groupes. Veuillez contacter le bureau national ou directement l'auberge en question.

Les auberges danoises pratiquent des prix différents pour les chambres privées et pour les lits en chambres communes ou dortoirs. Le prix d'une chambre privée varie entre 120 et 540 couronnes pour 2 à 6 personnes par nuit. Le prix maximum pour un lit et une nuit est de 85 couronnes. La nuitée est gratuite pour les enfants de moins de 2 ans. Prevenez-en l'auberge au moment de la réservation. Toutes les auberges sauf København Bellahøj ont des cuisines à la disposition des touristes, avec batterie de cuisine, mais il vous faudra fournir vos couverts et votre vaisselle. De nombreuses auberges servent des repas à des prix raisonnables.

A compter de 1997, Hostelling International Danemark introduit une classification par étoiles pour laquelle on accorde aux auberges une marque de une à cinq étoiles. Ces étoiles sont accordées en fonction de la qualité de 33 différents paramètres, dont le standing du bâtiment, des chambres, des sanitaires, des pièces communes de même que les services de base, pour n'en nommer que quelques-uns. Cinq étoiles constituent évidemment la marque la plus élevée. Les marques par étoiles seront affichées dans les auberges et dans le répertoire danois de 1997.

Hostelling International Danemark introduit présentement des auberges écologiques. Ce projet est réalisé en collaboration avec un organisme officiel dénommé "La Clef Verte". Jusqu'à présent, la Clef Verte n'a été attribuée qu'à une seule auberge - à Kalundborg - mais d'autres devraient suivre bientôt. Surveillez le fanion de la Clef Verte qui indique une auberge qui respecte l'environnement.

PASSEPORTS ET VISAS

Veuillez contacter l'ambassade ou le consulat danois de votre pays de résidence.

HEURES D'OUVERTURE DES BANQUES

Heures d'ouverture des guichets:

Du Lundi au Vendredi: 9h30-16h00 Jeudi: 9h30-18h00. De nombreuses agences dans les aéroports, gares maritimes et ferrovières sont ouvertes plus longtemps pour des raisons de change. Les heures d'ouverture peuvent varier quelque peu selon l'endroit. Les distributeurs rouges d'argent liquide 'Kontanten' acceptent les cartes Visa, Euro, Master et Cirrus pour le retrait de devises danoises. Ces distributeurs 'Kontanten' sont ouverts en permanence. Veuillez prendre note que les banques danoises sont susceptibles de refuser de changer les billets de banque étrangers de grosses dénominations.

BUREAUX DE POSTE

Ils sont en général ouverts en semaine de 9h/10h à 17h/17h30 et le samedi de 9h à 12h. Tous les bureaux de poste sont fermés le dimanche.

HEURES D'OUVERTURE DES MAGASINS

En général, les magasins sont ouverts de 9h à 17h30 du lundi au vendredi et de 9h à 13h le samedi. Cependant, les supermarchés et les magasins à rayons sont souvent ouverts jusqu'à 19h en semaine et jusqu'à 17h le samedi. Les boulangeries sont habituellement ouvertes le dimanche. Dans les villes et les stations-service, on peut trouver des boutiques ouvertes 24 heures.

DEPLACEMENTS

Avions

L'aéroport de Copenhague assure les vols intérieurs. Les aéroports nationaux sont généralement situés de façon à desservir plusieurs villes. Les temps de vol sont minimes. Les tarifs des vols intérieurs faisant l'objet de réductions sont nombreux, parmi lesquels les "départs verts", en plus de réductions pour enfants, jeunes adultes et groupes.

Trains

Les services interurbains représentent la pierre angulaire du réseau DSB et relient la plupart des villes danoises. Les lignes principales jouissent de services réguliers toutes les heures. Ces trains vont également sur les ferry-boats de la Grande Ceinture Nyborg-Korsør. Il faut réserver des places sur ces trains. Lorsque la traversée de la Grande Ceinture fait partie du voyage, les réservations de places sont obligatoires.

Un réseau ferroviaire métropolitain électrifié S-Train relie le centre de Copenhague à la banlieue toutes les 10 à 20 minutes. Les billets sont en vente à toutes les gares et doivent être compostés par les machines automatiques situées sur les quais avant de monter dans le train. Les billets aller-retour pour les gares se trouvant à l'extérieur de la zone centrale de trafic doivent être compostés à nouveau avant le retour. Les passagers voyageant sans billets validés risquent des amendes. Les S-Trains sont en service à partir de 5h en semaine et de 6h le dimanche jusqu'à 0h30 environ.

Plusieurs trains internationaux sont reliés au service intérieur pour former un réseau ferroviaire très complet.

Autobus/Autocar

De nombreuses liaisons locales sont assurées par un service de bus. Pour plus d'informations, adressez-vous aux guichets des gares ferroviaires. Les billets peuvent être obtenus auprès du conducteur. En montant dans le bus par l'avant, assurez-vous d'avoir votre argent ou vos billets à la main et dites au conducteur où vous voulez aller.

Ferry-boats

Le Danemark est un pays entouré d'eau et aucun endroit n'est à plus de 55km de la mer. Les nombreuses îles habitées sont reliées par un vaste réseau de services maritimes. La plupart des lignes maritimes sont bien établies et transportent des passagers, des voitures et/ou des trains. Il y a un peu plus de 90 services maritimes différents en partance des ports danois.

Tous les bateaux font partie du système de transport intégré du pays et sont ponctuels et fiables.

Automobiles

Votre permis de conduire doit indiquer clairement le type de véhicule auquel il se rapporte. La carte verte n'est pas obligatoire mais conseillée. Le triangle est obligatoire de même que le port des ceintures de sécurité. Il est obligatoire de rouler en codes 24h sur 24. Les véhicules avec conduite à droite doivent avoir des triangles noirs adhésifs que l'on peut souvent obtenir auprès des compagnies de ferry ou dans les magasins d'articles pour automobiles.

JOURS FERIES

Nouvel an, 1er janvier; Pâques, 27/31 mars; Grande journée de la prière, 25 avril; Ascension, 8 mai; Dimanche/lundi de Pentecôte, 18/19 juin; Fête de la Constitution, 5 juin; Noël, 24 à midi/25/26 décembre.

TELEPHONE

Indicatif International	Indicatif du Pays	Indicatifs régionaux des Villes principales
00	45	Copenhague 31

DEUTSCH

DÄNISCHE JUGENDHERBERGEN

Jugendherbergen in Dänemark haben ausgezeichnete Einrichtungen für Familien.

Die meisten Jugendherbergen sind von 08.00-12.00 Uhr und von 16.00-21.00 Uhr geöffnet aber einige Jugendherbergen sind 24 Stunden am Tag geöffnet (siehe jeweiligen JH-Eintrag). Die Gemeinschaftsbereiche sind ganztägig zugänglich. Wenn Sie Ihr Bett nicht bis spätestens 17.00 Uhr in Anspruch nehmen, müssen Sie die Herberge im voraus verständigen. Reservierungen sind vom 1.9-15.5 (Einzelreisenden) und vom 1.1-31.12 (Gruppen) unerläßlich. Die meisten Jugendherbergen akzeptieren Reservierungen von Gruppen. Bitte erkundigen Sie sich beim Nationalverband oder direkt bei der Jugendherberge.

Dänische Jugendherbergen haben verschiedene Preise für Privatzimmer und Betten in geteilten Schlafsälen. Für ein Privatzimmer für 2-6 Personnen ist mit einem Preis zwischen Dkk 120-540 pro Nacht zu rechnen. Der Höchstpreis für ein Bett ist Dkk 85 pro Nacht. Kinder unter 2 Jahren, sind kostenlos beherbergt. Alle Herbergen außer København Bellahøj haben Einrichtungen für Selbstversorger, einschließlich Töpfe und Pfannen. Sie müssen aber Ihr eigenes Besteck und Geschirr mitbringen. Viele Herbergen stellen Mahlzeiten zur Verfügung und sind sehr preiswert.

Hostelling International Denmark hat für 1997 eine neue, nationale Kategorisierung eingeführt, nach der Jugendherbergen von einem Stern bis zu fünf Sterne verliehen werden. Die Sterne werden nach der Qualität von 33 verschiedenen Parametern (z.B. Gebäudequalität, Schlafmöglichkeiten, Bade- und Duschgelegenheiten, Gemeinschaftsräume und grundlegende Dienstleistungen, um nur einige zu nennen) vergeben. Eine Herberge mit fünf Sternen ist dabei am höchsten eingestuft. Die Sterneinstufung ist in der jeweiligen Herberge ausgehängt, sowie im dänische Katalog von 1997 verzeichnet.

Hostelling International Denmark ist gerade dabei, Jugendherbergen auch unter dem Aspekt des Umweltschutzes einzustufen. Dies geschieht in Zusammenarbeit mit der offiziellen Organisation "The Green Key". Bislang ist der "Grüne Schlüssel" nur einer Herberge (Kalundborg) verliehen worden, weitere Herbergen werden jedoch bald folgen. Eine besonders umweltfreundliche Herberge ist an der Flagge mit dem grünen Schlüssel zu erkennen.

PÄSSE UND VISA

Bitte setzen Sie sich mit der dänischen Botschaft oder dem Konsulat in Ihrem Land in Verbindung.

GESCHÄFTSSTUNDEN DER BANKEN

Montags bis freitags 09.30-16.00, donnerstags 09.30-18.00. Wechselstuben auf den Flughäfen, Häfen und Bahnhöfen sind länger geöffnet. Öffnungszeiten sind von Ort zu Ort unterschiedlich. Bitte beachten Sie, daß dänische Banken sich weigern können, ausländische Banknoten mit einem hohen Nennwert zu wechseln.

Rote Bankautomaten "Kontanten" akzeptieren Visa, Euro, Master und Cirrus, um dänisches Bargeld zu erhalten.

POSTÄMTER

Im allgemeinen werktags von 09.00/10.00-17.00/17.30 Uhr und samstags von 09.00-12.00 Uhr. Alle Postämter sind sonntags geschlossen.

LADENÖFFNUNGSZEITEN

Im allgemeinen sind die Geschäfte montags bis freitags von 9.00 bis 17.30 Uhr, und samstags von 9.00 bis 13.00 Uhr geöffnet. Die Geschäftszeit von Supermärkten und Warenhäusern ist jedoch an Wochentagen oft bis 19.00 Uhr, und samstags bis 17.00 Uhr. Bäckerläden sind gewöhnlich auch sonntags geöffnet. In den Großstädten und an großen Tankstellen befinden sich oft Kioske, die rund um die Uhr aufhaben.

REISEN

Flugverkehr

Der Flughafen von Kopenhagen ist der Hauptflughafen für den Inlandsverkehr. Die Flughäfen für den Inlandsverkehr sind im allgemeinen so gelegen, daß sie mehreren Städten dienen. Die Flugzeiten sind minimal. Es gibt zahlreiche Nachlässe auf Inlandsflüge, darunter die sogenannten "grünen Abflüge" sowie Ermäßigungen für Kinder, Jugendliche und Gruppen.

Eisenbahn

Der Intercity-Verkehr ist die Hauptstütze des DSB-Netzes. Diese Züge verkehren zwischen den meisten Städten in Dänemark. Auf den Hauptstrecken verkehrt jede Stunde ein Zug. Die Züge fahren auch auf die Große Belt-Fähren Nyborg-Korsør. In diesen Zügen muß man einen Platz reservieren lassen. Wenn die Überfahrt über den Großen Belt Teil der Eisenbahnfahrt bildet, sind Platzreservierung obligatorisch.

Ein elektrifiziertes S-Bahn-Netz verbindet das Stadtzentrum von Kopenhagen mit den Außenbezirken. Die Züge verkehren alle 10-20 Minuten. Fahrkarten können auf allen Stationen gekauft werden und müssen in Automaten auf dem Bahnsteig vor Besteigen des Zuges mit einem Zeitstempel versehen und geknipst werden. Rückfahrkarten von und nach Stationen außerhalb des zentralen Verkehrsbereichs müssen vor Antritt der Rückfahrt wieder gestempelt werden. Passagiere ohne eine gültige, gestempelte Fahrkarte laufen Gefahr, mit einer Geldstrafe belegt zu werden. S-Bahnen verkehren werktags von 05.00 und sonntags von 06.00 bis gegen 00.30 Uhr.

Mehrere internationale Züge haben Anschluß an den Inlandsverkehr, so daß ein sehr umfangreiches Eisenbahnnetz geboten wird.

Busse

Es gibt viele örtliche Busverbindungen. Weitere Information sind auf den Bahnhöfen vorhanden. Fahrkarten können beim Busfahrer gekauft werden. Bitte vorne in den Bus einsteigen und immer Geld oder Fahrkarte bereithalten. Dem Fahrer sagen, wohin man fahren will.

Fähren

Da Dänemark von Wasser umgeben und an keiner Stelle mehr als 55 km vom Meer entfernt ist, gibt es viele bewohnte Inseln, die durch ein umfangreiches Fährnetz miteinander verbunden sind. Die meisten Strecken werden schon lange befahren, und es werden Passagiere, Autos und/oder Züge befördert. Von dänischen Häfen aus gibt es etwas mehr als 90 verschiedene Fährverbindungen.

Alle Schiffe gehören zu dem Verkehrsverbundsystem des Landes. Sie sind pünktlich und zuverlässig.

Autofahren

Ihr Führerschein muß deutlich angeben, daß er für ein Fahrzeug des benutzten Typs gilt. Eine grüne Versicherungskarte ist nicht obligatorisch, aber empfehlenswert. Ein Warndreieck ist obligatorisch, und auch das Tragen eines Sicherheitsgurtes ist Pflicht. 24 Stunden am Tag muß mit Abblendlicht gefahren werden. Autos mit Rechtssteuerung müssen ein schwarzes Dreieck tragen, das bei Kfz-Zubehörhandlungen und Fährbootunternehmen erhältlich ist.

FEIERTAGE

Neujahr, 1. Januar; Ostern, 27.-31. März; Tag des großen Gebets, 25 April; Himmelfahrt, 8. Mai; Pfingstsonntag/-montag, 18./19. Mai; Tag der Verfassung, 5. Juni; Weihnachten, ab mittag 24./25./26. Dezember.

FERNSPRECHINFORMATIONEN

Internationale Kennzahl	Landes- Kennzahl	größere Städte - Ortsnetzkennzahlen
00	45	Kopenhagen 31

ESPAÑOL

ALBERGUES DE JUVENTUD DANESES

Los albergues de juventud de Dinamarca son excelentes para viajar en familia.

La mayoría de los albergues daneses abren de 08.00 a 12.00 horas y de 16.00 a 21.00 horas, pero algunos están abiertos 24 horas al día (véase la información para cada albergue en particular). Hay acceso a las áreas comunes todo el día. Si no puede presentarse antes de las 17.00 horas para solicitar su cama, debe avisar al albergue con antelación. Es preciso que las reservas individuales se hagan entre 1.9-15.5 y las reservas de grupo entre 1.1-31.12. La mayoría de los albergues daneses aceptan reservas de grupo. Favor contactar con la Oficina Nacional o el albergue directamente para las reservas de grupo.

La mayoría de los albergues juveniles daneses tienen habitaciones privadas y dormitorios compartidos. Un cuarto privado cuesta entre 120-540 kr para 2 hasta 6 personas por noche. El precio máximo de una cama es de 85 kr por noche. A los niños de 2 años no se les cobra. Favor notificar tales detalles al hacer su reserva.

Todos los albergues excepto København Bellahøj tienen cocina para huéspedes, pero éstos deben traer su propia vajilla y cubertería. Muchos albergues también sirven comidas a precios razonables.

A partir de 1997, Hostelling International Denmark implantará un sistema de clasificación nacional en forma de estrellas, adjudicando a los albergues entre una y cinco estrellas. Las estrellas se otorgan conforme al nivel de 33 parámetros distintos, que incluyen la categoría de construcción, los dormitorios, los baños y las salas comunes, además de cinco elementos de servicio básicos, entre muchos otros. Evidentemente, cinco estrellas representan la clasificación más alta. La clasificación por estrellas será exhibida en los albergues y en el catálogo danés de 1997.

Hostelling International Denmark está estableciendo albergues que cumplen con las normas ambientales, en colaboración con un organismo oficial llamado La Llave Verde. Hasta el momento, La Llave Verde ha sido adjudicada a un solo albergue, el de Kalundborg, pero se prevé que será adjudicada a varios más. Busque la bandera de la Llave Verde, que indica un albergue favorable al medio ambiente.

PASAPORTES Y VISADOS

Favor contactar con la Embajada Danesa o el Consulado en su país de residencia.

HORARIO DE BANCOS

Horas de Oficina: De lunes a viernes de 09.30 a 16.00 horas, los jueves de 09.30 a 18.00 horas. Muchas sucursales en los aeropuertos, puertos y estaciones de tren están abiertas hasta más tarde para el cambio de divisas. Las horas pueden variar según la localidad. Los cajeros automáticos rojos "Kontanten" aceptan las tarjetas Visa Euro, Master y Cirrus para retirar moneda danesa. Los cajeros automáticos están siempre abiertos. Obsérvese que los bancos daneses pueden negarse a cambiar billetes bancarios extranjeros de gran valor.

CASAS DE CORREO

Normalmente abren los días laborables de 09.00 / 10.00 horas a 17.00 / 17.30 horas y los sábados de 09.00 a 12.00 horas. Todas las casas de correo están cerradas los domingos.

HORARIO COMERCIAL

En general, las tiendas abren de lunes a viernes de 09.00 a 17.30 horas y los sábados de 09.00 a 13.00 horas. No obstante, los supermercados y las grandes tiendas suelen estar abiertos hasta las 19.00 horas los días laborables y hasta las 17.00 horas los sábados. Las panaderías suelen abrir los domingos. En las ciudades y gasolineras importantes, es posible que haya quioscos abiertos 24 horas al día.

DESPLAZAMIENTOS

Avión

El aeropuerto de Copenhague es el centro de las rutas nacionales. Los aeropuertos nacionales suelen estar situados de manera que sirvan a varias poblaciones. El tiempo de vuelo es mínimo. Hay muchas tarifas rebajadas para vuelos nacionales, incluyendo las denominadas "salidas verdes" y reducciones para niños, jóvenes y grupos.

Tren

Los servicios intercity son lo mejor de la red de DSB y enlazan la mayoría de las ciudades danesas. En las rutas principales hay trenes regulares cada hora. Estos trenes también suben a los ferrys del Gran Cinturón Nyborg-Korsør. Para estos trenes se deben reservar los asientos. Si cruzar el Gran Cinturón forma parte del trayecto, la reserva de asientos es obligatoria.

Una red electrificada de tren metropolitano "S-Tren" conecta el centro de Copenhague con las afueras de la ciudad a intervalos de 10-20 minutos. Los billetes se pueden comprar en todas las estaciones y hay que marcarles la hora y pasarlos por las máquinas automáticas que se encuentran en el andén, antes de subir al tren. Los billetes de ida y vuelta a estaciones fuera de la zona central de tráfico también tienen que marcarse antes de volver. Los pasajeros que viajen sin un billete válido y debidamente marcado pueden ser multados. Los trenes metropolitanos "S-Tren" funcionan desde las 05.00 horas los días de entre semana y desde las 06.00 horas los domingos hasta las 00.30 horas.

Varios trenes internacionales enlazan con los servicios internos formando una red ferroviaria muy completa.

Autobús

Hay muchas conexiones locales de autobús. Se puede obtener la información en las estaciones de ferrocarril. Los billetes se pueden comprar al conductor del autobús. Se ruega tener siempre listo el dinero o los billetes al subir al autobús por la puerta delantera e indicar al conductor a dónde se desea ir.

Ferry

Rodeada por aguas y con el mar a un máximo de 55 kilómetros desde cualquier punto, Dinamarca es un país de numerosas islas habitadas. Estas están conectadas por una completa red de rutas de ferry. La mayoría de estas rutas son importantes y transportan pasajeros, coches y/o trenes. Hay algo más de 90 servicios distintos de ferry desde los puertos daneses.

Todos los barcos forman parte del sistema de transporte integrado del país y son puntuales y fiables.

Coche

Su permiso de conducir debe indicar claramente que es válido para el tipo de vehículo que desee utilizar. La carta verde no es obligatoria pero sí recomendable. Es obligatorio llevar un triángulo de advertencia y utilizar los cinturones de seguridad. Hay que llevar las luces de cruce encendidas 24 horas al día. Los coches con el volante a la derecha deben llevar triángulos negros adhesivos, que suelen encontrarse en las tiendas de las compañías de ferry o en las tiendas de automóviles.

DIAS FESTIVOS

Año Nuevo, 1 enero; Pascua, 27-31 marzo; Día de la Gran Oración, 25 abril; Día de la Ascensión, 8 mayo; Domingo/Lunes de Pentecostés, 18/19 mayo; Día de la Constitución, 5 junio; Navidad, desde el mediodía del 24 hasta el 26 inclusive.

INFORMACION TELEFONICA

Código Internacional	Código Nacional	Indicativo de área de las Ciudades principales
009	45	Copenhague 31

DISCOUNTS AND CONCESSIONS

Hertz Car Hire Service: Hertz Biludlejning, Vester Farimagsgade 1, 1606 Copenhagen V. Discount from 5% in the USA to 20% in Scandinavia, granted on normal time and kilometre rates. Obtainable on presentation of a CD-card which can be obtained by applying to Karin Thomsen ✆ 3313 4011 Ext 605.
Kattegatbroen, Mercandia Linierne I/S, Juelsminde Færgehavn, 7130 Juelsminde. 10% discount on all valid ferry fares. ✆ 7569 4800.

Free admission and discounts at many museums. Enquire for local discounts at hostel.

Aabenraa ▲ Sonderskovvej 100, 6200 Aabenraa. ✆ 74622699 **FAX** 74622939 **Open:** 1.3-31.10 ☎ 102 ⑩ ⚥ & ▣ ⊞ ℗ ⚓ ⛴ 2km ⊞ 10km ⊞ ap YH

Aalborg ⚐ 'Fjordparken', Skydebanevej 50, 9000 Aalborg. ✆ 98116044 **FAX** 98124711 **Open:** 1.2-15.12 ☎ 144 ⑩(B) ⚥ & ▣ ⊞ ℗ ⚓ ✈ Aalborg 10km A⊞ 8km ⊞ 3.5km ⊞ 8 from City Centre 8m

Århus ▲ ⬚3N⬚ 'Pavillonen', Marienlundsvej 10, 8240 Risskov. ✆ 86167298 **FAX** 86105560 **Open:** 20.1-20.12 ☎ 150 ⑩(B L) ⚥ & ⊞ ▣ ⊞ ℗ ⚓ ✈ Tirstrup 35km A⊞ City centre 3km ⛴ Århus 3km ⊞ Århus 3km ⊞ Marienlund 1 200m ⊞ 1, 2, 6, 8

Årup △ Årup-Hallen Skolegade 3, 5560 Årup. ✆ 64432034 **FAX** 64432034 **Open:** 15.1-15.12 ☎ 47 ⑩ ⚥ ① ⊞ ℗ ⊞ 300m

Assens ▲ Ungdommens hus, Adelgade 26, 5610 Assens. ✆ 64711357 **FAX** 64715657 **Open:** 1.3-31.10 ☎ 64 ⑩ ⚥ ① ⊞ ℗ ⚲ ⚓ ⊞ 500m

Billund ⚐ ⌖CC⌖ Ellehammers Alle 2, 7190 Billund. ✆ 75332777 **FAX** 75332877 **Open:** 15.1-14.12 ☎ 228 ⑩ ⚥ & ▣ ⊞ ℗ ⚲ ✈ Billund 250m

A⊞ 300m ⊞ Vejle 27km ⊞ Vejle 50m

Blokhus-Hune ▲ Kirkevej 26, 9492 Blokhus. ✆ 98249180 **FAX** 98209005 **Open:** 1.2-31.12 ☎ 100 ⑩(B D) ⚥ ⊞ ℗ ⚲ ⚓ ⊞ 200m

Brande ▲ Dr Arendsvej 2, 7330 Brande. ✆ 97182197 **FAX** 97182197 **Open:** 1.3-30.11 (Grps; 1.1-20.12) ☎ 54 ⑩(B) ⚥ ⊞ ℗ ⊞ Brande 800m ⊞ 100m Ⓡ

Brønderslev ▲ Brønderslev Hallen, Knudsgade 15, 9700 Brønderslev. ✆ 98821500 **FAX** 98800120 **Open:** 08.00-12.00hrs, 16.00-22.00hrs ☎ 49 ⚥ ▣ ⊞ ℗ ⚲ ⚓ ⊞ 1.5km ⊞ 1.5km

Copenhagen ☞ **København**

Ebeltoft ▲ Søndergade 43, 8400 Ebeltoft. ✆ 86342053 **FAX** 86342077 **Open:** 1.3-1.11 ☎ 72 ⑩(B) ⚥ ⊞ ℗ ⚓ ⛴ 4km ⊞ 400m

Enderupskov ▲ 6510 Gram. ✆ 74821711 **FAX** 74820782 **Open:** 1.3-31.10 ☎ 50 ⑩ ⚥ ▣ ⊞ ℗ ✈ Skrydstrup 25km ⛴ Esbjerg 45km ⊞ 200m

Esbjerg ▲ Vardevej 80, 6700 Esbjerg. ✆ 75124258 **FAX** 75136833 **Open:** 1.2-20.12 ☎ 124 ⑩ ⚥ & ⊞ ℗ ⚲ ⚓ ⛴ Esbjerg 2.6km ⊞ Esbjerg 2.7km ⊞ 100m ap YH

Fåborg ▲ Grønnegade 72, 5600
Fåborg. ✆ 62611203 **FAX** 62613508
Open: 1.4-1.10 ✉ 79 ⑩(B) ♔ 🏧 ①
♒ ♻ ⚓ ⛴ 12km 🚌 200m

Fakse ▲ Østervej 4, 4640 Fakse. ✆
56714181 **FAX** 56715492 **Open:**
8.1-23.12 ✉ 80 ⑩(B D) ♔ ♿ ① ♒
🅿 🚻 Fakse 1.5km 🚌 150m

Fjerritslev ⚠ Han Herred Fritidscenter,
Broendumvej 14-16, 9690 Fjerritslev.
✆ 98211190 **FAX** 98212522 ✉ 178
⑩ ♔ ♿ 🅿 ⚓ 🚌 200m

Fredensborg ⚠ Ostrupvej 3, 3480
Fredensborg. ✆ 48480315 **FAX**
48481656 **Open:** 07.00-23.00hrs ✉
94 ⑩ ♔ ① 🔲 ♒ 🅿 ♻ ⚓ ✈
Copenhagen 50km ⛴ Helsingør
15km 🚻 Fredensborg 800m 🚌 336
150m

Fredericia ⚠ [2 SE] [CC] Vestre Ringvej
98, 7000 Fredericia ✆ 75921287 **FAX**
75932905 **Open:** 07.00-21.00hrs,
2.1-1.12 ✉ 120 ⑩ ♔ ♿ 🔲 ♒ 🅿 ♻
⚓ ✈ Billund 60km 🚻 Fredericia 2km
🚌 100m

Frederikshavn ▲ [1 NE] 'Fladstrand',
Buhlsvej 6, 9900 Frederikshavn. ✆
98421475 **FAX** 98426522 **Open:**
2.2-19.12 ✉ 130 ⑩ ♔ ♿ ♒ 🅿 ⚓
⛴ 2km 🚻 Frederikshavn 1.5km
🚌 500m

Frederiksværk ▲ Strandgade 30, 3300
Frederiksværk. ✆ 47770725 **FAX**
42120766 **Open:** 1.2-30.11 ✉ 100 ⑩
♔ ♿ 🔲 ♒ 🅿 ♻ ⚓ ✈ Copenhagen
60km 🚻 Frederiksværk 500m

Givskud ⚠ Løveparkvej 2, 7323
Givskud. ✆ 75730500 **FAX** 75730530
Open: 1.2-1.12 ✉ 126 ⑩(B D) ♔ ♿
🔲 ♒ 🅿 ♻ ✈ Billund 15km 🚻 Give
8km 🚌 212, 500m

Gjerrild ⚠ 'Djursvold', Dyrehavevej 9,
Gjerrild, 8500 Grenå. ✆ 86384199
FAX 86384302 **Open:** 6.1-20.12 ✉

92 ⑩ ♔ ♿ 🔲 ♒ 🅿 ♻ ⚓ ⛴ Grenå
12km 🚻 Grenå 10km 🚌 100m

Grenå ⚠ [CC] Ydesvej 4, 8500 Grenå.
✆ 86326622 **FAX** 86321248 **Open:**
15.1-18.12 ✉ 108 ⑩ ♔ ♿ 🔲 ♒
♻ ⚓ ✈ Århus 22km ⛴ Grenå 2km
🚻 Grenå 3km 🚌 1.5km

Grindsted ▲ Morsbøl Skolevej 24,
7200 Grindsted. ✆ 75322605 **FAX**
75310905 **Open:** 1.4-31.9 (Grps
1.2-31.12) ✉ 80 ⑩ ♔ ♿ 🔲 ♒ 🅿 ♻
✈ Billund 15km 🚌 2km

Gudhjem ▲ Sct Jørgens Gård, 3760
Gudhjem. ✆ 53985035 **FAX**
56485635 **Open:** 24hrs ✉ 220 ⑩ ♔
① ♒ 🅿 ♻ ⚓ 🚌 5m

Haderslev ▲ Erlevvej 34, 6100
Haderslev. ✆ 74521347 **FAX**
74521364 **Open:** 1.2-30.11 ✉ 102
⑩(B) ♔ ♿ ♒ 🅿 ⚓ 🚻 Haderslev
1km 🚌 50m

Hadsund △ [CC] Stadionvej 33, 9560
Hadsund. ✆ 98574345 **FAX**
98574345 **Open:** 1.4-30.9 ✉ 48 ⑩
♔ 🔲 ♒ 🅿 ♻ ⚓ 🚌 1km

Hasle ▲ Fælledvej 28, 3790 Hasle. ✆
56964175 (1.11-1.5, 56966434) **FAX**
56964175 **Open:** 1.5-30.10 ✉ 100 ⑩
♔ ① ♒ 🅿 ⚓ 🚌 500m

Helsingør ⚠ [1.5 NW] [IBN] Ndr
Strandvej 24, 3000 Helsingør. ✆
49211640 FAX 49211399 Open:
1.2-1.12 ✉ 188 ⑩ ♔ ♿ ① ♒ 🅿 ⚓
⛴ Helsingør 2km 🚻 Helsingør
2km 🚌 100m

Henne St △ Strandvejen 458, 6854
Henne Strand. ✆ 75255075 **FAX**
75255075 **Open:** 21.6-23.8 ✉ 44
⑩(B) ♔ ♿ 🏧 ♒ 🅿 ⚓ 🚻 Nr Nebel
+ Henne- Stations By 🚌 Henne-
Stations By ap YH

Herning ⚠ [3 NW] Holingknuden 2,
Holing, 7400 Herning. ✆ 97123144

FAX 97216169 **Open:** 20.1-10.12 🏠
112 ⏹(B) ♦♦♦ ♿ 🗑 🖻 **P** 🚲 ✈ Karup
25km **A**🚌 Herning 4km 🚍
Herning 4km 🚌 1, 1km ap YH

Hirtshals ▲ Kystvejen 53, 9850
Hirtshals. 📞 98941248 **FAX**
98945655 **Open:** 1.2-30.11 🏠 72
⏹(B D) ♦♦♦ ♿ 🖬 **P** ⛵ 🚢 Hirtshals
1km 🚍 Hirtshals 1km 🚌 1km

Hjembæk ▲ Tornbrinken 2, Hjembæk,
Sjælland, 4450 Jyderup. 📞 53468181,
53468033 **Open:** 1.5-1.9 🏠 50 ⏹(B)
♦♦♦ ① 🗑 🚍 Jyderup 5km 🚌 100m
Ⓡ

Hjørring 🔺 Thomas Morildsvej, 9800
Hjørring. 📞 98926700 **FAX**
98901550 **Open:** 1.3-15.10 🏠 140
⏹(B) ♦♦♦ ♿ 🗑 🚍 **P** ⛵ 🚍 Hjørring
2km 🚌 100m

Hobro 🔺 Amerikavej 24, 9500 Hobro.
📞 98521847 **FAX** 98511847 **Open:**
1.2-30.11 🏠 116 ⏹(B) ♦♦♦ ♿ 🗑 🚍 **P**
🚲 ⛵ 🚍 Hobro 3.5km 🚌 100m

Holbæk ▲ Ahlgade 1 A, 4300 Holbæk.
📞 59442919 **FAX** 53439485 **Open:**
2.1-20.12 🏠 125 ⏹ ♦♦♦ ♿ 🏠 🗑 🚍 **P**
🚲 ⛵ ✈ Copenhagen 60km 🚍
Holbaek 250m 🚌 10m Ⓡ

Horsens 🔺 Flintebakken 150, 8700
Horsens. 📞 75616777 **FAX** 75610871
Open: 15.1-15.12 🏠 108 ⏹ ♦♦♦ ♿ 🗑
🚍 **P** ⛵ 🚍 Horsens 2.5km 🚌 300m

Hou ▲ Feriecenter, Søndergade 18,
Hou, 9370 Hals. 📞 98253212 **FAX**
98253090 🏠 85 ⏹ ♦♦♦ 🗑 🚍 **P** ⛵ ✈
Aalborg 35km 🚍 Frederikshavn
54km 🚍 Aalborg 32km 🚌 76;
300m

Hvide Sande ▲ 🆑 Numitvej 5, 6960
Hvide Sande 📞 97311505 **FAX**
97311906 **Open:** New hostel to open
1.4 🏠 88 (120; 1.7-7.8) ⏹ ♦♦♦ ♿ 🗑
🚍 **P** 🚲 ⛵ ✈ Billund Lufthavn 12km

🚢 Esbjerg 8km 🚍 Ringkøbing
Banegard 2.5km 🚌 ap Hvide Sande
Hallen

Jels 🔺 Jels Idrætscenter og
Vandrerhjem, Oerstedvej 10, Jels, 6630
Roedding. 📞 74552869 **FAX**
74553107 🏠 98 ⏹ ♦♦♦ ♿ 🗑 🚍 **P** 🚍
10km 🚌 1km

Juelsminde ▲ Rousthøj Alle 1, 7130
Juelsminde. 📞 75693066 **FAX**
75693957 **Open:** 1.5-1.9 🏠 66 ⏹(B)
♦♦♦ ♿ 🏠 🚍 **P** ⛵ 🚢 Juelsminde 500m
🚌 205, 105, 103

Jægerspris 🔺 ⏹2E⏹ 🆑 Skovnæsvej 2,
3630 Jægerspris 📞 42311032 **FAX**
42312832 🏠 100 ⏹ ♦♦♦ 🏠 🗑 **P** 🚲
⛵ ✈ Copenhagen/Kastrup 60km 🚢
Hundested 3.2km 🚍 Frederikssund
3km 🚌 500m

Kalundborg 🔺 ⏹1 W⏹ 🆑 Stadion Alle
5, DK-4400 Kalundborg. 📞 59561366
FAX 59564626 🏠 118 ● Dkr 85-300
⏹(B) (Grps only) ♦♦♦ ♿ 🗑 🚍 **P** 🚲 ⛵
✈ Copenhagen 100km 🚢
Kalundborg 500m 🚍 Kalundborg
1.5km 🚌 202 200m Ⓡ

Katrinedal ▲ 'Rast', Vellingvej 53,
8654 Bryrup. 📞 75756146 **FAX**
75757810 **Open:** 31.3-31.10 🏠 64 ⏹
♦♦♦ 🚍 **P** 🚌 200m

Kerteminde 🔺 Skovvej 46, 5300
Kerteminde. 📞 65323929 **FAX**
65323924 **Open:** 6.1-14.12 🏠 120
⏹(B) ♦♦♦ ♿ ① 🗑 🚍 **P** ⛵ 🚌 500m

Kolding ▲ ⏹1 SE⏹ Ørnsborgvej 10, 6000
Kolding. 📞 75509140 **FAX** 75509151
Open: 1.2-1.12 🏠 92 ⏹(B) ♦♦♦ 🗑 🚍
P 🚲 ⛵ 🚍 Kolding 1.5km 🚌
300m

Korsør 🔺 ⏹1.5 NE⏹ 🆑 Tovesvej 30F,
4220 Korsør. 📞 53571022 **FAX**
58356870 **Open:** 7.1-15.12 🏠 80
⏹(B) ♦♦♦ ♿ ① 🗑 🚍 **P** 🚲 ⛵ 🚢

Korsør/Halsskov 1km 🚻 Korsør 1km 🚌 500m

KØBENHAVN (2 Hostels)

København - Amager ▲ 4SE IBN
Vejlandsallé 200, 2300 København S.
📞 32522908 **FAX** 32522708 **Open:**
15.1-30.11 (check in from 13.00hrs)🖂
528 🍴(B D) 👫 ♿ 🖳 ♨ P ✈ 4km
A🚌 2505 +🚌 37, 10m 🚻
Copenhagen Central 4km 🚌
46,37,16 Toftegårds Plads 10m Ⓡ
(1.1-31.12)

København - Bellahøj ▲ 5NW IBN
Herbergvejen 8, 2700 Brønshøj. 📞
31289715 (From 29.4; 38289715)
FAX 38890210 **Open:** 1.3-15.1 🖂
299 🍴(B D) 👫 ♿ 🖳 ♨ P 🚲 ⛴
6km 🚻 Godthåbsvej 1.2km 🚌 2,
4E, 5, 7E, 8, 17E, 902, 905, 959 400m

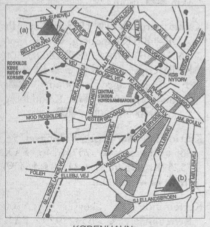

KØBENHAVN -
(a) "Bellahøj", (b) Amager

Køge ▲ 2.5W Lille Køgegaard,
Vamdrupvej 1, 4600 Køge. 📞
53651474 **FAX** 53660869 **Open:**
1.4-15.12 🖂 100 🍴 👫 Ⓘ 🖳 P 🚲
♨ 🚻 Køge 3km 🚌 210 400m Ⓡ

Lyngby (Raadvad) ▲ 7NE Raadvad,
2800 Lyngby. 📞 42803074 **FAX**
42803032 **Open:** 3.1-20.12 🖂 94 🍴
👫 Ⓘ ♨ P ♨ 🚻 Lyngby 7km 🚌
182, 183 1.5km E47 exit 15

Læsø ⚘ Lærkevej 6, 9950 Vesterø Havn,
Læsø. 📞 98499195 **FAX** 98499160
Open: 1.5-1.10 🖂 90 🍴(D) 👫 Ⓘ ♨
P ♨ 🚌 200m

Løgumkloster △ Forsamlingshuset,
Vænget 28, 6240 Løgumkloster. 📞
74743618 **FAX** 74743619 **Open:**
16.4-14.12 🖂 42 🍴 👫 ♨ P 🚌
1km

Maribo ▲ Sdr Boulevard 82B, 4930
Maribo. 📞 53883314 **FAX** 53883265
🖂 97 🍴(B L) 👫 Ⓘ 🚻 1km 🚌
ap YH

Marstal ▲ Færgestræde 29, 5960
Marstal. 📞 62531064 **FAX** 62531057
Open: 1.5-1.9 🖂 82 🍴(B D) 👫 Ⓘ
♨ P 🚲 ♨ 🚌 300m

Møn ▲ 'Møns Klint', Langebjergvej 1,
4791 Borre. 📞 55812030 **FAX**
55812818 **Open:** 1.5-1.10 🖂 105
🍴(B) 👫 Ⓘ P 🚲 ♨ 🚌 2km ap YH
(Su only)

Nakskov ▲ Branderslevvej 11, 4900
Nakskov. 📞 53922434 **FAX** 53923367
🖂 58 🍴(B D) 👫 ♿ Ⓘ 🖳 ♨ P ♨
⛴ Nakskov 3.5km 🚻 Nakskov
3.5km 🚌 100m

Næstved ▲ 1SE Frejasvej 8, 4700
Næstved. 📞 55722091 **FAX** 55725645
Open: 15.3-15.11 🖂 81 🍴(B) 👫 Ⓘ
♨ P 🚲 ♨ ✈ Copenhagen 85km 🚻
Næstved 1.5km 🚌 200m

Nyborg ⚘ Havnegade 28, 5800
Nyborg. 📞 65312704 **FAX** 65302604
Open: 08.00-12.00hrs, 16.00-20.00hrs,
15.5-1.9; 08.00-12.00hrs, 15.1-15.12
🖂 88 🍴(B) 👫 ♿ Ⓘ 🖳 ♨ P ♨ ✈
Beldringe 45km ⛴ Nyborg
(trainferry) 200m, Knudshoved
(carferry) 2.5km 🚻 Nyborg 100m
🚌 200m

Nykøbing Falster (Falster) ⚘ Østre
Alle 110, 4800 Nykøbing Falster. 📞

54856699 **FAX** 54823242 **Open:** 15.1-15.12 🚲 94 🍴(B D) ᭖ ᪥ ① 🖵 ᪥ 🅿 🚌 Nykøbing Falster 1.5km 🚌 ap YH

Nykøbing Mors (Jutland) ⚠ Morsø vandrerhjem, Østerstrand, 7900 Nykøbing Mors. 📞 97720617 **FAX** 97720776 **Open:** 1.2-20.12 🚲 129 🍴(B) ᭖ ᪥ ① 🖵 ᪥ 🅿 ⚓ ⛵ 🚌 1km

Nykøbing Sjælland (Sealand) ▲ Anneberg Vandrerhjem, Egebjergvej 162, 4500 Nykøbing Sj. 📞 59930062 **FAX** 59930062 **Open:** 15.1-15.12 🚲 56 🍴(B) ᭖ ᪥ ① 🖵 ᪥ 🅿 ⚓ ⛵ 🚌 50m

Odense ▲ [2 SE] [IBN] Kragsbjerggården, Kragsbjergvej 121, 5230 Odense M. 📞 66130425 **FAX** 65912863 **Open:** 15.2-1.12 🚲 170 🍴(B) ᭖ ᪥ ① 🖵 ᪥ 🅿 ✈ Odense-Beldringe 15km A🚌 city centre 2.5km 🚌 Odense 2km 🚌 2 150m

Oksbøl ▲ Præstegårdsvej 21, 6840 Oksbøl. 📞 75271877 **FAX** 75272544 🚲 106 🍴(B) ᭖ ᪥ ᪥ 🖵 ᪥ 🅿 ⚓ ⛵ ✈ Esbjerg 20km ⛴ Esbjerg 20km 🚌 Oksbøl 1km 🚌 1km

Randers ▲ [1 NW] Gethersvej 1, 8900 Randers. 📞 86425044 **FAX** 86419854 **Open:** 1.2-30.11 🚲 138 🍴(B) ᭖ ᪥ 🖵 ᪥ 🅿 ⚓ ⛵ 🚌 Randers 600m 🚌 1km

Rebild ⚠ Rebild, 9520 Skørping. 📞 98391340 **FAX** 98392740 **Open:** 26.1-22.12 🚲 100 🍴(B) ᭖ ᪥ 🖵 ᪥ 🅿 ⚓ ✈ Aalborg Lufthavn 30km 🚌 Skørping 2km 🚌 ap YH

Ribe ⚠ Ribehallen, Sct Pedersgade 16, 6760 Ribe. 📞 75420620 **FAX** 75424288 **Open:** 1.2-30.11 🚲 140 🍴(B) ᭖ ᪥ ᪥ 🅿 ⚓ 🚌 Ribe 500m

Ringe ▲ Søvej 34, 5750 Ringe 📞 62622151 **FAX** 62622154 **Open:**

10.1-20.12 🚲 50 🍴 ᭖ ᪥ ① 🖵 ᪥ 🅿 ⚓ 🚌 500m 🚌 500m

Ringkøbing ⚠ Kirkevej 26, Rindum, 6950 Ringkøbing. 📞 97322455 **FAX** 97324959 **Open:** 3.1-22.12 🚲 120 🍴(B D) ᭖ ᪥ 🖵 🅿 ⚓ 🚌 Ringkøbing 1.5km

Ringsted ⚠ St Bendtsgade 18, 4100 Ringsted. 📞 53611526 **FAX** 53613426 **Open:** 11.1-19.12 🚲 78 🍴 ᭖ ① 🖵 ᪥ 🅿 ⚓ 🚌 1km 🚌 200m

Roskilde ▲ [3.5 W] Hørgården, Hørhusene 61, 4000 Roskilde. 📞 46352184 **FAX** 46326690 **Open:** 1.5-1.10 🚲 84 (108, 1.7-31.8) 🍴(B) ᭖ ᪥ ① 🖵 ᪥ 🅿 🚌 Roskilde 4km 🚌 800m

Roslev ▲ 'Salling-Hallen', Viumvej 8, 7870 Roslev. 📞 97571385 **FAX** 97572052 **Open:** 5.1-15.12 🚲 100 🍴(B D) ᭖ ᪥ 🅿 ⚓ 🚌 Skive 17km 🚌 100m

Rudbøl ▲ Rudbølvej 19-21, Rudbøl, 6280 Højer. 📞 74738298 **FAX** 74738035 **Open:** 1.3-1.12 🚲 55 🍴 ᭖ ᪥ 🅿 ⚓ 🚌 Tønder 11km 🚌 ap YH

Rudkøbing ▲ Engdraget 11, 5900 Rudkøbing. 📞 62511830 **FAX** 62511830 **Open:** 1.3-30.11 (Grps 1.1-31.12) 🚲 66 🍴(B) ᭖ ᪥ ① 🖵 ᪥ 🅿 ⚓ ⛴ 🚌 500m 🚌 500m

Ry ▲ 'Knudhule', Randersvej 90, 8680 Ry. 📞 86891407 **FAX** 86892870 **Open:** 1.1-30.11 🚲 117 🍴(B) (Grps only) ᭖ 32 ᪥ 🖵 ᪥ 🅿 ⚓ ⛵ 🚌 Ry 2.5km 🚌 104; om

Rømø ▲ 'Poppelgården', Lyngvejen 7, 6792 Havneby. 📞 74755188 **Open:** 15.3-1.11 🚲 91 🍴(B) ᭖ ᪥ ① 🖵 🅿 ⛵ 🚌 500m

Rønde ▲ Kaløvej 2, 8410 Rønde. 📞 86371108 **FAX** 86371108 **Open:**

1.2-30.11 🏖 60 🍴(B D) 👥 ♿ 🏭 🅿
⛴ � 300m

Rønne ▲ ⎡CC⎤ Arsenalvej 12, 3700
Rønne, Bornholm 📞 56951340 **FAX**
56950132 Open: 4.4-31.10 🏖 150 🍴
👥 🏛 ① 🖥 🏭 🅿 🚴 ⛴ ✈ 5km A�
⛴ 1km � 1km

Sakskøbing 🔺 ⎡CC⎤ Saxe's alle 10, 4990
Sakskøbing. 📞 54706045 **FAX**
54706041 Open: 3.1-19.12 🏖 82
🍴(B D) 👥 ♿ ① 🏭 🅿 ⛴ ⛴ Rødby
Færgehavn 25km 🚂 Sakskøbing
500m � 500m

Samsø ▲ Klintevej 8, Ballen, 8305
Samsø. 📞 86592044 **FAX** 86592343
Open: 1.3-31.10 🏖 100 🍴(B) 👥 ①
🖥 🏭 🅿 🚴 ⛴ � 300m

Sandvig ▲ Sjøljan, Hammershusvej 94,
3770 Allinge. 📞 56480362 **FAX**
56481862 Open: 1.4-31.10 🏖 100
🍴(B) 👥 ① 🏭 🅿 🚴 ⛴ � 100m

Sejerø △ Sejerbyvej 4, Sejerby, 4592
Sejerø. 📞 53490290, 44980504
(7.8-22.6) Open: 23.6-6.8 🏖 35
🍴(B L) 👥 ① 🏭 🅿 🚴 ⛴ ⛴ 300m
Ⓡ

Silkeborg ▲ Åhavevej 55, 8600
Silkeborg. 📞 86823642 **FAX**
86812777 Open: 1.3-30.11 🏖 93
🍴(B) (Grps only) 👥 22 ♿ 🖥 🏭 🅿 🚴
⛴ 🚂 Silkeborg 300m � 300m

Skagen 🔺 Skagen NY Vandrerhjem,
Rolighedsvej 2, 9990 Skagen. 📞
98442200 **FAX** 98442255 Open:
15.2-30.11 🏖 112 🍴(B) 👥 ♿ 🖥 🏭
🅿 🚴 ⛴ ⛴ Frederikshavn 41km 🚂
Skagen 200m � Skagen 200m Ⓡ
(Write or **FAX**)

Skanderborg 🔺 Dyrehaven, 8660
Skanderborg. 📞 86511966 **FAX**
86511334 Open: 1.5-1.10 🏖 122 🍴
👥 🖥 🏭 🅿 🚴 ⛴ 🚂 Skanderborg 3km
� 500m

Skælskor △ Kildehuset, Kildehusvej,
4230 Skælskor. 📞 58191121 **FAX**
58192550 Open: 5.1-20.12 🏖 51
🍴(B) 👥 ① 🏭 🅿 ⛴ � 500m

Slagelse ▲ Bjergbygade 78, 4200
Slagelse. 📞 53522528 **FAX** 53522540
Open: 15.1-10.12 🏖 125 🍴 👥 ①
🏭 🅿 ⛴ 🚂 Slagelse 2km � 100m

Sorø 🔺 ⎡6SW⎤ ⎡CC⎤ Skalskørvej 34, 4180
Sorø 📞 53649200 **FAX** 53649201
Open: 09.00-19.00hrs 🏖 80 🍴 👥 ♿
🏛 ① 🖥 🅿 ✈ Kastrup Copenhagen
80km A� Copenhagen Railway
Station SAS 75km ⛴ Roedby 125km
- Halsskov 30km 🚂 Sorø 4km �
83 4km ap Lynge Eskildstrup 4km

Store Heddinge ▲ Ved Munkevænget
1, 4660 Store Heddinge. 📞 53702022
FAX 53702022 Open: 1.4-31.9 🏖 63
🍴(B) 👥 ① 🏭 🅿 🚴 ⛴ 🚂 Store
Heddinge 600m

Struer 🔺 Bremdal, Fjordvejen, 7600
Struer. 📞 97855313 **FAX** 97840950
Open: 15.1-30.11 🏖 80 🍴(B) 👥 ♿
🖥 🏭 🅿 ⛴ 🚂 2km � 200m ap YH
Ⓡ (15.9-15.4)

Stubbekøbing 🔺 ⎡1.2W⎤ ⎡CC⎤ Gl.
Landevej 27, 4850 Stubbekøbing 📞
54442095 40322095 (mobile) **FAX**
54442098 Open: 1.5-30.9 🏖 64
🍴(B D) 👥 ① 🏭 🅿 🚴 ⛴ ✈ Kastrup
(Copenhagen) 125km ⛴ Gedser
65km Rødby 45km 🚂 Nørre Alslev
10km

Svaneke 🔺 Reberbanevej 9, 3740
Svaneke. 📞 56496242 **FAX** 56497383
Open: 22.3-1.10 🏖 152 🍴(B D) 👥
① 🖥 🏭 🅿 ⛴ � ap YH

Svendborg 🔺 Vestergade 45, 5700
Svendborg. 📞 62216699 **FAX**
62202939 Open: 8.1-22.12 🏖 230
🍴(B D) 👥 🏛 ① 🖥 🏭 🅿 ⛴ ✈ 50km
A� 800m 🚂 Svendborg 1km �
800m

Sæby Sæbygaardsvej 32, 9300 Sæby 98463650 **FAX** 98467630 **Open:** 08.00-22.00hrs 156 12km 200m

SØNDERBORG (2 Hostels)

Sønderborg - **Kærvej** Kærvej 70, 6400 Sønderborg. 74423112 **FAX** 74425631 **Open:** 1.2-30.11 200 (B D) 1km Sønderborg 1.5km ap YH

Sønderborg - **Vollerup** 'Abildgården', Mommarkvej 22, Vollerup, 6400 Sønderborg. 74423990 **FAX** 74425290 120 10km 6km ap YH

Thisted Skinnerup, Kongemøllevej 8, 7700 Thisted. 97925042 **FAX** 97925150 **Open:** 1.3-31.10 86 (B) Thisted 4km 22, 40 ap YH

Tisvildeleje St Helene Centeret, Bygmarken, 3220 Tisvildeleje 42309850 **FAX** 42309897 160 500m

Tønder 'Kogsgården', Sønderport 4, 6270 Tønder. 74723500 **FAX** 74722797 **Open:** 1.2-20.11 124 (B D) Tønder 1km 100m

Varde Ungdomsgården, Pramstedvej 10, 6800 Varde. 75221091 **FAX** 75223338 **Open:** 15.3-1.10 48 (B) Varde 800m ap YH

Vejle CC Gl Landevej 80, 7100 Vejle. 75825188 **FAX** 75831783 116 (B) 30km A 2.5km Vejle 3.5km 2 200m St E45, exit turn 61

Viborg 'Søndersø', Vinkelvej 36, 8800 Viborg. 86671781 **FAX** 86671788 **Open:** 1.3-30.11 122 (B) (Grps only) Viborg 3km 300m

Ærøskøbing Smedevejen 15 62521044 **FAX** 62521644 **Open:** 1.4-30.9 87 (B L) Ærøskøbing 1km 200m

Australie ***02 9261 1111***
Angleterre ***0171 836 1036***
Nouvelle-Zélande ... ***09 379 4224***
Irlande du Nord .. ***01232 324733***
République d'Irlande .. ***01 301766***
Écosse ***0141 332 3004***
États-Unis ***0202 783 6161***

Les réservations par carte de crédit sont courantes pour les réservations téléphoniques effectuées dans l'un de ces centres IBN.

*You can obtain your
Membership Card from the YHA
of the country where you live.*

*Wherever you travel, Hostelling International
offers you the company of like-minded
people, a friendly welcome and affordable
accommodation all over the world.*

EGYPT
EGYPTE
ÄGYPTEN
EGIPTO

Egyptian Youth Hostels Association,
1 El-Ibrahimy Street, Garden City,
Cairo, Egypt.

☎ (20) (2) 3561448, 3540527
FAX (20) (2) 3550329

Office Hours: Monday-Thursday, Saturday, Sunday,
08.30-15.30hrs

Travel Section: Travel and Camping Department,
7 Dr Abdel Hamid Saiid St, Maarouf,
Cairo, Egypt.

☎ (20) (2) 779773
FAX (20) (2) 5791953

Capital:	Cairo
Language:	Arabic
Currency:	LE (Egyptian pound) = 100 piastres
Population:	60,000,000
Size:	1,001,449 sq km

EGYPT

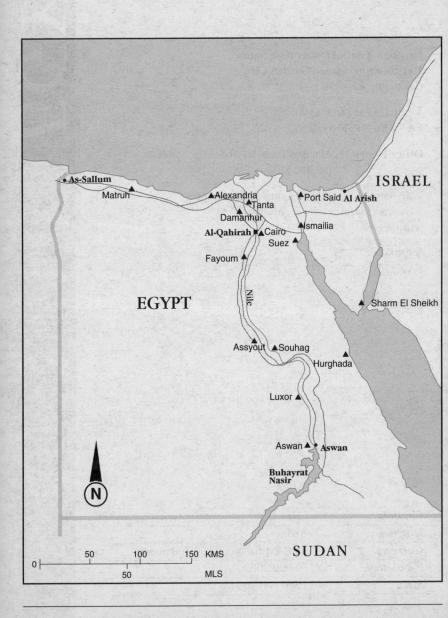

ISRAEL

As-Sallum

Matruh

Alexandria
Tanta
Damanhur
Al-Qahirah ■▲Cairo
Suez

Port Said Al Arish

Ismailia

Fayoum

EGYPT

Nile

Sharm El Sheikh

Assyout ▲Souhag

Hurghada

Luxor ▲

Aswan ▲ Aswan

Buhayrat
Nasir

N

0   50   100   150 KMS

50   MLS

SUDAN

EGYPTIAN HOSTELS

Whether it is the mystery of the pyramids, the Nile sunset or the bustle of Cairo, there is a hostel to help you get there.

Hostels are open 24hrs. Expect to pay in the region of 10.50LE for one night's bed and breakfast. There are self-catering facilities everywhere except Aswan, Assyout, Damanhour, El Fayoum, Sohag and Tant.

PASSPORTS AND VISAS

Visas are required and must be valid for 3 months from date of issue and for 30 days' stay. Visas can be obtained at point of entry or in some Egyptian diplomatic missions for a fee.

HEALTH

Innoculation requirements must be met.

BANKING HOURS

Normal banking hours are weekdays 08.30-14.00hrs. Banks are off on Saturdays and Fridays.

POST OFFICES

Post offices are open weekdays 08.30-14.00hrs.

SHOPPING HOURS

Shops are normally open weekdays 10.00-21.00hrs.

TRAVEL

Rail
Trains are available from Cairo to all major cities.

Bus
The network of buses covers the whole country.

Ferry
There are ferry services from the Mediterranean ports to Alexandria.

Driving
Hire cars are available.

PUBLIC HOLIDAYS

Sham El Nasim (Changeable Date); Sinai Liberation Day, 25 April; Labourers Day, 1 May; Independence Day, 18 June; National Day, 23 July; Military Forces Day, 6 October. In addition there are a number of Islamic holidays which are determined by the phases of the moon.

TELEPHONE INFORMATION

International Code	Country Code	Main City Area Codes	
00	20	Alexandria	3
		Aswan	97
		Cairo	2
		Hurghada	65
		Ismailia	64
		Luxor	95
		Sharmel-shiek	62

FRANÇAIS

AUBERGES DE JEUNESSE EGYPTIENNES

Que vous vouliez voir les mystérieuses pyramides, un coucher de soleil sur le Nile ou faire l'expérience de la vie affairée du Caire, il se trouve toujours une auberge pour vous aider à y arriver.

Les auberges sont ouvertes 24 heures. Une nuit et le petit déjeuner vous coûteront environ 10.50LE. Il est possible de faire la cuisine soi-même partout sauf à El Fayoum, Tantah, Aswan, Sohay, Assyorat et Damasshour.

PASSEPORTS ET VISAS

Les visas sont nécessaires et doivent être valides 3 mois à partir de leur date d'émission et pour un séjour de 30 jours. Ils peuvent être obtenus à l'entrée dans le pays ou dans certaines missions diplomatiques égyptiennes, moyennant un paiement.

SOINS MEDICAUX

Les exigences concernant les vaccinations doivent être satisfaites.

HEURES D'OUVERTURE DES BANQUES

Les banques sont fermée le Samedi et le Vendredi.

BUREAUX DE POSTE

Les bureaux de poste sont ouverts en semaine de 8h30 à 14h.

HEURES D'OUVERTURE DES MAGASINS

Les magasins sont en principe ouverts en semaine de 10h à 21h.

DEPLACEMENTS

Trains
Les trains desservent toutes les grandes villes à partir du Caire.

Autobus
Le réseau d'autobus dessert tout le pays.

Ferry-boats
Les services maritimes relient les ports méditerranéens à Alexandrie.

Automobiles
Il est possible de se procurer des voitures de location.

JOURS FERIES

Sham El Nassem (date variable) ; Fête de la libération du Sinaï, 25 avril; Fête du travail, 1er mai; Fête de l'Indépendance, 18 juin; Fête nationale, 23 juillet; Fête des Forces armées, 6 octobre. Il y a en outre un certain nombre de fêtes islamiques qui sont en fonction des phases de la lune.

TELEPHONE

Indicatif International	Indicatif du Pays	Indicatifs régionaux des Villes principales	
00	20	Alexandrie	3
		Aswan	97
		Le Caire	2
		Hurghada	65
		Ismailia	64
		Luxor	95
		Sharmel-shiek	62

DEUTSCH

ÄGYPTISCHE JUGENDHERBERGEN

Ob Sie das Geheimnis der Pyramiden kennenlernen, den Sonnenuntergang am Nil bewundern oder das Leben und Treiben in Kairo erleben wollen, finden Sie bestimmt in der Nähe eine Jugendherberge.

Die Herbergen sind von 24.00 Uhr geöffnet. Es ist mit einem Preis von 10.50LE. Pro Übernachtung mit Frühstück zu rechnen. Überall, außer in Aswan, Assyorat, Damasshour, el-Faijum, Sohay und Tant, gibt es auch Einrichtungen für Selbstversorger.

PÄSSE UND VISA

Es wird ein Visum benötigt, das vom Tag der Ausstellung an für einen Aufenthalt von 30 Tagen 3 Monate gültig sein muß. Das Visum kann bei der Einreise oder in einer ägyptischen diplomatischen Mission gegen eine Gebühr erworben werden.

GESUNDHEIT

Die Impfvorschriften müssen erfüllt werden.

GESCHÄFTSSTUNDEN DER BANKEN

Banken sind Frietags und Samstags Geschlossen.

POSTÄMTER

Die Postämter sind werktags von 08.30-14.00 Uhr geöffnet.

LADENÖFFNUNGSZEITEN

Die Geschäfte sind im allgemeinen werktags von 10.00-21.00 Uhr geöffnet.

REISEN

Eisenbahn
Zwischen Kairo und allen größeren Städten gibt es einen Zugverkehr.

Busse
Das Busnetz erstreckt sich über das ganze Land.

Fähren
Von den Mittelmeerhäfen nach Alexandria gibt es einen Fährenverkehr.

Autofahren
Es gibt Mietwagen.

FEIERTAGE

Sham El Nasim, (Veränderliches Datum); Tag der Befreiung Sinais, 25. April; Maitag, 1. Mai; Unabhängigkeitstag, 18. Juni; Nationalfeiertag, 23. Juli; Tag der Streitkräfte, 6. Oktober. Außerdem gibt es einige islamische Feiertage, die sich nach den Mondphasen richten.

FERNSPRECHINFORMATIONEN

Internationale Kennzahl	Landes- Kennzahl	größere Städte - Ortsnetzkennzahlen	
00	20	Alexandria	3
		Aswan	97
		Kairo	2
		Hurghada	65
		Ismailia	64
		Luxor	95
		Sharmel-shiek	62

ESPAÑOL

ALBERGUES DE JUVENTUD EGIPCIOS

Tanto si desea ver el misterio de las pirámides, una puesta de sol sobre el Nilo o el bullicio del Cairo, siempre habrá un albergue donde alojarse.

Los albergues abren las 24.00 horas del día. Suelen cobrar unas 10.50LE por una noche con desayuno incluido. Disponen de cocina para huéspedes excepto en Aswan, Assyorat, Damasshour, El Fayoum, Sohay y Tant.

PASAPORTES Y VISADOS

Se requiere un visado válido para 3 meses a partir de la fecha de expedición y para una estancia de 30 días. Se pueden obtener visados en el punto de entrada al país y en algunas misiones diplomáticas egipcias abonando una suma.

SANIDAD

Deben cumplirse los requisitos de vacunación.

HORARIO DE BANCOS

Los bancos están cerrados los sábados y los viernes.

CASAS DE CORREO

Las casas de correo abren los días laborables de 08.30 a 14.00 horas.

HORARIO COMERCIAL

Las tiendas suelen abrir los días laborables de 10.00 a 21.00 horas.

DESPLAZAMIENTOS

Tren
Existen servicios de tren desde El Cairo a las principales ciudades.

Autobús
La red de autobuses cubre todo el país.

Ferry
Hay servicios de ferry desde los puertos del Mediterráneo a Alejandría.

Coche
Se pueden alquilar coches.

DIAS FESTIVOS

Sham El Nasim, (La fecha puede cambiar); Día de la Liberación del Sinaí, 25 abril; Día del Trabajador, 1 mayo; Día de la Independencia, 18 junio; Día Nacional, 23 julio; Día de las Fuerzas Armadas, 6 octubre. Además se celebra una serie de festividades islámicas en función de las fases lunares.

INFORMACION TELEFONICA

Código Internacional	Código Nacional	Indicativo de área de las Ciudades principales	
00	20	Alejandría	3
		Aswan	97
		El Cairo	2
		Hurghada	65
		Ismailia	64
		Luxor	95
		Sharmel-shiek	62

DISCOUNTS AND CONCESSIONS

Your membership entitles you to discounts on rail travel and some shops, check with the travel office.

Hostels in this country may also display this symbol.

Les auberges de ce pays pourront également afficher ce symbole.

Jugendherbergen in diesem Land können auch dieses Symbol zeigen.

Es posible que los albergues de este país exhiban además este símbolo.

Alexandria 2NE 32 Port Said St, Shatbi, Raml, Alexandria. ☎ (3) 5975459 **FAX** (3) 5964759 ✉ 200 ● 17-27LE BBinc ⍫ ♙ ⛭ P ✈ Elnozha 20km ⛴ Alexandria 10km ▦ Alexandria 3km ⛍ 20 ▦ 1

ALEXANDRIA

Assyout Bldg 503 El Walidia, Assyout. ☎ (88) 324846 ✉ 40 ● 6-15LE ♂ ⛭ P ▦ Assyout 3km

Aswan 96 Abtaal El Tahrir St, Aswan. ☎ (97) 322313 ✉ 80 ● 6-15LE BBinc ♂ ⛭ P ✈ Aswan 5km ▦ Aswan 500m

Cairo 2S 135 Abdel Aziz Al Saoud St, El Manial, Kobri El Gamaa (University Bridge), Cairo. ☎ (2) 3640729 **FAX** (2) 984107 ✉ 204 ● 12-22LE BBinc ⍫ ♂ ♙ ⬡ ⛭ P ✈ Cairo 20km A⛍ 400 Tahrir Square 20km ▦ Cairo 10km ⛍ 95 Ramses Square, 8900 Tahrir Square 20km ap YH

١٣٥ شارع عبد العزيز آل سعــود
بجوار كوبرى الجامعــة ــ القاهرة

CAIRO

Damanhour 9 El Shaheed Gawad Hosni St, Damanhour. ☎ (45) 314056 ✉ 30 ● 6LE ♂ ⛭ ▦ Damanhour 2km

El Fayoum   Lux Housing Block of Flats, Hadaka, Block 7, Flat No 7, 8, Fayoum. ☎ (84) 323682, 320005 ✉ 48 ● 6LE 🅿 🚂 El Fayoum 3km

Hurghada   New Tourist Centre, Hurghada. ☎ (65) 442432 ✉ 45 ● 17-27LE ᴮᴮ ⁱⁿᶜ 🍴 ☕ 🏤 🅿 ✈ Hurghada 10km

Ismailia   Emara Touristic Rd, Temsah Lake. ☎ (64) 331429 **FAX** (64) 322850 ✉ 200 ● 12-22LE ᴮᴮ ⁱⁿᶜ 🍴 ☕ 👫 ① on a lake 🖥 🏤 🅿 🚲 ⚓ 🚂 Ismailia 5km 🚌 Ismailia from Cairo Station

Luxor   16 Maabad El Karnak St, near the Education and Administration Centre: approach via City Gate nearest to airport. ☎ (95) 370539 **FAX** (95) 372139 ✉ 275 ● 17-27LE ᴮᴮ ⁱⁿᶜ 🍴 ☕ 👫 🖥 🏤 🅿 ✈ Luxor 25km 🚂 Luxor 5km

Mersa Matrouh   behind 4 El Galaa St, Salloum Rd, Mersa Matrouh. ☎ (3) 932331 ✉ 60 ● 8LE ᴮᴮ ⁱⁿᶜ 🍴 ☕ 🏤 🅿 🚂 Mersa Matrough 2km

Port Said   El Amin St & Kornaish (near Sport Stadium), Port Said. ☎ (66) 228702 **FAX** (66) 226432 ✉ 210 ● 17-27LE ᴮᴮ ⁱⁿᶜ 🍴 ☕ 👫 🏤 🅿 🅿 🚢 Port Said 2km 🚂 Port Said 2km 🚌 Port Said-Cairo 3km

Sharm-El-Sheikh   PO 46619: 290km SE of Suez. ☎ (62) 600317 **FAX** (62) 600317 ✉ 105 ● 17-27LE ᴮᴮ ⁱⁿᶜ 🍴 🖥 🏤 🅿 ✈ Sharm-El-Sheikh 3km 🚌 from Cairo

Sohag   5 Port Said St, Sohag. ☎ (93) 324395 ✉ 28 ● 6-15LE ☕ 🏤 🅿 🚂 Sohag 1.5km 🚌 from Cairo

Suez   Sharia Tariq El Horia (near Sport Stadium), PO 171, Suez. ☎ (62) 221945 ✉ 100 ● 12-22LE ᴮᴮ ⁱⁿᶜ 🍴 ☕ 🏤 🅿 🚂 Port Said 3km 🚌 from Cairo

Tanta   Shobra Malas, Mahala El Kobra Rd, Tanta. ☎ (40) 337978 ✉ 24 ● 6LE 🏤 🅿 🚌 from Cairo

ENGLAND & WALES
ANGLETERRE & PAYS DE GALLES
ENGLAND & WALES
INGLATERRA Y GALES

ASSURED STANDARD

YHA (England & Wales) Limited,
Trevelyan House, 8 St Stephen's Hill,
St Albans, Hertfordshire, AL1 2DY, England

☎ (44) (1727) 855215, **FAX** (44) (1727) 844126
Customer Services
☎ (44) (1727) 845047, **FAX** (44) (1727) 844126

Office Hours: Monday-Friday, 09.00-17.30hrs

London Membership and Information Centre
and YHA Adventure Shop,
14 Southampton Street, Covent Garden,
London, WC2E 7HY, England.

☎ (44) (171) 836 1036, **FAX** (44) (171) 8366372

and 52 Grosvenor Gardens, London SW1W 0AG, England.
☎ (44) (171) 730 5769, **FAX** (44) (171) 7305779
Opening Hours: Monday-Friday, 09.30-17.30hrs

Central London Booking Service ☎ (44) (171) 2486547
Opening Hours: Monday-Friday, 09.00-17.30hrs

IBN Booking Centres for outward bookings
■ London, *via London Membership and Information Centre above.*
■ London-YHA Victoria, Campus Travel,
    52 Grosvenor Gardens, Victoria, London, SW1W 0AG.
    ☎ (44) (171) 7305769, **FAX** (44) (171) 7305779.
■ London-USIT Agent Services.
■ Totnes Devon - Western Air Travel, Bickham, Totnes, Devon.

Capital:	London
Language:	English
Currency:	£ Sterling (Pound)
Population:	51,277,000
Size:	151,207 sq km

ENGLAND & WALES

ENGLAND & WALES

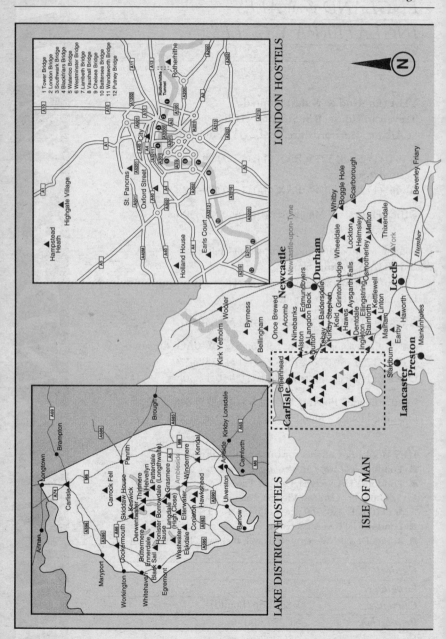

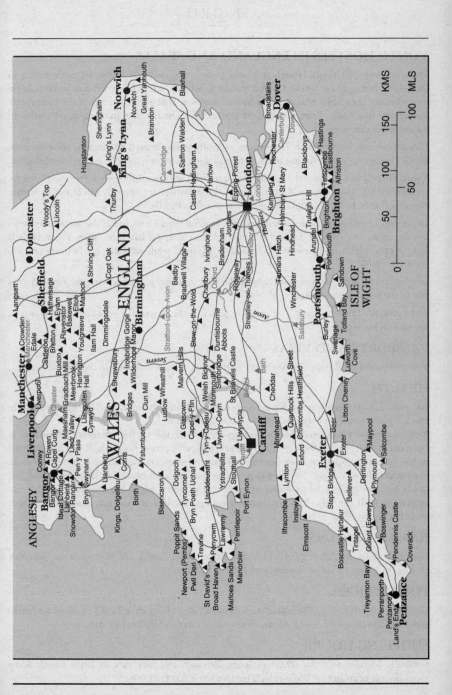

ENGLISH

YOUTH HOSTELS IN ENGLAND AND WALES

There are over 240 Youth Hostels to choose from in England and Wales, all participating in Hostelling International's new Assured Standards Scheme, see page six for details. Hostels are located along the tourist trail of major historic towns as well as in the heart of the countryside and around the coast. From Land's End to the Lake District and from medieval castles to remote mountain huts.

City centre and larger Youth Hostels are generally open through the season, however some smaller hostels are closed for one night or more a week - always telephone to check availability.

Youth Hostels in London and a number of large cities are open 24hrs, with reception open for booking in 07.30-23.00hrs. Most YHA's in the provinces are open 07.00-23.00hrs, with a closed period of 10.00-17.00hrs, except where stated in this Guide.

Prices vary according to location and facilities, ranging from £5.65 to £12.50 outside London - less for under 18s - which includes the price of sheet sleeping bag hire. Many Youth Hostels serve meals, which may have to be booked in advance, while self-catering facilities are also widely available.

It is recommended that accommodation is booked in advance - particularly for family rooms and in the busy summer months.

Some provincial hostels adopt a no smoking policy in the interests of your comfort. Enquire at the time of booking.

PASSPORTS AND VISAS

You will need a valid passport. Not many visitors now require visas but do check in advance.

HEALTH

An international Certificate of Vaccination is not required to enter the UK, but you should check if one is needed on your re-entry into your own country.

Medical Insurance is essential because visitors are only eligible for free **emergency** treatment at National Health Service Accident and Emergency departments of hospitals. If you are admitted to hospital as an in-patient, even from an accident and emergency department, or referred to an out-patient clinic, you will be asked to pay unless you are a national of an EC country, resident in any member country, or a national or resident of a country which has a reciprocal health care agreement with the UK. You are therefore strongly advised to take out adequate insurance cover before travelling to Britain.

BANKING HOURS

Generally open weekdays 09.30-17.00hrs. Most major banks are also open on Saturday mornings. All are closed on Sundays and Public Holidays.

POST OFFICES

Open weekdays 09.00-17.30hrs (although most sub post offices shut 13.00-14.00hrs for lunch) and Saturdays 09.00-12.30hrs. All are closed on Sundays and Public Holidays.

SHOPPING HOURS

Generally Monday-Saturday 09.00-17.30hrs, although this may vary in larger towns. Some shops do stay open late on Wednesday/Thursday until 20.00/21.00hrs.

TRAVEL

Air

It is possible to travel around by air to many places in Britain but as many of the distances are relatively short, travel by train or coach is cheaper.

Rail

There is a comprehensive rail network linking the country. Rail transport is a good, reasonably inexpensive way to travel. Inter-Rail and Britrail cards are valid.

Bus

Coach travel is cheaper than rail and there is a large network of services operated by 2/3 major companies. Most towns are served with good local services.

Ferry

Various routes available.

Driving

If you want to drive a motor vehicle in Britain you must be over the age of 17. Driving is on the left-hand side of the road. Seat belts are required to be worn in both the front and back of cars, if seat belts are fitted. The drink driving laws are very strict so don't do it! The AA and RAC are just two of the motoring organizations offering, amongst other things, breakdown and recovery services.

PUBLIC HOLIDAYS

New Year's Day, 1 January; Good Friday, 28 March; Easter Monday, 31 March; May Day, 6 May; Bank Holiday, 26 May; Bank Holiday, 23 August; Christmas 25/26 December.

TELEPHONE INFORMATION

International Code	Country Code	Main City Area Codes	
00	44	London	171 or 181
		Cardiff	1222
		Chester	1244
		York	1904
		Manchester	161

FRANÇAIS

AUBERGES DE JEUNESSE ANGLAISES ET GALLOISES

Vous pouvez choisir parmi plus de 240 auberges en Angleterre et au Pays de Galles et elles participent toutes au nouveau Plan Hostelling International pour la Garantie des Normes en Auberge - voir page 15 pour un complément d'informations. Elles sont situées le long des itinéraires touristiques menant aux principales villes historiques ainsi qu'au coeur de la campagne et le long de la côte. De Land's End au Lake District, vous n'êtes jamais bien loin d'une auberge, qu'elle ait la forme d'un château médiéval ou d'une cabane isolée dans une montagne.

Les auberges situées au coeur des villes ainsi que les auberges les plus importantes restent généralement ouvertes toute la saison. Mais il arrive que de plus petites auberges soient fermées une nuit ou plus par semaine. Il est conseillé de toujours vérifier les disponibilités par téléphone.

Les auberges de jeunesse de Londres et de certaines grandes villes sont ouvertes 24 heures sur 24 et la réception accueille les voyageurs de 7h30 à 23h. En région, la plupart des auberges sont ouvertes de 7h à 23h, et ferment entre 10h et 17h, sauf indication contraire mentionnée dans le guide.

Les prix varient selon les endroits et les services offerts et vont de 5,65 livres à 12,50 livres en dehors de Londres - moins pour les moins de 18 ans - location de draps comprise. Un grand nombre d'auberges servent des repas, qui doivent parfois être réservés à l'avance, tandis que la plupart des auberges ont une cuisine à la disposition des visiteurs.

Il est conseillé de réserver des places à l'avance - surtout pour des chambres familiales et pendant l'été.

Dans certaines auberges en région, il est interdit de fumer afin d'assurer le confort des voyageurs. Informez-vous lorsque vous réservez.

PASSEPORTS ET VISAS

Les voyageurs doivent être munis d'un passeport valide. De nos jours, peu de visiteurs doivent avoir un visa mais vérifiez à l'avance.

SOINS MEDICAUX

Il n'est pas nécessaire d'être muni d'un certificat international de vaccination mais il vous est conseillé de vérifier qu'il ne vous en faudra pas un pour rentrer dans votre pays.

Il est essentiel d'être couvert par une assurance maladie car les visiteurs ne peuvent bénéficier que d'un traitement **d'urgence** gratuit dans les services d'accidents et d'urgence des hôpitaux de la Sécurité sociale. Si vous êtes hospitalisé, même à la demande d'un service d'accidents et d'urgence, ou si vous êtes envoyé dans un service de consultation externe, il vous faudra payer à moins d'être un citoyen d'un pays de la CE, de donc résider dans un pays membre ou d'être un citoyen ou de résider dans un pays ayant passé un accord médical réciproque avec le Royaume-Uni. Il vous est donc fortement conseillé de souscrire à une police d'assurance avant votre départ pour la Grande-Bretagne.

HEURES D'OUVERTURE DES BANQUES

Les banques sont en général ouvertes en semaine de 9h30 à 17h. La plupart des grandes banques sont aussi ouvertes le samedi matin. Elles ferment toutes le dimanche et les jours fériés.

BUREAUX DE POSTE

Les bureaux de poste sont ouverts en semaine de 9h à 17h30 (bien que la plupart des bureaux de poste auxiliaires ferment entre 13h et 14h) et le samedi de 9h à 12h30. Ils sont tous fermés le dimanche et les jours fériés.

HEURES D'OUVERTURE DES MAGASINS

Les magasins sont en général ouverts du lundi au samedi, de 9h à 17h30, bien que cela puisse varier dans les grandes villes. Certains magasins restent ouverts plus longtemps les mercredi/jeudi jusqu'à 20h/21h.

DEPLACEMENTS

Avions

Il est possible de se rendre par avion dans beaucoup de régions du pays, mais vu que la plupart des distances est relativement courte, il est moins cher de se déplacer par le train ou en car.

Trains

Un réseau ferroviaire étendu dessert le pays. Le train est un bon moyen de voyager, et s'avère assez économique. Les cartes Inter-Rail et Britrail sont valides.

Autobus

Les cars sont moins chers que le train et de nombreux services, assurés par 2/3 grandes compagnies, sont offerts. La plupart des villes sont desservies par de bons services locaux.

Ferry-boats

Diverses traversées possibles.

Automobiles

Si vous voulez conduire une voiture en Grande-Bretagne, vous devez être âgé de plus de 17 ans. La conduite est à gauche. Le port des ceintures de sécurité à l'avant et à l'arrière du véhicule, s'il en est équipé, est obligatoire. Les lois concernant l'alcool au volant sont très strictes; ne prenez pas de risques! Les organisations automobiles AA et RAC (et elles ne sont pas les seules) offrent, entre autres, des services de dépannage et de recouvrement de véhicule.

JOURS FERIES

Nouvel an, 1er janvier; Vendredi saint, 28 mars; Lundi de Pâques, 31 mars; Fête du travail, 6 mai; Jour férié, 26 juin; Jour férié, 23 août; Noël, 25 et 26 décembre.

TELEPHONE

Indicatif International	Indicatif du Pays	Indicatifs régionaux des Villes principales	
00	44	Londres	171 ou 181
		Cardiff	1222
		Chester	1244
		York	1904
		Manchester	161

DEUTSCH

JUGENDHERBERGEN IN ENGLAND UND WALES

In England und Wales, gibt es eine Wahl von mehr als 240 Herbergen, die sich alle dem "Assured Standards" Schema des Hostelling Internationals ungeschlossen haben (siehe Seite 24 für weitere Einzelheiten). Herbergen befinden sich in historischen Städten auf dem Tounstenweg sowie auf dem Land und an der küste. Von Land's End bis zum Lake District, von mittelalterlichen Burgen bis zu entlegenen Berghütten.

Jugendherbergen im Stadtzentrum und große Jugendherbergen sind normalerweise ganzjährig geöffnet. Einige der kleineren Jugendherbergen können für eine oder mehrere Tage in der Woche geschlossen sein. Fragen Sie nach, ob Zimmer zur Verfügung stehen.

Die Jugendherbergen in London und auch einige in anderen großen Städten sind 24 Stunden geöffnet. Die Rezeption ist aber für Buchungen von 07.30-23.00 Uhr geöffnet. Die meisten Herbergen auf dem Land sind von 07.00-23.00 Uhr geöffnet, schließen aber zwischendurch von 10.00-17.00 Uhr, außer wenn in diesem Führer etwas anderes steht.

Die Preise hängen von der Lage und den Einrichtungen ab und liegen außerhalb Londons zwischen £5,65 und £12,50 - billiger für Jugendliche unter 18 Jahren. Die Gebühr für die Bettwäsche ist im Preis enthalten. Viele Jugendherbergen bieten Mahlzeiten, die oft aber im voraus bestellt werden müssen. In vielen Herbergen gibt es auch Einrichtungen für Selbstversorger.

Es empfiehlt sich, die Unterkunft im voraus zu buchen - besonders für familienzimmer und in den Sommermonaten, wenn viel Betrieb herrscht.

Manche Jugendherbergen auf dem Land haben ein Rauchverbot im Interesse Ihres Komforts. Bitte bei der Buchung nachfragen.

PÄSSE UND VISA

Sie brauchen einen gültigen Reisepaß. Ein Visum wird nur noch von wenigen Reisenden benötigt. Sie sollten sich aber im voraus erkundigen.

GESUNDHEIT

Für die Einreise nach Großbritannien benötigt man kein Impfzeugnis. Erkundigen Sie sich aber, ob Sie bei der Rückkehr in Ihr eigenes Land eines brauchen.

Eine Krankenversicherung ist erforderlich, da Besucher nur **in Notfällen** Anspruch auf kostenlose Behandlung durch die Unfall- oder Notfallabteilung des National Health Service in Krankenhäusern haben. Wenn Sie (ob von der Unfall- oder Notfallabteilung eines Krankenhauses oder von einem anderen Arzt) zur stationären Behandlung in ein Krankenhaus eingewiesen oder an die ambulante Abteilung überwiesen werden, müssen Sie selbst bezahlen, es sei denn, Sie besitzen die Staatsangehörigkeit eines EU-Landes oder Sie sind in einem Mitgliedsstaat wohnhaft oder Sie besitzen die Staatsangehörigkeit eines Landes, mit dem Großbritannien einen gegenseitigen Vertrag über die Gesundheitspflege abgeschlossen hat, bzw Sie sind in einem solchen Land wohnhaft. Ehe Sie nach Großbritannien reisen, raten wir Ihnen deshalb dringend zum Abschluß einer ausreichenden Versicherung.

GESCHÄFTSSTUNDEN DER BANKEN

Im allgemeinen werktags von 09.30-15.30 Uhr geöffnet, aber viele schließen erst eine Stunde später. Die meisten größeren Banken sind auch am Samstagvormittag geöffnet. An Sonn- und Feiertagen sind alle Banken geschlossen.

POSTÄMTER

Öffnungszeiten: werktags von 09.00-17.30 Uhr (die meisten Nebenpostämter machen jedoch eine Mittagspause von 13.00-14.00 Uhr) und samstags von 09.00-12.30 Uhr. An Sonn- und Feiertagen sind alle Postämter geschlossen.

LADENÖFFNUNGSZEITEN

Im allgemeinen montags bis samstags von 09.00-17.30 Uhr, in größeren Städten oft anders. Einige Geschäfte sind mittwochs/donnerstags bis 20.00/21.00 Uhr geöffnet.

REISEN

Flugverkehr

Viele Orte in Großbritannien sind zwar mit dem Flugzeug erreichbar, aber da die Entfernungen im allgemeinen relativ kurz sind, ist es billiger, mit der Bahn oder dem Bus zu reisen.

Eisenbahn

Über das ganze Land erstreckt sich ein umfangreiches Schienennetz. Es wird ein guter Eisenbahnverkehr angeboten, und das Reisen mit der Bahn ist auch verhältnismäßig preiswert. Es gelten sowohl Inter-Rail als auch Britrail-Karten.

Busse

Reisebusse sind billiger als die Eisenbahn, und 2 oder 3 größere Unternehmen bieten in einem großen Netz gute Verbindungen. Die meisten Städte haben einen guten Ortsverkehr.

Fähren

Auf verschiedenen Strecken wird ein Fährverkehr angeboten.

Autofahren

Wer in Großbritannien ein Kraftfahrzeug führen will, muß über 17 Jahre alt sein. Es herrscht Linksverkehr. Sowohl auf den Vorder- als auch auf den Rücksitzen müssen im Auto, sofern vorhanden, Sicherheitsgurte angelegt werden. Die Gesetze über das Autofahren nach dem Genuß von Alkohol sind sehr streng - unterlassen Sie es daher! Die AA und der RAC sind nur zwei Kraftfahrzeugorganisationen, die u.a. einen Pannen- und Rückführdienst bieten.

FEIERTAGE

Neujahr, 1. Januar; Karfreitag, 28. März; Ostermontag, 31. März; Maifeiertag, 5. Mai; Feiertag, 26. Juni; Feiertag, 23. August; Weihnachten, 25./26. Dezember.

FERNSPRECHINFORMATIONEN

Internationale Kennzahl	Landes- Kennzahl	größere Städte - Ortsnetzkennzahlen
00	44	London . . . . . 171 oder 181
		Cardiff 1222
		Chester 1244
		York 1904
		Manchester 161

ESPAÑOL

ALBERGUES DE JUVENTUD EN INGLATERRA Y GALES

Hay más de 240 albergues de juventud entre los que elegir en Inglaterra y Gales, situados tanto en itinerarios turísticos en las principales poblaciones históricas como en pleno campo y en la costa. Todos los albergues juveniles participan en el nuevo Plan Hostelling International de Normas Garantizadas (ver la página 33 para más información). Desde Land's End al Distrito de los Lagos, nunca estará lejos de un albergue juvenil que puede ocupar desde un castillo medieval a una remota cabaña en las montañas.

Los albergues situados en el centro de las ciudades, así como los albergues con mayor capacidad, están abiertos todo el año. Sin embargo, algunos albergues pequeños están cerrados una noche o más por semana. Compruebe por teléfono la disponibilidad de camas antes de viajar.

Los albergues de Londres y de algunas ciudades grandes están abiertos 24 horas al día, abriendo la recepción para reservas de 07.30 a 23.00 horas. La mayoría de los albergues en las provincias abren de 07.00 a 23.00 horas, estando cerrados entre 10.00 y 17.00 horas, salvo que la guía indique lo contrario.

Los precios varían según la ubicación y los servicios ofrecidos, desde £5,65 a £12,50 fuera de Londres - menos para menores de 18 años - incluyendo el alquiler de la ropa de cama. Muchos albergues sirven comidas, que en algunos casos hay que pedir con antelación, mientras que muchos ofrecen también cocina para huéspedes.

Se recomienda reservar el alojamiento con antelación, sobre todo las habitaciones familiares y durante los meses de verano.

En algunos albergues provinciales se prohíbe fumar, para su mayor comodidad. Consulte en el momento de hacer la reserva.

PASAPORTES Y VISADOS

Se necesita un pasaporte válido. En la actualidad, muy pocos visitantes requieren visado, pero se recomienda confirmarlo con antelación.

SANIDAD

Para entrar en el Reino Unido no se precisa un Certificado Internacional de Vacunación, pero se aconseja verificar la necesidad de presentar uno al regresar a su país de origen.

Un seguro médico es fundamental porque los visitantes sólo tienen derecho a tratamiento gratuito de **urgencia** en el departamento de Accidentes y Urgencias de los hospitales del Servicio Nacional de Sanidad. Si se le ingresa en un hospital como paciente interno, aunque venga del departamento de urgencias, o se le manda a una consulta para pacientes externos, se le pedirá que pague el coste del servicio a menos que sea ciudadano de un país de la CE, residente en cualquier país miembro, o ciudadano o residente en un país que tenga un acuerdo de asistencia sanitaria mutua con el Reino Unido. Por lo tanto, se recomienda encarecidamente suscribir un seguro adecuado antes de viajar al Reino Unido.

HORARIO DE BANCOS

Por lo general, abren los días laborables de 09.30 a 17.00 horas. Los grandes bancos abren también los sábados por la mañana. Todos los bancos cierran los domingos y festivos.

CASAS DE CORREO

Abren los días laborables de 09.00 a 17.30 horas (si bien muchas casas de correo secundarias cierran de 13.00 a 14.00 horas para el almuerzo) y los sábados de 09.00 a 12.30 horas. Todas cierran los domingos y festivos.

HORARIO COMERCIAL

Por lo general, las tiendas abren de lunes a sábado de 09.00 a 17.30 horas aunque el horario puede variar en las poblaciones más importantes. Algunas tiendas abren hasta más tarde los miércoles/jueves, hasta las 20.00/21.00 horas.

DESPLAZAMIENTOS

Avión

Se puede viajar en avión a muchos puntos de Gran Bretaña, pero como las distancias son relativamente cortas, viajar en tren o autobús resulta más barato.

Tren

Existe una completa red ferroviaria que se extiende por todo el país. El tren es una buena forma de viajar y relativamente barata. Las tarjetas Inter-Rail y Britrail son válidas.

Autobús

Viajar en autobús resulta más barato que viajar en tren y hay una gran red de servicios ofrecidos por 2/3 grandes compañías. La mayoría de las ciudades cuentan con un buen servicio local.

Ferry

Existen varias rutas.

Coche

Para conducir un automóvil en Gran Bretaña hay que ser mayor de 17 años. La conducción es por la izquierda de la carretera. Es obligatorio llevar cinturones de seguridad en los asientos delanteros y en los traseros de haberlos. La legislación sobre la conducción bajo la influencia del alcohol es muy estricta. ¡No se arriesgue! El AA y el RAC son dos de las organizaciones de automovilismo que ofrecen, entre otros, servicios de asistencia en carretera y de grúa.

DIAS FESTIVOS

Año Nuevo, 1 enero; Viernes Santo, 28 marzo; Lunes de Pascua, 31 marzo; Fiesta de Mayo, 6 mayo; Festivo, 26 junio; Festivo, 23 agosto; Navidad 25/26 diciembre.

INFORMACION TELEFONICA

Código Internacional	Código Nacional	Indicativo de área de las Ciudades principales	
00	44	Londres	171 ó 181
		Cardiff	1222
		Chester	1244
		York	1904
		Manchester	161

DISCOUNTS AND CONCESSIONS

Your membership entitles you to a wide range of discounts in England and Wales, including reduced admissions to attractions near Youth Hostels, reduced equipment hire and travel.

In addition the following national discount applies:

YHA Adventure Shops: 10% discount.

Hostels in this country may also display this symbol.

Les auberges de ce pays pourront également afficher ce symbole.

Jugendherbergen in diesem Land können auch dieses Symbol zeigen.

Es posible que los albergues de este país exhiban además este símbolo.

Acomb △ ⋐CC⋑ Main St, Acomb, Hexham, Northumberland NE46 4PL. ✆ (1434) 602864 ⇋ 40 ⊜ £3.85-5.65 🚹 👫 🏠 🚲 ⛵ 🚂 Hexham 3km

Alfriston ▲ ⋐CC⋑ Frog Firle, Alfriston, Polegate, East Sussex BN26 5TT. ✆ (1323) 870423 **FAX** (1323) 870615 **Open:** 1.2-14.12; 24-28.12 ⇋ 68 ⊜ £5.70-8.50 🍽 🚹 🏠 🏠 🅿 🚲 ⛴ Newhaven 🚂 Seaford 5km 🚌 713 Eastbourne-Alfriston-Brighton

Alston ▲ ⋐CC⋑ The Firs, Alston, Cumbria CA9 3RW. ✆ (1434) 381509 **FAX** (1434) 381509 **Open:** 21.3-1.11 ⇋ 30 ⊜ £5.15-7.70 🍽 🚹 👫 🏠 🅿 🚌 888 from Penrith Station

Ambleside ⚠ ⋐IBN⋑ ⋐CC⋑ Waterhead, Ambleside, Cumbria LA22 0EU. ✆ (15394) 32304 **FAX** (15394) 34408 **Open:** 07.00-24.00hrs ⇋ 226 ⊜ £6.30-9.40 🍽 🚹 👫 🏠 🅿 🚲 ⛵ 🚂 Windermere 5km; Waterhead 555 🚌 YHA minibus collects from Station

Arnside ▲ ⋐CC⋑ Oakfield Lodge, Redhills Rd, Arnside, Carnforth, Lancashire LA5 0AT. ✆ (1524) 761781 **FAX** (1524) 762589 **Open:** 1-4.1; 31.1-30.11; 22-28.12 ⇋ 72 ⊜ £5.70-8.50 🍽 🚹 🏠 🅿 🚲 ⛵ 🚂 Arnside 1.5km 🚌 CMS 552 from Kendal

Arundel ▲ ⋐CC⋑ Warning Camp, Arundel, West Sussex BN18 9QY. ✆

(1903) 882204 **FAX** (1903) 882776 **Open:** 17.2-1.11 ⇋ 60 ⊜ £5.15-7.70 🍽 🚹 👫 🏠 🅿 🚌 Arundel 1.5km 🚌 Stagecoach coastline 11, Worthing-Bognor Regis ap Arundel Station 1.5km

Aysgarth Falls ▲ ⋐CC⋑ Aysgarth, Leyburn, North Yorkshire DL8 3SR. ✆ (1969) 663260 **FAX** (1969) 663110 **Open:** 24.1-30.11 ⇋ 65 ⊜ £5.15-7.70 🍽 🚹 👫 🏠 🅿 🚲

Badby △ ⋐CC⋑ Church Green, Badby, Daventry, Northamptonshire NN11 3AS. ✆ / **FAX** (1327) 703883 **Open:** 25.3-25.10 ⇋ 32 ⊜ £4.75-6.95 🚹 🚌 🏠 🅿 (limited) 🚌 Long Buckby 10km

Bakewell ▲ ⋐CC⋑ Fly Hill, Bakewell, Derbyshire DE45 1DN. ✆ (1629) 812313 **FAX** (1629) 812313 **Open:** 3.1-20.12 ⇋ 36 ⊜ £4.75-6.95 🍽 🚹 👫 🏠 🅿 🚲 🚌 Matlock 13km

Baldersdale △ ⋐CC⋑ Blackton, Baldersdale, Barnard Castle, Co Durham DL12 9UP. ✆ (1833) 650629 **FAX** (1833) 650629 **Open:** 21.3-4.10 ⇋ 46 ⊜ £4.70-6.95 🍽 🚹 👫 🏠 🅿

Bangor ▲ ⋐CC⋑ Tan-y-Bryn, Bangor, Caernarfonshire LL57 1PZ. ✆ (1248) 353516 **FAX** (1248) 371176 **Open:** 1.1-1.11; 27-31.12 ⇋ 84 ⊜ £5.70-8.50 🍽 🚹 🏠 🅿 ⛵ ⛴ Holyhead 27km 🚂 Bangor 2km

Bassenthwaite ☞ **Skiddaw House**

Bath ▲ ⟦1E⟧ ⟦IBN⟧ ⟦CC⟧ Bathwick Hill,
Bath, Avon BA2 6JZ. ☏ (1225) 465674
FAX (1225) 482947 **Open:** 24hrs ⌇
121 ⊖ £6.30-9.40 ⍾◻ ▥ 🚌 Bath
Spa 2km 🚌 Badgerline 18 opposite
station ⓡ

BATH

Beer ▲ ⟦CC⟧ Bovey Combe, Townsend,
Beer, Seaton, Devon EX12 3LL. ☏
(1297) 20296 **FAX** (1297) 23690
Open: 24.3-30.10 ⌇ 40 ⊖
£5.70-8.50 ⍾◻ ⑂ ▥ ⚓ 🚌
Axminster 16km

Bellever ▲ ⟦CC⟧ Postbridge, Yelverton,
Devon PL20 6TU. ☏ (1822) 880227
FAX (1822) 880302 **Open:** 24.3-1.11
⌇ 36 ⊖ £5.70-8.50 ⍾◻ ⑂ ▥ 🚲
⚓ 🚌 Newton Abbott 28km 🚌 82
Exeter - Plymouth (May- Sept only),
Western National 98/A Tavistock -
Princetown 6m ap Postbridge 1m

Bellingham △ Woodburn Rd,
Bellingham, Hexham, Northumberland
NE48 2ED. ☏ (1434) 220313 **Open:**
2.3-30.10 ⌇ 34 ⊖ £4.25-6.25 ◻ ⑂
▥ 🚲 ⚓ 🚌 Hexham 30km 🚌
880 from Hexham

Beverley ▲ ⟦CC⟧ The Friary, Friar's
Lane, Beverley, East Yorkshire HU17
0DF. ☏ (1482) 881751 **FAX** (1482)
880118 **Open:** 21.3-1.11 ⌇ 34 ⊖

£4.75-6.95 ⍾◻ ◻ ⑂ ♿ ▥ 🚌
Beverley 400m

Blackboys △ Uckfield, East Sussex
TN22 5HU. ☏ (1825) 890607 **FAX**
(1825) 890104 **Open:** 24.3-27.9 ⌇ 29
⊖ £4.75-6.95 ◻ ▥ 🚌 Buxted 4km
🚌 218, 728 Eastbourne- Uckfield
ap Blackboys

Black Sail △ ⟦CC⟧ Black Sail Hut,
Ennerdale, Cleator, Cumbria CA23
3AY. **Open:** 21.3-1.11 ⌇ 17 ⊖
£4.25-6.25 ⍾◻ ◻ ▥ ⓡ (Alston YH)

Blaencaron △ Tregaron, Cardiganshire
SY25 6HL. ☏ (1974) 298441 **Open:**
25.3-6.9 ⌇ 16 ⊖ £3.85-5.65 ◻ ▣

Blaxhall ▲ ⟦CC⟧ Heath Walk, Blaxhall,
Woodbridge, Suffolk IP12 2EA. ☏
(1728) 688206 **Open:** 24.3-30.10 ⌇
40 ⊖ £5.15-7.70 ⍾◻ ◻ ▥ ▣ ⚓
Harwich and Felixstowe 27km 🚌
Wickham Market 5km 🚌 80/1, 99
Ipswich-Aldeburg

Boggle Hole ▲ ⟦CC⟧ Mill Beck,
Fylingthorpe, Whitby, North
Yorkshire YO22 4UQ. ☏ (1947)
880352 **FAX** (1947) 880987 **Open:**
13.00-23.00hrs, 3.1-1.11; 27.12-2.1.98
⌇ 80 ⊖ £5.70-8.50 ⍾◻ ◻ ⑂ ▥ ▣
🚌 Whitby (not Sun: Oct-May) 15km
🚌 Tees & District 93A Whitby
1.5km ap Robin Hood Bay

Borrowdale (Longthwaite) ▲ ⟦CC⟧
Longthwaite, Borrowdale, Keswick,
Cumbria CA12 5XE. ☏ (17687) 77257
FAX (17687) 77393 **Open:**
13.00-23.00hrs, 1.1-3.1.98 ⌇ 95 ⊖
£5.70-8.50 ⍾◻ ◻ ⑂ ▥ ▣ ⚓

Borth ▲ ⟦CC⟧ Morlais, Borth,
Cardiganshire SY24 5JS. ☏ (1970)
871498 **FAX** (1970) 871827 **Open:**
14.2-26.10 ⌇ 68 ⊖ £5.70-8.50 ⍾◻ ◻
⑂ ▥ ▣ ⚓ 🚌 Borth 1km 🚌 511,
512, 520 or 524 from Aberystwyth

Boscastle Harbour △ 〔CC〕 Palace Stables, Boscastle, Cornwall PL35 0HD. ☎ (1840) 250287 **FAX** (1840) 250615 **Open:** 19.3-2.11 ⚮ 25 ⊖ £5.70-8.50 ⏺ ⛺ 🏠 ⚘ 🅿 🚅 52/B BR Bodmin Parkway-Boscastle

Boswinger △ 〔CC〕 Gorran, St Austell, Cornwall PL26 6LL. ☎ (1726) 843234 **Open:** 27.3-1.11 ⚮ 38 ⊖ £5.15-7.70 ⏺ ⛺ 👨‍👩‍👧 🖥 ⚘ 🅿 🚲 ⛵ 🚻 St Austell 16km 🚌 26A BR St Austell 7km ap Mevagissay

Bradenham △ 〔CC〕 Village Hall, Bradenham, High Wycombe, Buckinghamshire HP14 4HF. ☎ (1494) 562929 **FAX** (1494) 564743 **Open:** 3.1-20.12 ⚮ 18 ⊖ £4.25-6.25 ⛺ ⚘ 🅿 🚻 Saunderton (not Sun) 2km Ⓡ (G Lee, 54A Brixham Crescent, Ruislip Manor, Middx HA4 8TX) ☎ (1895) 673188)

Bradwell Village ▲ 〔CC〕 Manor Farm, Vicarage Rd, Bradwell, Milton Keynes, Buckinghamshire MK13 9AJ. ☎ (1908) 310944 **FAX** (1908) 310944 **Open:** 24.3-31.8 ⚮ 38 ⊖ £4.75-6.95 ⛺ ⚘ 🅿 🚲 ⛵ 🚻 Milton Keynes Central 1.5km

Brandon ▲ 〔CC〕 Heath House, off Warren Close, Bury Rd, Brandon, Suffolk IP27 0BU. ☎ (1842) 812075 **FAX** (1842) 812075 **Open:** 14.2-20.12 ⚮ 36 ⊖ £5.70-8.50 ⏺ ⛺ 👨‍👩‍👧 ⚘ 🅿 🚲 🚻 Brandon 1km

Bretton △ Nether Bretton, Derbyshire. ☎ (114) 2884541 **Open:** Sat+Bank Holidays ⚮ 18 ⊖ £4.25-6.25 ⛺ 👨‍👩‍👧 🅿 🚻 Grindleford 6km Ⓡ (7 New Bailey, Crane Moor, Nr Thurgoland, Near Sheffield S30 7AT)

Bridges Long Mynd △ Ratlinghope, Shrewsbury SY5 0SP. ☎ (1588) 650656 **FAX** (1588) 650656 **Open:** 1.3-15.11 ⚮ 35 ⊖ £4.75-6.95 ⏺ ⛺ 🏠 🅿 🚲 🚻 Church Stretton 8km

Brighton ▲ 〔6NW〕 〔CC〕 Patcham Place, London Rd, Brighton, Sussex BN1 8YD. ☎ (1273) 556196 **FAX** (1273) 509366 **Open:** 07.00-10.00hrs, 13.00-23.00hrs, 1.1-27.12 ⚮ 84 ⊖ £6.30-9.40 ⏺ ⛺ 🏠 ⚘ 🅿 ⛵ 🚻 Preston Park 4 km, Brighton 6km

Bristol ▲ 〔3N〕 〔IBN〕 〔CC〕 International YHA, Hayman House, 14 Narrow Quay, Bristol BS1 4QA. ☎ (117) 9221659 **FAX** (117) 9273789 **Open:** 24hrs, 2.1-21.12 ⚮ 124 ⊖ £7.65-11.20 ⏺ ⛺ 👨‍👩‍👧 ♿ 🖥 🚲 ⛵ 🚻 Bristol Temple Meads 1km

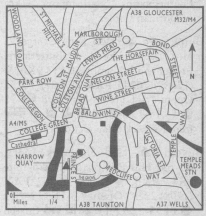

BRISTOL

Broad Haven ▲ 〔CC〕 Haverfordwest, Pembrokeshire SA62 3JH. ☎ (1437) 781688 **FAX** (1437) 781100 **Open:** 14.2-1.11 ⚮ 74 ⊖ £5.70-8.50 ⏺ ⛺ 👨‍👩‍👧 ♿ 🖥 ⚘ 🅿 🚲 ⛵ 🚢 Fishguard 28km 🚻 Haverfordwest 11km 🚌 311 Haverfordwest

Broadstairs ▲ 〔0.5W〕 〔CC〕 Thistle Lodge, 3 Osborne Rd, Broadstairs, Isle-of-Thanet, Kent CT10 2AE. ☎ (1843) 604121 **FAX** (1843) 604121 **Open:** 23.3-16.11 ⚮ 37 ⊖ £5.70-8.50 ⛺ 👨‍👩‍👧 🖥 🚲 ⛵ 🚢 Ramsgate 4km 🚻 Broadstairs 100m 🚌 From Ramsgate, Margate, Canterbury and Sandwich.

Bryn Gwynant ▲ 〔CC〕 Nant Gwynant, Caernarfon, Caernarfonshire LL55 4NP.

📞 (1766) 890251 **FAX** (1766) 890479
Open: 2.1-2.11; 28.12-3.1.98 🛏 67
🍴 £5.70-8.50 🍴 👕 👪 🛒 🅿 ⛵

Bryn Poeth Uchaf △ Hafod- y-Pant,
Cynghordy, Llandovery, Carmarthenshire
SA20 0NB. 📞 (1550) 750235 **Open:**
25.3-6.9 🛏 22 🍴 £3.85-5.65 👕 👪 🅿

Burley ▲ 🆑 Cottesmore House, Cott
Lane, Burley, Ringwood, Hampshire
BH24 4BB. 📞 (1425) 403233 **FAX**
(1425) 403233 **Open:** 16.2-20.12 🛏
36 🍴 £5.70-8.50 🍴 👕 👪 👪 🅿 🚂
Brockenhurst   10km   🚌   X1
Bournemouth- Southampton   1km
ap Durmast Corner

Buttermere ▲ 🆑 King George VI
Memorial   Hostel,   Buttermere,
Cockermouth, Cumbria CA13 9XA. 📞
(17687) 70245 **FAX** (17687) 70231
Open: 1.1-1.11; 28.12-3.1.98 🛏 71
🍴 £5.15-7.70 🍴 👕 👪 👪 🅿 ⛵ 🚌
from Keswick (May-Oct only)

Buxton ▲ 🆑 Sherbrook Lodge,
Harpur Hill Rd, Buxton, Derbyshire
SK17 9NB. 📞 (1298) 22287 **FAX**
(1298) 22287 **Open:** 7.3-21.12 🛏 55
🍴 £4.75-6.95 🍴 👕 👪 🅿 🚂 Buxton
1.5km

Byrness △ 🆑 7 Otterburn Green,
Byrness, Newcastle-upon-Tyne, NE19
1TS. 📞 (1830) 520425 **Open:**
23.3-30.9 🛏 28 🍴 £4.25-6.25 👕 👪
🔲 👪 🅿

Cambridge ▲ 2SE 🆔 🆑 97
Tenison Rd, Cambridge CB1 2DN. 📞
(1223) 354601 **FAX** (1223) 312780
Open: 24hrs 🛏 105 🍴 £7.00-10.30
🍴 👕 👪 🔲 🅿 🚲 👪 Cambridge 400m

Canterbury ▲ 1SE 🆔 🆑 54 New
Dover Rd, Canterbury, Kent CT1 3DT.
📞 (1227) 462911 **FAX** (1227) 470752
Open: 07.00-10.00hrs, 1.2-30.12;
13.00-23.00hrs, 2.1-30.11 🛏 91 🍴
£6.30-9.40 🍴 👕 🔲 👪 🅿 🚲 ⛵ 👪

Canterbury East 1km, Canterbury West
2km

Capel Curig ▲ 🆑 Plas Curig, Capel
Curig, Betws-y-Coed, Aberconwy LL24
0EL. 📞 (1690) 720225 **FAX** (1690)
720270 **Open:** 14.2-14.12; 25-27.12
🛏 60 🍴 £5.70-8.50 🍴 👕 👪 👪 🅿 ⛵
👪 Betws-y-Coed (not Sun: Sept-June)
8km

Capel- y-Ffin △ 🆑 Abergavenny,
Gwent NP7 7NP. 📞 (1873) 890650
Open: 7.2-29.11 🛏 40 🍴 £4.75-6.95
🍴 👕 👪 🅿 👪 Abergavenny 23km

Cardiff ▲ 🆔 🆑 2 Wedal Rd,
Roath Park, Cardiff CF2 5PG. 📞 (1222)
462303 **FAX** (1222) 464571 **Open:**
07.00-10.00hrs,   15.00-23.00hrs,
2.1-30.11 🛏 68 🍴 £6.30-9.40 🍴 👕
♿ 🔲 🅿 ⛵ ✈ Cardiff 20km 👪 Cardiff
Central 2.5km 🚌 78,80,82 from
Cardiff station

Carlisle ▲ 🆑 Etterby House, Etterby,
Carlisle, Cumbria CA3 9QS. 📞 (1228)
23934 **FAX** (1228) 23934 **Open:**
14.2-1.11 🛏 56 🍴 £4.25-6.25 🍴 👕
🔲 👪 🅿 👪 Carlisle 3km

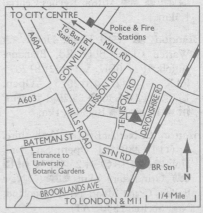

CAMBRIDGE

Carrock Fell △ 🆑 High Row
Cottage,   Haltcliffe,   Hesket
Newmarket, Wigton, Cumbria CA7
8JT. 📞 (16974) 78325 **FAX** (16974)

78325 **Open:** 21.3-1.11 🛏 20 ⏺
£4.75-6.95 🍴 👕 🏭 🅿 🚂 Penrith
24km

Castle Hedingham ▲ ⊂CC⊃ 7 Falcon
Square, Castle Hedingham, Halstead,
Essex CO9 3BU. ☎ (1787) 460799
FAX (1787) 461302 **Open:**
16.2-19.12 🛏 50 ⏺ £5.70-8.50 🍴 👕
👪 ♿ 🏭 🍺 🚲 ⛵ 🚢 Harwich 38km
🚂 Sudbury (not Sun: Oct-May) 11km,
Braintree 13km 🚌 89/A from
Braintree

Castleton ▲ ⊂CC⊃ Castleton Hall,
Castleton, Sheffield S30 2WG. ☎
(1433) 620235 **FAX** (1433) 621767
Open: 07.00-23.00hrs, 9.2-23.12 🛏
150 ⏺ £5.70-11.20 🍴 👕 👪 🏭 🍺 🅿
🚲 🚂 Hope 5km 🚌 272,274 from
Sheffield

Charlbury ▲ ⊂CC⊃ The Laurels, The
Slade, Charlbury, Oxfordshire OX7
3SJ. ☎ (1608) 810202 **Open:** 1.1-31.10
🛏 50 ⏺ £5.15-7.70 🍴 👕 ♿ 🎞 🍺 🅿
🚲 🚂 Charlbury 1.5km

Cheddar ▲ ⊂CC⊃ Hillfield, Cheddar,
Somerset BS27 3HN. ☎ (1934) 742494
FAX (1934) 744724 **Open:**
21.3-20.12; 23-29.12 🛏 56 ⏺
£4.75-6.95 🍴 👕 👪 🎞 🍺 🅿 ⛵ 🚂
Weston-Super-Mare 17.5km, Weston
Milton 16km 🚌 126, 826 Weston-
Super-Mare to Wells ap Cheddar

Chester ⚠ 2SW IBN ⊂CC⊃ Hough
Green House, 40 Hough Green, Chester
CH4 8JD. ☎ (1244) 680056 FAX
(1244) 681204 Open: 07.00-10.00hrs,
15.00-23.00hrs, 10.1-20.12 🛏 130 ⏺
£6.30-9.40 🍴 👕 🎞 🍺 🅿 ⛵ 🚂 Chester
2.5km

Clun Mill △ ⊂CC⊃ The Mill, Clun, Nr
Craven Arms, Shropshire SY7 8NY. ☎
(1588) 640582 **FAX** (1588) 640582
Open: 26.3-2.9 🛏 24 ⏺ £4.75-6.95
👕 🎞 🍺 🅿 🚲 🚂 Broome or Hopton
10km, Craven Arms 15km 🚌

Midland Red West 741-5 from Ludlow
🚐 ap (Pass BR Ludlow) Clun

Cockermouth △ ⊂CC⊃ Double Mills,
Cockermouth, Cumbria CA13 0DS. ☎
(1900) 822561 **FAX** (1900) 822561
Open: 21.3-1.11 🛏 28 ⏺ £4.75-6.95
🍴 👕 👪 🎞 🍺 🅿 🚲 ⛵ 🚂 Workington
13km

Coniston (Holly How) ▲ ⊂CC⊃ Holly
How, Far End, Coniston, Cumbria
LA21 8DD. ☎ (15394) 41323 **FAX**
(15394) 41803 **Open:** 17.1-23.11 🛏
69 ⏺ £5.15-7.70 🍴 👕 🍺 🅿 🚲 ⛵ 🚂
Ulverston 21km

Coniston Coppermines △ ⊂CC⊃
Coppermines House, Coniston,
Cumbria LA21 8HP. ☎ (15394) 41261
FAX (15394) 41261 **Open:** 21.3-1.11
🛏 31 ⏺ £4.75-6.95 🍴 👕 👪 🍺 🅿 🚲
⛵ 🚂 Windermere 13km

Conwy ▲ ⊂CC⊃ Larkhill, Sychnant Pass
Road, Conwy, Aberconwy, LL32 8AJ ☎
(1492) 593571 🛏 85 ⏺ £6.30-9.40
🍴 👕 👪 ♿ 🍺 🅿 ⛵ ✈ Manchester
120km A🚐 46km 🚢 Hollyhead
🚂 Conwy 1km

Copt Oak △ ⊂CC⊃ Whitwick Rd,
Markfield, Leicester LE67 9QB. ☎
(1530) 242661 **Open:** 26.3-27.10 🛏
18 ⏺ £4.25-6.25 👕 🍺 🅿 ⛵ 🚂 BR
Leicester 🚌 117-119 Leicester
ap Flying Horse Garage (Carousel Pub)
1km

Corris △ Old School, Old Rd, Corris,
Machynlleth, Powys SY20 9QT. ☎
(1654) 761686 **Open:** 24.3-2.11 🛏 46
⏺ £5.15-7.70 🍴 👕 👪 🍺 🅿 🚲 🚂
Machynlleth 9km 🚌 34
Machynlleth-Corris

Coverack ▲ ⊂CC⊃ Park Behan, School
Hill, Coverack, Helston, Cornwall
TR12 6SA. ☎ (1326) 280687 **FAX**
(1326) 280119 **Open:** 24.3-8.11 🛏 38
⏺ £5.70-8.50 🍴 👕 👪 🎞 🍺 🍺 🚲 ⛵

🚆 Penryn or Penmere (not Sun: Oct-Apr) 29km 🚌 326 Helston-Coverack

Crowcombe Heathfield ▲ CC Denzel House, Crowcombe Heathfield, Taunton, Somerset TA4 4BT. 📞 (1984) 667249 **FAX** (1984) 667249 **Open:** 24.3-5.9 🏠 44 ● £4.75-6.95 👔 🍺 P 🚲 🚆 Taunton 16km 🚌 28/C Taunton-Minehead 1km ap Triscombe Cross

Crowden- in- Longdendale ▲ CC Peak National Park Hostel, Crowden, Hadfield, Hyde, Cheshire SK14 7HZ. 📞 (1457) 852135 **FAX** (1457) 852135 **Open:** 2.3-23.12 🏠 50 ● £4.75-6.95 🍽 👔 🚹 🍺 P ⛵ 🚆 Hadfield 8km

Cynwyd △ CC The Old Mill, Cynwyd, Corwen, Denbighshire LL21 0LW. 📞 (1490) 412814 **Open:** 26.1-27.9 🏠 30 ● £3.85-5.65 👔 🏘 🍺 P ⛵ 🚆 Ruabon 28km 🚌 94 Wrexham-Barmouth

Dartington △ CC Lownard, Dartington, Totnes, Devon TQ9 6JJ. 📞 (1803) 862303 **FAX** (1803) 865171 **Open:** 25.3-3.11 🏠 30 ● £5.70-8.50 👔 🚹 🏘 🗄 🍺 P 🚲 🚆 Totnes 3km 🚌 X80 800m ap Shinner's Bridge

Dentdale ▲ CC Cowgill, Dent, Sedbergh, Cumbria LA10 5RN. 📞 (15396) 25251 **FAX** (15396) 25251 **Open:** 31.1-21.12; 27.12-3.1.98 🏠 40 ● £5.15-7.70 🍽 👔 🚹 🏘 🍺 P 🚆 Dent (not Sun: Oct-March) 3km

Derwentwater ▲ CC Barrow House, Borrowdale, Keswick, Cumbria CA12 5UR. 📞 (17687) 77246 **FAX** (17687) 77396 **Open:** 13.00-23.00hrs 1.1-1.11; 28.12-3.1.98 🏠 95 ● £6.30-9.40 🍽 👔 🚹 🏘 🍺 P ⛵

Dimmingsdale △ CC Little Ranger, Dimmingsdale, Oakamoor, Stoke-on-Trent, Staffordshire ST10 3AS. 📞 (1538) 702304 **Open:** 24.3-1.11 🏠 26

● £4.25-6.25 👔 🍺 P 🚆 Blythe Bridge 10km

Dolgoch △ Tregaron, Cardiganshire SY25 6NR. 📞 Wales Regional Office (1222) 222122 **Open:** 25.3-6.9 🏠 22 ● £3.85-5.65 👔 P ● (Remote YH rough track - take care)

Dover ▲ IBN CC 306 London Rd, Dover, Kent CT17 0SY. 📞 (1304) 201314 **FAX** (1304) 202236 **Open:** 07.00-10.00hrs, 13.00-23.00hrs 🏠 110 ● £6.30-9.40 🍽 👔 🚹 🏘 🗄 🍺 🚲 ⛵ 🚢 Dover 2.5km 🚆 Dover Priory 1.5km

Dufton ▲ CC 'Redstones', Dufton, Appleby, Cumbria CA16 6DB. 📞 (17863) 51236 **FAX** (17683) 51236 **Open:** 31.1-1.11 🏠 40 ● £5.15-7.70 🍽 👔 🚹 🗄 🍺 P 🌿 ⛵ 🚆 Appleby (not Sun: Oct-Mar) 5km

Duntisbourne Abbots ▲ CC Cirencester, Glos GL7 7JN. 📞 (1285) 821682 **FAX** (1285) 821697 **Open:** 17.1-29.12 🏠 59 ● £5.15-7.70 🍽 👔 🚹 🗄 P ⛵ 🚆 Kemble 16km

Earby △ CC Katherine Bruce Glasier Memorial Hostel, Glen Cottage, Birch Hall Lane, Earby, Colne, Lancashire BB8 6JX. 📞 (1282) 842349 **Open:** 24.3-30.9 🏠 23 ● £4.25-6.25 👔 🚹 🍺 P 🚆 Colne 8km

Eastbourne △ CC East Dean Rd, Eastbourne, East Sussex BN20 8ES. 📞 (1323) 721081 **FAX** (1323) 721081 **Open:** 27.3-29.9 🏠 32 ● £5.15-7.70 👔 🍺 P 🚲 ⛵ 🚆 Eastbourne 2.5km 🚌 712 Brighton-Eastbourne

Edale ▲ CC Hostel and Activity Centre, Rowland Cote, Nether Booth, Edale, Derbyshire S30 2ZH. 📞 (1433) 670302 **FAX** (1433) 670243 **Open:** 4.1-1.12; 07.00-23.00hrs 🏠 139 ● £6.30-9.40 🍽 👔 🚹 🗄 🍺 🚲 ⛵ 🚆 Edale 3km

Edmundbyers △ ⊂⊂ Low House, Edmundbyers, Consett, Co Durham DH8 9NL. ☎ (1207) 55651 **FAX** (1207) 255345 **Open:** 21.3-30.10 ⊠ 40 ● £4.25-6.25 ✦ ⁂ ♿ ⌂ ♒ P

Ellingstring △ Lilac Cottage, Ellingstring, Ripon, North Yorks HG4 4PW. ☎ (1677) 460216 **Open:** 24.3-31.10 ⊠ 20 ● £3.85-5.65 ✦ ⁂ ♿ ♒ P

Elmscott △ ⊂⊂ Hartland, Bideford, Devon EX39 6ES. ☎ (1237) 441367 **FAX** (1237) 441910 **Open:** 28.3-30.9 ⊠ 36 ● £4.25-6.25 ✦ ⌂ ♒ P ⚓ ⛟ Barnstable 37km ⛟ Barnstaple-Hartland 5.5km ap Hartland

Elterwater ▲ ⊂⊂ Ambleside, Cumbria LA22 9HX. ☎ (15394) 37245 **FAX** (15394) 37120 **Open:** 1-4.1; 14.2-27.12 ⊠ 46 ● £5.15-7.70 ⊚ ✦ ⁂ ♒ ⚓ ⛟ Windermere 14km

Elton △ ⊂⊂ Elton Old Hall, Main St, Elton, Matlock, Derbyshire DE4 2BW. ☎ (1629) 650394 **Open:** 28.2-1.11; 27.12-1.1.98 ⊠ 32 ● £4.25-6.25 ⊚ ✦ ⁂ ⌂ ♒ P ⛟ Matlock (not Sun: Oct to Mar) 8km

Ennerdale (Gillerthwaite) △ ⊂⊂ Cat Crag, Ennerdale, Cleator, Cumbria CA23 3AX. ☎ (1946) 861237 **Open:** 22.3-1.11 ⊠ 24 ● £4.25-6.25 ⊚ ✦ ⁂ ♒

Epping Forest △ ⊂⊂ Wellington Hall, High Beach, Loughton, Essex IG10 4AG. ☎ (181) 5085161 **FAX** (181) 5085161 **Open:** 3.3-1.11 ⊠ 36 ● £4.75-6.95 ✦ ⁂ ♒ P ⚓ ⛟ Chingford 5.5km ⛟ 250 Waltham Cross-Loughton 1km ap Volunteer Inn Ⓤ Loughton 3km

Eskdale ▲ ⊂⊂ Boot, Holmrook, Cumbria CA19 1TH. ☎ (19467) 23219 **FAX** (19467) 23163 **Open:** 1.1-28.12 ⊠ 54 ● £5.70-8.50 ⊚ ✦ ⁂ ♒ P ⚲ ⛟ Eskdale 2.5km

Exeter ▲ ③SE ⊂⊂ 47 Countess Wear Rd, Exeter, Devon EX2 6LR. ☎ (1392) 873329 **FAX** (1392) 876939 **Open:** 1.1-7.12; 27.12-5.1.98 ⊠ 90 ● £6.30-9.40 ⊚ ✦ ⁂ ⌂ ♒ P ⚓ ⛟ Exeter Central 5km ⛟ K, T, Exeter High St

Exford ▲ ⊂⊂ Exe Mead, Exford, Minehead, Somerset TA24 7PU. ☎ (164383) 1288 **FAX** (164383) 1650 **Open:** 14.2-1.11 ⊠ 51 ● £5.70-8.50 ⊚ ✦ ⁂ ⌂ ♒ P ⚓ ⛴ Taunton 40km ⛟ Minehead- Porlock 11km ap Porlock

Eyam ▲ ⊂⊂ Hawkhill Rd, Eyam, Sheffield S30 1QP. ☎ (1433) 630335 **FAX** (1433) 630335 **Open:** 7.2-26.12 ⊠ 60 ● £5.15-7.70 ⊚ ✦ ⁂ ♒ ⌂ P ⚲ ⛟ Grindleford 5.6km

Glascwm △ The School, Glascwm, Llandrindod Wells, Powys LD1 5SE. ☎ (1982) 570415 **Open:** 1.1-27.12 ⊠ 22 ● £3.85-5.65 ✦ ♒ P

Golant ▲ ⊂⊂ Penquite House, Golant, Fowey, Cornwall PL23 1LA. ☎ (1726) 833507 **FAX** (1726) 832947 **Open:** 31.1-2.11; 22-28.12 ⊠ 94 ● £6.30-9.40 ⊚ ✦ ⁂ ⌂ ⌂ ♒ P ⚓ ⛟ Par (not Sun: Oct-May) 5km ⛟ 24 St Austell- Fowey 2km ap Castle Dore Cross Rds

Gradbach Mill ▲ ⊂⊂ Gradbach, Quarnford, Buxton, Derbyshire SK17 0SU. ☎ (1260) 227625 **FAX** (1260) 227334 **Open:** 13.00hrs, 7.2-6.12; 27.12-3.1.98 ⊠ 96 ● £5.70-8.50 ⊚ ✦ ⁂ ♿ ⌂ ⌂ ♒ P ⛟ Buxton 11km

GRASMERE (2 Hostels)

Grasmere - Butterlip How ▲ ⊂⊂ Grasmere, Ambleside, Cumbria LA22 9QG. ☎ (15394) 35316 **FAX** (15394) 35798 **Open:** 13.00-23.00hrs, 1.1-27.12 ⊠ 96 ● £5.70-8.50 ⊚ ✦ ⁂ ⌂ ♒ P ⚓ ⛟ Windermere 13.6km

Grasmere - Thorney How ▲ ⅭⅭ Grasmere, Ambleside, Cumbria LA22 9QW. ☎ (15394) 35591 **FAX** (15394) 35866 **Open:** 14.2-20.12; 28.12-3.1.98 ⇌ 48 ⚫ £5.70-8.50 �🍽 ♂ ♙♙♙ ▣ ♨ ▣ ⚲ ⚓ 🚃 Windermere 14km

Great Yarmouth ▲ ⅭⅭ 2 Sandown Rd, Great Yarmouth, Norfolk NR30 1EY. ☎ (1493) 843991 **FAX** (1493) 843991 **Open:** 26.3-31.8 ⇌ 40 ⚫ £5.70-8.50 🍽 ♂ ♙♙♙ ♨ ⚓ 🚃 Great Yarmouth 1.5km

Greenhead ▲ ⅭⅭ Carlisle, Cumbria CA6 7HG. ☎ (16977) 47401 **FAX** (16977) 47770 **Open:** 1.1-20.12 ⇌ 40 ⚫ £4.75-6.95 🍽 ♂ ♙♙♙ ♨ 🚃 Haltwhistle 5km

Grinton ▲ ⅭⅭ Grinton Lodge, Grinton, Richmond, North Yorkshire DL11 6HS. ☎ (1748) 884206 **FAX** (1748) 884876 **Open:** 1.1-2.11; 27.12-3.1.98 ⇌ 70 ⚫ £4.75-6.95 🍽 ♂ ♙♙♙ ♨ ▣

Hartington ▲ ⅭⅭ Hartington Hall, Hartington, Buxton, Derbyshire SK17 0AT. ☎ (1298) 84223 **FAX** (1298) 84415 **Open:** 13.00-23.00hrs, 7.2-3.1.98 ⇌ 120 ⚫ £5.70-11.20 🍽 ♂ ♙♙♙ ⛪ ▣ ♨ ▣ ⚓ 🚃 Buxton 19km

Hastings ▲ ⅭⅭ Guestling Hall, Rye Rd, Guestling, Hastings, East Sussex TN35 4LP. ☎ (1424) 812373 **FAX** (1424) 814273 **Open:** 14.2-31.12 ⇌ 57 ⚫ £5.70-8.50 🍽 ♂ ♙♙♙ ♨ ▣ 🚃 Three Oaks 4km, Hastings 9.5km 🚌 11/711 Hastings-Rye

Hathersage ▲ ⅭⅭ Castleton Rd, Hathersage, Sheffield S30 1AH. ☎ (1433) 650493 **FAX** (1433) 650493 **Open:** 3.1-29.11 ⇌ 42 ⚫ £5.15-7.70 🍽 ♂ ♙♙♙ ♨ ▣ 🚃 Hathersage 800m 🚌 272 from Sheffield

Hawes ▲ ⅭⅭ Lancaster Terrace, Hawes, North Yorkshire DL8 3LQ. ☎ (1969) 667368 **FAX** (1969) 667368 **Open:** 1.3-27.12 ⇌ 60 ⚫ £5.70-8.50 🍽 ♂ ♙♙♙ ▣ ♨ ▣ ⚲ 🚃 Garsdale (not Sun: Oct-Mar) 10km

Hawkshead ▲ ⅭⅭ Esthwaite Lodge, Hawkshead, Ambleside, Cumbria LA22 0QD. ☎ (15394) 36293 **FAX** (15394) 36720 **Open:** 13.00hrs, 14.2-3.1.98 ⇌ 117 ⚫ £6.30-9.40 🍽 ♂ ♙♙♙ ⛪ ▣ ♨ ▣ ⚲ ⚓ 🚃 Windermere (by ferry) 11km

Haworth ▲ ⅭⅭ Longlands Hall, Longlands Drive, Lees Lane, Haworth, Keighley, West Yorkshire BD22 8RT. ☎ (1535) 642234 **FAX** (1535) 643023 **Open:** 07.30-23.00hrs, 31.1-21.12 ⇌ 90 ⚫ £5.70-8.50 🍽 ♂ ♙♙♙ ♨ ▣ 🚃 Keighley 6km

Helmsley ▲ ⅭⅭ Carlton Lane, Helmsley, North Yorkshire YO6 5HB. ☎ (1439) 770433 **FAX** (1439) 770433 **Open:** 7.1-1.11 ⇌ 40 ⚫ £5.15-7.70 🍽 ♂ ♙♙♙ ♨ ⚲

Helvellyn ▲ ⅭⅭ Greenside, Glenridding, Penrith, Cumbria CA11 0QR. ☎ (17684) 82269 **FAX** (17684) 82269 **Open:** 1.1-1.11; 28.12-3.1.98 ⇌ 64 ⚫ £5.15-7.70 🍽 ♂ ♙♙♙ ♨ ▣ ⚲ ⚓ 🚃 Penrith 22.4km

High Close ☞ **Langdale**

Hindhead △ ⅭⅭ Devils Punchbowl, off Portsmouth Rd, Thursley, Nr Godalming, Surrey GU8 6NS ☎ (142) 8604285 **Open:** 24.3-31.8 ⇌ 16 ⚫ £4.25-6.25 ♂ ▣ 🚃 Haslemere 7km 🚌 Stagecoach Hants and Surrey 18/9, 518/9 Aldershot-Haselmere (Pass close BR Haslemere), 271, 292, 571 from Guildford ap Hindhead

Holford ☞ **Quantock Hills**

Holmbury St Mary ▲ ⅭⅭ Radnor Lane, Holmbury St Mary, Dorking, Surrey RH5 6NW. ☎ (1306) 730777 **FAX** (1306) 730933 **Open:**

17.2-31.12 ✉ 52 ● £5.70-8.50 🍴 ✿
♟ ⌂ P ♿ ⛲ Gomshall 4.5km 🚌
22 Guildford-Dorking ap Woodhouse
Farm

Honister Hause △ ⟨CC⟩ Seatoller,
Keswick, Cumbria CA12 5XN. ☎
(17687) 77267 **Open:** 21.3-1.11 ✉ 30
● £4.25-6.25 🍴 ✿ ♟ ⌂ P

Hunstanton ▲ ⟨CC⟩ 15 Ave Rd,
Hunstanton, Norfolk PE36 5BW. ☎
(1485) 532061 **FAX** (1485) 532632
Open: 28.2-1.11; (7.11-20.12 Fri/Sat
only) ✉ 48 ● £5.70-8.50 🍴 ✿ ♟ ▣
⌂ ⛵ ⛲ Kings Lynn 25km 🚌
410,411 from Kings Lynn

Idwal Cottage ▲ ⟨CC⟩ Nant Ffrancon,
Bethesda, Bangor, Caernarfonshire
LL57 3LZ. ☎ (1248) 600225 **FAX**
(1248) 602952 **Open:** 2.1-25.10;
28.12-3.1.98 ✉ 56 ● £4.75-6.95 🍴
✿ ⌂ P ⛵ ⛲ Bangor 18km

Ilam ▲ ⟨CC⟩ Ilam Hall, Ashbourne,
Derbyshire DE6 2AZ. ☎ (1335) 350212
FAX (1335) 350350 **Open:**
07.00-23.00hrs, 31.1-23.11 (24-26.12
♟) ✉ 148 ● £6.30-9.40 (♟
£7.45-10.90) 🍴 ✿ ♟ ♿ ⛪ ▣ ⌂ P ⛵
⛲ Matlock 22km

Ilfracombe ▲ ⟨CC⟩ Ashmour House, 1
Hillsborough Terrace, Ilfracombe,
Devon EX34 9NR. ☎ (1271) 865337
FAX (1271) 862652 **Open:** 24.3-4.10
✉ 50 ● £5.70-8.50 🍴 ✿ ♟ ⌂ P ♿
⛵ ⛲ Barnstaple 21km 🚌
Barnstaple-Ilfracombe 30, 62, 300 (Red
Bus)

Ingleton ▲ ⟨CC⟩ Greta Tower, Ingleton,
Carnforth, Lancashire LA6 3EG. ☎
(15242) 41444 **FAX** (15242) 41854
Open: 3.1-2.11; 23.12-3.1.98 ✉ 66
● £4.75-6.95 🍴 ✿ ♟ ⌂ P ♿ ⛵ ⛲
Bentham 5km

Instow ▲ ⟨CC⟩ Worlington House,
New Rd, Instow, Bideford, Devon
EX39 4LW. ☎ (1271) 860394 **FAX**

(1271) 860055 **Open:** 16.2-2.11 ✉ 58
● £5.70-8.50 🍴 ✿ ♟ ⛪ ▣ ⌂ P ♿
⛵ ⛲ Barnstable 9.5km 🚌
Barnstable-Instow 1, 2, 8 (Red Bus) 1km
ap Instow

Ironbridge Gorge ▲ ⟨CC⟩ Paradise,
Coalbrookdale, Telford, Shropshire TF8
7NR. ☎ (1952) 433281 **FAX** (1952)
433166 **Open:** 31.1-1.11 ✉ 97 ●
£6.30-9.40 🍴 ✿ ⛪ ▣ ⌂ P ⛲ Telford
8km 🚌 BR Telford-Ironbridge

Ivinghoe ▲ ⟨CC⟩ The Old Brewery
House, Ivinghoe, Leighton Buzzard,
Bedfordshire LU7 9EP. ☎ (1296)
668251 **FAX** (1296) 662903 **Open:**
31.1-20.12 ✉ 54 ● £5.15-7.70 🍴 ✿
⛪ ⌂ P ⛲ Cheddington 2.5km,
Tring 5km 🚌 61 Aylesbury-Luton
ap Ivinghoe

Jordans △ ⟨CC⟩ Welders Lane, Jordans,
Beaconsfield, Buckinghamshire HP9
2SN. ☎ (1494) 873135 **FAX** (1494)
875907 **Open:** 17.3-28.10 ✉ 24 ●
£4.75-6.95 ✿ ⌂ P ⛲ Seer Green 1km
🚌 305 High Wycombe-Uxbridge
1km; 353 Slough-Berkhampstead
1.5km ap Seer Green; Chalfont Leisure
Centre

Keld ▲ ⟨CC⟩ Keld Lodge, Upper
Swaledale, Keld, Richmond, North
Yorkshire DL11 6LL. ☎ (1748) 886259
FAX (1748) 866013 **Open:** 3.1-30.11;
27.12-3.1.98 ✉ 46 ● £4.75-6.95 🍴
✿ ♟ ⌂

Kemsing ▲ ⟨CC⟩ Church Lane,
Kemsing, Sevenoaks, Kent TN15 6LU.
☎ (1732) 761341 **FAX** (1732) 763044
Open: 31.1-28.12 ✉ 50 ●
£5.70-8.50 🍴 ✿ ⌂ P ⛲ Kemsing
(not Sun) 2.4km, Otford 3km 🚌
425/436 Sevenoaks- Kemsing
ap Kemsing PO

Kendal ▲ ⟨CC⟩ 118 Highgate, Kendal,
Cumbria LA9 4HE. ☎ (1539) 724066
FAX (1539) 724906 **Open:**

14.2-20.12; 28.12-3.1.98 🎪 50 ⊖
£5.70-8.50 🍴 ⚲ ♀♀ 🏠 ⛲ 🅿 ♿ �";
Kendal 1km

Keswick ▲ 𝗖𝗖 Station Rd, Keswick,
Cumbria CA12 5LH. ☎ (17687) 72484
FAX (17687) 74129 **Open:**
13.00-23.00hrs, 1.1-4.1; 14.2-18.12;
28.12-3.1.98 🎪 91 ⊖ £6.30-9.40 🍴
⚲ ♀♀ ⊟ ⛲ 🅿 ♿ ⛵ 🚌 Penrith 27km
🚍 888 Penrith

Kettlewell ▲ 𝗖𝗖 Whernside House,
Kettlewell, Skipton, North Yorkshire
BD23 5QU. ☎ (1756) 760232 **FAX**
(1756) 760402 **Open:** 13.00hrs,
31.1-20.12; 27.12-3.1.98 🎪 58 ⊖
£5.15-7.70 🍴 ⚲ ⛲ 🅿 ♿ ⛵

Kings, Dolgellau ▲ 𝗖𝗖 Kings,
Penmaenpool, Dolgellau,
Merlonethshire LL40 1TB. ☎ (1341)
422392 **FAX** (1341) 422477 **Open:**
6.2-30.8; 16.9-22.11; 28.12-3.1.98 🎪
56 ⊖ £4.75-6.95 🍴 ⚲ ♀♀ ⛲ 🅿 🚌
Morfa Mawddach 8km

King's Lynn ▲ 𝗖𝗖 Thoresby College,
College Lane, King's Lynn, Norfolk
PE30 1JB. ☎ (1553) 772461 **FAX**
(1553) 764312 **Open:** 27.3-31.8 🎪 36
⊖ £5.15-7.70 ⚲ 🏠 ⛲ ♿ 🚌 Kings
Lynn 1.2km

Kirk Yetholm ☞ Scotland

Kirkby Stephen ▲ 𝗖𝗖 Fletcher Hill,
Market St, Kirkby Stephen, Cumbria
CA17 4QQ. ☎ (17683) 71793 **FAX**
(17683) 71793 **Open:** 14.2-20.12 🎪
44 ⊖ £5.15-7.70 🍴 ⚲ ♀♀ ⊟ ⛲ 🅿 ♿
⛵ 🚌 Kirkby Stephen (not Sun: Oct-
Mar) 2.5km

Land's End ▲ 𝗖𝗖 Letcha Vean, St Just,
Penzance, Cornwall TR19 7NT. (7km
N of Land's End) ☎ (1736) 788437 **FAX**
(1736) 787337 **Open:** 18.2-29.11;
23-27.12 🎪 44 ⊖ £5.70-8.50 🍴 ⚲
⛲ 🅿 ♿ ⛵ 🚌 Penzance 13km 🚍
10/A/B, 11/A Penzance-St Just 1.2km
ap St Just

Langdale (High Close) ▲ 𝗖𝗖 High
Close, Loughrigg, Ambleside, Cumbria
LA22 9HJ. ☎ (15394) 37313 **FAX**
(15394) 37101 **Open:** 10.1-1.11 🎪 96
⊖ £5.70-8.50 🍴 ⚲ ♀♀ 🏠 ⛲ 🅿

Langdon Beck ▲ 𝗖𝗖 Forest- in-
Teesdale, Barnard Castle, Co Durham
DL12 0XN. ☎ (1833) 622228 **FAX**
(1833) 622228 **Open:** 7.2-30.11 🎪 34
⊖ £5.70-8.50 🍴 ⚲ ♀♀ ⊟ ⛲ 🅿 ⛵

Langsett △ Nr Penistone, Sheffield S30
5GY. ☎ (114) 2884541 **Open:** 1.1-24.7
(Sat + Bank Holidays, 25.7-31.12 Sat
only) 🎪 36 ⊖ £4.25-6.25 ⚲ ♀♀ 🅿 🚌
Penistone 5km ⓡ (c/o John & Elaine
Whittington, 7 New Bailey, Crane
Moor, Nr Sheffield S30 7AT ☎ (114)
2884541)

Lincoln ▲ 2SE 𝗖𝗖 77 South Park,
Lincoln LN5 8ES. ☎ (1522) 522076
FAX (1522) 567424 **Open:**
16.2-21.12; 27-31.21 🎪 44 ⊖
£5.70-8.50 🍴 ⚲ ♀♀ 🏠 ⛲ 🅿 ♿ ⛵ 🚌
Lincoln 1.5km

Linton ▲ 𝗖𝗖 The Old Rectory,
Linton- in- Craven, Skipton, North
Yorkshire BD23 5HH. ☎ (1756)
752400 **FAX** (1756) 752400 **Open:**
6.1-2.3; 21.3-20.12 🎪 38 ⊖
£5.70-8.50 🍴 ⚲ ♀♀ ⛲ 🅿 ♿ ⛵ 🚌
Skipton 13km

Litton Cheney △ 𝗖𝗖 Dorchester,
Dorset DT2 9AT. ☎ (1308) 482340
Open: 26.3-27.9 🎪 30 ⊖ £3.85-5.65
⚲ ⛲ ⛵ 🚢 Weymouth 22km 🚌
Dorchester 16km 🚍 31 Weymouth-
Taunton ap Whiteway

Liverpool (*see town plan on next page*) ▲
𝗖𝗖 Chalenor Street, Liverpool **Open:**
Spring '97 🎪 100 🍴 ⚲ ♀♀ ⊟ ⛲ 🅿 ⛵
✈ Manchester ⛴ Liverpool Docks
1km 🚌 Lime Street 1.5km Ⓤ James
Street 700m ⓡ (Prior to opening
contact: Central Reservations ☎ (171)
248 6547, **FAX** (171) 236 7681)

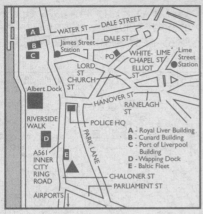

LIVERPOOL

A - Royal Liver Building
B - Cunard Building
C - Port of Liverpool Building
D - Wapping Dock
E - Baltic Fleet

Llanbedr ▲ CC Plas Newydd, Llanbedr, Merionethshire LL45 2LE. ☎ (1341) 241287 **FAX** (1341) 241389 **Open:** 3.1-1.11 ⌘ 47 ● £5.15-7.70 ⛱ ☕ ♟ 🚾 🎒 🚂 Llanbedr 800m

Llanberis ▲ CC Llwyn Celyn, Llanberis, Caernarfon, Caernarfonshire LL55 4SR. ☎ (1286) 870280 **FAX** (1286) 870936 **Open:** 3.1-25.10; 28.12-3.1.98 ⌘ 67 ● £5.15-7.70 ⛱ ♟ 🎒 ⚓ 🚂 Bangor 17.5km 🚌 77 from Bangor

Llanddeusant △ CC The Old Red Lion, Llanddeusant, Llangadog, Carmarthenshire SA19 6UL. ☎ (1550) 740634, 740619 **Open:** 24.3-4.9 ⌘ 28 ● £4.25-6.25 ♟ ☕ 🎒 🚾 Llangadog (not Sun: Oct-Apr) 11km

Llangollen ▲ CC Field Study & Activity Centre, Tyndwr Hall, Tyndwr Rd, Llangollen, Denbighshire LL20 8AR. ☎ (1978) 860330 **FAX** (1978) 861709 **Open:** 07.00-23.00hrs, 3.1-21.12 ⌘ 124 ● £5.70-8.50 ⛱ ♟ 🍴 🖥 🎒 🚾 🚲 ⚓ 🚂 Chirk 9km

Lledr Valley ▲ CC Lledr House, Pont-y-Pant, Dolwyddelan, Aberconwy LL25 0DQ. ☎ (1690) 750202 **Open:** 14.2-31.10 ⌘ 60 ● £5.15-7.70 ⛱ ♟

🎒 🚗 🚲 🚾 Pont-y-Pant (not Sun: Sept-June) 1.2km

Llwyn y Celyn ▲ CC Libanus, Brecon, Powys LD3 8NH. ☎ (1874) 624261 **FAX** (1874) 624261 **Open:** 19.2-13.9; 29.9-29.11 ⌘ 42 ● £4.75-6.95 ⛱ ♟ 🚗 🚲 ⚓ 🚂 Merthyr Tydfil 17.6km

Llwynypia ▲ CC Glyncornel Centre, Llwynypia, Rhondda, Mid Glamorgan CF40 2JF. ☎ (1443) 430859 **FAX** (1443) 423415 **Open:** 15.2-22.2; 3.3-24.10 ⌘ 62 ● £5.70-8.50 ⛱ ♟ ♿ 🍴 🎒 🚗 🚾 Llwynypia 800m

Lockton △ CC The Old School, Lockton, Pickering, North Yorkshire YO18 7PY. ☎ (1751) 460376 **Open:** 23.3-27.9 ⌘ 26 ● £3.85-5.65 ♟ 🚗 🚾 Levisham 3.2km

LONDON (8 Hostels)

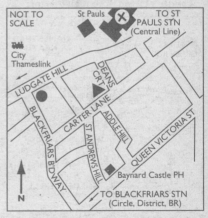

LONDON - City of London

Open: 24hrs ⚑ 154 ⊖ £15.80-18.00 BB inc ⚏ ⚑ ▢ ♨ ⚲ 🚂 Kensington 1.5km U Piccadilly or District; Earl's Court 400m

LONDON - Earls Court

1831 **FAX** (181) 341 0376 Open: 07.00-24.00hrs, 1.2-18.12 ⚑ 70 ⊖ £8.65-12.50 ⚏(B) ⚑ ♨ P 🚌 271, 210 U Archway

LONDON - Highgate

London - **Hampstead Heath** ▲ 9NW IBN CC 4 Wellgarth Rd, Golders Green, London NW11 7HR. ☎ (181) 458 9054/7196 **FAX** (181) 209 0546 Open: 24hrs ⚑ 198 ⊖ £12.80-15.00 ⚏ ⚑ 👫 🏠 ▢ ♨ P 🚌 Hampstead Heath 2.5km 🚌 From City Centre 13, from U 210 .+ 268 U Northern; Golder's Green 400m Ⓡ (Grps)

LONDON - Hampstead Heath

London - **Highgate Village** ▲ 9NW IBN CC 84 Highgate West Hill, Highgate, London N6 6LU ☎ (181) 340

London - **Holland House** ▲ 6SW IBN CC Holland House, Holland Walk, Kensington, London W8 7QU ☎ (171) 937 0748 **FAX** (171) 376 0667 Open: 24hrs ⚑ 201 ⊖ £15.80-18.00 BB inc ⚏ ⚑ 🏠 ▢ ♨ U Central: 800m ap Holland Park, District: Kensington High St

LONDON - Holland House

London - **Rotherhithe** ▲ IBN CC Salter Rd, London SE16 1PP ☎ (171) 232 2114 **FAX** (171) 237 2919 Open: 24hrs ⚑ 320 ⊖ £17.20-20.50 BB inc ⚏

🚹 🏃 ♿ 📻 ⚒ 🅿 🚲 🚂 Waterloo 6km
Ⓤ East London; Rotherhithe 300m

contact: **Central Reservations** 📞 (171)
248 6547 **FAX** (171) 236 7681)

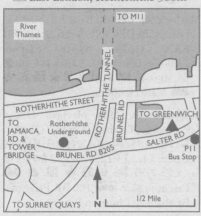

LONDON - Rotherhithe

London - Oxford Street 🔺 IBN CC
14 Noel St, London W1V 3PD. 📞 (171)
7341618 **FAX** (171) 7341657 **Open:**
24hrs 🛏 89 ⚫ £14.65-18.00 🚹 ⚒ 🚂
Charing Cross 1.2km Ⓤ Central,
Bakerloo and Victoria Lines to Oxford
Circus 400m, or Northern and Central
Lines to Tottenham Court Road 500m
Ⓡ

LONDON - Oxford Street

London - St Pancras 🔺 CC 79-81
Euston Road, London N1 **Open:** Su '97
🛏 150 🍽 🚹 ⚒ 📻 ⚒ 🅿 🚂 St Pancras,
Kings Cross & Euston 100m Ⓤ St
Pancras 100m Ⓡ (Prior to opening

LONDON - St Pancras

Longthwaite ☞ **Borrowdale**

Ludlow 🔺 CC Ludford Lodge,
Ludford, Ludlow, Shropshire SY8 1PJ.
📞 (1584) 872472 **FAX** (1584) 872095
Open: 14.2-22.12; 27-31.12 🛏 50 ⚫
£4.75-6.95 🍽 🚹 🚻 ⚒ 🚲 ⛵ 🚂
Ludlow 1km 🚌 192, 292
Birmingham-Hereford

Lulworth Cove 🔺 CC School Lane,
West Lulworth, Wareham, Dorset
BH20 5SA. 📞 (1929) 400564 **FAX**
(1929) 400640 **Open:** 16.2-1.11 🛏 34
⚫ £5.70-8.50 🍽 🚹 🚻 ⚒ 🅿 🚂 Wool
8km 🚌 225 BR Wool- Lulworth
Cove, 220 Dorchester-Lulworth Cove

Lynton 🔺 CC Lynbridge, Lynton,
Devon EX35 6AZ 📞 (1598) 753237
FAX (1598) 753305 **Open:**
14.2-13.12; 23-28.12 🛏 38 ⚫
£5.15-7.70 🍽 🚹 ⚒ 🅿 ⛵ 🚂
Barnstaple 32km 🚌 310 Barnstaple-
Lynton

Maeshafn △ CC Holt Hostel,
Maeshafn, Mold, Denbighshire CH7
5LR. 📞 (1352) 810320 **Open:**
26.3-30.8 🛏 31 ⚫ £4.75-6.95 🚹 ⚒
🅿 🚂 Buckley 13km; Chester 23km

R (**Shut:** ☎ Wales Regional Office
(1222) 396766)

Malham ▲ CC John Dower Memorial
Hostel, Malham, Skipton, North
Yorkshire BD23 4DE. ☎ (1729)
830321 **FAX** (1729) 830551 **Open:**
1.1-20.12; 27.12-3.1.98 🏃 80 ⬤
£6.30-9.40 🍽 ☞ 👬 ♿ 🏠 🏚 **P** 🚂
Skipton 20km

Malton ▲ CC Derwent Bank, York Rd,
Malton, North Yorkshire YO17 0AX.
☎ (1653) 692077 **FAX** (1653) 692077
Open: 6.1-6.9 🏃 60 ⬤ £4.75-6.95 🍽
☞ 👬 🏚 **P** 🚲 🚂 Malton 1.2km

Malvern Hills ▲ CC 18 Peachfield Rd,
Malvern   Wells,   Malvern,
Worcestershire WR14 4AP. ☎ (1684)
569131 **FAX** (1684) 565205 **Open:**
14.2-26.12 🏃 59 ⬤ £5.15-7.70 🍽 ☞
🏚 **P** 🚂 Great Malvern 2.5km

Manchester ▲ IBN Potato Wharf,
Castlefield, Manchester M3 ☎ (161)
8399960 FAX (161) 8352054 Open:
24hrs 🏃 160 ⬤ £8.65-12.50 🍽 ☞ 👬
♿ 🏠 🏚 P ✈ Manchester 16km A🚌
757 16km 🚢 Liverpool 43.5km 🚂
Picadilly (Manchester) 1.5km 🚌 30,
31 800m ap Picadilly Station 🚃
Metrolink 500m ap G-Mex

Mankinholes ▲ CC Todmorden,
Lancashire OL14 6HR. ☎ (1706)
812340 **FAX** (1706) 812340 **Open:**
31.1-30.11 🏃 40 ⬤ £4.75-6.95 🍽 ☞
👬 🏠 🏚 **P** ⚓ 🚂 Todmorden 3.2km

Manorbier ▲ CC Nr Tenby,
Pembrokeshire SA70 7TT. ☎ (1834)
871803 **FAX** (1834) 871101 **Open:**
14.2-30.8; 12.9-25.10 🏃 68 ⬤
£5.70-8.50 🍽 👬 ♿ 🏠 🏚 **P** ⚓ ⛴
Pembroke Dock 16km 🚂 Manorbier
4km

Marloes Sands △ Runwayskiln,
Marloes, Haverfordwest, Pembrokeshire
SA62 3BH. ☎ (1646) 636667 **Open:**
24.3-27.9 🏃 30 ⬤ £4.25-6.25 ☞ 🏚

P ⛴ 🚐 Pembroke Dock 12km 🚂
Milford Haven 17km

Matlock ▲ CC 40 Bank Rd, Matlock,
Derbyshire DE4 3NF. ☎ (1629) 582983
FAX   (1629)   583484   **Open:**
13.00-23.00hrs, 2.1-3.1.98 🏃 49 ⬤
£6.30-9.40 🍽 ☞ 👬 ♿ 🏠 🏚 **P** 🚲 ⚓
🚂 Matlock 400m

Maypool ▲ CC Maypool House,
Galmpton, Brixham, Devon TQ5 0ET.
☎ (1803) 842444 **FAX** (1803) 845939
Open: 14.2-13.12; 27-31.12 🏃 93 ⬤
£5.15-7.70 🍽 ☞ 🏠 🏚 **P** ⚓ 🚂
Paignton 8km 🚐 100 BR Paignton-
Brixham ap Churston Pottery

Meerbrook △ Old School, Meerbrook,
Leek, Staffordshire ST13 8SJ. ☎ (1629)
650394 **Open:** 24.3-1.11 🏃 22 ⬤
£4.25-6.25 ☞ 👬 🏚 **P** **R** (c/o Mrs I
Carlile, Elton YH, Elton Old Hall, Main
St, Elton, Matlock ☎ (1629) 650394)

Milton Keynes ☞ **Bradwell Village**

Minehead ▲ CC Alcombe Combe,
Minehead, Somerset TA24 6EW. ☎
(1643) 702595 **FAX** (1643) 703016
Open: 25.3-1.11 🏃 36 ⬤ £5.70-8.50
🍽 ☞ 👬 🏚 **P** 🚂 Taunton 40km 🚐
Southern National No 28 1km
ap Alcombe

Newport ▲ Lower St Mary's St,
Newport,   Pewmbrokeshire,   Dyfed
SA42 0TS. ☎ (1239) 820080 **FAX**
(1239) 820080 **Open:** 28.2-27.10
Shut: Some Tues and Wed 🏃 28 ⬤
£5.15-7.70 ☞ 👬 ♿ 🏚 **P** ⛴
Fishguard 10km

Newcastle upon Tyne ▲ IBN CC
107 Jesmond Rd, Newcastle upon Tyne
NE2 1NJ. ☎ (191) 2812570 FAX (191)
2818779 Open: 1.2-30.11 🏃 60 ⬤
£5.15-7.70 🍽 ☞ 👬 🏚 P ⚓ 🚂
Newcastle 2.5km U Jesmond 500m

Ninebanks △ Orchard House, Mohope,
Ninebanks, Hexham, Northumberland

NE47 8DO. ☎ (1434) 345288 **FAX**
(1434) 345288 **Open:** 5.1-23.12 ⊠ 26
⊖ £3.85-5.65 ✶ ♦♦♦ ⊞ 🅿

Norwich ▲ 2W CC3 112 Turner Rd,
Norwich NR2 4HB. ☎ (1603) 627647
FAX (1603) 629075 **Open:** 1.2-21.12
⊠ 68 ⊖ £5.70-8.50 🍴 ✶ ♦♦♦ ⊞ 🅿 ☋
⚓ 🚂 Norwich 3km

Once Brewed ▲ CC3 Military Rd,
Bardon Mill, Hexham, Northumberland
NE47 7AN. ☎ (1434) 344360 **FAX**
(1434) 344045 **Open:** 13.00hrs,
31.1-29.11 ⊠ 76 ⊖ £5.70-8.50 🍴 ✶
♦♦♦ ♿ (limited) ⊠ ⊞ 🅿 🚂 Maroon
Mill 4km

Osmotherley ▲ CC3 Cote Ghyll,
Osmotherley, Northallerton, North
Yorkshire DL6 3AH. ☎ (1609) 883575
FAX (1609) 883715 **Open:** 31.1-8.11
⊠ 80 ⊖ £5.70-8.50 🍴 ✶ ♦♦♦ 🏧 ⊞ 🅿
🚂 Northallerton 13km

Oxford ▲ 3NE IBN CC3 32 Jack
Straw's Lane, Oxford OX3 0DW. ☎
(1865) 762997 FAX (1865) 769402
Open: 24hrs, 13.1-31.12 ⊠ 112 ⊖
£6.30-9.40 🍴 ✶ ♦♦♦ ⊠ ⊞ 🅿 ☋ ⚓ 🚂
Oxford 4km

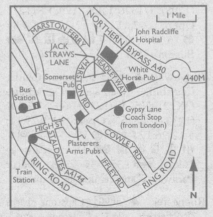

OXFORD

Patterdale ▲ CC3 Goldrill House,
Patterdale, Penrith, Cumbria CA11
0NW ☎ (17684) 82394 **FAX** (17684)

82034 **Open:** 07.00-23.00hrs,
14.2-21.12 ⊠ 82 ⊖ £6.30-9.40 🍴 ✶
⊠ ⊞ 🅿 ☋ ⚓ 🚂 Penrith 24km

Pendennis Castle ▲ CC3 Falmouth,
Cornwall TR11 4LP. ☎ (1326) 311435
FAX (1326) 315473 **Open:**
17.2-29.11; 27-31.12 ⊠ 76 ⊖
£5.70-8.50 🍴 ✶ ♦♦♦ 🏧 ⊠ ⊞ ☋ ⚓ 🚂
Falmouth Docks (not Sun: Sep- Jun)
1.5km

Pentlepoir △ CC3 The Old School,
Pentlepoir, Saundersfoot, Pembrokeshire
SA9 9BJ. ☎ (1834) 812333 **Open:**
28.3-25.10 ⊠ 34 ⊖ £4.75-6.95
🍴 (B D) ✶ ⊞ 🅿 ⚓ 🚂 Saundersfoot
(not Sun: Oct-Apr) 1.2km

Penycwm (Solva) ▲ 4SE Solva, Hafod
Lodge, White House, Penycwm, Nr
Solva, Haverfordwest, Pembrokeshire
SA61 6LA. ☎ (1437) 720959 **FAX**
(1437) 720959 **Open:** 28.2-25.10 ⊠
26 ⊖ £5.70-8.50 🍴 ✶ ♦♦♦ 🅿 ☋ ⚓
🚂 Haverfordwest 18km R (Nov-
Feb)

Pen- y-Pass ▲ CC3 Nant Gwynant,
Caernarfon, Caernarfonshire LL55 4NY
☎ (1286) 870428 **FAX** (1286) 872434
Open: 07.00-10.00hrs, 13.00-23.00hrs,
1.1-26.10; 28.12-3.1.98 ⊠ 104 ⊖
£5.70-8.50 🍴 ✶ ♦♦♦ ♿ ⊞ 🅿 🚂
Bangor 29km

Penzance (*see town plan on next page*) ▲
CC3 Castle Horneck, Alverton,
Penzance, Cornwall TR20 8TF. ☎
(1736) 362666 **FAX** (1736) 362663
Open: 2.2-22.12; 29.12-3.1.98 ⊠ 84
⊖ £6.30-9.40 🍴 ✶ 🏧 ⊠ ⊞ 🅿 ☋ ⚓
🚂 Penzance 3km 🚌 From BR
Station 5B, 6B, 10B ap Pirate Pub

Perranporth △ CC3 Droskyn Point,
Perranporth, Cornwall TR6 0DS. ☎
(1872) 573812 **Open:** 27.3-30.9 ⊠ 24
⊖ £5.15-7.70 ✶ ⊞ ☋ ⚓ 🚂 Truro
or Newquay (not Sun: Oct-May) 16km
🚌 87A, B, C, 88A Truro-Newquay

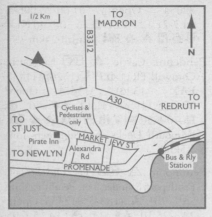

PENZANCE

Plymouth ▲ 4S CC Belmont House, Belmont Place, Stoke, Plymouth PL3 4DW. ☎ (1752) 562189 **FAX** (1752) 605360 **Open:** 2.1-27.12 ⌂ 68 ● £6.30-9.40 🍴 ☞ 🏥 🏠 🏢 🅿 ♿ ⚓ 🚢 Plymouth 🚌 Plymouth 2.5km, Davenport 500m 🚆 33,34A from city centre ap Stoke

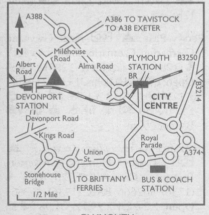

PLYMOUTH

Poppit Sands ▲ CC 'Sea View', Poppit, Cardigan, Cardiganshire SA43 3LP. ☎ (1239) 612936 **Open:** 25.3-25.10 **Shut:** Some Mon ⌂ 30 ● £4.75-6.95 ☞ 🅿 ♿ 🚌 Fishguard 32km

Port Eynon ▲ CC The Old Lifeboat House, Port Eynon, Swansea SA3 1NN.

☎ (1792) 390706 **FAX** (1792) 390706 **Open:** 14.2-29.11 ⌂ 32 ● £4.75-6.95 ☞ 🏥 🏢 ⚓ 🚢 Swansea 24km 🚌 Swansea 24km ● See also Stouthall

Portsmouth ▲ 6NE CC Wymering Manor, Old Wymering Lane, Cosham, Portsmouth, Hampshire PO6 3NL. ☎ (1705) 375661 **FAX** (1705) 214177 **Open:** 2.1-20.12 ⌂ 66 ● £5.70-8.50 🍴 ☞ 🏥 🏢 🅿 ⚓ 🚢 Portsmouth 3km 🚌 Cosham 1km

Pwll Deri ▲ CC Castell Mawr, Tref Asser, Goodwick, Pembrokeshire SA64 0LR. ☎ (1348) 891233 **Open:** 24.3-25.10 **Shut:** some Sun and Mon ⌂ 32 ● £4.75-6.95 ☞ 🏢 🅿 🚢 Fishguard 7.5km 🚌 Fishguard Harbour 7.5km

Quantock Hills △ CC Sevenacres, Holford, Bridgwater, Somerset TA5 1SQ. ☎ (1278) 741224 **Open:** 25.3-31.8 ⌂ 24 ● £4.75-6.95 ☞ 🅿 🚌 Bridgwater 22km 🚆 Southern National 15 from Bridgewater

Ravenstor ▲ CC Millers Dale, Buxton, Derbyshire SK17 8SS. ☎ (1298) 871826 **FAX** (1298) 871275 **Open:** 7.2-23.12; 27.12-3.1.98 ⌂ 84 ● £6.30-9.40 🍴 ☞ 🏥 🗄 🏢 🅿 ♿ 🚌 Buxton 13km

Ridgeway ▲ CC Ridgeway Centre, Courthill, Wantage, Oxfordshire OX12 9NE. ☎ (12357) 60253 **FAX** (12357) 68865 **Open:** 31.1-29.11; 5.12-26.12 ⌂ 59 ● £5.15-9.40 🍴 ☞ 🏥 ♿ 🗄 🏢 🅿 🚌 Didcot Parkway 16km 🚆 32, 35, 36A Didcot Parkway-Wantage 3km ap Wantage

Rochester ▲ CC Capstone Farm (Rochester), 377 Capstone Road, Gillingham, Kent ME7 3JE ☎ (1634) 400788 **FAX** (1634) 400794 **Open:** 3.1-31.12 ⌂ 46 ● £5.70-8.50 🍴 🏥 ♿ 🏥 🗄 🏢 🅿 ♿ ✈ Gatwick 🚢

Sheerness to Vlissigen 18km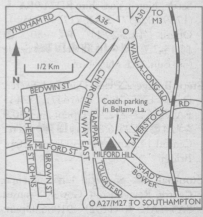
Chatham 4km 114 ap Wagan at
Hale PH 500m

Rowen △ Rhiw Farm, Rowen, Conwy,
Aberconwy LL32 8YW. **Open:**
26.3-30.8 🛏 24 ⊖ £3.85-5.65 ⚓ 🅿
 Tal-y-Cafn (not Sun: Sep-Jun) 5km
Ⓡ (The Warden, Colwyn Bay YH)

Saffron Walden ▲ ⌖ 1 Myddylton
Place, Saffron Walden, Essex CB10
1BB. ☎ (1799) 523117 **Open:**
28.2-21.12 🛏 38 ⊖ £5.15-7.70 🍴 ⚓
🏮 ♿ 🅿 ✈ Stanstead Audley End
4km BR Audley End- Saffron
Walden

St Briavels Castle ▲ ⌖ The Castle,
St Briavels, Lydney, Gloucestershire
GL15 6RG. ☎ (1594) 530272 **FAX**
(1594) 530849 **Open:** 7.2-11.12;
24-27.12 🛏 70 ⊖ £6.30-9.40 🍴 ⚓
🏮 ♿ 🅿 ⚓ Chepstow 11km

St David's △ ⌖ Llaethdy, St David's,
Haverfordwest, Pembrokeshire SA62
6PR. ☎ (1437) 720345 **FAX** (1437)
721831 **Open:** 24.3-27.9 🛏 40 ⊖
£4.25-6.25 ⚓ ♿ 🅿 🚲 ⚓
Fishguard 24km

Salcombe ▲ ⌖ 'Overbecks',
Sharpitor, Salcombe, Devon TQ8 8LW.
☎ / **FAX** (154884) 2856 **Open:**
24.3-1.11 🛏 54 ⊖ £5.15-7.70 🍴 ⚓
🏮 ♿ 🅿 ⚓ Totnes 32km

Salisbury ▲ ⌊IBN⌋ ⌖ Milford Hill
House, Milford Hill, Salisbury,
Wiltshire SP1 2QW. ☎ (1722) 327572
FAX (1722) 330446 **Open:**
07.00-10.00hrs, 13.00-23.00hrs 🛏 74
⊖ £6.30-9.40 🍴 ⚓ 🚻 🏮 🗊 ♿ 🅿
Salisbury 1.5km

Sandown ▲ ⌖ The Firs, Fitzroy St,
Sandown, Isle of Wight PO36 8JH. ☎
(1983) 402651 **FAX** (1983) 403565
Open: 21.3-1.11 🛏 64 ⊖ £5.70-8.50
🍴 ⚓ 🚻 ① ♿ 🅿 🚲 ⚓ 🚢 Ryde

10km, East Cowes 19km Sandown
800m

Scarborough ▲ ⌖ The White
House, Burniston Rd, Scarborough,
North Yorkshire YO13 0DA. ☎ (1723)
361176 **FAX** (1723) 500054 **Open:**
31.1-27.12 🛏 64 ⊖ £4.75-6.95 🍴 ⚓
🚻 ♿ 🅿 🚲 ⚓ Scarborough 3.2km

Sheringham ▲ ⌖ 1 Cremer's Drift,
Sheringham, Norfolk NR26 8HX. ☎
(1263) 823215 **FAX** (1263) 823215
Open: 1.2-6.12; 23.12-3.1.98 🛏 109
⊖ £6.30-9.40 🍴 ⚓ 🚻 ♿ 🏮 🅿 🚲 ⚓
 Sheringham 400m 758/9,
761,58/X58 Norwich-Sheringham

Shining Cliff △ Shining Cliff Woods,
near Ambergate. ☎ (1629) 650394
Open: 24.3-1.11 🛏 26 ⊖ £3.85-5.65
⚓ 🚻 🅿 Ambergate 3km Ⓡ (Mrs
I Carlile, Elton YH, Main St, Elton,
Near Matlock, Derbyshire DE4 2BW)

Shrewsbury ▲ ⌖ The Woodlands,
Abbey Foregate, Shrewsbury,
Shropshire SY2 6LZ. ☎ (1743) 360179
FAX (1743) 357423 **Open:**
14.2-20.12 🛏 60 ⊖ £5.70-8.50 🍴 ⚓
🗊 ♿ 🅿 ⚓ Shrewsbury 1.5km Ⓡ
(Ironbridge Gorge YH ☎ (1952)
433281)

SALISBURY

Skiddaw House △ ⟨CC⟩ YHA Bothy, Bassenthwaite, Cumbria. ☏ (16974) 78325 **FAX** (16974) 78325 **Open:** 21.3-1.11 ⋈ 15 ● £3.85-5.65 ♂ ♟ ♣ ● Remote location, no one turned away, no access by car

Slaidburn △ ⟨CC⟩ King's House, Slaidburn, Clitheroe, Lancashire BB7 3ER. ☏ (1200) 446656 **Open:** 27.3-30.10 ⋈ 36 ● £3.85-5.65 ⊙ ♂ ♨ 🅿 ♣ ♻ Long Preston 16km ⓡ (except 15.7-3.9: PO Box 11, Matlock, Derbyshire ☏ (1629) 825850 **FAX** (1629) 824571)

Slimbridge ▲ ⟨CC⟩ Shepherd's Patch, Slimbridge, Gloucestershire GL2 7BP. ☏ (1453) 890275 **FAX** (1453) 890625 **Open:** 1.1-30.11; 27-31.12 ⋈ 56 ● £6.30-9.40 ⊙ ♂ ♟ ▣ ♨ 🅿 ♻ Cam and Dursley 5km ♻ 308 Bristol-Gloucester, 91 Gloucester- Dursley ap Slimbridge Cross-rds

Snowdon Ranger ▲ ⟨CC⟩ Rhyd Ddu, Caernarfon, Caernarfonshire LL54 7YS. ☏ (1286) 650391 **FAX** (1286) 650093 **Open:** 14.2-21.12 ⋈ 67 ● £5.70-8.50 ⊙ ♂ ♨ 🅿 ⚓ ♻ Bangor 25.5km

Solva ☞ **Penycwm**

Stainforth ▲ Taitlands, Stainforth, Settle, North Yorkshire BD24 9PA. ☏ (1729) 823577 **FAX** (1729) 825404 **Open:** 14.2-29.11 ⋈ 50 ● £5.15-7.70 ⊙ ♂ ♟ ♨ ♣ 🅿 ♻ Settle (not Sun: Oct-Mar) 4km

Steps Bridge △ ⟨CC⟩ Dunsford, Exeter, Devon EX6 7EQ. ☏ (1647) 252435 **FAX** (1647) 252948 **Open:** 23.3-30.9 ⋈ 24 ● £4.25-6.25 ♂ ♣ 🅿 ♻ Exeter Central 14.5km ♻ 359 Exeter-Steps Bridge

Stouthall ▲ Stouthall Environmental Centre, Reynoldston, Gower, Swansea SA3 1AP. ☏ (1792) 391086 **Open:** 26.7-31.8 ⋈ 60 ● £6.30-9.40 ⊙ ♂

♟ ♣ 🅿 ✈ Cardiff 90km ⛴ Swansea 25.7km ● Annexe for Port Eynon YH

Stow- on- the- Wold ▲ ⟨CC⟩ Cheltenham, Gloucestershire GL54 1AF. ☏ (1451) 830497 **FAX** (1451) 870102 **Open:** 1.2-14.12; 28.12-1.1.98 ⋈ 56 ● £5.15-7.70 ⊙ ♂ ♨ ▣ ♣ ♻ Kingham 6.5km

Stratford- upon- Avon ▲ ⟨IBN⟩ ⟨CC⟩ Hemmingford House, Alveston, Stratford- upon- Avon, Warwickshire CV37 7RG. ☏ (1789) 297093 **FAX** (1789) 205513 **Open:** 6.1-14.12 ⋈ 148 ● £9.65-12.95 ⟨BB⟩inc ⊙ ♂ ♟ ▣ ♣ 🅿 ♨ ✈ Birmingham 32km ♻ Stratford 4.8km ♻ 18 Stratford-Leamington Spa

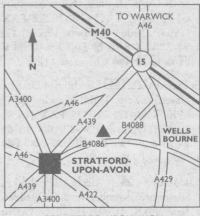

STRATFORD-UPON-AVON

Streatley- on- Thames ▲ ⟨CC⟩ Hill House, Reading Rd, Streatley, Reading, Berks RG8 9JJ. ☏ (1491) 872278 **FAX** (1491) 873056 **Open:** 31.1-13.12; 27-31.12 ⋈ 51 ● £6.30-9.40 ⊙ ♂ ♟ ♣ 🅿 ♻ Goring & Streatley 1.5km ♻ 105 Reading-Oxford ap Bull Hotel

Street △ ⟨CC⟩ The Chalet, Ivythorn Hill, Street, Somerset BA16 0TZ. ☏ (1458) 442961 **FAX** (1458) 442738 **Open:** 26.3-30.10 ⋈ 32 ● £5.15-7.70 ♂ ♟ ♣ 🅿 ♻ Castle Cary 17.5km, Bridgwater 21km ♻ 29A Bristol-Yeovil 500m ap Marshalls Elm

Swanage ▲ CC Cluny, Cluny Crescent, Swanage, Dorset BH19 2BS. ☎ (1929) 422113 **FAX** (1929) 426327 **Open:** 14.2-1.11; 23-26.12 ⊠ 106 ● £6.30-9.40 ⚎ 🍴 🔒 🖥 🏠 🅿 🚅 Wareham 16km 🚌 150 Bournemouth-Swanage, 142/4 Poole-Swanage 500m

Tanners Hatch △ CC Polesden Lacey, Dorking, Surrey RH5 6BE. ☎ (1372) 452528 ⊠ 28 ● £4.25-6.25 🔒 🏠 🏠 🚅 Box Hill & W. Humble 3km, Dorking Town 4km 🚌 465 Kingston- Horsham 3.5km ap West Humble

Tebay △ The Old School, Tebay, Penrith, Cumbria CA10 3TP. ☎ (15396) 24286 **FAX** (15396) 24286 **Open:** 7.2-29.11 **Shut:** Thurs ⊠ 46 ● £5.15-7.70 🍴 👬 🖥 🏠 🅿 ⚓ 🚅 Kendal 17.5km

Telscombe △ Bank Cottages, Telscombe, Lewes, East Sussex BN7 3HZ. ☎ (1273) 301357 **Open:** 24.3-31.8 ⊠ 22 ● £4.75-6.95 🔒 🏠 🏠 ⚎ Newhaven 8km 🚅 Southease 4km, Lewes 10km, Brighton 11km 🚌 Stagecoach South Coast 123 BR Lewes- Newhaven (will go to YH on request) R (☎ (1825) 890607)

Thirlmere △ CC The Old School, Stanah Cross, Keswick, Cumbria CA12 4TQ. ☎ (17687) 73224 **FAX** (17687) 73224 **Open:** 21.3-8.11 ⊠ 33 ● £3.85-5.65 🍴 🔒 🚹 🏠 🅿 🚅 Penrith 29km

Thixendale △ CC The Village Hall, Thixendale, Malton, North Yorkshire YO17 9TG. ☎ (1377) 288238 **Open:** 27.3-30.9 ⊠ 18 ● £3.85-5.65 🔒 🏠 🏠 🅿 🚅 Malton 16km

Thurlby △ CC 16 High St, Thurlby, Bourne, Lincolnshire PE10 0EE. ☎ (1778) 425588 **Open:** 24.3-29.10 ⊠ 34 ● £5.15-7.70 🔒 👬 🚹 🏠 🏠 🅿 ⚓

🚅 Peterborough 24km 🚌 Peterborough-Thurlby

Tintagel △ CC Dunderhole Point, Tintagel, Cornwall PL34 0DW. ☎ (1840) 770334 **FAX** (1840) 770733 **Open:** 21.3-5.10 ⊠ 26 ● £5.15-7.70 🔒 🏠 🏠 🅿 🚅 Bodmin Parkway 32km 🚌 123 BR Bodmin Parkway-Tintagel ap Tintagel

Totland Bay ▲ CC Hurst Hill, Totland Bay, Isle of Wight PO39 0HD. ☎ (1983) 752165 **FAX** (1983) 756443 **Open:** 7.2-1.11 ⊠ 76 ● £6.30-9.40 🍴 🔒 👬 🖥 🏠 🅿 🚴 🛶 ⚓ ⛴ Yarmouth 5km, West Cowes 24km 🚌 1B/C Ryde- Totland ap Totland War Memorial

Trevine ▲ CC Trevine, Haverfordwest, Pembrokeshire SA62 5AU. ☎ (1348) 831414 **Open:** 11.3-25.10 ⊠ 26 ● £4.75-6.95 🔒 👬 🏠 🅿 ⚓ ⚎ Fishguard 19km 🚅 Fishguard Harbour 19km

Treyarnon Bay ▲ CC Tregonnan, Treyarnon, Padstow, Cornwall PL28 8JR. ☎ (1841) 520322 **FAX** (1841) 520322 **Open:** 24.3-1.11 ⊠ 42 ● £5.70-8.50 🍴 🔒 🏠 🅿 ⚓ 🚅 Bodmin Parkway 32km 🚌 Western National 55 BR Bodmin Parkway - Padstow ap Padstow

Truleigh Hill ▲ CC Tottington Barn, Truleigh Hill, Shoreham-by-Sea, West Sussex BN43 5FB. ☎ (1903) 813419 **FAX** (1903) 812016 **Open:** 17.2-2.11 ⊠ 64 ● £5.70-8.50 🍴 🔒 👬 🏠 🅿 🚅 Shoreham-by-Sea 6.5km

Tyncornel △ Llanddewi- Brefi, Tregaron, Cardiganshire SY25 6PH. ☎ Wales Regional Office (1222) 222122 **Open:** 25.3-6.9 ⊠ 16 ● £3.85-5.65 🔒 🅿 R (☎ (1222) 222122)

Ty'n- y-Caeau ▲ CC Groesffordd, Brecon, Powys LD3 7SW. ☎ (1874)

665270 **FAX** (1874) 665278 **Open:**
14.2-24.11 🎒 55 ● £5.15-7.70 🍴 ☕
🏛 🅿 🚲

Wastwater ▲ 🆔 Wasdale Hall,
Wasdale, Seascale, Cumbria CA20 1ET.
📞 (19467) 26222 **FAX** (19467) 26056
Open: 9.1-1.11; 28.12-3.1.98 🎒 50
● £5.70-8.50 🍴 ☕ 🏕 🏛 🅿 🚲 ⚠
🚌 Seascale (not Sun) 14.5km

Welsh Bicknor ▲ 🆔 The Rectory,
Welsh Bicknor, Nr Goodrich, Ross-on-
Wye, Herefordshire HR9 6JJ. 📞 (1594)
860300 **FAX** (1594) 861276 **Open:**
14.2-13.12 🎒 80 ● £5.70-8.50 🍴 ☕
🏕 🅾 🏛 🅿 🚲 ⚠ 🚌 Lydney 20km

Whitby ▲ 🆔 East Cliff, Whitby,
North Yorkshire YO22 4JT. 📞 (1947)
602878 **FAX** (1947) 602878 **Open:**
1.1-13.12; 31.12-3.1.98 🎒 66 ●
£4.75-6.95 🍴 ☕ 🏕 🏛 🅿 🚲 🚌
Whitby (not Sun: Oct-Apr) 800m

Wight, Isle of ☞ Sandown and Totland
Bay

Wilderhope Manor ▲ 🆔 The John
Cadbury Memorial Hostel, Easthope,
Much Wenlock, Shropshire TF13 6EG.
📞 (1694) 771363 **FAX** (1694) 771520
Open: 1.3-1.11 🎒 58 ● £5.70-8.50
🍴 ☕ 🏕 🏛 🅿 🚌 Church Stretton
13km

Winchester ▲ 🆔 The City Mill, 1
Water Lane, Winchester, Hampshire
SO23 0ER. 📞 (1962) 853723 **FAX**
(1962) 855524 **Open:** 14.2-20.12 🎒
31 ● £5.70-8.50 🍴 ☕ 🏕 🏛 🚌
Winchester 1.5km

Windermere ▲ 🆔 High Close,
Bridge Lane, Troutbeck, Windermere,
Cumbria LA23 1LA. 📞 (15394) 43543
FAX (15394) 47165 **Open:**
13.00-23.00hrs, 1.1-15.11; 28.12-3.1.98
🎒 73 ● £5.15-7.70 🍴 ☕ 🏛 🅿 🚌
Windermere 3.2km

Windsor ▲ 🆔 Edgeworth
House, Mill Lane, Windsor, Berkshire

SL4 5JE. 📞 (1753) 861710 **FAX** (1753)
832100 **Open:** 13.00-23.00hrs,
2.1-23.12 🎒 82 ● £6.30-9.40 🍴 ☕
🏕 🅾 🏛 🅿 🚌 Windsor & Eton 1.5km

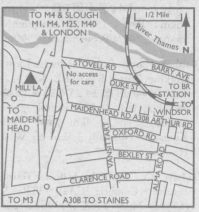

WINDSOR

Woody's Top △ 🆔 Ruckland, near
Louth, Lincs LN11 8RQ 📞 (1722)
337494 **FAX** (1722) 414027 **Open:**
24.3-30.9 🎒 22 ● £4.25-6.25 ☕ 🏛
🅿 🚲 ⚠ 🚌 Grimsby Town 35km,
Lincoln 40km 🚌 Grimsby- Louth
9km, Lincoln-Louth 9km ap Louth Ⓡ
(South England Region Bookings Office
(1722) 337494)

Wooler ▲ 🆔 30 Cheviot St, Wooler,
Northumberland NE71 6LW. 📞 (1668)
281365 **FAX** (1668) 282368 **Open:**
14.2-27.11 🎒 52 ● £5.15-7.70 🍴 ☕
🏕 ♿ 🅾 🏛 🅿 🚲

York (*see town plan on next page*) ▲ 2NW
🆔 🆔 YHA York International,
Water End, Clifton, York, Yorkshire
YO3 6LT. 📞 (1904) 653147 **FAX**
(1904) 651230 **Open:** 24hrs,
17.1-3.1.98 🎒 146 ● £10.30-13.85
BB inc 🍴 ☕ 🏕 🏛 🅾 🏛 🅿 🚌 York
1.5km

Youlgreave ▲ 🆔 Fountain Square,
Youlgreave, Bakewell, Derbyshire DE4
1UR. 📞 (1629) 636518 **FAX** (1629)
636518 **Open:** 7.2-23.12; 31.12-3.1.98

🚂 46 ⚫ £5.15-7.70 🍴 👕 👨‍👩‍👧 🏫 🅿 🚲
🚆 Matlock 17.5km

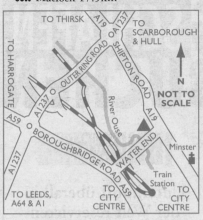

YORK

Ystradfellte △ ⏣ Tai'r Heol, Ystradfellte, Aberdare, Powys CF44 9JF. 📞 (1639) 720301 **Open:** 24.3-29.10 🚪 28 ⚫ £4.25-6.25 👕 🅿 🚆 Aberdare 16km

Ystumtuen △ ⏣ Glantuen, Ystumtuen, Aberystwyth, Cardiganshire

SY23 3AE. 📞 (1970) 890693 **Open:** 25.3-6.9 🚪 24 ⚫ £3.85-5.65 👕 🅿 🚆 Aberystwyth 18km

SUPPLEMENTARY ACCOMMODATION OUTSIDE THE ASSURED STANDARDS SCHEME

Harlow Corned House, Netteswell Cross, Harlow, Essex CM20 2QD 📞 (1279) 421702 ⚫ £4.75-6.95 ⚫ (Reopens in early '97, 📞 for more information)

Wheathill Malthouse Farm, Wheathill, Bridgnorth, Shropshire WV16 6QT. 📞 (1746) 787236 **Open:** 1.1-21.12; 27-31.12 🚪 28 ⚫ £3.85-5.65 👕 🏠 🏫 🅿 🚆 Ludlow 11km

Wheeldale ⏣ Wheeldale Lodge, Goathland, Whitby, North Yorkshire YO22 5AP. 📞 (1947) 896350 **Open:** 1.4-1.10 🚪 32 ⚫ £3.85-5.65 🍴 👕 🏫 🅿 🚆 Grosmont (not Sun: Oct-Apr) 10km

FINLAND
FINLANDE
FINNLAND
FINLANDIA

Suomen Retkeilymajajärjestö-SRM ry,
Yrjönkatu 38 B 15, 00100 Helsinki,
Finland.

☎ (358) (9) 6940377
FAX (358) (9) 6931349

Office Hours: Monday-Friday, 09.00-16.00hrs

Travel Section:
SRM Travel, Yrjönkatu 38 B15,
00100 Helsinki, Finland.

☎ (358) (9) 6940377
FAX (358) (9) 6931349

Capital:	Helsinki
Language:	Finnish and Swedish
Currency:	FIM (markka)
Population:	5,116,826
Size:	338,145 sq km

FINLAND

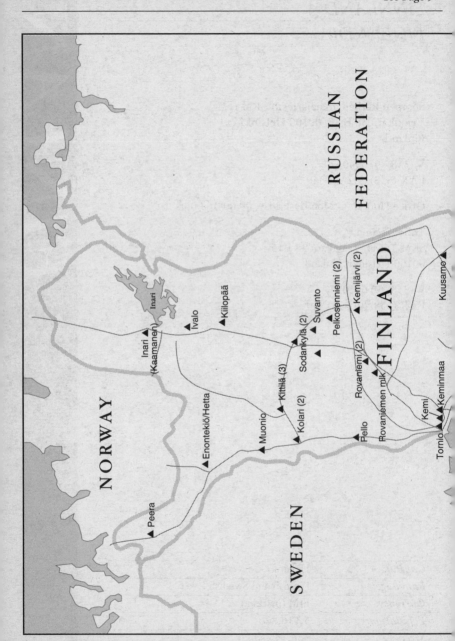

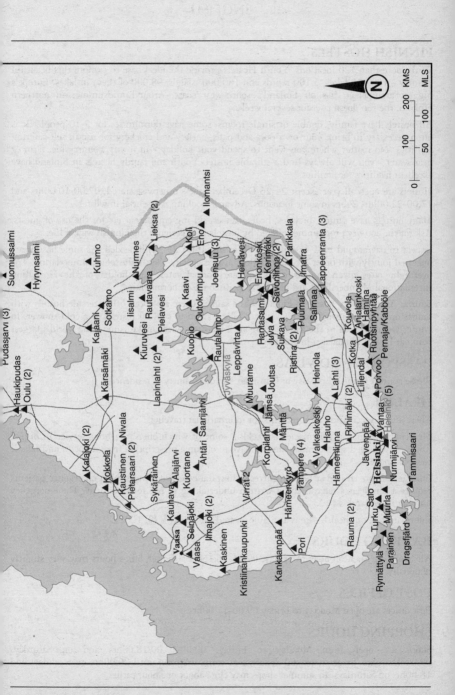

N

KMS
MLS

0   50   100   100   200

Suomussalmi
Hyrynsalmi
Kuhmo
Lieksa (2)
Nurmes
Koli
Eno
Ilomantsi
Iisalmi
Rautavaara
Joensuu (3)
Sotkamo
Kajaani
Heinävesi
Enonkoski
Kaavi
Outokumpu
Kerimäki
Kiuruvesi
Pielavesi
Savonlinna (2)
Parikkala
Rautalampi
Raņtasalmi
Imatra
Lappeenranta (3)
Lapinlahti (2)
Kuopio
Juva
Puumala
Saimaa
Kärsämäki
Rautjärvi
Sulkava
Kouvola
Pudasjärvi (3)
Leppävirta
Ristiina (2)
Anjalankoski
Haukipudas
Muurame
Jyväskylä
Heinola
Kotka
Hamina
Oulu (2)
Joutsa
Liljendal
Ruotsinpyhtää
Jämsä
Lahti (3)
Nivala
Korpilahti
Porvoo
Pernaja/Kabböle
Kalajoki (2)
Mänttä
Kokkola
Kaustinen
Valkeakoski
Riihimäki (2)
Pietarsaari (2)
Ähtäri
Saarijärvi
Hauho
Järvenpää
Sykäräinen
Kuortane
Virrat 2
Hämeenlinna
Vantaa
Alajärvi
Tampere (4)
Helsinki (5)
Kauhava
Hämeenkyrö
Nurmijärvi
Seinäjoki
Tammisaari
Vaasa
Ilmajoki (2)
Turku
Sato
Vaasa
Pori
Muurla
Kaskinen
Rauma (2)
Paraınen
Rymättylä
Kankaanpää
Dragsfjärd
Kristiinahkaupunki

$$\boxed{\text{ENGLISH}}$$

FINNISH HOSTELS

With more than 120 locations, Youth Hostels provide the ideal base to explore this beautiful country - 188,000 lakes, 5,100 rapids and 180,000 islands, 98,000 of them in lakes. Europe's biggest archipelago lies off Finland's south-west coast. Around midsummer in northern Finland, the sun doesn't set for several weeks.

All hostels have family, double or single rooms, some have dormitories for 5-10 people. It is often necessary to bring your own pots and pans, cutlery and crockery for use in self-catering facilities. No matter where you want to spend your holiday - in towns, countryside, farm or near water - you will always find a suitable hostel. Youth and family hostels in Finland have excellent facilities for families.

Hostels are open all year except 24-26 December unless otherwise stated, 07.00-10.00hrs and 17.00-22.00hrs, 24hrs in some locations. Advance booking is essential in winter.

Many hostels have saunas, bicycles, boats, canoes, ski-ing equipment etc for the use of guests. Ask for the activity programmes offered by hostels to experience the Finnish way of life.

Expect to pay around FIM 45-150 plus sheet hire (FIM 25-30) if needed. As some hostels are operated jointly with other accommodation, always specify Youth Hostel accommodation. The overnight rates given in this handbook are normal rates. The holder of the Hostelling International Membership Card gets FIM 15 discount on normal rates.

Sauna: Almost every hostel in Finland has a sauna. There are about 50 waterside hostels with saunas operated by using water - you can take a swim to cool off instead of a cold shower. In winter you can crawl in the snow. There are 11 hostels with smoke sauna - the world's largest being at Hostel Rauhalahti in Kuopio.

PASSPORTS AND VISAS

Please contact Finnish Embassy or Consulate in your country of residence.

HEALTH

There are no vaccination requirements for international travellers.

Medicines are sold at pharmacies (apteekki), some of which offer a 24-hour service in bigger towns. If you need special medicine you have to obtain a prescription from a doctor and take it to a pharmacy.

Emergencies are treated at health centres or hospital emergency units. Non-emergency patients require a physician's referral and a written undertaking to pay for treatment. The emergency number in Finland is 112.

Information about health care is available around the clock, ☏ (9) 10023.

BANKING HOURS

All banks are open Monday to Friday, 09.15-16.15hrs although office hours may vary slightly regionally.

POST OFFICES

Post offices are open Monday to Friday 09.00-17.00hrs.

SHOPPING HOURS

Shops are open from Monday to Friday, 09.00-17.00/18.00hrs and on Saturdays 09.00-15.00hrs. Some shops and department stores are open until 20.00hrs on weekdays and 18.00hrs on Saturdays. In summer shops may close about one hour earlier.

TRAVEL

Air

Finnair's network covers 50 international destinations. Finnair, Karair and Finnaviation fly to 21 destinations within Finland. There are good connections by air from Helsinki to the Baltic countries and Russia.

Rail

An excellent train network covers the whole of Finland up to Rovaniemi and Kemijärvi (Lapland), which are situated in the Arctic Circle. Ask for economical Finnrailpass! You can take your car with you by train overnight to Arctic Circle or vice versa.

There are two daily connections to St Petersburg and one night train to Moscow.

Bus

There is also an excellent coach network covering the whole of Finland. There are nearly 40,000 long distance departures daily, of which over 800 are express services.

Oy Matkahuolto Ab's 150 customer service points throughout Finland give additional information and sell tickets. Coach Holiday Tickets are available.

Ferry

The main harbours for passenger traffic are in Helsinki and Turku. There are excellent services between Sweden and Finland, as well as good connections to Tallinn in Estonia and Travemünde in Germany.

Many boats make local trips off the coast, and lake traffic is worth experiencing. Some Finnish hostels can be reached by boat.

Driving

Traffic drives on the right. Roads are well maintained all year round. Winter weather can make driving hazardous and motorists can hire snow tyres at ISKO shops. Drivers need to look out for elk and reindeer, and if you are involved in a collision with one, you should report it to local police without delay. You must carry a red warning triangle in your car to place on the road in case of a breakdown.

A driving licence is required and the nationality of foreign vehicles must be clearly marked. Headlights must be used at all times outside built-up areas. Seat belts must be worn in the front and back. Driving under the influence of alcohol or drugs carries heavy penalties. All drivers of foreign vehicles should carry a green card or arrange insurance immediately on arrival in Finland.

PUBLIC HOLIDAYS

New Year's Day, 1 January; Epiphany, 6 January; Good Friday, 28 March; Easter, 30/31 March; May Day, 1 May; Ascension Day, 8 May; Whitsun, 18 May; Midsummer Day, 21 June; All Saints Day, 1 November; Independence Day, 6 December; Christmas, 25/26 December.

There are celebrations all over Finland on May Day Eve (30 April), Midsummer's Eve (20 June) and New Year's Eve (31 December).

TELEPHONE INFORMATION

International Code	Country Code	Main City Area Codes	
00	358	Helsinki	9
		Tampere	3
		Turku	2

When dialling long distance calls within Finland dial "0" before the area code.

FRANÇAIS

AUBERGES DE JEUNESSE FINLANDAISES

Plus de 120 auberges de jeunesse vous offrent un point de départ idéal pour vous permettre d'explorer ce si beau pays - 188 000 lacs, 5 100 rapides et 180 000 îles, dont 98 000 sont situées dans des lacs. L'archipel le plus grand d'Europe se trouve au large de la côte sud-ouest de la Finlande. Au nord du pays, aux environs de la Saint-Jean, le soleil ne se couche pas pendant plusieurs semaines.

Toutes les auberges sont équipées de chambres familiales, à deux lits ou à un lit et certaines auberges ont des dortoirs pour 5 à 10 personnes. Nous vous conseillons d'apporter votre batterie de cuisine et vos assiettes et couverts si vous voulez cuisiner à l'auberge vous-même, ces articles n'étant pas souvent fournis. Où que vous souhaitiez passer vos vacances - dans les villes, à la campagne, dans une ferme ou bien au bord de l'eau - vous trouverez toujours une auberge à votre goût. Les auberges de jeunesse et les auberges familiales sont très bien équipées pour recevoir les familles.

Les auberges sont ouvertes toute l'année, sauf du 24 au 26 décembre, à moins qu'il en soit indiqué autrement, de 7h à 10h et de 17h à 22h, et jusqu'à 24h dans certains endroits. En hiver, il est nécessaire de réserver.

De nombreuses auberges offrent aux voyageurs la possibilité d'utiliser des saunas, des vélos, des bateaux, des canoës, du matériel de ski etc. Renseignez-vous sur les programmes d'activités que vous proposent nos auberges pour vous faire goûter le mode de vie finlandais.

Une nuit vous coûtera entre 45 et 150 MF, plus location de draps (25-30 MF) le cas échéant. Du fait que certaines auberges sont gérées conjointement avec d'autres types d'hébergement, n'oubliez pas de préciser à la réservation que vous souhaitez rester dans une auberge de jeunesse. Le tarif par nuit indiqué dans ce guide est le tarif normal. Le détenteur d'une carte de membre des auberges de jeunesse (Hostelling International) profite d'un rabais de 15 MF sur le tarif normal.

Saunas Presque toutes les auberges finlandaises sont équipées d'un sauna. Environ 50 d'entre elles sont implantées au bord de l'eau et disposent de saunas qui fonctionnent avec de l'eau - on peut aller nager pour se rafraîchir au lieu de prendre une douche froide. En hiver, on peut se rouler dans la neige. Il existe 11 auberges avec saunas à fumée et le plus grand du monde se trouve à l'auberge de Rauhalahti à Kuopio.

PASSEPORTS ET VISAS

Veuillez contacter l'ambassade ou le consulat finlandais de votre pays de résidence.

SOINS MEDICAUX

Aucune vaccination n'est requise pour les voyageurs internationaux.

Les médicaments sont vendus en pharmacie (apteekki). Dans les grandes villes, certaines pharmacies sont ouvertes jour et nuit. Si vous avez besoin de médicaments particuliers, il vous faudra obtenir une ordonnance chez un médecin et la présenter à un pharmacien.

Les cas urgents sont traités dans les centres médicaux ou dans les services d'urgences des hôpitaux. Les personnes requérant des soins non urgents doivent y être envoyées par un docteur et s'engager par écrit à payer le traitement. Le numéro de téléphone pour les urgences est le 112.

Des renseignements sur les soins médicaux offerts sont disponibles nuit et jour, ✆ (9) 10023.

HEURES D'OUVERTURE DES BANQUES

Toutes les banques sont ouvertes du lundi au vendredi, de 9h15 à 16h15, bien que les horaires puissent varier légèrement selon les régions.

BUREAUX DE POSTE

Les bureaux de poste sont ouverts du lundi au vendredi de 9h à 17h.

HEURES D'OUVERTURE DES MAGASINS

Les magasins sont ouverts du lundi au vendredi, de 9h à 17h/18h et le samedi de 9h à 15h. Certains magasins et grands magasins sont ouverts jusqu'à 20h en semaine et jusqu'à 18h le samedi. En été, il est possible que les magasins ferment une heure plus tôt.

DEPLACEMENTS

Air

Le réseau aérien de Finnair couvre 50 destinations internationales. Finnair, Karair et Finnaviation offrent 21 vols nationaux. De bonnes connexions aériennes existent entre Helsinki et les Etats Baltes et la Russie.

Trains

La Finlande possède un excellent réseau ferroviaire qui dessert tout le pays jusqu'aux villes de Rovaniemi et Kemijärvi (Laponie), situées dans le cercle polaire arctique. Demandez les billets économiques 'Finnrailpass'! Il est possible de transporter votre voiture sur le train de nuit vers et en provenance du cercle arctique.

Deux trains par jour partent à destination de Saint-Petersbourg et il y a un train de nuit pour Moscou.

Autobus

Toute la Finlande est également bien desservie par un excellent réseau d'autobus. Il y a presque 40 000 départs journaliers pour des voyages sur longue distance, parmi lesquels plus de 800 sont des services express.

Vous pourrez vous procurer des billets et de plus amples renseignements auprès des 150 bureaux d'information et de réclamation d'Oy Matkahuolto Ab répartis dans toute la Finlande. Des billets 'Vacances en Car' sont en vente.

Ferry-boats

Les ports d'Helsinki et de Turku sont les ports principaux accueillant les voyageurs. Il existe d'excellents services entre la Suède et la Finlande ainsi que de bonnes liaisons à destination de Tallinn en Estonie et Travemünde en Allemagne.

De nombreux bateaux assurent de petits trajets en mer et nous vous conseillons de faire l'expérience d'un voyage sur un lac. Certaines auberges finlandaises peuvent être atteintes par bateau.

Automobiles

La conduite est à droite. Les routes sont bien entretenues toute l'année. Les conditions climatiques en hiver peuvent rendre la conduite dangereuse et les automobilistes peuvent louer des pneus-neige dans les magasins Isko. Les conducteurs doivent être vigilants en ce qui concerne les élans et les rennes. Si vous entrez en collision avec l'un de ces animaux, vous devez en informer la police locale sans tarder. Vous devez avoir dans votre véhicule un triangle rouge de présignalisation et le placer sur la route en cas de panne.

Les conducteurs doivent être munis d'un permis de conduire et en ce qui concerne les étrangers, la nationalité de leur véhicule doit être clairement indiquée. Les phares doivent être allumés en tout temps en dehors des agglomérations. Le port des ceintures de sécurité à l'avant et à l'arrière est obligatoire. Les conducteurs trouvés coupables d'avoir conduit leur véhicule sous l'influence d'alcool ou de drogues seront fortement pénalisés. Tous les conducteurs de véhicules étrangers doivent être munis d'une carte verte ou prendre des dispositions pour s'assurer dès qu'ils arrivent en Finlande.

JOURS FERIES

Nouvel an, 1er janvier; Epiphanie, 6 janvier; Vendredi saint, 28 mars; Pâques, 30/31 mars; Fête du travail, 1er mai; Ascension, 8 mai; Pentecôte, 18 mai; Fête de la Saint-Jean, 21 juin; Toussaint, 1 novembre; Fête de l'Indépendance, 6 décembre; Noël, 25/26 décembre.

Il y a des célébrations dans toute la Finlande la veille de la Fête du travail (30 avril), la veille de la Saint-Jean (20 juin) et la veille du Nouvel an (31 décembre).

TELEPHONE

Indicatif International	Indicatif du Pays	Indicatifs régionaux des Villes principales
00	358	Helsinki 9
		Tampere 3
		Turku 2

Lors des appels longue distance à l'intérieur de la Finlande, composez "0" avant le code régional.

DEUTSCH

FINNISCHE JUGENDHERBERGEN

Die mehr als 120 Jugendherbergen, die es in Finnland gibt, sind ein idealer Ausgangspunkt zum Kennenlernen dieses schönen Landes mit 188.000 Seen, 5.100 Stromschnellen und 180.000 Inseln, 98.000 davon in Seen. Das größte Archipel Europas liegt vor der Südwestküste Finnlands. Um die Sommersonnenwende geht die Sonne in Nordfinnland mehrere Wochen lang nicht unter.

Alle Herbergen haben Familienräume, Doppel- und Einzelzimmer. Einige haben auch Schlafsäle für 5 bis 10 Personen. Oft müssen Selbstversorger ihre eigenen Töpfe und Pfannen und eigenes Besteck und Geschirr mitbringen. Egal, wo man Urlaub machen will - in Städten, auf dem Land, in einem Bauernhof, oder am Wasser - es gibt immer eine geeignete Jugendherberge in der Nähe. Jugend- und Familienherbergen in Finnland haben ausgezeichnete Einrichtungen für Familien.

Die Herbergen sind, außer vom 24.-26. Dezember, ganzjährig von 07.00-10.00 Uhr und von 17.00-22.00 Uhr geöffnet, sofern nichts anderes angegeben ist. An einigen Orten sind sie sogar 24 Stunden geöffnet. Im Winter ist Voranmeldung unerläßlich.

Viele Herbergen können den Gästen zur Benutzung Saunas, Fahrräder, Boote, Kanus, Skiausrüstungen usw. zur Verfügung stellen. Erkundigen Sie sich über Aktivprogramme in Jugendherbergen, wo Sie die finnische Lebensweise kennenlernen können.

Es ist mit einem Preis von ca FIM 45-150 ozuzüglich, bei Bedarf, einer Leihgebühr für die Bettlaken (FIM 25-30) zu rechnen. Da einige Herbergen gemeinsam mit anderen Unterkünften verwaltet werden, sollte immer 'Jugendherbergsunterkunft' angegeben werden. Die Übernachtungspreise in diesem Handbuch sind die normalen Preise. Besitzer einer Hostelling International-Mitgliedskarte erhalten FIM 15 Rabatt auf die normalen Preise.

Sauna: In Finnland hat fast jede Jugendherberge eine Sauna. Es gibt ungefähr 50 am Wasser gelegene Jugendherbergen mit Wassersaunas. Um sich abzukühlen kann man schwimmen gehen statt sich kalt zu duschen. Im Winter kann man sich im Schnee rollen.

Es gibt 11 Jugendherbergen, die Rauchsaunas haben. Die größte der Welt liegt in der Jugendherberge Rauhalahti in Kuopio.

PÄSSE UND VISA

Bitte erkundigen Sie sich vor der Abreise bei der finnischen Botschaft oder dem Konsulat in Ihrem Land.

GESUNDHEIT

Für international Reisende gibt es keine Impfvorschriften.

Arzneimittel werden in Apotheken (apteekki) verkauft, die in größeren Städten zum Teil 24 Stunden geöffnet sind. Zum Erhalt eines speziellen Medikamentes ist ein ärztliches Rezept erforderlich, das in einer Apotheke vorzulegen ist.

Notfälle werden in Gesundheitszentren oder im Krankenhaus in der Abteilung für Notfälle behandelt. In nicht dringenden Fällen sind eine ärztliche Überweisung und eine schriftliche Verpflichtung zur Bezahlung für die Behandlung erforderlich. Die Notruf-Nummer ist in Finnland 112.

Informationen über die Gesundheitspflege sind rund um die Uhr über ✆ (9) 10023 erhältlich.

GESCHÄFTSSTUNDEN DER BANKEN

Alle Banken sind montags bis freitags von 09.15-16.15 Uhr geöffnet. Die Geschäftsstunden können sich aber von Region zu Region etwas unterscheiden.

POSTÄMTER

Postämter sind montags bis freitags von 09.00-17.00 Uhr geöffnet.

LADENÖFFNUNGSZEITEN

Die Geschäfte sind montags bis freitags von 09.00-17.00/18.00 Uhr und samstags von 09.00-15.00 Uhr geöffnet. Einige Geschäfte und Warenhäuser sind werktags bis 20.00 Uhr und samstags bis 18.00 Uhr geöffnet. Im Sommer schließen viele Geschäfte etwa eine Stunde früher.

REISEN

Flugverkehr
Mit Finnair kann man 50 internationale Zielorte anfliegen.

Finnair, Karair und Finnaviation fliegen 21 Zielorte innerhalb Finnlands an.

Es gibt auch gute Flugverbindungen von Helsinki nach den Ostseeländern und nach Rußland.

Eisenbahn
Über ganz Finnland bis hinauf nach Rovaniemi und Kemijärvi (Lappland) im Nördlichen Polarkreis erstreckt sich ein ausgezeichnetes Schienennetz.

Fragen Sie nach dem preisgünstigen Finnrailpass. Sie können Ihr Auto über Nacht auf dem Zug zum Polarkreis oder auf der Rückreise mitnehmen.

Täglich fahren zwei Züge nach St Petersburg, nach Moskau gibt es einen Nachtzug.

Busse
Es gibt auch ein ausgezeichnetes Busnetz, das sich über ganz Finnland erstreckt. Täglich verkehren nahezu 40.000 Fernverkehrsbusse, wovon mehr als 800 Expreßbusse sind.

In ganz Finnland gibt es 150 Servicestellen von Oy Matkahuolto Ab, die weitere Auskunft erteilen und Fahrkarten verkaufen. Fahrkarten für Ferienreisen mit dem Bus sind auch zum Verkauf.

Fährboote
Die Haupthäfen für den Passagierverkehr befinden sich in Helsinki und Turku. Zwischen Schweden und Finnland gibt es ausgezeichnete Verbindungen, sowie gute Verbindungen nach Tallinn in Estland und Travemünde in Deutschland.

Von der Küste aus fahren viele Schiffe in die nähere Umgebung, und auch auf den Seen werden lohnenswerte Schiffsreisen angeboten. Einige finnische Herbergen können mit dem Schiff erreicht werden.

Autofahren

Es herrscht Rechtsverkehr. Die Straßen werden das ganze Jahr über gut instandgehalten. Im Winter kann das Autofahren wegen des Wetters gefährlich sein. Autofahrer können jedoch in ISKO-Läden Schneereifen mieten. Für den Fall einer Panne, muß man ein rotes Dreieck auf die Straße gestellt werden.

Die Fahrer müssen auf Elche und Rentiere achten. Wenn ein solches Tier angefahren wird, ist der Unfall unverzüglich der örtlichen Polizei zu melden.

Man braucht einen Führerschein, und bei ausländischen Fahrzeugen muß deutlich sichtbar sein, aus welchem Land Sie kommen. Außerhalb geschlossener Ortschaften müssen immer die Scheinwerfer eingeschaltet sein. Sowohl vorne als auch hinten müssen Sicherheitsgurte getragen werden. Das Lenken eines Fahrzeugs unter unter Alkohol- und Drogeneinfluß wird schwer bestraft. Alle Fahrer eines ausländischen Fahrzeugs sollten eine grüne Karte mit sich führen oder sofort nach der Ankunft in Finnland eine Versicherung abschließen.

FEIERTAGE

Neujahr, 1. Januar; Erscheinungsfest, 6. Januar; Karfreitag, 28. März; Ostern, 30./31. März; Maitag, 1. Mai; Himmelfahrt, 8. Mai; Pfingsten, 18. Mai; Sommersonnwendfest, 21. Juni; Allerheiligen, 1. November; Unabhängigkeitstag, 6. Dezember; Weihnachten, 25./26. Dezember.

Am Vorabend des Maitags (30. April), am Vorabend der Sommersonnenwende (20. Juni) und an Silvester (31. Dezember) wird in ganz Finnland gefeiert.

FERNSPRECHINFORMATIONEN

Internationale Kennzahl	Landes- Kennzahl	größere Städte - Ortsnetzkennzahlen
00	358	Helsinki 9
		Tampere 3
		Turku 2

Für Ferngespräche innerhalb Finnlands ist vor der Ortsvorwahl eine "0" zu wählen.

ESPAÑOL

ALBERGUES DE JUVENTUD FINLANDESES

Con más de 120 centros, los albergues de juventud son la base ideal para explorar este hermoso país: 188.000 lagos, 5.100 rápidos y 180.000 islas, 98.000 de las cuales están en lagos. El mayor archipiélago de Europa está en la costa suroeste de Finlandia. En el norte de Finlandia, hacia el día de San Juan, el sol no se pone durante varias semanas.

Todos los albergues tienen habitaciones familiares, individuales o dobles, algunos tienen dormitorios para 5-10 personas. A menudo es necesario llevarse los cacharros, cubiertos y platos para la cocina. Dondequiera que pase sus vacaciones, ya sea en la ciudad, en el campo, o en una granja o cerca del mar, siempre encontrará un albergue juvenil según sus necesidades. Los albergues de juventud y los albergues familiares en Finlandia ofrecen excelentes instalaciones para las familias.

Si no se indica otra cosa, los albergues estarán abiertos todo el año excepto del 24 al 26 de diciembre, de 07.00 a 10.00 horas y de 17.00 a 22.00 horas, y las 24 horas en algunos lugares. En invierno es esencial reservar con antelación.

Muchos albergues tienen saunas, bicicletas, barcas, canoas, artículos de esquí, etc. para sus huéspedes. Infórmese sobre los programas de actividades que ofrecen los albergues juveniles para conocer el modo de vivir finlandés.

Tendrá que pagar unos FIM 45-150, más el alquiler de las sábanas (FIM 25-30). A la hora de reservar, indique claramente que quiere alojarse en un albergue, ya que funcionan conjuntamente con otros tipos de alojamiento. Las tarifas por noche indicadas en este manual son las normales. Los titulares de la tarjeta de afiliación a Hostelling International reciben un descuento de FIM 15 sobre las tarifas normales.

Sauna: Casi todos los albergues finlandeses tienen sauna. Existen unos 50 albergues ribereños con saunas que funcionan con agua - usted puede nadar para referescarse en vez de darse una ducha fría. En invierno, usted puede revolcarse en la nieve. Existen 11 albergues con saunas que funcionan con humo. La más grande del mundo se encuentra en el Albergue Rauhalahti en Kuopio.

PASAPORTES Y VISADOS

Rogamos ponerse en contacto con la Embajada o Consulado finlandeses en su proprio país.

SANIDAD

No se exige ninguna vacuna a los viajeros internacionales.

Los medicamentos se venden en farmacias (apteekki), algunas de las cuales ofrecen un servicio ininterrumpido de 24 horas en las poblaciones más grandes. Si necesita algún medicamento especial, debe obtener una receta médica y presentarla en la farmacia.

Las emergencias se tratan en centros de salud o en unidades de urgencia hospitalaria. Los pacientes que no sean de urgencia tienen que ir enviados por un médico y firmar una garantía de pago del tratamiento. El número de emergencias en Finlandia es el 112.

La información de cuidados médicos funciona ininterrumpidamente, ☎ (9) 10023.

HORARIO DE BANCOS

Todos los bancos abren de lunes a viernes de 09.15 a 16.15 horas, aunque las horas de oficina pueden variar ligeramente según las regiones.

CASAS DE CORREO

Las casas de correo abren de lunes a viernes de 09.00 a 17.00 horas.

HORARIO COMERCIAL

Las tiendas abren de lunes a viernes de 09.00 a 17.00 o 18.00 horas y los sábados de 09.00 a 15.00 horas. Algunas tiendas y grandes almacenes permanecen abiertos hasta las 20.00 horas entre semana y hasta las 18.00 horas los sábados. En verano las tiendas pueden cerrar una hora antes.

DESPLAZAMIENTOS

Avión
La red aérea de Finnair cubre 50 rutas internacionales. Finnair, Karair y Finnaviation ofrecen un servicio aéreo que cubre 21 rutas nacionales en el país. Hay buenos enlaces aéreos de Helsinki a los países bálticos y Rusia.

Tren
Existe una red ferroviaria excelente que recorre Finlandia por completo, hasta Rovaniemi y Kemijärvi (Laponia), ya en el círculo polar ártico. ¡Solicite el billete económico especial Finnrailpass! Puede llevar su coche consigo en tren en viaje nocturno de ida o de regreso del círculo polar ártico.

Hay dos enlaces diarios a San Petersburgo y un tren nocturno a Moscú.

Autobús
También es excelente la red de autocares, que cubre Finlandia por completo. Hay casi 40.000 viajes diarios de largo recorrido, de los que 800 son servicios directos.

Las 310 oficinas de información y reclamaciones de Oy Matkahuolto Ab, repartidas por toda Finlandia, dan información adicional y venden billetes. Se pueden conseguir billetes de "vacaciones en autocar".

Ferry
Los principales puertos para el transporte de pasajeros están en Helsinki y Turku. Hay servicios excelentes entre Suecia y Finlandia, así como salidas a Tallinn en Estonia y Travemünde en Alemania.

Muchos barcos realizan recorridos cortos bordeando la costa y merece la pena ver el tráfico de los lagos. A algunos albergues finlandeses puede llegarse en barco.

Coche
El tráfico circula por la derecha. Las carreteras se mantienen bien todo el año. El tiempo en el invierno puede hacer que conducir sea peligroso y los conductores pueden alquilar neumáticos para la nieve en las tiendas ISKO. Hay que tener cuidado con los alces y los renos, y si atropellas uno tendrás que avisar inmediatamente a la policía. Se debe llevar en el coche el triángulo rojo como señal de advertencia en caso de avería.

Hace falta permiso de conducir, y la nacionalidad de los vehículos extranjeros debe estar claramente indicada. Las luces largas se usan en todo tiempo fuera de las zonas edificadas. Es obligatorio el uso de cinturones de seguridad tanto delante como detrás. Conducir bajo los efectos del alcohol o de drogas acarrea fuertes multas. Los conductores de vehículos extranjeros deben tener una carta verde o concertar un seguro nada más llegar a Finlandia.

DIAS FESTIVOS

Año Nuevo, 1 enero; Reyes (Epifanía), 6 enero; Viernes Santo, 28 marzo; Pascua, 30 y 31 marzo; Fiesta de Mayo, 1 mayo; Ascensión, 8 mayo; Pentecostés, 18 mayo; Solsticio de Verano, 21 junio; Día de Todos los Santos, 1 noviembre; Día de la Independencia, 6 diciembre; Navidad 25 y 26 diciembre.

En toda Finlandia hay celebraciones las vísperas del Día del Trabajo (30 abril), del Solsticio de Verano (20 junio) y en Nochevieja (31 diciembre).

INFORMACION TELEFONICA

Código Internacional	Código Nacional	Indicativo de área de las Ciudades principales
00	358	Helsinki 9
		Tampere 3
		Turku 2

Al efectuar conferencias dentro de Finlandia, marque un "0" antes del código de zona.

DISCOUNTS AND CONCESSIONS

Your Hostelling International membership entitles you to a wide range of discounts in Finland, including reduced admissions to attractions near hostels, reduced equipment hire and travel. "Go-as-You-Please" packages combining transport with hostel overnights are available from SRM Travel, and can represent good value. In addition the following national discounts apply:

Europcar Interrent: 10% discount on car hire in Finland. **Agencies:** Helsinki, Hyvinkää, Hämeenlinna, Ivalo, Joensuu, Jyväskylä, Kajaani, Kemi, Kittilä, Kokkola, Kotka, Kouvola, Kuopio, Kuusamo, Lahti, Lappeenranta, Oulu, Pori, Rovaniemi, Salo, Savonlinna, Seinäjoki, Tampere, Tornio, Turku, Vaasa, Vantaa and Varkaus.

Finnish Passenger Ship Association: 10% discount on most lake routes.

Transwell 15% discount on car hire - **Agencies:** Helsinki, Hämeenlinna, Jyväskylä, Järvenpää, Kerava, Kuopio, Lahti, Oulu, Rovaniemi, Salo, Tampere and Turku. St Petersburg in Russia.

Take Off: 5-20% reduction on mountain bikes, windsurfing, skis, snowboards, clothes and equipment (Nervanderinkatu 11, 00100 Helsinki, ☎ (9) 441739).

Eestin Linjat: 10% discount on regular traffic (not cruises) Helsinki-Tallinn (Estonia)-Helsinki. Tickets: Eestin Linjat, Keskuskatu 1, Helsinki, ☎ (9) 228 8544

Special discount on train ticket from Helsinki to St. Petersburg. Ticket available only at Eurohostel, Linnankatu 9, Helsinki.

Hostels in this country may also display this symbol.

Les auberges de ce pays pourront également afficher ce symbole.

Jugendherbergen in diesem Land können auch dieses Symbol zeigen.

Es posible que los albergues de este país exhiban además este símbolo.

Ähtäri Hostel Oulu Vesi, Koulutie 16, 63700 Ähtäri. ☎ (6) 5337482 **FAX** (6) 5337479 **Open:** 18.00-10.00hrs ⊭ 60; Wi 8 ● FIM 70-90 ♂ ♦♦♦ 🅿 ♿ 🍴 Ähtäri 600m 🚌 200m

Alajärvi 6W Hostel Kuusiniemi, Heikinkankaantie 44, 62710 Kurejoki. ☎ (6) 5574542 **Open:** 09.00-21.00hrs ⊭ 50 ● FIM 60 🍴(B) ♂ ♦♦♦ 🅿 ♿ ✈ Vaasa 120km ⛴ Vaasa 130km 🍴 Seinäjoki 70km 🚌 300m

Alvettula ☞ **Hauho**

Anjalankoski Rauhala, Itäasemantie 17, 46800 Myllykoski. ☎ (5) 3656061 ⊭ 15 ● FIM 60-80 🍴(B) ♂ ♦♦♦ 🍴 Myllykoski 100m 🚌 400m

Dragsfjärd Dragsfjärds vandrarhotell, Kulla, 25870 Dragsfjärd. ☎ (2) 424553 **FAX** (2) 424553 **Open:**

09.00-21.00hrs, 15.3-31.12 ⊭ 39 ● FIM 70-120 🍴 ♂ ♦♦♦ ① ⚒ 🅿 ♿ ▲ 🍴 Perniö 55km 🚌 100m ap Dragsfjärds Pensionat

Ekenäs ☞ **Tammisaari**

Eno Jokipirtin Majatalo, Uimaharjuntie 751, 81270 Paukkaja. ☎ (13) 774607 **FAX** (13) 774607 **Open:** 24hrs, 1.5-30.10 ⊭ 38 ● FIM 60-90 🍴 ♂ ♦♦♦ 🅿 ♿ ▲ 🍴 Uimarju 5km 🚌 500m ap Paukkajan kauppa

Enonkoski Kievari Enonhovi, Urheilukentäntie 1, 58175 Enonkoski. ☎ (15) 479431 **FAX** (15) 479435 **Open:** 24hrs ⊭ 22 ● FIM 100-160 sheets inc. 🍴 ♦♦♦ 🅿 ✈ Savonlinna 19km 🍴 Savonlinna 33km 🚌 Enonkoski 100m

Enontekiö ☞ **Hetta, Peera**

Hämeenkyrö 15E Finnhostel Pinsiön Majat, Sasintie 400, 39150 Pinsiö. ☎ (3) 3406191 **Open:** 08.00-18.00hrs, 1.3-15.12 ⊠ 29 ● FIM 110-160, Dorm FIM 50 (sheets inc for small rooms). ⬚◎(B) ☞ ⅲ 🖫 ⌨ 🅿 ⚲ ⚓ ₩ Tampere 22km ₩ 100m ap Pinsiön Majat

Hämeenlinna 2S Hostel Hattelmala, Hattelmala- Keskus, Rakennus C1, 13100 Hämeenlinna. ☎ (3) 6166564 **FAX** (3) 6166574 ⊠ 55 ● FIM 90-150 ◎(B) ☞ ⅲ 🖫 ⌨ 🅿 ✈ Tampere 75km ₩ Hämeenlinna 3.5km ₩ 50m ap Hattelmala- Keskus

Hamina Summer hostel Anna, Annankatu 1, 49400 Hamina. ☎ (5) 3447747 **FAX** (5) 3447747 **Open:** 1.6-15.8 ⊠ 96 ● FIM 125-150 sheets inc. ᴮᴮ ⁱⁿᶜ ☞ ⅲ ⌨ 🅿 ✈ Helsinki 130km ₩ Kotka 25km ₩ 30m ap Alakaupunki

Hattuvaara ☞ **Lieksa (Loma-Kitsi)**

Hauho 6W Hostel Miekka, Häränvattantie 67, 14680 Alvettula. ☎ (3) 6545122 **FAX** (3) 6545321 **Open:** 08.00-20.00hrs, 15.5-31.8 ⊠ 43 ● FIM 160 Sheets Inc. ᴮᴮ ⁱⁿᶜ ⅲ 🏠 🅿 ⚲ ⚓ ✈ Tampere 60km ⛴ Alvettula 2km ₩ Hämeenlinna 30km ₩ 1km ap YH

Haukipudas 12SW Finnhostel Virpiniemi, Hiihtomajantie 27, 90820 Kello ☎ (8) 5401222, 5401945 **FAX** (8) 5401945 **Open:** 08.30-16.00hrs (08.30-21.00hrs, 1.6-31.8) ⊠ 101 ● FIM 60-75 ◎ ☞ ⅲ ⚅ ⌨ 🅿 ⚲ ✈ Oulu 38km ₩ Oulu 25km ₩ 5km ap Virpiniemen tienhaara ● (☎ for pick-up from ₩ ap)

Heinävesi 18S Pohjataipaleen kartan, Pyylintie 8, 79700 Heinävesi. ☎ (17) 566419 ⊠ 20 ● FIM 65-75 ◎(B L) ☞ ⅲ 🅿 ⚓ ⛴ Pohjataival 150m ₩ Heinävesi 12km ₩ 18km

Heinola 1.2N Finnhostel Heinola, Opintie 3, 18200 Heinola. ☎ (3) 141655 **FAX** (3) 8475211 **Open:** 07.00-23.30hrs, 1.6-7.8 ⊠ 80 ● FIM 70 ◎(B) ☞ ⅲ ⌨ 🅿 ✈ Helsinki 130km ₩ Lahti 30km ₩ 1.2km

HELSINKI (6 Hostels)
(see town plan on next page)

Helsinki - Eurohostel 2SE IBN CC Linnankatu 9, 00160 Helsinki. ☎ (9) 6220470 FAX (9) 655044 Open: 24hrs ⊠ 255 ● FIM 115-175 sheets inc. ◎ ☞ ⅲ 🖫 ✈ Helsinki-Vantaa 20km ⛴ 500m ₩ Helsinki 2km ₩ 2km ₩ 4 100m ap Eurohostel

Helsinki - Stadion 2N Stadion Hostel, Pohj Stadiontie 3 B, 00250 Helsinki. ☎ (9) 496071 **FAX** (9) 496466 **Open:** 08.00-02.00hrs (08.00-10.00hrs, 16.00-02.00hrs, 15.9-15.6) ⊠ 164 ● FIM 70-140 (26.4-11.5 FIM 85-155) ◎ ☞ ⅲ 🏠 🖫 ⌨ 🅿 ✈ Helsinki-Vantaa 18km A ₩ Finnair ₩ Helsinki 2km ₩ 3B, 7 500m

Helsinki - Vantaa 15N CC Vantaan retkeilymaja, Tikkurilan Urheilupuisto, Valkoisen-lähteentie 52, 01300 Vantaa. ☎ (9) 8393310 **FAX** (9) 8394366 ⊠ 21 ● FIM 55-125 ◎(B) ☞ ⅲ 🅿 ✈ Helsinki- Vantaa 4km ₩ Tikkurila 1km ₩ 50m

Helsinki - Academica 1W CC Hostel Academica, Hietaniemenkatu 14, 00100 Helsinki. ☎ (9) 4020206 **FAX** (9) 441201 **Open:** 24hrs, 1.6-1.9 ⊠ 66 ● FIM 90-115 ◎ ☞ ⅲ 🖫 ⌨ 🅿 ✈ Helsinki- Vantaa 18km ₩ Helsinki 700m ₩ 50m

Helsinki - Satakuntalo 1SW CC Lapinrinne 1A, 00180 Helsinki. ☎ (9) 695851 **FAX** (9) 6942226 **Open:** 24hrs, 29.5-1.9 ⊠ 55 ● FIM 70-185 ◎ ⅲ 🖫 🅿 ✈ Helsinki-Vantaa 18km

🚻 Helsinki 500m 🚌 50m Ⓤ
Kamppi 200m

Helsinki - **Erottajanpuisto** ⏚ Hostel
Erottajanpuisto, Uudenmaankatu 9,
00120 Helsinki. 📞 (9) 642169 **FAX** (9)
6802757 **Open:** 24hrs ⊯ 54 ● FIM
130-200 sheets inc. 🍽(B) 👬 ✈
Helsinki 24km 🛥 Helsinki 1km 🚻
Helsinki 800m 🚋 10

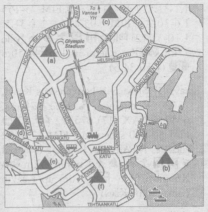

HELSINKI - (a) Stadion, (b) Eurohostel,
(c) Vantaa, (d) Academica,
(e) Satakuntatalo, (f) Erottajanpuisto

Hetta ⏚ Finnhostel Hetta, 99400
Enontekiö. 📞 (16) 521361 **FAX** (16)
521049 **Open:** 24hrs, 15.2-2.5;
1.6-20.9 ⊯ 39 ● FIM 85-160 sheets
inc. 🍽 👬 🅿 ⚲ ♿ ⚓ 🚻 Kolari
170km 🚌 50m

Hyrynsalmi Hostel Iston koulu Koskitie
2, 89400 Hyrynsalmi. 📞 (8) 741711,
741722 **FAX** (8) 742086 **Open:**
15.00-22.00hrs, 26.6-31.7 ⊯ 32 ✆ 👬
🗐 🅿 🚻 Kontiomaki 50km 🚌 100m
ap 5-tie Ⓡ

Iisalmi Iisalmen NMKY:n hostel,
Sarvikatu 4C, 74120 Iisalmi. 📞 (17)
23940 **FAX** (17) 23940 **Open:**
08.00-12.00hrs, 17.00-23.00hrs,
1.6-31.7 ⊯ 46 ● FIM 100, peak
seasons (when festivals) FIM 150 🍽(B)
✆ 👬 🗐 🅿 ♿ ✈ Kuopio 70km 🚻
Iisalmi 1km 🚌 100m

ILMAJOKI (2 Hostels)

Ilmajoki - **Viitala** 10W Hostel Viitala,
Ristimäentie 207, 61350 Huissi. 📞 (6)
4227657 **Open:** 1.6-31.8 ⊯ 16 ● FIM
75 🍽(B) ✆ 👬 🅿 ♿ ✈ Seinäjoki 25km
🚻 Seinäjoki 25km 🚌 2km

Ilmajoki - **Palonkortteeri** ⏚ Hostel
Palonkortteeri, Kauppatie 26, 60800
Ilmajoki. 📞 (6) 4240000 **FAX** (6)
4240057 **Open:** 09.00-24.00hrs ⊯
160 ● FIM 135-205 sheets inc. 🍽 👬
✈ Seinäjoki 25km 🚻 Seinäjoki 16km
🚌 Station 500m

Ilomantsi 7E Finnhostel Haapakallio,
Varisvaarantie 8, 82900 Ilomantsi. 📞
(13) 843107 **FAX** (13) 844199 **Open:**
16.00-21.00hrs, 1.6-31.8 ⊯ 29 ●
FIM 55-150 🍽(B) ✆ 👬 🅿 ✈ Joensuu
95km 🚻 Joensuu 80km 🚌 2km
ap Kuuksenvaara

Imatra 3SE Ukonlinna, Leiritie, 55420
Imatra. 📞 (5) 4321270 **Open:**
09.00-22.00hrs, 1.5-30.9; 10.00-18.00hrs,
1.10-30.4 ⊯ 20 ✆ 👬 🅿 ⚲ ♿ ⚓ ✈
Lappeenranta 40km 🚻 3km 🚌
500m ap Imatra Kylpylä

Inari ☞ **Ivalo, Kaamanen, Kiilopää**

Ivalo Motelli Petsamo, Petsamontie 16,
99800 Ivalo 📞 (16) 661106, 661621
FAX (16) 661628 ⊯ 54 ● FIM
55-115, FIM 95-165 sheets inc. 🍽 ✆
👬 ♿ 🗐 ✈ Ivalo 10km 🚻 Rovaniemi
300km 🚌 200m

Jämsä 7S Ratsastuskievari (Riding-
hostel), Lopeistontie 75, 42100 Jämsä.
📞 (14) 762388 **FAX** (14) 762389 ⊯
30 ● FIM 60-80 🍽(B) (Advance
booking essential) 👬 🎠 🅿 ✈ Jyväskla
85km 🚻 Jämsä 7km 🚌 100m
ap Olkkolan koulu

Järvenpää 25S ⏚ Hostel,
Stålhanentie, 04400 Järvenpää. 📞 (9)
287775 **FAX** (9) 2911441 **Open:**
08.00-23.00hrs, (Wi 09.00-19.00hrs)

◪ 23 ● FIM 43-85 ⚹|ᗺ⦿| (Advance booking essential) ♂ (Su) ⅲⅲ 🅿 ⚓ ⬢ ✈ Helsinki- Vantaa 20km 🚾 Järvenpää 3km 🚋 50m ap Terveyskeskus

JOENSUU (3 Hostels)

Joensuu - **Joensuun Elli** ⌷CC⌷ Kesähotelli Joensuun Elli, Länsikatu 18, 80110 Joensuu. ☎ (13) 225927 **FAX** (13) 225763 **Open:** 08.00-16.00hrs, 15.5-31.5; 24hrs, 1.6-24.8 ◪ 53 ● FIM 80-90, FIM 135-200 sheets inc. ⚹|ᗺ⦿|(B) ♂ ⅲⅲ 🔲 🏛 🅿 🚲 ✈ Joensuu 8km 🚾 Joensuu 2km 🚋 500m

Joensuu - **Partiotalo** ⌷1S⌷ Vanamokatu 25, 80130 Joensuu. ☎ (13) 123381 **Open:** 08.00-12.00hrs, 16.00-22.00hrs, 1.6-31.8 ◪ 44 ● FIM 53-75 ♂ ⅲⅲ 🅿 ✈ Joensuu 8km 🚾 Joensuu 2km 🚋 500m

Joensuu - ⌷0.5W⌷ Finnhostel Joensuu, Itä-Suomen Liikuntaopisto, Kalevankatu 8, 80110 Joensuu. ☎ (13) 2675076, 2675077 **FAX** (13) 2675075 **Open:** 08.00-20.00hrs, 1.1-31.5; 1.9-31.12, (08.00-21.00hrs, 1.6-31.8) ◪ 72 ● FIM 115-190 sheet inc. (1.1-31.5) FIM 130 from 1.6 ⚹|ᗺ⦿| ♂ ⅲⅲ 🅿 ⚓ ⬢ ✈ Joensuu 12km 🚾 Joensuu 2km 🚋 600m ap Koskikadun linja-autoasema

Joutsa ⌷16NW⌷ Vaihelan tila, Vaihelantie 24, 19920 Pappinen. ☎ (14) 889107 **FAX** (14) 889197 **Open:** 07.00-22.00hrs ◪ 14 ● FIM 65-130 ⚹|ᗺ⦿| (Advance booking essential) ♂ ⅲⅲ 🅿 ⚓ 🚲 ⬢ ✈ Jyväskylä 90km 🚾 Jyväskylä 65km 🚋 1km ap Pappinen

Juva ⌷9SE⌷ Hostel Toivio, Toivio, 51900 Juva. ☎ (15) 459622 **FAX** (15) 459605 ◪ 25 ● FIM 75-85, FIM 140-180 sheets inc. ⚹|ᗺ⦿|(B) ♂ ⅲⅲ 🅿 ⚓ 🚾 Mikkeli 50km 🚋 50m ap Toivio

Jyväskylä ⌷4W⌷ ⌷IBN⌷ ⌷CC⌷ Finnhostel Laajari, Laajavuorentie 15, 40740

Jyväskylä. ☎ (14) 253355 **FAX** (14) 253355 Open: 07.00-03.00hrs ◪ 109 ● FIM 80 sheets inc. (FIM 115-160 sheets inc.) ⌷BB⌷ⁱⁿᶜ ⚹|ᗺ⦿| ♂ ⅲⅲ 🔲 🏛 🅿 ⚓ ✈ Jyväskylä 20km 🚾 Jyväskylä 4km 🚋 200m

Kaamanen ⌷1.5S⌷ Hostel Jokitörmä, 99910 Kaamanen. ☎ (16) 672725 **FAX** (16) 672745 ◪ 50 1.6-30.9 (8 1.1-31.5; 1.10-31.12) ● FIM 75-155 1.6-30.9 (FIM 95-155 1.1-31.5; 1.10-31.12) ⚹|ᗺ⦿|(B) ⅲⅲ 🅿 ⚓ ⬢ ✈ Ivalo 77km 🚾 Rovaniemi 367km 🚋 50m Ⓡ (1.10-31.5)

Kaavi ⌷17NE⌷ Kaavin Lomakeskus Kaavi, 73620 Kortteinen. ☎ (17) 675333, 675216 **FAX** (17) 675222 ◪ 60 ● FIM 85-130 sheets inc; FIM 120-402 cottages ⚹|ᗺ⦿| Advance booking essential ♂ ⅲⅲ 🅿 ⚓ 🚲 ⬢ ✈ Kuopio 55km 🚾 Kuopio 70km 🚋 50m ap Kaavin Lomakeskus Kaavi

Kabböle ☞ Pernaja

Kajaani ⌷0.6SE⌷ ⌷CC⌷ Hostel Huone ja Aamiainen, Pohjolankatu 4, 87100 Kajaani. ☎ (8) 622254 **FAX** (8) 622254 **Open:** 24.00-12.00hrs, 16.00-24.00hrs; (Sat, Sun 24.00-12.00hrs, 18.00-24.00hrs) ◪ 48 ● FIM 75-145 sheets inc. ⌷BB⌷ⁱⁿᶜ ⅲⅲ 🏛 ✈ Kajaani 7km 🚾 Kajaani 200m 🚋 600m ap 🚋 Station

KALAJOKI (2 Hostels)

Kalajoki - **Tapion Tupa** Finnhostel Tapion Tupa, Hiekkasärkät, 85100 Kalajoki. ☎ (8) 466622 **FAX** (8) 466699 ◪ 36 ● FIM 100-220 sheets inc. ⌷BB⌷ⁱⁿᶜ ⚹|ᗺ⦿| ♂ ⅲⅲ ♿ 🚆 🏛 🅿 ⚓ 🚲 ✈ Kruunupyy 80km 🚾 Kokkola 60km 🚋 50m ap Tapion Tupa

Kalajoki - **Kaju** Hostel Kaju, Opintie 1, 85100 Kalajoki. ☎ (8) 462933 **FAX** (8) 462319 **Open:** 08.00-12.00hrs, 17.00-23.00hrs, 15.6-31.7 ◪ 80 ● FIM 80 ♂ ⅲⅲ 🅿 ✈ Kruunupyy 80km

Ylivieska 39km 100m ap Shell-Simpukka

Kankaanpää Finnhostel Kankaanpää, Neuvoksenkatu 2, 38700 Kankaanpää. (2) 5722299 **Open:** 08.00-17.00hrs, 1.6-8.8 35 FIM 75-100 Pori 50km Parkano 40km 1km

Kärsämäki Hostel Suomela, 86710 Kärsämäki. (8) 771455 **Open:** 08.00-10.00hrs, 17.00-22.00hrs, 1.6-15.8 10 FIM 75-100 (B) Haapamäki 35km 200m

Kaskinen Björnträ vandrarhem, Raatihuoneenkatu 22, 64260 Kaskinen. (6) 2227007 **FAX** (6) 2227007 **Open:** 1.6-5.8 15 FIM 85-95 Seinajoki 110km Seinäjoki 110km 400m

Kauhava Tuppiroska, Yrittäjäopisto, Kauppatie 109, 62200 Kauhava. (6) 4315350 **FAX** (6) 4342240 **Open:** 07.30-23.30hrs (Fri, Sat 07.30-01.00hrs), 1.6-14.8 200 sheets inc. Seinäjoki 40km Kauhava 1km 50m

Kaustinen - **Koskelan Lomatalo** Finnhostel Koskelan Lomatalo, Känsäläntie 123, 69600 Kaustinen. (6) 8611338 **Open:** 08.00-22.00hrs 31 FIM 70-95 Kokkola 45km Kokkola 45km 1km

Kemi Hostel Turisti, Valtakatu 39, 94100 Kemi (16) 250876 **Open:** 24hrs 32 FIM 90-120 sheets inc. Kemi-Tornio 5km Kemi 200m 50m ap Kaupungintalon Pysäkki

KEMIJÄRVI (2 Hostels)

Kemijärvi - **Matkatupa** 26S A725 Ulkuniemi PL, 98100 Kemijärvi. (16) 888517 **Open:** 24hrs, 1.5-31.10

76 FIM 65-170 Advance booking essential Rovaniemi 80km Kemijärvi 27km 100m ap Ulkuniemi

Kemijärvi - **Kemijärvi** 0.3W Hostel Kemijärvi, Lohelankatu 1, 98100 Kemijärvi. (16) 813253, 813341 **FAX** (16) 813342 **Open:** 24hrs 100 FIM 85-150 Rovaniemi 80km Kemijärvi 1km 300m ap Station

Keminmaa Kapernaumin Lomakylä, Heimarintie 90, 94500 Lautiosaari. (16) 288166 **FAX** (16) 288166 **Open:** 24hrs 30 FIM 85-350 Kemi 14km Kemi 20km

Kerimäki Korkeamäen Majatalo, Ruokolahdentie 545, 58200 Kerimäki. (15) 442186, 544827 **Open:** 08.00-11.00hrs, 17.00-22.00hrs, 1.6-31.8 49 FIM 60-200 (B) Savonlinna 30km Retretti 9km 6km ap Kerimäki

Kiilopää CC Hostel Ahopää, Tunturikeskus Kiilopää, 99830 Saariselkä (16) 667101 **FAX** (16) 667121 **Open:** 09.00-17.00hrs (08.00-22.00hrs peak season) 36 FIM 80-150 sheets inc. Ivalo 40km Rovaniemi 280km 50m ap Kiilopää

Kilpisjärvi Peera

KITTILÄ (3 Hostels)

Kittilä CC Hostel Kittilä, Valtatie 220, 99100 Kittilä (16) 642002 **FAX** (16) 642016 **Open:** 08.00-11.00hrs, 16.00-22.00hrs, 1.6-17.8 **Shut:** (Wi only grps) 48 FIM 75 Kittilä 5km Rovaniemi 160km 50m

Kittilä - **Hostel Majari** Valtatie 5, 99100 Kittilä. (16) 648508 **Open:**

07.00-10.00hrs,   17.00-23.00hrs, 10.6-5.8 ⚐ 65 ⊜ FIM 60-90 ⦿(B) ♂ ♟ ⚒ P ✈ Kittilä 5km ⛟ Kolari 80km ⛆ 100m

Kittilä - Sillankorva Hostel Sillankorva, 99140 Köngäs. ☎ (16) 653428 **Open:** 07.00-10.00hrs, 16.00-22.00hrs ⚐ 15 ⊜ FIM 115 sheets inc. BBinc ♂ ♟ P ⚲ ⊿ ✈ Kittilä 22km ⛟ Kolari 100km ⛆ 50m ap Köngäs

Kiuruvesi, Matkamaja Kiurusoppi Museokatu 17, 74700 Kiuruvesi. ☎ (17) 754444 **FAX** (17) 753286 **Open:** 07.00-10.00hrs,   16.00-23.00hrs, 1.6-10.8 ⚐ 32 ⊜ FIM 75 ♂ ♟ ▣ P ⛟ Kiuruvesi 700m ⛆ 500m ap Station

Kokkola ⟦2.5N⟧ Hostel Tankkari, Vanhansatamanlahti, 67100 Kokkola. ☎ (6) 8314006, (Wi) 8311902 **FAX** (6) 8310306   **Open:**   07.00-24.00hrs, 1.6-31.8 ⚐ 23 ⊜ FIM 85-100 ⦿(B) ♂ ♟ ⚒ P ⚲ ⊿ ✈ Kruunupyy 22km ⛟ Kokkola 2.5km ⛆ 2.5km ap Station

KOLARI (2 Hostels)

Kolari - **Vaattovaara** ⟦0.7S⟧ Vaattovaaran retkeilymaja, KP2, 95900 Kolari. ☎ (16) 561086 Open: 24hrs ⚐ 12 ⊜ FIM 70-100 ⦿(B) ♂ ♟ ▣ P ⚲ ✈ Kittilä 80km ⛟ Kolari 5km ⛆ 200m

Kolari - **Lappean Loma** ⟦28S⟧ Hostel Lappean Loma, PPA 3, 95900 Kolari. ☎ (16) 563155 **FAX** (16) 563165 **Open:** 08.00-22.00hrs ⚐ 42 ⊜ FIM 75-80 ⦿ ♂ ♟ ⚒ P ⚲ ⊿ ✈ Kittilä 100km ⛟ Kolari 33km ⛆ 28km ap Station

Koli ☞ Lieksa (Koli)

Korpilahti ⟦20W⟧ Finnhostel Loma-Surkee, 41800 Korpilahti. ☎ (14) 827437 **Open:** 08.00-22.00hrs ⚐ 38 ⊜ FIM 65-95 ⦿ (Advance booking

essential) ♂ ♟ P ⚲ ⊿ ✈ Jyväskylä 70km ⛟ Jyväskylä 40km ⛆ 22km ap Korpilahti

Kotka ⟦5W⟧ Kärkisaaren retkeilymaja, Kärkisaarentie, Mussalo, 48310 Kotka. ☎ (5) 604215 **Open:** 07.00-12.00hrs, 16.00-22.00hrs, 15.5-15.9 ⚐ 47 ⦿(B) ♂ ♟ P ⚲ ⚾ ⊿ ✈ Helsinki 134km ⛟ Kotka 5km ⛆ 700m

Kouvola ⟦2E⟧ Kouvonpesä Utinkatu 39, 45200 Kouvola ☎ (5) 3751337 **FAX** (5) 3751013 **Open:** 07.00-12.00hrs, 16.00-22.00hrs, 1.6-4.8 ⚐ 50 ⊜ FIM 105-130 sheets inc. ⦿(B) ♂ ♟ P ✈ Lappeenranta 85km ⛟ Kouvola 1.5km ⛆ 100m ap Utinkatu

Kristiinankaupunki ⟦30S⟧ Hostel Kilstrand, Kilen, 64490 Sideby. ☎ (6) 2225611 **FAX** (6) 2225615 **Open:** 11.00-19.00hrs, 1.6-15.8 ⚐ 38 ⊜ FIM 85 ⦿(B L) ♟ P ⊿ ✈ Vaasa 130km ⛟ Pori 80km ⛆ 10m ap Kiili

Kuhmo Hostel, Piilolan koulu, 88900 Kuhmo. ☎ (8) 6556245 **FAX** (8) 6556139   **Open:**   07.00-15.00hrs, 17.00-01.00hrs, 1-31.7 ⚐ 33 ♟ P ⚾ ✈ Kajaani 110km ⛟ Kajaani 101km ⛆ 150m

Kuopio ⟦5S⟧ 【CC】 Hostel Rauhalahti, Katiskaniementie 8, 70700 Kuopio. ☎ (17) 473111 **FAX** (17) 473470 ⚐ 63 ⊜ FIM 120-220 sheets inc. ⦿ ♟ ⚒ P ⚲ ⚾ ⊿ ✈ Kuopio 23km ⛴ Rauhalahti 150m ⛟ Kuopio 6km ⛆ 10m ap Rauhalahti

Kuortane Finnhostel Virtaniemen Lomatila, Virtala, 63100 Kourtane. ☎ (6) 5256689 **FAX** (6) 5256694 **Open:** 07.00-22.00hrs ⚐ 62 ⊜ FIM 90-110 sheets inc. ⦿ ♂ ♟ ▣ P ⚲ ⚾ ⊿ ✈ Seinäjoki 55km ⛟ Seinäjoki 49km ⛆ 300m

Kuusamo Hostel Kuusamon Kansanopisto, Kitkantie 35, 93600 Kuusamo. ℃ (8) 8522132 **FAX** (8) 8521134 **Open:** 17.00-21.00hrs, 1.6-31.8 (08.00-15.45hrs Mon- Fri 1.9-31.5) ✄ 86 ● FIM 60-105, FIM 115 sheets inc. 🍽 ✶ ⋔ 🖻 **P** ✈ Kuusamo 8km 🚌 Kemijärvi 145km 🚃 200m

LAHTI (3 Hostels)

Lahti - Lahden kaupungin retkeilymaja, Kivikatu 1, 15700 Lahti. ℃ (3) 7826324 **FAX** (3) 7826324 **Open:** 10.00-22.00hrs, 1.6-31.8 (10.00-12.00hrs, 13.00-18.00hrs Mon - Fri, 1.9-31.5) ✄ 30 ● FIM 70 ✶ ⋔ **P** ⊥ ⨝ ✈ Helsinki- Vantaa 100km 🚌 Lahti 2km 🚃 200m

Lahti - Kansanopisto ⊏CC⊐ Lahden kansanopisto, Harjukatu 46, 15100 Lahti ℃ (3) 7523344 **FAX** (3) 7523322 **Open:** 08.00-12.00hrs, 16.00-20.00hrs, 2.6-17.8 ✄ 72 ● FIM 80-145 sheets inc. ᴮᴮ^{inc} ⋔ **P** ✈ Helsinki- Vantaa 100km 🚌 Lahti 300m 🚃 100m

Lahti - Mukkula 4N ⊏CC⊐ Ritaniemenkatu 10, 15240 Lahti. ℃ (3) 8823500 **FAX** (3) 8823522 **Open:** 24hrs ✄ 146 (Wi 10) ● FIM 135-185 sheets inc. ᴮᴮ^{inc} 🍽 ✶ ⋔ **P** ⊥ ⨝ ⬣ ✈ Helsinki-Vantaa 100km 🚌 Lahti 4km 🚃 100m

LAPINLAHTI (2 Hostels)

Lapinlahti - Nerkoon Retkeilymaja 8N Iisalmentie 770, 73120 Nerkoo ℃ (17) 735281 **Open:** 08.00-23.00hrs, 2.6-3.8 ✄ 37 ● FIM 55-75 🍽(B) ⋔ ⬚ **P** ✈ Kuopio 60km 🚌 Lapinlahti 7km 🚃 100m ap Nerkoon Koulu

Lapinlahti - Hostel Portaanpää 2S 73100 Lapinlahti ℃ (17) 768860 **FAX** (17) 731998 **Open:** 08.00-21.00hrs 1.6-15.8 ✄ 72 ● FIM 70-130 🍽 ⋔ ⬚ **P** ⬣ ✈ Kuopio 50km 🚌

Lapinlahti 1km 🚌 ap Matin Ja Liisan Asema 1km

Lappea ☞ **Kolari (Lappean Loma)**

LAPPEENRANTA (3 Hostels)

Lappeenranta - 2W ⊏CC⊐ Finnhostel Lappeenranta, Kuusimäenkatu 18, 53810 Lappeenranta. ℃ (5) 4515555 **FAX** (5) 4515558 **Open:** 07.00-22.00hrs, 15.1-15.12 ✄ 80 ● FIM 100-210 sheets inc. 🍽 ✶ ⋔ ⬣ **P** ⊥ ⨝ ⬣ ✈ Lappeenranta 2km ⛴ Lappeenranta 3km 🚌 Lappeenranta 3km 🚃 200m

Lappeenranta - Huhtiniemi 2W ⊏CC⊐ Hostel Huhtiniemi, Kuusimäenkatu 18, 53810 Lappeenranta ℃ (5) 4515555 **FAX** (5) 4515558 **Open:** 24hrs, 1.6-15.8 ✄ 24 ● FIM 55 🍽 ✶ 🖻 ⨝ ⬣ ✈ Lappeenranta 2km 🚌 Lappeenranta 3km

Lappeenranta - Karelia Park 2W Karelia-Park, Korpraalinkuja 1, 53810 Lappeenranta. ℃ (5) 675211, 4530405, **FAX** (5) 4528454 **Open:** 06.00-22.00hrs, 1.6-31.8 ✄ 50 ● FIM 85 🍽 ⋔ 🖻 **P** ✈ Lappeenranta 2km ⛴ Lappeenranta 2.5km 🚌 Lappeenranta 3km 🚃 100m

Leppävirta Hirvola, Timolantie 100, 78480 Timola ℃ (17) 5581188 **FAX** (17) 5581188 ✄ 16 ● FIM 150 sheets inc. ᴮᴮ^{inc} 🍽 ⋔ **P** ⨝ ⬣ ✈ Varkaus 22km 🚌 Varkaus 7km 🚃 300m ap Mansikkamäentie

LIEKSA (3 Hostels)

Lieksa - Loma-Kitsi 42E Kitsintie 86 A, 81650 Hattuvaara. ℃ (13) 539114 **FAX** (13) 539114 **Open:** 07.00-22.00hrs, 15.5-15.10 ✄ 24 ● FIM 50-60 (Cottages FIM 200-350) 🍽 ✶ ⋔ **P** ✈ Joensuu 100km 🚌 Lieksa 45km 🚃 9km

Lieksa - **Herranniemi** 27S Finnhostel Herranniemi, Vuonislahdentie 185, 81590 Vuonislahti. ✆ (13) 542110 **FAX** (13) 542110 **Open:** 08.00-23.00hrs, 15.5-15.10 ✄ 70 ⊖ FIM 60-160 ⦿ ☞ ⚥ ⊡ P ⚲ ⚓ ✈ Joensuu 80km ⛴ Vuonislahti 1km ⛟ Vuonislahti 600m ⛍ 100m

Lieksa - **Koli** Koli retkeilymaja, Niinilahdentie 47, 83960 Koli. ✆ (13) 673131 **Open:** 24hrs ✄ 46 ⊖ FIM 55-65 ⦿ (Advance booking essential) ☞ ⚥ ⛟ ⊡ P ✒ ⚲ ✈ Joensuu 85km ⛴ Koli 6km ⛟ Joensuu 75km ⛍ 6km ap Koli

Liljendal Hostel Embom, Embom 461-A, 07880 Liljendal. ✆ (19) 616354 **Open:** 17.00-10.00hrs 1.5-30.9 ✄ 23 ⊖ FIM 60-70 ☞ ⚥ P ⚲ ⚓ ✈ Helsinki-Vantaa 80km ⛟ Helsinki 90km ⛍ 4km ap Liljendalin tienhaara

Mänttä Mäntän retkeilymaja, Koulukatu 6, 35800 Mänttä. ✆ (3) 4888641 **FAX** (3) 4888500 **Open:** 08.00-10.00hrs, 16.00-21.00hrs, 2.6-10.8 ✄ 30 ⊖ FIM 80 ☞ ⚥ P ✈ Tampere 100km ⛟ Vilppula 7km ⛍ 400m

Muonio 0.5W Lomamaja Pekonen, Lahenrannantie 10, 99300 Muonio. ✆ (16) 532237 **FAX** (16) 532237 **Open:** 08.00-22.00hrs ✄ 54 ⊖ Rooms FIM 130/Pers sheets inc., Cottages FIM 140-360 ☞ ⚥ P ✒ ⚓ ✈ Kittilä 80km ⛟ Kolari 80km ⛍ 100m

Muurame CC Hostel Riihivuori, Riihivuorentie, 40950 Muurame. ✆ (14) 3110911 **FAX** (14) 3110911 **Open:** 07.00-22.00hrs, 1.4-20.12 ✄ 36 ⊖ FIM 100 ☞ ⚥ P ✈ Jyväskylä 40km ⛟ Jyväskylä 20km ⛍ 4km

Muurla Kesähostelli Muurlan Evankelinen Opisto, Muurlantie 365, 25130 Muurla ✆ (2) 7320511 **FAX** (2)

7320533 **Open:** 07.00-22.00hrs, 1.6-15.8 ✄ 58 ⊖ FIM 50-105 ⦿ ☞ ⚥ P ✈ Turku 60km ⛟ Salo 12km ⛍ 50m

Myllykoski ☞ **Anjalankoski**

Nerkoo ☞ **Lapinlahti, Nerkoo**

Nivala Hostel Nivala, Maliskyläntie 2, 85500 Nivala ✆ (8) 443171 **FAX** (8) 442555 **Open:** 08.00-10.00hrs, 16.00-23.00hrs, 6.6-31.7 ✄ 112 ⊖ FIM 70-110 ⦿(B) ☞ ⚥ ⛟ P ⚲ ⛟ Nivala 2km ⛍ 300m

Nurmes - Hyvärilä CC Hyvärilän Matkailukeskus, Lomatie 75500 Nurmes. ✆ (13) 481770 **FAX** (13) 481775 **Open:** 08.00-16.00hrs, (07.00-23.00hrs, 1.6-15.8) ✄ 79 ⊖ FIM 55-220 ⦿ ☞ ⚥ ⚳ ⛟ P ✒ ⚲ ⚓ ✈ Kuopio 130km ⛟ Nurmes 4km ⛍ 200m

Nurmijärvi Lomakoti Kotoranta, Kotorannantie 74, 05250 Kiljava. ✆ (9) 2765879 **FAX** (9) 2765928 **Open:** 24hrs ✄ 34 ⊖ FIM 155-195 sheets inc. BB inc ⦿ ⚥ ⚳ P ✒ ⚲ ⚓ ✈ Helsinki-Vantaa 30km ⛟ Hyvinkää 20km ⛍ 1km

OULU (2 Hostels)

Oulu-**Otokylä** 2SE CC Hostel Otokylä, Haapanatie 2, 90150 Oulu. ✆ (8) 5308413 **FAX** (8) 5308327 **Open:** 07.00-22.45hrs, 15.5-15.8 ✄ 115 ⊖ FIM 65-170 ⦿(B) ⚥ ⊡ P ✈ Oulu 8km ⛟ Oulu 2km ⛍ 100m ap YH

Oulu-**Välkkylä** CC Summer Uni Hostel Välkkylä, Kajaanintie 36, 90100 Oulu. ✆ (8) 3118060 **FAX** (8) 3136754 **Open:** 07.00-24.00hrs, 2.6-30.8 ✄ 154 ⊖ FIM 65-85 ⦿(B) ☞ ⚥ ⊡ P ✈ Oulu 10km ⛟ Oulu 1km ⛍ 100m ap Välkkylä

Outokumpu Muurajan kartano, Suvisrannantie 15, 83500 Outokumpu.

☎ (1) 3552309 **Open:** 07.00-10.00hrs, 16.00-22.00hrs, 1.5-30.9 ✉ 41 ●
FIM 50-80 ⛽(B) ♂ ⛎ P ♿ ✈ Joensuu 35km 🍴 Viinijärvi 18km 🚂 50m

Parainen ⌊1.5N⌋ ⌈CC⌉ Hostel Norrdal, Solliden Camping, Norrby, 21600 Parainen. **☎** (2) 4585955 **FAX** (2) 4585955 **Open:** 08.00-22.00hrs, 1.6-15.8 ✉ 20 ● FIM 60-80 ⛽(B) ♂ ⛎ 🗐 ♨ P ▲ ✈ Turku 33km 🍴 Turku 23km 🚂 1km

Parikkala ⌊4S⌋ ⌈CC⌉ Karjalan Lomahovi, 59100 Parikkala. **☎** (5) 430851 **FAX** (5) 470597 **Open:** 08.00-22.30hrs, 1.6-31.8 ✉ 20 ● FIM 60-70 ⛽ ♂ ⛎ ♨ P ♿ ▲ 🍴 Parikkala 4km 🚂 4km

Paukkaja ☞ Eno

Peera Peeran Retkeilykeskus, 99490 Kilpisjärvi. **☎** (16) 532659 **FAX** (16) 532659 **Open:** 07.00-22.00hrs, 20.2-31.10 ✉ 45 ● FIM 90-135 ⛽ ♂ ⛎ ♨ P 🎿 ✈ Enontekiö 160km 🍴 Kolari 280km 🚂 300m ap Peera

Pelkosenniemi ☞ Suvanto

Pelkosenniemi ⌊12S⌋ Saukkoaavan retkeilykeskus, A 758 Saukkoaapa 2, 98999 Kemijärvi. **☎** (16) 853402 **FAX** (16) 853402 **Open:** 07.00-23.00hrs ✉ 70 ● FIM 60-75 ⛽ Advance booking essential ♂ ⛎ 🗐 ♨ P 🎿 🔧 ✈ Rovaniemi 100km 🍴 Kemijärvi 45km 🚂 10m

Pello Kittisvaaran hiihto-ja leirikeskus, Vaaranperä, 95700 Pello. **☎** (16) 586155 **Open:** 07.00-10.00hrs, 16.00-23.00hrs, 1.6-15.8 ✉ 30 ⛽(B) ♂ ⛎ ♨ P 🍴 Pello 4km 🚂 500m

Pernaja Kabböle vandrarhem, Kabböle, 07750 Isnäs, **☎** (19) 635643 **Open:** 08.00-22.00hrs, 1.5-30.9 ✉ 18 ● FIM 65 ⛽ ⛎ P ▲ ✈ Helsinki-Vantaa

70km 🍴 Helsinki 80km 🚂 10m ap Kabböle

Pielavesi Hostelli ⌈CC⌉ Laurinpurontie 23, 72400 Pielavesi. Postal address; Säviän Kyläkeskus, 72550 Säviä **☎** (17) 862970 **FAX** (17) 887270 **Open:** 10.6-10.8 ✉ 63 ● FIM 100 sheets inc. ⛽ ⛎ P ♿ ✈ Kuopio 70km 🍴 Iisalmi 45km 🚂 300m ap Station

PIETARSAARI (2 Hostels)

Pietarsaari - Svanen/Joutsen ⌊4N⌋ Hostel Svanen/Joutsen, Luodontie 50, 68600 Pietarsaari **☎** (6) 7230660 **Open:** 09.00-22.00hrs, 15.5-31.8 ✉ 24 ● FIM 45 ⛽(B) ♂ ⛎ 🗐 P ♿ ▲ ✈ Kruunupyy 36km 🍴 Pännäinen 15km 🚂 500m ap Alheda

Pietarsaari - Bodgärdet ⌊1S⌋ Pitäjäntie 5, 68600 Pietarsaari. **☎** (6) 7246610 **Open:** 24hrs, 3.6-4.8 ✉ 62 ● FIM 60-70 ⛽(B) ♂ ⛎ 🗐 ♨ P ✈ Kruunupyy 15km 🍴 Pännäinen 10km 🚂 100m ● (Partly under reconstruction '97)

Pinsiö ☞ Hämeenkyrö

Pori ⌊5W⌋ ⌈CC⌉ Hostel Tekunkorpi, Tekniikantie 4, 28600 Pori. **☎** (2) 6378400, (Wi) 6378125 **FAX** (2) 6378125 **Open:** 07.00-22.00hrs, 15.5-15.8 ✉ 160 ● FIM 75; FIM 95 sheets inc. ⛽(B) ♂ ⛎ 🗐 P ♿ ✈ Pori 5km 🍴 Pori 5km 🚂 200m ap Ulasoorintie

Porvoo Hostel, Linnankoskenkatu 1-3, 06100 Porvoo. **☎** (19) 5230012 **FAX** (19) 5230012 **Open:** 06.00-10.00hrs, 16.00-23.00hrs, 2.1-20.12 ✉ 41 ● FIM 65-140 ⛽ ⛎ ♨ P 🎿 ✈ Helsinki-Vantaa 50km 🍴 Helsinki 50km 🚂 1km ap Station

PUDASJÄRVI (3 Hostels)

Pudasjärvi - **Pudas- Maja** Finnhostel, Pudas- Maja, Sähkötie 3, 93100

Pudasjärvi. ✆ (8) 823220 **Open:**
07.00-10.00hrs,   17.00-22.00hrs,
1.6-30.9 ⊠ 34 ⬤ FIM 70-130 sheets
inc. ﹒◯❙(B) (Advance booking essential)
ⁱⁱⁱ P ♺ **Ⅲ** Oulu 90km 🚌 300m
ap Pudasjärvi

Pudasjärvi - **Kunto-Syöte** 50NE Hostel
Kunto-Syöte, PPA 2, 93280 Syöte. ✆
(8) 838167 **FAX** (8) 453120 **Open:**
08.00-22.00hrs ⊠ 50 ⬤ FIM 70-210
❙◯❙ ♂ ⁱⁱⁱ ⇆ **P** ⚲ Alt 192m ♺ ✈ Oulu
150km **Ⅲ** Oulu 150km 🚌 10m
ap Kunto-Syöte

Pudasjärvi - **Syöte** 55NE CC⫶ Hostel
Syöte, PPA 2, Pikku- Syöte tunturi,
93280 Syöte ✆ (8) 838172 **FAX** (8)
838173 ⊠ 50 ⬤ FIM 80 ❙◯❙ ♂ ⁱⁱⁱ ⓔ
P ⚲ ♺ ⬤ ✈ Oulu 150km **Ⅲ** Oulu
140km 🚌 10m (once a day) ⬤ ✆ YH
about 🚌 connections

Punkaharju ☞ **Kerimäki**

Puumala 2NW CC⫶ Hostel Reissumaja,
Koskenseläntie 98, 52200 Puumala. ✆
(15) 4381119 **FAX** (15) 4381809
Open: 24hrs ⊠ 23 ⬤ FIM 60-120
❙◯❙(B) ♂ ⁱⁱⁱ ⓔ **P** ⚲ ♺ ⬤ ✈ Mikkeli
80km **Ⅲ** Imatra 62km 🚌 1km
ap Koskenselän tienhaara

Rantasalmi Ranta-Pyyvilä, Pyyviläntie
240, 58900 Rantasalmi. ✆ (15) 440124
Open: 07.00-10.00hrs, 16.00-22.00hrs,
1.5-30.9 ⊠ 26 ⬤ FIM 60-120 ♂ ⁱⁱⁱ
P ⬤ **Ⅲ** Savonlinna 45km 🚌 3km

Raudanjoki ☞ **Sodankylä (Visatupa)**

RAUMA (2 Hostels)

Rauma - **Poroholma** Hostel Poroholma,
Camping Site, 26100 Rauma. ✆ (2)
8224666 Open: 15.5-31.8 ⊠ 38 ❙◯❙(B)
♂ ⁱⁱⁱ ⓔ ⇆ **P** ♺ ⬤ **Ⅲ** Rauma 2km
🚌 2km

Rauma - **Rauma** CC⫶ Hostel Rauma,
Satamakatu 20, 26100 Rauma. ✆ (2)
8240130   **Open:**   07.00-22.00hrs,

1.6-31.8 ⊠ 195 ⬤ FIM 125-195
sheets inc. BBⁱⁿᶜ ♂ ⁱⁱⁱ **P** ✈ Pori 50km
Ⅲ Rauma 300m 🚌 600m

Rautalampi 2N Korholan Kartano,
77700 Rautalampi. ✆ (17) 530320
Open: 08.00-22.00hrs, 1.1-21.12 ⊠
40 ⬤ FIM 75-85 sheets inc. ❙◯❙(B) ♂
ⁱⁱⁱ ⇆ ⓔ **P** ⚲ ♺ ⬤ ✈ Kuopio 70km
Ⅲ Suonenjoki 17km 🚌 2km
ap Station

Rautavaara   24E   Finnhostel
Metsäkartano, Metsäkartanontie 700,
73900 Rautavaara. ✆ (17) 780510 **FAX**
(17) 780515 **Open:** 07.00-23.00hrs,
1.6-31.8; 08.00-21.00hrs, 1.9-31.5 ⊠
131 ⬤ FIM 130-160 sheets inc. BBⁱⁿᶜ
❙◯❙ ♂ ⁱⁱⁱ ♿ ⓔ **P** ⚲ ♺ ⬤ ✈ Kuopio
100km **Ⅲ** Nurmes 36km 🚌 7km

RIIHIMÄKI (2 Hostels)

Riihimäki - **Riihimäki** Finnhostel
Riihimäki, Merkuriuksenkatu 7,
11130 Riihimäki. ✆ (400) 876169
Open: 07.00-23.00hrs, 15.5-15.8 ⊠
139 ⬤ FIM 60-155 sheets inc. ❙◯❙(B)
♂ ⁱⁱⁱ **P** ✈ Helsinki-Vantaa 60km **Ⅲ**
Riihimäki   300m   🚌   100m
ap Peltosaari

Riihimäki - **Seurahuone** CC⫶ Riihimäen
Seurahuone, Hämeenkatu 29, 11100
Riihimäki. ✆ (19) 7721 **FAX** (19)
729027 ⊠ 20 ⬤ FIM 200/double
room, sheets inc. ❙◯❙ ♂ ⁱⁱⁱ ✈ Helsinki
66km **Ⅲ** Riihimäki 500m ⬤ Hostel
reception at Sokos Hotel, Hämeenaukio
1 (400m from YH)

RISTIINA (2 Hostels)

Ristiina - **Löydön kartano** 6N Löydön
retkeilymaja, Kartanontie 71, 52300
Ristiina ✆ (15) 664101 **FAX** (15)
664109 ⊠ 58 (Wi 17) ⬤ FIM 70-130
❙◯❙ (Advance booking recommended)
ⁱⁱⁱ ⇆ **P** ⚲ ⬤ ✈ Mikkeli 18km **Ⅲ**
Mikkeli 15km 🚌 300m ap **Vitsiälä**

Ristiina - **Brahe** CC Hostel Brahe, Brahentie 54, 52300 Ristiina ✆ (15) 661078 **FAX** (15) 455115 **Open:** 11.00-03.00hrs,1.6-31.8;11.00-22.00hrs, 1.9-31.5 ✍ 74 ● FIM 65; FIM 95-160 sheets inc. ⑩ ⅲ P 🚲 ▲ ✈ Mikkeli 25km 🚢 Ristiina 300m 🚌 Mikkeli 22km 🚐 500m

Rovaniemen maalaiskunta ③N TH-Kievari Gasthaus, Kemintie 1956, 97130 HIrvas ✆ (16) 382017 **FAX** (16) 382191 ✍ 40 ● FIM 75-120 ⑩ ⅲ P ✈ Rovaniemi 30km 🚌 Muurola 3km 🚐 200m ap Hirvas

ROVANIEMI (2 Hostels)

Rovaniemi - **Hostel Tervashonka** Hallituskatu 16, 96100 Rovaniemi. ✆ (16) 344644 **FAX** (16) 344644 **Open:** 06.00-10.00hrs, 17.00-22.00hrs ✍ 60 ● FIM 85-95 ⑩(B) ⅲ P 🚲 ✈ Rovaniemi 10km 🚌 Rovaniemi 800m 🚐 500m

Rovaniemi - **Aari Hostel** ③SE CC Pöykkölä, 96460 Rovaniemi ✆ (16) 362906 **FAX** (16) 362906 **Open:** 08.00-10.00hrs, 15.00-22.00hrs (Wi: Grps only), 1.6-18.8 ✍ 152 ● FIM 105-135 ⑩ ⅲ 🛏 P ✈ Rovaniemi 12km 🚌 Rovaniemi 4km 🚐 ap 100m

Rymättylä Hostel Päiväkulma ③SE Kuristentie 225, 21140 Rymättylä. ✆ (2) 2521894 **Open:** 24hrs, 1.5-31.8 ✍ 50 ● FIM 60-150 ⑩(B) (Advance booking essential) 🍴 ⅲ ① 🛏 P ▲ ✈ Turku 45km 🚌 Turku 35km 🚐 3km ap Kirkonkylä (village centre)

Ruotsinpyhtää Ruotsinpyhtään Ruukkialue Oy, Krouvinmäki, 07970 Ruotsinpyhtää. ✆ (19) 618474 **FAX** (19) 618475 **Open:** 08.00-18.00hrs (10.00-18.00hrs Sat, Sun), 1.6-15.8; 08.00-16.00hrs Mon- Fri, 16.8-31.5 **Shut:** Sat, Sun reception ✍ 18 ● FIM 120 sheets inc. ⑩ 🍴 ⅲ 🎣 🛏 P ▲ ✈

Helsinki-Vantaa 110km 🚌 Kouvola 55km 🚐 10m

Saarijärvi Leiriharju- Menninkäinen, Kolkanlahdentie 294, 43100 Saarijärvi ✆ (14) 439711 **FAX** (14) 439716 ✍ 88 ⑩ ⅲ 🎣 P 🚲 ▲ ✈ Jyväskylä 55km 🚌 Jyväskylä 70km 🚐 100m ap Metsäoppilaitos

Saariselka ☞ **Kiilopää**

Salo Retkeilymaja, Laurin koulu, Venemestarinkatu 37,24240 Salo. ✆ (2) 7784409 **Open:** 08.00-11.00hrs, 17.30-22.30hrs, 1.6-10.8 ✍ 60 ● FIM 45-110 🍴 ⅲ P ✈ Turku 60km 🚌 Salo 2km 🚐 100m

SAVONLINNA (2 Hostels)

Savonlinna - **Malakias** CC Hostel Malakias, Pihlajavedenkuja 6, 57170 Savonlinna. ✆ (15) 533283 **FAX** (15) 272524 **Open:** 07.00-23.00hrs, 30.6-3.8 ✍ 30 ● FIM 110-170 ⑩(B) 🍴 ⅲ 🛏 P ✈ Savonlinna 17km 🚌 Savonlinna 1.5km 🚐 100m ap Malakias

Savonlinna - **Vuorilinna** CC Kylpylaitoksentie, 57130 Savonlinna. ✆ (15) 7395495 **FAX** (15) 272524 **Open:** 07.00-23.00hrs, 2.6-24.8 ✍ 30 ● FIM 110-170 ⑩ 🍴 ⅲ ① 🛏 P 🚲 ▲ ✈ Savonlinna 15km 🚌 Savonlinna 150m 🚐 150m ap Savonlinna

Seinäjoki CC Marttilan Kortteeri, Puskantie 38, 60100 Seinäjoki. ✆ (6) 4204800 **FAX** (6) 4234145 **Open:** 08.30-21.00hrs, 1.6-11.8 ✍ 157 ● FIM 100-205 sheets inc. ⑩(B) 🍴 ⅲ 🛏 P 🚲 ✈ Seinäjoki 10km 🚌 Seinäjoki 700m 🚐 200m ap Vapaudentie

SODANKYLÄ (2 Hostels)

Sodankylä-**Lapin Opisto** ②E CC Hostel Lapin Opisto, Kansanopistontie 5, 99600 Sodankylä. ✆ (16) 612181 **FAX** (16) 611503 **Open:** 07.00-23.00hrs,

31.5-15.8 ✄ 29 ● FIM 80 ⦿(B) ♂
♟ P ⚹ ✈ Rovaniemi 130km 🚂
Rovaniemi 130km 🚌 2km
ap Sodankylä

Sodankylä - **Raudanjoki** Hostel
Visatupa, 99510 Raudanjoki. ☎ (16)
634133 **FAX** (16) 634101 **Open:**
07.00-22.00hrs ✄ 55 ● FIM 95-240
⦿ ♂ ♟ 🖥 P ⚲ ♺ ⚹ ✈ Rovaniemi
73km 🚂 Rovaniemi 83km 🚌 4km
ap Raudanjoki

Sotkamo Hostel Tikkanen, Kainuuntie
31, 88600 Sotkamo. ☎ (8) 6660541
Open: 07.00-12.00hrs,
16.00-22.00hrs ✄ 38 ● FIM 60-70
⦿(B) ♂ ♟ P ⚲ ♺ ✈ Kajaani 40km
🚂 Vuokatti 7km 🚌 300m
ap Sotkamo

Sulkava ⟦16S⟧ Partalansaaren Lomakoti,
Hirviniementie 5, 58720
Kaartilankoski. ☎ (15) 478850 ✄ 47
● FIM 75-90 ⦿ ♂ ♟ ① P ⚲ ♺ ⚹
✈ Savonlinna 70km 🚂 Savonlinna
57km 🚌 200m ap Hirviniemi ● ☎
for pick-up

Suomussalmi ⟦75SE⟧ Finnhostel Domnan
Pirtti, Kuivajärventie 195, 89840
Ylivuokki. ☎ (8) 723179 **FAX** (8)
711189 **Open:** 09.00-21.00hrs,
1.4-30.9 ✄ 37 ● FIM 70-125 sheets
inc. ⦿ ♟ 🏠 ⚖ P ⚹ 🚂 Kontiomäki
150km 🚌 20km

Sykäräinen Finnhostel, Hirvikosken
kurssikeskus, Tornikoskentie 50,
69410 Sykäräinen. ☎ (6) 8623086 **FAX**
(6) 8623080 ✄ 84 ● FIM 130-200
sheets inc. ⟦BB⟧inc ⦿ ♂ ♟ 🖥 ⚖ P ✈
Kruunupyy 90km 🚂 Kannus 45km
🚌 500m

Pelkosenniemi - Suvanto ⟦20N⟧
Finnhostel Mettiäinen, 98550 Suvanto.
☎ (16) 854112 **FAX** (16) 854112
Open: 10.00-22.00hrs ✄ 10 ● FIM
80-120 ⦿ ♂ ♟ P ⚲ ⚹ ✈ Rovaniemi
100km 🚂 Kemijärvi 56km 🚌 9km

Taivalkoski ⟦25SE⟧ Finnhostel
Jokimutka, Parviainen, 93420 Jurmu.
☎ (8) 845762 **Open:** 10.6-31.7 ✄ 24
● FIM 65-100 sheets inc. ⦿ ♂ ♟ P
⚹ ✈ Oulu 135km 🚂 Oulu 135km
🚌 5km ap Tutulampi

Tammisaari Ekenäs vandrarhem,
Tammisaaren retkeilymaja,
Höijersvägen 10, 10600 Ekenäs. ☎ (19)
2416393 **FAX** (19) 2413917 **Open:**
09.00-12.00hrs, 15.00-21.00hrs,
16.5-20.8 ✄ 88 ● FIM 65-110 ⦿(B)
♂ ♟ P ♺ ✈ Helsinki-Vantaa 80km
🚂 Tammisaari 1km 🚌 50m

TAMPERE (4 Hostels)

Tampere - YWCA Hostel Tampere
(YWCA), Tuomiokirkonk 12 A, 33100
Tampere. ☎ (3) 2544020 **FAX** (3)
2544022 **Open:** 08.00-10.00hrs,
16.00-23.00hrs, 1.6-25.8 ✄ 81 ●
FIM 70-120 ⦿(B) ♂ ♟ P ✈ Tampere
15km ⛴ Tampere 1.5km 🚂
Tampere 500m 🚌 100m

Tampere - Domus ⟦2E⟧ ⟦CC⟧
Pellervonkatu 9, 33540 Tampere. ☎ (3)
2550000 **FAX** (3) 2550009 **Open:**
24hrs, 1.6-31.8 ✄ 40 ● FIM 120-200
sheets inc. ⟦BB⟧inc ⦿ ♂ ♟ 🖥 P ♺ ✈
Tampere 15km A🚌 Sammonkatu-
Uintikeskus 🚂 Tampere 1.5km

Tampere - Hostel Uimahallin Maja
Pirkank 10-12, 33230 Tampere. ☎ (3)
2229460 **FAX** (3) 2229940 **Open:**
07.00-11.00hrs, 15.30-23.30hrs,
1.9-11.5; 24hrs, 12.5-31.8 **Shut:** Sun
22.00hrs-Mon 08.00hrs, 12.5-31.8 ✄
89 ● FIM 95-190 sheets inc. ⦿ ♟ ⚲
🚂 Tampere 1.5km 🚌 50m

Tampere - Summer Hostel Härmälä
Nuolialantie 50, 33900 Tampere. ☎ (3)
2651355 **Open:** 2.6-27.8 ✄ 45 ⦿ ♟
P ♺ ⚹ ✈ Tampere 5km 🚂 Tampere
5km 🚌 10m ap Härmälän asuntola

Toholampi ☞ Sykäräinen

Tornio Hostel Suensaari, Kirkkokatu 1, 95400 Tornio. ☎ (16) 481682 **FAX** (16) 480048 **Open:** 06.00-11.00hrs, 16.00-23.00hrs, 5.6-8.8 ⊭ 82 ● FIM 80 ⑩(B) ☞ 👬 🔲 🍴 🅿 🏍 ✈ Kemi-Tornio 20km 🚌 Kemi 25km 🚐 500m

Turku ⎡2S⎤ Hostel Turku, Linnankatu 39, 20100 Turku. ☎ (2) 2316578 **FAX** (2) 2311708 **Open:** 06.00-10.00hrs, 15.00-24.00hrs ⊭ 120 ● FIM 60-115 ⑩(B) ☞ 👬 ♿ 🔲 🅿 ✈ Turku 10km 🚌 Turku 2km 🚐 50m ap Boren Puisto, poliisiasema

Vaasa ⎡3N⎤ ⎡CC⎤ Hostel Tekla, Palosaarentie 58, 65200 Vaasa. ☎ (6) 3276411 **FAX** (6) 3213989 **Open:** 08.00-23.30hrs, 1.9-30.5; 24hrs, 1.6-31.8 ⊭ 200 (Wi 85) ● FIM 115-205 sheets inc. ⑩ ☞ 👬 🔲 🅿 🏍 ✈ Vaasa 8km 🚌 Vaasa 3km 🚐 5m ap YH

Valkeakoski Finnhostel Apia, Apiankatu 43, 37600 Valkeakoski. ☎ (3) 5766405 **Open:** 08.00-24.00hrs, 1.6-15.8 ⊭ 70 ● FIM 70, FIM 130-190 sheets inc. ⎡BB⎤ⁱⁿᶜ ⑩ 👬 🅿 ⚓ ✈ Tampere 35km 🚌 Toijala 21km 🚐 500m ap Station

Vantaa ☞ Helsinki

VIRRAT (2 Hostels)

Virrat - Domus Domus Virrat, Sipiläntie 3, 34800 Virrat. ☎ (3) 4755600 **FAX** (3) 4755605 **Open:** 24hrs, 1.6-15.8 ⊭ 78 ● FIM 85-145, FIM 115-190 sheets inc. ⎡BB⎤ⁱⁿᶜ ⑩ ☞ 👬 ♿ 🔲 🍴 🅿 🏍 ⚓ ✈ Tampere 100km 🚌 Parkano 60km 🚐 1km ap Virrat

Virrat - Haapamäki ⎡20S⎤ Finnhostel Haapamäki, 34710 Vaskivesi. ☎ (3) 4758845 **FAX** (3) 4758811 **Open:** 09.00-22.00hrs, 1.5-30.9 ⊭ 55 ● FIM 95 ⑩ Advance booking recommended ☞ 👬 🅿 ⚖ 🏍 ⚓ ✈ Tampere 80km 🚌 Tampere 80km 🚐 1.5km

Vuonislahti ☞ Lieksa (Herranniemi)

GET THERE FOR LESS

The International Student Identity Card (ISIC) ○ gives access to thousands of discounts & services worldwide ○ is carried by more than 2 million full time students in 93 countries ○ offers 24-hour **FREE** travel advice and emergency service ○ is worldwide proof of student status ○ is recognised by **UNESCO**

INTERNATIONALLY ACCEPTED PROOF OF STUDENT STATUS

ISIC

FRANCE
FRANCE
FRANKREICH
FRANCIA

**Fédération Unie des Auberges de Jeunesse,
27 rue Pajol, 75018 Paris, France.**

☎ (33) (1) 44898727
FAX (33) (1) 44898710

Office Hours: Monday-Friday, 09.30-18.00hrs
                    Saturday, 10.00-17.00hrs

Travel Section: Service Groupes,
Fédération Unie des Auberges de Jeunesse,
27 rue Pajol, 75018 Paris, France.

☎ (33) (1) 44898727
FAX (33) (1) 44898749

IBN Booking Centres for outward bookings
- Boulogne, FUAJ Pays de Calais, Place Rouget de Lisle.
- **Paris FUAJ**, Rue Pajol, *via National Office above.*
- **Paris FUAJ**, Beaubourg, 9 rue Brantôme.
  ☎ (33) 20570894 **FAX** (33) 20639893

Capital:	Paris
Language:	French
Currency:	F (franc)
Population:	54,426,000
Size (includes Corsica):	547,026 sq km

FRANCE

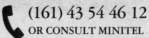
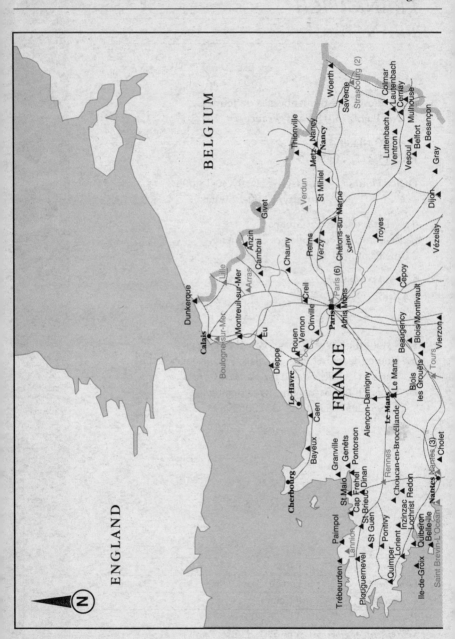

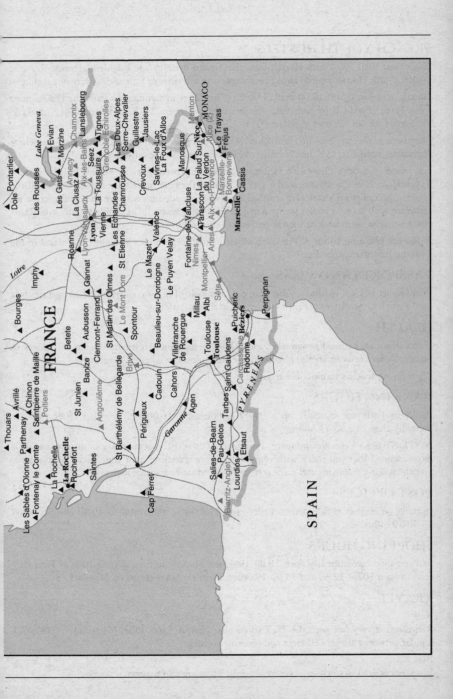

ENGLISH

FRENCH YOUTH HOSTELS

With more than 190 Youth Hostels from the Alps to Brittany and the Mediterranean to Paris, French Youth Hostels are the ideal base for sporting activities or for the discovery of a region.

Hostels are open 07.00-10.00 and 17.00-22.00hrs, later in summer. In Paris the D'Artagnan, Jules Ferry, Paris-Clichy and Cité des Sciences are open 24 hrs. (Price: 114F, breakfast included; Cité des Sciences in winter 95F).

Elsewhere expect to pay in the region of 30-68F plus bedlinen and residence tax where applicable, breakfast; 19F, lunch/dinner: 49F. Most hostels have self-catering facilities.

Fax France has been created to facilitate pre-booking overnights in French Youth Hostels. Youth Hostels in the scheme send a special form to the next hostel(s) you wish to visit; if the booking is confirmed a stamp is attached, payment is made immediately and confirmation fax complete with stamp entitles you to a bed in the hostel booked. Fax replies usually take 24hrs but it is advisable to book as soon as possible to ensure a bed.

If you are planning to use a Visa card whilst in France please see the note at the end of the Banking Information section.

PASSPORTS AND VISAS

EC passport holders require a valid passport, nationals of other countries should contact their local French Consulate to obtain a visa by personal application.

HEALTH

If you are an EC national get an E111 form DSS for emergency treatment during a short stay in France. Other nationals should obtain private health insurance before travelling.

There are no specific vaccinations required.

BANKING HOURS

Banks in Paris are normally open 09.00-17.00hrs (or 16.00hrs). In other cities they are normally closed 12.30-13.30hrs.

NOTE: To use a Visa card in France, a confidential code (PIN) is necessary in many places. It is recommended that you check with your bank, before travelling, that your Visa card meets the French banking standards and if the code can be used for financial transactions.

POST OFFICES

In main cities Post Offices are normally open Monday to Friday 08.30-19.00 and Saturdays 08.30-12.30hrs.

SHOPPING HOURS

In Paris shops are normally open 10.00-19.00hrs, Monday to Saturday. Outside of Paris they tend to open 10.00-12.30 and 14.00-19.00hrs. Some shops are closed on Mondays.

TRAVEL

Rail

Rail travel is very fast with the TGV (Bordeaux, Nantes, Lyon, Lille, Marseille). Other SNCF regular networks are very efficient and serve main cities.

Bus

Bus services exist in towns to serve local needs. There are also regional services.

Ferry
There are many ferries from England to Northern France. Some lines are available from France to Corsica and Northern Africa.

Driving
An international driving licence is required.

PUBLIC HOLIDAYS

New Year, 1 January; Easter, 30/31 March; Labour Day, 1 May: Liberation Day - 2nd World War, 8 May; Bastille Day, 14 July; Assumption Day, 15 August; All Saints Day, 1 November; Armistice Day - 1st World War, 11 November; Christmas, 25 December.

TELEPHONE INFORMATION

International Code	Country Code	Main City Area Codes
00	33	Paris 1

FRANÇAIS

AUBERGES DE JEUNESSE FRANÇAISES

Avec plus de 190 auberges de jeunesse, des Alpes à la Bretagne et de la Méditerranée à Paris, les Auberges de Jeunesse françaises constituent une base idéale, que ce soit pour les activités sportives ou de la découverte d'une région.

Les auberges sont ouvertes de 7h à 10h et de 17h à 22h, et plus tard en été. A Paris, les auberges D'Artagnan, Jules Ferry, Paris-Clichy et Cité des Sciences sont ouvertes 24h sur 24. (Prix: 114F, petit déjeuner compris; Cité des Sciences 95F durant les mois d'hiver).

Ailleurs, une nuit vous coûtera environ de 30 à 68F plus draps et taxe de séjour dans certains cas, petit déjeuner: 19F, déjeuner/dîner: 49F. La plupart des auberges ont une cuisine à la disposition des touristes.

France Fax a été créé pour faciliter la réservation de nuitées dans les auberges de jeunesse françaises. Les auberges qui participent au projet envoient un formulaire spécial à la ou les prochaines auberges dans lesquelles vous souhaitez séjourner; si la réservation est confirmée, un tampon est apposé, le réglement s'effectue immédiatement et le fax de confirmation tamponné vous donne droit à un lit dans l'auberge réservée. Il faut environ 24h pour recevoir une réponse par fax mais il est recommandé de réserver dès que possible pour être sûr d'avoir un lit.

Si vous envisagez utiliser une carte VISA lors de votre séjour en France, reportez-vous à la remarque située à la fin de la section consacrée aux informations bancaires.

PASSEPORTS ET VISAS

Les voyageurs en possession d'un passeport de la communauté européenne doivent avoir un passeport valide. Les citoyens d'autres pays doivent contacter leur consulat français local afin d'obtenir un visa pour lequel ils devront faire une demande personnelle.

SOINS MEDICAUX

Si vous habitez un pays du Marché commun, il vous faut obtenir un formulaire E111 DSS en cas de traitement d'urgence pendant un court séjour en France. Il est conseillé aux citoyens d'autres pays de souscrire à une police d'assurance maladie privée avant leur départ.

Aucune vaccination spéciale n'est requise.

HEURES D'OUVERTURE DES BANQUES

A Paris, les banques sont normalement ouvertes de 9h à 17h (ou 16h). Dans les autres villes, elles ferment en principe entre 12h30 et 13h30.

REMARQUE: Pour l'utilisation d'un carte VISA en France, un code confidentiel (Pincode) est nécessaire dans la plupart des cas. Veuillez vérifier, avant votre départ, auprès de votre banque, si votre carte VISA correspond aux normes bancaires françaises et si le code peut être utilisé dans les opérations financières.

BUREAUX DE POSTE

Dans les grandes villes, les bureaux de poste sont normalement ouverts du lundi au vendredi de 8h30 à 19h et le samedi de 8h30 à 12h30.

HEURES D'OUVERTURE DES MAGASINS

A Paris, les magasins sont normalement ouverts de 10h à 19h, du lundi au samedi. En dehors de Paris, ils sont en principe ouverts de 10h à 12h30 et de 14h à 19h. Certains magasins ferment le lundi.

DEPLACEMENTS

Trains
Les trains sont très rapides avec le TGV (Bordeaux, Nantes, Lyon, Lille, Marseille). Les autres réseaux standard de la SNCF assurent un service très efficace et desservent les grandes villes.

Autobus
Les services d'autobus urbains satisfont les besoins locaux. Il existe également des services régionaux.

Ferry-boats
De nombreux ferry-boats relient l'Angleterre au nord de la France. Certaines lignes relient la France à la Corse et à l'Afrique du Nord.

Automobiles
Un permis de conduire international est nécessaire.

JOURS FERIES

Nouvel an, 1er janvier; Pâques, 30 et 31 mars; Fête du Travail, 1er mai; Victoire 1945, 8 mai; Pentecôte, 4 et 5 juin; Fête nationale, 14 juillet; Assomption, 15 août; Toussaint, 1er novembre; Armistice 1918, 11 novembre; Noël, 25 décembre.

TELEPHONE

Indicatif International	Indicatif du Pays	Indicatifs régionaux des Villes principales
00	33	Paris 1

DEUTSCH

FRANZÖSISCHE JUGENDHERBERGEN

In Frankreich gibt es von den Alpen bis zur Bretagne und vom Mittelmeer bis nach Paris 190 Jugendherbergen - ein idealer Ausgangspunkt zum Skilaufen oder für andere Sportaktivitäten oder zum kennelernen der Region.

Die Herbergen sind von 07.00-10.00 und von 17.00-22.00 Uhr geöffnet, im Sommer länger. In Paris sind D'Artagnan, Jules Ferry, Paris-Clichy und Cité des Sciences 24 Stunden geöffnet. (Preis: 114F, einschließlich Frühstück; Cité des Sciences 95F im Winter).

An anderen Orten liegt der Preis zwischen 30 und 68F plus Miete für Bettwäsche und ggf Kurtaxe. Fruhstück: 19F, Mittag- oder Abendessen: 49F. Die meisten Herbergen haben Einrichtungen für Selbstversorger.

Fax France ermöglicht die Vorausbuchung von Übernachtungen in FUAJ-Herbergen. Teilnehmende Jugendherbergen schicken ein Formular an die nächste Herberge, in der Sie übernachten wollen. Das abgestempelte Telefax gibt Ihnen den Anspruch auf ein Bett in der nächsten Jugendherberge. Antworten per Telefax dauert meistens 24 Stunden; es empfiehlt sich jedoch, einen Platz so bald wie möglich zu reservieren. Nach Bestätigung wird das Fax abgestempelt, die Bezahlung erfolgt umgehend.

Siehe den obenstehenden Abschnitt über Bankgeschäft in Frankreich, wenn Sie vorhaben, eine Visa-Karte in Frankreich zu benutzen.

PÄSSE UND VISA

Wer einen EG-Paß besitzt, braucht einen gültigen Paß. Staatsangehörige anderer Länder sollten beim Französischen Konsulat in ihrem Land persönlich ein Visum beantragen.

GESUNDHEIT

Staatsangehörige eines EG-Landes sollten sich für dringende ärztliche Behandlung während eines kurzen Aufenthaltes in Frankreich das Formular E111 DSS besorgen. Staatsangehörige anderer Länder sollten vor Antritt ihrer Reise eine private Krankenversicherung abschließen.

Es werden keine speziellen Impfungen verlangt.

GESCHÄFTSSTUNDEN DER BANKEN

In Paris sind die Banken im allgemeinen von 09.00-17.00 Uhr (oder 16.00 Uhr) geöffnet. In anderen Städten schließen sie gewöhnlich zwischen 12.30 und 13.30 Uhr.

Wenn man eine Visa-Karte in Frankreich benutzt, braucht man in vielen Standorten eine Personalausweisnummer. Erkundigen Sie sich bei Ihrer Bank über die Gültigkeit Ihrer Karte in Frankreich im voraus, gleichfalls ob Ihre Ausweisnummer für Bankgeschäfte in Frankreich gültig ist.

POSTÄMTER

In größeren Städten sind die Postämter im allgemeinen montags bis freitags von 08.30-19.00 und samstags von 08.30-12.30 Uhr geöffnet.

LADENÖFFNUNGSZEITEN

In Paris sind die Geschäfte im allgemeinen montags bis samstags von 10.00-19.00 Uhr geöffnet. Außerhalb von Paris sind sie oft von 10.00-12.30 und von 14.00-19.00 geöffnet. Einige Geschäfte sind montags geschlossen.

REISEN

Eisenbahn
Die Hochgeschwindigkeitszüge (TGV) fahren nach Bordeaux, Nantes, Lyon, Lille, Marseille. Auch der übrige SNCF-Verkehr ist sehr effizient, und die Züge fahren in alle größeren Städte.

Busse
Der Busverkehr in den Städten ist auf den örtlichen Bedarf ausgerichtet. Es gibt auch einen Regionalverkehr.

Fähren
Es gibt viele Fähren von England nach Nordfrankreich und auch einige Fährverbindungen zwischen Frankreich und Korsika bzw Nordafrika.

Autofahren
Es wird ein internationaler Führerschein verlangt.

FEIERTAGE

Neujahr, 1. Januar; Ostern, 30. und 31. Marz; Maifeiertag, 1. Mai; Befreiungstag (1945), 8. Mai; Pfingsten, 4./5. Juni; Staatsfeiertag, 14. Juli; Mariä Himmelfahrt, 15. August; Allerheiligen, 1. November; Tag des Waffenstillstands (1918), 11. November; Weihnachten, 25. Dezember.

FERNSPRECHINFORMATIONEN

Internationale Kennzahl	Landes-Kennzahl	größere Städte - Ortsnetzkennzahlen
00	33	Paris 1

ESPAÑOL

ALBERGUES DE JUVENTUD FRANCESES

Con más de 190 albergues de juventud desde los Alpes a Bretaña y desde el Mediterráneo a París, los albergues de juventud franceses son una base ideal para las actividades deportivas o el descubrimiento de una región.

Los albergues abren de 07.00 a 10.00 horas y de 17.00 a 22.00 horas, en verano hasta más tarde. En París, el D'Artagnan, Jules Ferry, Paris-Clichy y Cité des Sciences están abiertos las 24 horas del día. (Precio: 114 francos incluyendo el desayuno; Cité des Sciences 95F en invierno).

En las demás poblaciones, se suele pagar entre 30 y 68 francos, más la ropa de cama y el impuesto de residencia donde corresponda, desayuno: 19F, almuerzo/cena: 49F. La mayoría de los albergues cuentan con cocina para huéspedes.

Fax France ha sido creado para facilitar la reserva de estancias por adelantado en los albergues juveniles franceses. Los albergues juveniles que participan en el proyecto envían un formulario especial al albergue o a los albergues siguientes donde usted desee alojarse; una vez confirmada la reserva, se sella el fax y se efectúa el pago en el acto. Este fax de confirmación sellado le da derecho a una cama en el albergue reservado. Generalmente, la respuesta por fax tarda 24 horas, pero se recomienda reservar lo antes posible para asegurar su cama.

Si piensa utilizar su tarjeta Visa durante su estancia en Francia, vea la nota al final de la sección de información bancaria.

PASAPORTES Y VISADOS

Los titulares de pasaportes de la CE necesitan un pasaporte válido. Los ciudadanos de otros países deben ponerse en contacto con su respectivo Consulado francés para obtener un visado mediante una solicitud personal.

SANIDAD

Si es ciudadano de la CE, solicite un formulario E111 en el Departamento de Seguridad Social por si necesita tratamiento de urgencia durante una corta estancia en Francia. Se recomienda a los ciudadanos de otros países hacerse un seguro de enfermedad privado antes de viajar.

No se requiere ninguna vacuna en particular.

HORARIO DE BANCOS

En París, los bancos suelen abrir de 09.00 a 17.00 horas (ó 16.00 horas). En las demás ciudades, acostumbran a cerrar entre las 12.30 y las 13.30 horas.

NOTA: Para poder utilizar su tarjeta Visa en Francia, en muchos lugares se exige el código confidencial (PIN). Antes de viajar, se recomienda que confirme con su banco si su tarjeta Visa cumple con las normas bancarias francesas y si se puede utilizar el código para realizar transacciones financieras.

CASAS DE CORREO

En las ciudades principales, las casas de correo abren de lunes a viernes de 08.30 a 19.00 horas y los sábados de 08.30 a 12.30 horas.

HORARIO COMERCIAL

En París, las tiendas normalmente están abiertas de 10.00 a 19.00 horas de lunes a sábado. Fuera de París tienden a abrir de 10.00 a 12.30 horas y de 14.00 a 19.00 horas. Algunas tiendas cierran los lunes.

DESPLAZAMIENTOS

Tren
Viajar en tren es muy rápido con el TGV (tren de alta velocidad) (a Burdeos, Nantes, Lyon, Lille y Marsella). Otros servicios regulares de la SNCF funcionan muy bien y llegan a las principales ciudades.

Autobús
Las distintas poblaciones cuentan con servicios de autobús para cubrir trayectos locales. También existen servicios regionales.

Ferry
Hay muchos ferrys desde Inglaterra al norte de Francia. También hay algunas líneas entre Francia y Córcega y el norte de Africa.

Coche
Se requiere un permiso de conducir internacional.

DIAS FESTIVOS

Año Nuevo, 1 enero; Pascua, 30 y 31 marzo; Fiesta del Trabajo, 1 mayo; Día de la Liberación - Segunda Guerra Mundial, 8 mayo; Toma de la Bastilla, 14 julio; Día de la Asunción, 15 agosto; Todos los Santos, 1 noviembre; Día del Armisticio - Primera Guerra Mundial, 11 noviembre; Navidad, 25 diciembre.

INFORMACION TELEFONICA

Código Internacional	Código Nacional	Indicativo de área de las Ciudades principales
00	33	París 1

DISCOUNTS AND CONCESSIONS

Your Hostelling International membership entitles you to a wide range of discounts in France, including reduced admissions to attractions near hostels, reduced rates on equipment hire, excursions and travel, ask for details at the Youth Hostel on your arrival.

Hostels in this country may also display this symbol.

Les auberges de ce pays pourront également afficher ce symbole.

Jugendherbergen in diesem Land können auch dieses Symbol zeigen.

Es posible que los albergues de este país exhiban además este símbolo.

Agen 17 rue Léo Lagrange, 47000 Agen (Lot-et-Garonne). ☎ (5) 53661898 **FAX** (5) 53477881 **Open:** 18.00-23.00hrs ⊨ 60 ⵌ(B) ⌀ 🗑 ⚲ 🚍 Agen 2km 🚍 Lalande ap Léon Blum

Aix-en-Provence [2W] (IBN) Le Jas de Bouffan, 3 Ave Marcel-Pagnol, 13090 Aix-en-Provence ☎ (4) 42201599 **FAX** (4) 42593612 **Open:** 07.00-12.00hrs, 17.00-23.00hrs, 1.2-20.12 (1.7-30.9; 24hrs); book in by 22.00hrs ⊨ 100 [BB]ⁱⁿᶜ ⵌ ⌖ 🗑 🏭 🅿 ⚲ ✈ Marseille/Provence 18km A🚍 direct 🚍 Aix-en-Provence 2km 🚍 12 ap Jas de Bouffan Vasarely ⓡ

Aix-les-Bains [3NW] (IBN) Promenade du Sierroz, 73100 Aix-les-Bains (Savoie). ☎ (4) 79883288 **FAX** (4) 79611405 **Open:** 07.00-10.00hrs, 18.00-22.00hrs, 4.2-4.11; 19,12-5.1.98 ⊨ 90 ⵌ ⌀ ⵌ ⌖ 🗑 🅿 ⵌ ⚲ ⚓ ✈ Geneve 70km 🚍 Aix-les Bains TGV 3km 🚍 2 Grand Port ap Camping ⓡ (Grps)

Albi (Assoc) AJ MJC, 13 Rue de la Republique, 81000 Albi (Tarn). ☎ (5) 63545365 **FAX** (5) 63546155 ⊨ 35 ⵌ 🗑 🅿 🚍 Albi Ville 2.5km 🚍 2, 5 ap Rascol ⓡ

Alençon- Damigny Lieudit 'La Croisette' 1, rue de la Paix, 61250 Damigny (Orne). ☎ (2) 33290048 ⊨

45 ⵌ ⌀ ⵌ 🗑 🚍 Alençon 3km 🚍 3 daily

Anglet ☞ **Biarritz**

Angoulême [2N] (IBN) Ile de Bourgines, 16000 Angoulême (Charente). ☎ (5) 45924580 **FAX** (5) 45959071 **Open:** 5.1-21.12 ⊨ 84 ⵌ ⌀ ⵌ 🅿 ⚓ 🚍 Angoulême 2km 🚍 7 ap Pont St Antoine ⓡ

Annecy (IBN) 4 Route du Semnoz, 74000 Annecy (Haute-Savoie). ☎ (4) 50453319 **FAX** (4) 50527752 ⊨ 117 ● 66F + 2F [BB]ⁱⁿᶜ ⵌ ⌀ ⵌ ⵌ 🗑 🅿 ⵌ ✈ Geneve 40km A🚍 🚍 Annecy 3km 🚍

Anzin (Assoc) Auberge de Jeunesse, 43 rue des Martyrs, 59410 Anzin (Nord). ☎ (3) 27469063 **FAX** (3) 27301091 ⊨ 40 ⌀ 🚍 Valenciennes 🚍 2 St Amand, 3 Beauvrage ap Rousseau ⓡ

Arles [1SE] (IBN) (CC) 20 Ave Foch, 13200 Arles (Bouches- du- Rhône). ☎ (4) 90961825 **FAX** (4) 90963126 **Open:** 6.2-16.12 ⊨ 100 [BB]ⁱⁿᶜ ⵌ 🗑 ⚲ ✈ Nimes/Arles A🚍 🚍 Arles 1.8km 🚍 8 ap Fournier ⓡ (1.3-15.7)

Arras [2N] (IBN) 59 Grand-Place, 62000 Arras (Pas-de-Calais). ☎ (3) 21227002 **FAX** (3) 21074615 **Open:** 07.30-10.00hrs, 17.00-23.00hrs, 1.2-30.11 ⊨ 54 ⵌ(B) ⌀ ⵌ 🗑 ⚲ 🚍

Arras 1km 🚌 Ligne D Grand-Place
Ⓡ (📞 (3) 21326161) Dec/Jan)

Aubusson (Assoc) FJT 14c Rue des Fusillés, 23200 Aubusson. 📞 (5) 55661359 **FAX** (5) 55663531 **Open:** 1.6-30.9 (Sun 12.00-20.00hrs) ✉ 10 ● 58F ᴮᴮⁱⁿᶜ 🍽 🔲 ✈ Clermont Fd 100km 🚍 Aubusson 2km 🚌 Hall Polyvalent Ⓡ

Auch (Assoc) CC FJT Cité du Garros, BP 563, 36 rue des Canaries, 32022 Auch Cedex 9 (Gers). 📞 (5) 62053480 **FAX** (5) 62600044 **Open:** 08.00-22.00hrs ✉ 17 ● 56F-66F 🍽 🔲 🅿 ✈ Toulouse 'Blagnac' 🚍 Auch 1km 🚌 ap Grand Garros

Avrillé- Langeais (Assoc) Rue des Tilleuls, 37340 Avrillé. 📞 (2) 47249600 **FAX** (2) 47249754 **Open:** 1.4-31.10 ✉ 35 🍽 ♂ 👪 ♿ 🔲 ⛪ 🚲 🚍 Langeais (shuttle ask YH) 15km Ⓡ (Grps: **FAX** AJ Tours (2) 47482659)

Banize (Assoc) AJ Cha "Lou Pélélé", 23120 Banize (Creuse). 📞 (5) 55660648 ✉ 29 ♂ 👪 🔲 🚍 Aubusson 16km 🚌 from Aubusson direction Limoges ap Courcelles/Banize or "Chez Cadet"

Bayeux (Assoc) "International-Family-Home", 39, Rue Gal de Dais, 14400 Bayeux 📞 (2) 31921522 **FAX** (2) 31925572 ✉ 127 ᴮᴮⁱⁿᶜ 🍽 ♂ 👪 ♿ ⛪ 🔲 ⛪ 🅿 🚲 🚍 Bayeux 1km

Beaugency Hameau de Vernon, 152 route de Châteaudun, 45190 Beaugency (Loiret). 📞 (2) 38446131 **FAX** (2) 38441473 **Open:** 1.3-31.12 ✉ 100 ● 48F 🍽 ♂ 👪 ♿ 🅿 🚲 🚍 Beaugency 2km Ⓡ

Beaulieu- sur- Dordogne 'La Riviéra Limousine', Place du Monturu, 19120 Beaulieu-sur-Dordogne (Corrèze). 📞 (5) 55911382 **FAX** (5) 55912606 **Open:** 1.4-30.9 ✉ 30 🍽(B) ♂ 🔲 🚍

Bretenoux- Biars 7km 🚍 Brive-Beaulieu

Belfort (Assoc) 1S Résidence Madrid, FJT, 6 rue de Madrid, 90000 Belfort. 📞 (3) 84213916 **FAX** (3) 84285895 ✉ 20 ● 60F 🍽 👪 ♿ 🔲 ✈ 80km A 🚍 Bale-Mulhouse 🚍 Belfort 500m 🚍 1 ap Madrid

Belle-Ile en Mer CC Haute Boulogne, Belle-Ile, 56360 Le Palais (Morbihan). 📞 (2) 97318133 **FAX** (2) 97315838 **Open:** 1.1-30.9; 1.11-31.12 ✉ 93 ● 49F 🍽 ♂ 👪 ♿ 🔲 🔲 🅿 🚲 ⛵ ⛴ Belle-Ile 🚍 Quiberon or Auray 🚍 Belle-Ile Ⓡ

Besançon CC 48 rue des Cras, 25000 Besançon. 📞 (3) 81884311 **FAX** (3) 81807797 **Open:** 09.00-19.00hrs ✉ 30 🍽 🔲 ⛪ 🅿 🚍 Besançon Viotte 1.5km 🚌 7 Orchamps ap les oiseaux

Betete (Assoc) AJ Verte/Country Hostel, AJ- Centre d'Animation de l'Abbaye de Prebenoit, Prebenoit, 23270 Betete (Creuse). 📞 (5) 55807891 **FAX** (5) 55677428 **Open:** 1.4-31.10 ✉ 51 ● 40F 🍽 ♂ 👪 ⛪ 🔲 🚲 🚍 Gueret 35km, la Chatre 30km 🚍 Chateauroux 30km ap Genouillac Ⓡ

Biarritz- Anglet IBN CC "Gazte Etxea", 19 Route des Vignes, Quartier Chiberta, 64600 Anglet (Pyrénées Atlantiques). 📞 (5) 59587000 **FAX** (5) 59587007 **Open:** 20.1-20.12 ✉ 96 🍽 ♂ (1.2-15.5, 30.9-30.11) 🔲 ⛵ ✈ Biarritz 10km 🚍 Biarritz 6km from 🚍 L2 ap Hotel de Ville + L4 🚍 From 🚍 Bayonne L4 direct, from 🚍 L2 ap Hotel de Ville + L4 ap AJ ● CC Jul/Aug

BLOIS (2 Hostels)

Blois - **Les Grouëts** 4W 18 rue de l'Hôtel Pasquier, Les Grouëts, 41000 Blois (Loir-et-Cher). 📞 (2) 54782721 **Open:** 1.3-15.11 ✉ 48 ● 40F 🍽(B) ♂ 🚍

Blois 4.5km 🚌 4 Blois-Les Grouëts ap Eglise or YH **ⓡ**

Blois - Montlivault AJ Verte/Country Hostel, Montlivault Village, Cedex 181, 41350 Vineuil (Loir- et- Cher). (Carrefour D951/D84 Montlivault 1km; by la Loire, Chambord 8km, Blois 10km) ☎ (2) 38446131 **FAX** (2) 38441473 **Open:** 15.6-15.9 🛏 37 ⊖ 40F ⑩ ♂ ♙♙ ♿ 🚇 Blois 10km **ⓡ** (AJ Beaugency, 152 Rte de Châteaudun, 45190 Beaugency)

Boulogne- sur- Mer **IBN** **CC** Place Rouget de Lisle, 62200 Boulogne-sur-Mer (Pas- de- Calais). ☎ (3) 21801450 **FAX** (3) 21804562 Open: 07.30-01.00hrs 🛏 134 ⊖ 80F ⑧ inc ⑩ ♂ ♙♙ ♿ 🅿 ⚓ 🚢 Catamaran Seacat 1km 🚇 Boulogne-sur-Mer 40m **ⓡ**

Bourges "Jacques Coeur", 22 rue Henri Sellier, 18000 Bourges (Cher). ☎ (2) 48245809 **FAX** (2) 48655146 **Open:** 6.1-18.12 **Shut:** 12.00-14.00hrs Mon-Fri, (12.00-17.00hrs Sat-Sun) 🛏 74 ⑩ ♂ ⑥ 🚇 Bourges 3km 🚌 1, 2 ap Maison de la Culture **ⓡ** (Festival: "Spring de Bourges")

Brive **IBN** 56 Av Maréchal Bugeaud, Parc Monjauze, 19100 Brive (Corrèze). ☎ (5) 55243400 **FAX** (5) 55848280 Open: 08.00-23.00hrs 🛏 107 ⑩ ♂ ♙♙ ⑥ ♿ 🚇 Brive 1.5km

Cadouin 24480 Cadouin ☎ YH Brive (5) 55243400 **FAX** YH Brive (5) 55848280 **Open:** 1.3 🛏 60 ⊖ 66F ⑧ inc ⑩ ♂ ♙♙ ♿ 🏠 ⑥ 🚇 🅿 ⚓ ⚓ ✈ Bergerac 30km 🚇 Le Buisson de Cadouin 5km **ⓡ** (YH Brive)

Caen (Assoc) Residence Robert Reme, 68 rue Eustache Restout, 14300 Caen (Calvados). ☎ (2) 31521996 **FAX** (2) 31842949 **Open:** 1.6-30.9 🛏 58 ⊖ 60F ⑧ inc 70F) ♙♙ ⑥ 🚢 Ouistremar 12km 🚇 Caen 2km 🚌 5, 17 Grace de Dieu ap Lycée Fresnel **ⓡ**

Cahors (Assoc) FJT, 20 Rue F Suisse, 46000 Cahors. ☎ (5) 65356471, (5) 65539702 **FAX** (5) 65359592 **Open:** 09.00-23.00hrs 🛏 30 ⊖ 49F ⑩ (except Sat+Sun) ♂ ♙♙ 🏠 ⑥ 🚇 🅿 ⚓ ✈ Toulouse 120km 🚇 Cahors 500m **ⓡ** (1.9-30.6)

Calvi (Assoc) **CC** BVJ Corsotel, Ave de la République, 20260 Calvi (Corse). ☎ (4) 95651415 **FAX** (4) 95653372 **Open:** 25.3-31.10 🛏 133 ⊖ 120F ⑧ inc ⑩(B D) ♙♙ ① ✈ Calvi St Catherine ⚓ Calvi 🚇 Calvi 25m

Cambrai (Assoc) "Etape", 22 Rue de Crevecoeur, 54900 Cambrai ☎ (3) 27749803 **FAX** (3) 27830072 **Open:** 08.00-21.00hrs 🛏 73 ⑩ ♂ ♙♙ 🚇 Cambrai

Cannes ☞ **Le Trayas**

Cap Ferret AJ Verte/Country Hostel, 87 Ave de Bordeaux, 33970 Cap Ferret (Gironde). ☎ (5) 56606462 **Open:** 1.7-31.8 🛏 36 ♂ 🚇 Arcachon

Cap Fréhel AJ Verte/Country Hostel, Kérivet la ville Hardrieux, 22240 Cap Fréhel/Plévenon (Côtes-d'Armor). ☎ (2) 96414898 **FAX** (2) 96782747 **Open:** 15.4-15.9 🛏 60 ⊖ 44F ⑩ ♂ ♙♙ ♿ ⑥ 🚇 Lamballe, Saint-Brieuc 45km 🚌 Plévenon Fréhel ap Vieux Bourg

Carcassonne **IBN** **CC** Rue du Vicomte Trencavel, Cité Médiévale, 11000 Carcassonne (Aude). ☎ (4) 68252316 **FAX** (4) 68711484 Open: 07.00-01.00hrs: Sat/Sun 07.00-12.00hrs, 17.00-01.00hrs, 1.2-14.12 🛏 120 ⑩ ♂ ♙♙ 🏠 ⑥ 🚋 ♿ ✈ Beziers 60km-Toulouse 100km 🚇 Carcassonne 2.5km 🚌 4 ap La Cité

Cassis Les Calanques, La Fontasse, 13260 Cassis (Bouches- du- Rhône). ☎ (4) 42010272 🛏 65 ♂ ⑥ ✈ Marseille 20km 🚇 Cassis 6km 🚌 enquire at Tourism Office

Cepoy 25 Quai du Port, 45120 Cepoy (Loiret): (Montargis 6km N). (2) 38932545 **FAX** (2) 38931925 **Open:** 08.00-22.00hrs, 1.2-19.12 100 Orly or Roissy Montargis 6km 2 ap St Loup/Autoroute A6; Paris/Province Dordives, Province/Paris Courtenay, N7 Paris/Lyon

Cernay MJC/AJ 16a, Faubourg de Colmar, 68700 Cernay (Haut-Rhin). (3) 89754459 **FAX** (3) 89758748 **Open:** 2.1-15.12 50 Cernay 1.5km Elgise ap Cernay

Châlons- sur- Marne rue Kellermann, "Square Antral", 51000 Châlons- sur-Marne (Marne). (3) 26681356 **Open:** 5.7-4.9 41 (B) Châlons 1km Vallée Saint Pierre ap Doulcet

Chambord ☞ **Blois-Montlivault**

Chamonix IBN 127 Montée J Balmat, Les Pélerins d'en Haut, 74400 Chamonix (Haute- Savoie). (4) 50531452 **FAX** (4) 50559234 Open: 1.12-15.10 118 Alt 1085m Genève 90km Les Pélerins 700m 300m ap Les Pélerins école R (16-30.10)

Chamrousse Le Recoin, 38410 Chamrousse. (4) 76899131 **Open:** 1.12-1.5; 1.6-30.9 85 Alt 1650m Grenoble 30km Voie Ferrée du Dauphiné ap Le Recoin R

Chaumont (Assoc) 2S FJT, 1 rue de Carcassonne, 52000 Chaumont. (3) 25032277 **Open:** 15.00-21.00hrs 34 62F BB inc Chaumont 1km 1 ap Cavalier

Chauny Bd Bad- Kostritz, 02300 Chauny (Aisne). (3) 23520996 **FAX** (3) 23399092 40 + 20 Chauny 2km

Chinon (Assoc) Centre Animation Accueil, Rue Descartes BP 233, 37502 Chinon. (2) 47981048 **FAX** (2) 47984498 Open: 2.1-29.12 40 45F Chinon 200m 200m R

CHOLET (2 Hostels)

Cholet - Les Goelands (Assoc) Les Goelands, 2 rue Hallouin, BP 133, 49301 Cholet Cedex (Maine et Loire). (2) 41622357 **FAX** (2) 41554861 **Open:** Reception 08.00-19.30hrs Mon-Fri 20 70F (60F) Nantes Nantes Cholet 1km A, B ap St Bernadette R

Cholet - Les Pâquerettes (Assoc) FJT "Les Pâquerettes", 5 rue de la Casse, BP 316, 49303 Cholet Cedex (Maine et Loire). (2) 41713636 **FAX** (2) 41626222 Open: 15.6-15.9, and school holidays 30 61F Nantes Nantes Cholet 1 ap Saint-Pierre R

Choucan- en- Brocéliande AJ Verte/Country Hostel, Choucan, Paimpont, 35380 Plélan-le-Grand (Ille-et- Vilaine). (Concoret/56 2km) (2) 97227675 **Open:** 15.4-30.9 24 Rennes 45km Tiv 12km ap Paimpont

Clermont- Ferrand 2S "Auberge du Cheval Blanc", 55 Ave de l'URSS, 63000 Clermont- Ferrand (Puy- de-Dôme). (4) 73922639 **FAX** (4) 73929996 Open: 1.3-31.10 58 Clermont-Ferrand 150m

Colmar (Assoc) 2 Rue Pasteur, 68000 Colmar (Haut-Rhin). (3) 89805739 **FAX** (3) 89807616 **Open:** 15.1-15.12 110 Strasbourg, Bâle, Mulhouse Colmar 2km 4 ap Lycèe Technique

Corsica ☞ **Calvi**

Creil (Assoc) Centre de Formation des Cadres Sportifs, rue du Général Leclerc, 60100 Creil (Oise). ✆ (3) 44253766 **FAX** (3) 44242445 **Open:** until 21.00hrs Mon-Sat (19.00hrs Sun) ⊟ 70 ● 62F (inc sheets) ⏻⏻ ⏻ ✈ Paris Roissy 25km ⏻⏻ Creil 2km ⏻⏻ 1 ap Buhl or Champrelle **R**

Crevoux (Assoc) Auberge de Jeunesse, Crevoux, 05200 Embrun (Hautes Alpes). ✆ (4) 92431818 **FAX** (4) 92434980 **Open:** 15.12-30.4 ⊟ 84 ⏻⏻ ⏻⏻ ⏻ ✈ Alt 1600m ✈ Grenoble ⏻⏻ Embrun 15km **R**

Dieppe 2SW 48 Rue Louis Fromager, Quartier Janval, 76550 Saint Aubin S/Scie (Seine-Maritime): access Eglise de Janval/Chámps des Oiseaux. ✆ (2) 35848573 **FAX** (2) 35848962 ⊟ 46 (+ 20 Su) BB|inc ⏻⏻ ⏻ ⏻⏻ ⏻ ⏻ 2km ⏻⏻ Dieppe 2km ⏻⏻ 2 ap Château Michel

Dijon (Assoc) CC Centre de Rencontres Internationales/AJ, 1 bd Champollion, 21000 Dijon (Cote d'Or). ✆ (3) 80729520 **FAX** (3) 80700061 **Open:** 2.1-30.12 ⊟ 110 BB|inc ⏻⏻ ⏻⏻ ⏻ ⏻ ⏻ ✈ Dijon-Longvic ⏻⏻ Dijon Ville ⏻⏻ 5, 6 ap Epirey **R**

Dinan 2.5N Moulin de Méen, Vallée de la Fontaine des Eaux, 22100 Dinan (Côtes d'Armor). ✆ (2) 96391083 **FAX** (2) 96391062 ⊟ 70 (+12 Su) ⏻⏻ ⏻ ⏻⏻ ⏻ ⏻ ⏻⏻ Dinan 2.5km

Dole (Assoc) "FJT le St Jean", Place Jean XXIII, BP 164, 39101 Dole Cedex (Jura). ✆ (3) 84823674 **FAX** (3) 84791769 ⊟ 60 ● 65F ⏻⏻ 40F ⏻⏻ ⏻ ✈ Dole Tavaux ⏻⏻ Dole 1km ⏻⏻ ap St Jean

Dunkerque 2N Place Paul Asseman, 59140 Dunkerque (Nord): opposite the skating rink. ✆ (3) 28633634 **FAX** (3) 28632454 **Open:** 18.00-23.00hrs,

2.1-22.12 ⊟ 120 ⏻⏻ ⏻⏻ ⏻ ⏻⏻ Dunkerque 3km ⏻⏻ 3 ap Piscine

Etsaut (Assoc) Auberge de Jeunesse, Vallée d'Aspe, 64490 Etsaut (Pyrénées Atlantiques). ✆ (5) 59348898 **FAX** (5) 59348691 **Open:** 09.00-12.00hrs, 14.00-18.00hrs ⊟ 70 ● 45F ⏻⏻ ⏻ ⏻⏻ ⏻ ⏻ ⏻⏻ ✈ Pau A⏻⏻ Pau Gare ⏻⏻ Oloron 35km ⏻⏻ Etsaut 50m ap Eglise **R**

Eu - Le Treport (Assoc) CC Centre des Fontaines, rue des Fontaines, BP 123, 76260 Eu (Seine Maritime). ✆ (2) 35860503 **FAX** (2) 35864512 **Open:** 5.1-19.12 ⊟ 55 ⏻⏻ ⏻⏻ ⏻ ⏻ ⏻⏻ **R**

Evian (Assoc) CC Centre International de Séjour, ave de Neuvecelle, BP 31, 74501 Evian les Bains Cedex (Haute Savoie). ✆ (4) 50753587 **FAX** (4) 50754567 **Open:** 08.00-20.00hrs **Shut:** Weekends - ✆ YH ⊟ 50 ● 66/90F ⏻⏻ ⏻ ⏻ ✈ Genève 35km ⏻⏻ Evian les Bains 1.5km **R**

Fontaine-de-Vaucluse Chemin de la Vignasse, 84800 Fontaine-de-Vaucluse (Vaucluse). ✆ (4) 90203165 **FAX** (4) 90202620 **Open:** 15.2-15.11 ⊟ 50 ● 43F ⏻⏻(B) ⏻ ⏻⏻ ⏻ ⏻ ⏻⏻ Isle sur Sorgue 7km

Fontenay-le-Comte (Assoc) Foyer Sud Vendée "Les Trois Portes", 16 Rue des Gravants, BP 347, 85206 Fontenay le Comte. ✆ (2) 51691344 **FAX** (2) 51690423 **Open:** 1.7-31.9 ⊟ 30 ● 66F ⏻⏻ ⏻ ⏻⏻ ⏻ ⏻ ⏻⏻ ⏻ ⏻ Fontenay le Comte 1km **R**

Fréjus Chemin du Counillier, 83600 Fréjus (Var). ✆ (4) 94531875 **FAX** (4) 94532586 **Open:** 08.00-10.00hrs, 18.00-23.00hrs Su, (22.00hrs Wi) ⊟ 120 BB|inc ⏻⏻ ⏻ (Wi only) ⏻⏻ ⏻ ⏻⏻ ⏻ ⏻ ✈ Nice ⏻⏻ Fréjus 2km ⏻⏻ St Raphaël 5km ⏻⏻ Platform 7 at 18.00hrs ap "leschênes" **R** (⏻⏻/Grps)

Gannat (Assoc) `CC` Maison du Folklore, Route de St Priest, 03800 Gannat. ☎ (4) 70902829 **FAX** (4) 70902264 **Open:** 08.00-19.00hrs ⊯ 58 (+ 100 Annex) ⬤ 60F ⑩ ⅲ ▣ ✚ Aulnat 40km 🚌 Vichy 18km, Gannat 2km **R** (4 Ave de la République, 03800 Gannat)

Givet AJ Verte/Country Hostel, Château 'Mon Bijou', Route des Chaumières, 08600 Givet (Ardennes). ☎ Mr Lelong: (3) 24420960 **FAX** (3) 24420244 **Open:** 17.00-20.00hrs ⊯ 50 ☌ ⅲ 🚌 Givet ap Bon Secours 1km **R**

Granville (Assoc) Centre Régional de Nautisme, Bd des Amiraux, BP 135, 50400 Granville (Manche). ☎ (2) 33501895 **FAX** (2) 33505199 **Open:** 6.1-23.12 ⊯ 60 ⑩ ⅲ ▣ 🚌 Granville 500m

Gray (Assoc) Le Foyer, 2 Rue André Maginot, 70100 Gray. ☎ (3) 84648260 **FAX** (3) 84651623 ⊯ 10 ⬤ 47F ⑩ ☌ ⅲ ▣ ⚙ 🚌 Besançon 🚌 ap Gare Routière

Grenoble-Echirolles `4 SW` `IBN` `CC` 10 Ave du Grésivaudan, Lieudit 'La Quinzaine', 38130 Echirolles (Isère). ☎ (4) 76093352 **FAX** (4) 76093899 Open: 07.30-23.00hrs ⊯ 130 ⬤ 68F `BB`inc ⑩ ☌ ⅲ ⅊ ▣ ⅉ Alt 220m ✚ St Geoirs-Satolas 🚌 Grenoble 5km 🚌 8, 11 + Tramway ap La Quinzaine

Guillestre (Assoc) les Quatre Vents, Route de la Gare, "La Rochette", 05600 Guillestre (Hautes Alpes) ☎ (4) 92450432 **Open:** 1.1-30.9; 1.11-31.12 ⊯ 65 ⬤ 45F Su; 51F Wi ⑩ ☌ ⅲ ▣ ✚ Marseille 🚌 Guillestre- Mont Dauphin **R**

Ile- de- Groix Le Méné, 56590 Groix (Morbihan). ☎ (2) 97868138 **FAX** (2) 97865243 **Open:** 1.4-15.10 ⊯ 50 ⑩(B) ☌ ⅲ ⅉ ▣ 🄿 ⛴ Lorient Quai de l'Estacade 12km 🚌 Lorient

Imphy (Assoc) Agafimp, "Foyer le Vignot", 8 Rue Jean Sounié, 58160 Imphy. ☎ (3) 86687200 **FAX** (3) 86383187 ⊯ 50 ⬤ 64F 1st Day; 48F till 7th Day ⑩ ☌ ⅲ ▣ ✚ 20km 🚌 Imphy 1km 🚌 Nevers ap Macon André Dubois **R**

Inzinzac- Lochrist AJ Verte/Country Hostel, Ferme du Gorée, 56650 Inzinzac- Lochrist (Morbihan). ☎ (2) 97360808 **FAX** (2) 97369083 **Open:** 1.3-31.10 ⊯ 35 ⬤ 61F (43F Bed only) `BB`inc ⑩(L D) only for groups on **R** ☌ ⅲ ♿ 1 room 🄿 ⚙ 🚌 Lorient 15km 🚌 I, H ap le Gorée

Jausiers (Assoc) Le Mas des Loups, 04850 Jausiers. ☎ (4) 92810649 **FAX** (4) 91089544 **Open:** 15.10-15.9 ⊯ 42 ⑩ ⅲ ⅊ Alt 1240m ⚙ ✚ Marignane ⛴ Marseille 🚌 Gap 🚌 SNCF line ap Barcelonette **R** (Aroeven, 7 av du Général Leclercq, 13003 Marseille ☎ 91508741)

La Clusaz `3 SE` Chalet "Le Marcoret", Route du Col de la Fry, Lieudit "Les Etages", 74220 La Clusaz (Haute-Savoie). ☎ (4) 50024173 **FAX** (4) 50026585 **Open:** ☎ or **FAX** for further information ⊯ 50 ⑩ 🄿 ⅊ Alt 1250m ⚙ 🚌 Annecy 32km 🚌 Annecy-La Clusaz (hostel 3Km) **R**

La Foux d'Allos 04260 La Foux Allos (Alpes- de- Haute- Provence). ☎ (4) 92838108 **FAX** (4) 92838370 **Open:** 1.12.96-7.5; 1.6-30.9 ⊯ 70 ⬤ 45F ⑩ (1.12-7.5) ☌ June/Sept/Dec ⅲ ⅊ Alt 1815m ✚ Nice 🚌 Nice/Digne les Bains/Thorame- Haute 🚌 La Foux Allos in Wi/Jul/Aug, Allos in Jun and Sep 8km

La Palud-sur-Verdon "Immense Botte de Paille", Route de la Maline, 04120 La Palud-sur-Verdon (Alpes-de-Haute-Provence). ☎ (4) 92773872 **FAX** (4) 92773048 **Open:** 17.00-10.00hrs,

1.4-31.10 🛏 65 ● 64F [BB]inc ♂ ⁇ 🖭
🅿 ♿ ✈ Marseille Marignane or Nice
🚌 Manosque 70km (R)

La Rochelle [2S] Centre International de
Séjour/Auberges de Jeunesse, Les
Minimes, BP 305, 17013 La Rochelle
Cedex (Charente- Maritime). ☎ (5)
46444311 FAX (5) 46454148 Open:
08.00-24.00hrs, 1.6-20.12 🛏 230 (+
20 Su) ⁇ ⁇ ♿ 🖭 ♿ ⛴ Port Les
Minimes 🚌 La Rochelle 1.8km 🚌
10 ap YH

La Toussuire Fontcouverte, 73300 St-
Jean- de- Maurienne (Savoie). ☎ (4)
79567204 FAX (4) 79830093 Open:
30.11.96-30.4; 1.7-15.9 🛏 72 ⁇ ⁇
⁇ Alt 1800m ✈ Genève 🚌 St Jean-
de-Maurienne 18km 🚌 RDTS - La
Toussuire

LANNION (2 Hostels)

Lannion - Beg Leguer AJ Verte/Country
Hostel, Route de Goalagorn, Beg
Leguer, 22300 Lannion. ☎ (2)
96472486 FAX (2) 96370206 🛏 12
⁇ ((R) only) ⁇ ♿ 🚌 Lannion 4km
🚌 (Su only) ap Plage Goalagorn (R)

Lannion - Les Korrigans [IBN] 22300
Lannion (Cotes D'Armor). ☎ (2)
96379128 FAX (2) 96370206 🛏 80
⁇ ♂ ⁇ ♿ 🖭 ⁇ 🅿 ✈ Lannion 2km
🚌 Lannion 200m (R)

Lanslebourg/Valcenis Hameau des
Champs, 73480 Lanslebourg/Val-Cenis
(Savoie). ☎ (4) 79059096 FAX (4)
79058252 Open: 1.1-30.4; 1.6-20.9;
11-31.12; (Grps 1.1-31.12) 🛏 75 ⁇
⁇ ⁇ Alt 1450m ♿ ✈ Genève-Turin
🚌 Modane 25km 🚌 Lans le Villard
ap Hameau-des-Champs (R) (Grps)

Lautenbach AJ Verte/Country Hostel,
"Dynamo", La Schellimat, 68610
Lautenbach (Haut- Rhin): access via
Guebwiller and Munster Valleys). ☎ (3)
89742681 Open: weekends & school

holidays 🛏 30 ♂ 🚌 Mulhouse 25km
🚌 Kunegel ap Maison forestière (R)
● Accessible only on foot from car park
Col du Boenlesgrab (30 min)

Le Mans (Assoc) [1N] AJ-FJT le Flore, 23
rue Maupertuis Ave Bollée, 72000 le
Mans (Sarthe). ☎ (2) 43812755 FAX
(2) 43810610 Open: 07.00-22.00hrs
🛏 28 ● 64F [BB]inc ⁇(L D) ⁇ ♿ 🖭 ⁇
🚌 le Mans TGV 🚌 4, 12 ap Erpell
50m (R)

Le Mazet St Voy (Assoc) AJ "Ferme du
Besset", Foyer de ski de fond de Lizieux,
La Bataille, 43520 Le Mazet St Voy
(Haute Loire). ☎ (4) 71650035 FAX
(4) 71650544 🛏 30 ♂ ⁇ ⁇ 🚌 Le
Puy- St Etienne 🚌 St Etienne
ap Chambon (R)

Le Mont- Dore [IBN] [CC] "Le Grand
Volcan", au pied du Sancy, 63240 Le
Mont- Dore (Puy- de- Dome). ☎ (4)
73650353 FAX (4) 73652639 🛏 90
● 48F ⁇ ♂(Su) ⁇ 🖭 🅿 ⁇ Alt 1300m
♿ ✈ Clermont 🚌 Le Mont-Dore 3km
(R)

Le Puy en Velay (Assoc) Centre Pierre
Cardinal, 9 Rue Jules Vallès, 43000 Le
Puy en Velay. ☎ (4) 71055240 FAX (4)
71056124 Open: 07.00-24.00hrs (Sun
+ Holidays 07.00-12.00hrs,
20.00-22.00hrs), 1.4-30.9 (1.10-31.3
Mon-Fri) 🛏 70 ● 39F ⁇ ♂ ⁇ 🖭 ⁇
🅿 ♿ 🚌 Le Puy en Velay 500m

Le Trayas (Théoule-sur-Mer) 9 Av de
la Véronèse, Le Trayas, 06590 Théoule-
sur- Mer (Alpes- Maritimes). ☎ (4)
93754023 FAX (4) 93754345 Open:
1-5.1; 15.2-31.12 🛏 100 ⁇(B) ♂ 🖭
🚌 Le Trayas 2km 🚌 St Raphaël
20km ap Auberge Blanche (R)
(1.5-15.9 FAX (4) 93754345)

Le Treport ☞ Eu

Les Deux Alpes "Les Bruleurs de
Loups", 38860 Les Deux Alpes (Isère).

📞 (4) 76792280 **FAX** (4) 76792615
Open: 25.10.96-30.4; 23.6-31.8 ✉ 55
⬤ 48F 🍴 👫 ⛪ 🅿 ⚓ Alt 1600m 🚲
🚮 Grenoble 70km 🚌 Cars VFD ap I
Ⓡ

Les Echandes 2NW AJ Verte/Country
Hostel, Lieudit "Le Pertuiset", 42240
Unieux (Loire): St Etienne 17km. 📞 (4)
77357294 **Open:** 1.6-30.9, (Grps
1.1-15.12) ✉ 40 ⬤ 43F 🚹 👫 🔲 🚮
Firminy 5km 🚌 Firminy/Pertuiset

Les Gets "Les Farfadets", Le Poncet,
74260 Les Gets. 📞 (4) 50791486
(Morzine YH) **Open:** Grps only ✉ 69
⚓ Alt 1180m ✈ Geneva 70km A🚌
W 🚮 Cluses 25km 🚌 Cluses-
Morzine ap Le Poncet ⬤ (minimum age
6 years)

Les Rousses 3S Ⓒ Ⓒ Le Bief de la Chaille,
39220 Les Rousses (Jura). 📞 (3)
84600280 **FAX** (3) 84600967 **Open:**
22.12.96-19.4; 17.5-30.9 (Grps
1.1-31.12) ✉ 50 🍴 🚹 👫 ⚓ Alt
1100m ✈ Genève 45km/La Cure 2km
by train 🚮 Morez 10km 🚌
Morez/Les Rousses

Les Sables d'Olonne Ancien
Sémaphore, rue du Sémaphore, La
Chaume, 85100 Les Sables d'Olonne
(Vendée). 📞 (2) 51957621 **FAX** (2)
51957621 ✉ 36 ⬤ 67F BB inc 🍴 🚹 👫
🔲 ⛪ 🅿 🚲 ⛴ ✈ Nantes-Atlantique
A🚌 ⛴ Les Sables d'Olonne 🚮 Les
Sables d'Olonne 3km 🚌 2
ap Armandèche Ⓡ

Lille IBN 12 Rue Malpart, 59000 Lille
📞 (3) 20570894 **FAX** (3) 20639893
Open: 3.97 ✉ 160 BB inc 🍴(L D) 👫
♿ 🔲 🅿 🚮 Lille-Flanders

Lorient 2SW Auberge de Jeunesse du Ter,
41 rue Victor Schoelcher, 56100 Lorient
(Morbihan). 📞 (2) 97371165 **FAX** (2)
97879549 **Open:** 1.2-22.12 ✉ 104 🍴
🚹 👫 ♿ 🔲 ✈ 12km 🚮 Lorient 3km
🚌 C ap YH

Lourdios/ Ichere - Aramits (Assoc) AJ,
Estivade d'Aspe Pyrénées, "Maison
Pelou", 64570 Lourdios Ichère
(Pyrénées Atlantique). 📞 (5) 59344639
FAX (5) 59344804 ✉ 21 🍴 👫 ⛪ ⚓
Alt 400m 🚲 🚮 Oloron Ste Marie
22km 🚌 Oloron 13km ap ASASP-
Arros Ⓡ

Luttenbach ☞ **Munster**

Lyon- Vénissieux 4SE IBN 51 rue
Roger Salengro, 69200 Vénissieux
(Rhône). 📞 (4) 78763923 **FAX** (4)
78775111 **Open:** 07.00-00.30hrs ✉
130 🍴 🚹 👫 🔲 🅿 ✈ 15km A🚌 from
Partdieu Station 🚆 Lyon Partdieu or
Perrache 4km 🚌 36 from Lyon
Partdieu Station or 53 from Perrache
ap Viviani-J.Curie (36) or Viviani (53)
Ⓤ Bellecour + 🚌 35 ap Georges Levy
⬤ at 23.40hrs Ⓤ "D" from Bellecour ap
Parilly, + 53 "Perrache"(sortie sud) at
00.07hrs ap YH

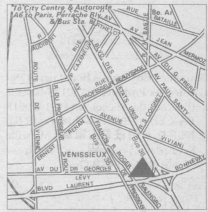

LYON - Vénissieux

Maël-Pestivien (Assoc) "Manoir-Ferme
de Kérauffret", 22160 Maël Pestivien.
📞 (2) 96457528 ✉ 20 ⬤ 44F 🍴 🚹 👫
🔲 🅿 ✈ St Brieuc 50km ⛴ Roscoff
50km 🚮 Coat Guégan 10km

Manosque 2S Parc de la Rochette,
04100 Manosque (Alpes de Haute-
Provence). 📞 (4) 92875744 **FAX** (4)

92724391 ⛵ 60 🍽 (Grps) ♂ 👫 �ⓦ
Manosque 4km 🚌 35 ap Centre Ville

MARSEILLE (2 Hostels)

Marseille - **Bonneveine** ⑥S ⒾⒷⓃ ⒸⒸ
Av J Vidal (Impasse du Dr Bonfils),
13008 Marseille (Bouches-du-Rhône).
📞 (4) 91732181 **FAX** (4) 91739723
Open: 1.2-31.12 **Shut:** 01.00hrs ⛵
150 [BB]inc 🍽 👫 ♿ 🔲 🅿 🚲 ⚓ ✈
Marignane 30km 🚍 Marseille St
Charles 5km 🚌 44 ap Place
Bonnefons Ⓤ 2 Prado Ⓡ (Grps)

MARSEILLE - Bonneveine

Marseille - **Château de Bois-Luzy** 4.5 NE
Allée des Primevères, 13012 Marseille
(Bouches-du-Rhône). 📞 (4) 91490618
FAX (4) 91490618 ⛵ 80 (+ 10 Su)
🍽(B D) ♂ 👫 🏠 🔲 🛏 🅿 🚍 Marseille
St Charles 4.5km 🚌 6 ap J Thierry or
Marius-Richard Ⓡ Grps

MARSEILLE - Château de Bois-Luzy

Martinique - Morne Rouge Av Jean
Jaurés, Haut du Bourg, 97260 Morne
Rouge. 📞 (596) 523023 **FAX** (596)
523964 ⛵ 40 ⊖ 71F [BB]inc 🍽(B D) ♂

👫 ♿ 🏠 🛏 🅿 🚲 ⚓ ✈ Fort de France
26km A🚌 Morne Rouge

Menton ⒾⒷⓃ Plateau St-Michel, 06500
Menton (Alpes- Maritimes). 📞 (4)
93359314 **FAX** (4) 93359307 **Open:**
07.00-12.00hrs,   17.00-24.00hrs,
1.2-30.11 ⛵ 80 🍽 🔲 🅿 ✈ Nice 28km
🚍 Menton 2km 🚌 ap Camping St-
Michel Ⓡ

Metz (Assoc) ⒸⒸ Carrefour, 6 rue
Marchant, 57000 Metz (Moselle). (near
Cathédrale, Place d'Armes) 📞 (3)
87750726 **FAX** (3) 87367144 **Open:**
24hrs ⛵ 60 [BB]inc 🍽 37F ♂ 👫 🔲 🛏
🚲 ⚓ ✈ Metz Louvigny 20km A🚌
🚍 Metz 2km 🚌 Circuit B ap Ste
Ségolene   50m   or   lines
3,4,5,7,9,11,24,25,29 400m ap Place
d'Armes Ⓡ (Grps)

Metz (Assoc) ⒸⒸ 1 Allée de Metz Plage,
Place de Pontiffroy, BP 573, 57010
Metz cedex (near Police Office and
University) 📞 (3) 87304402 **FAX** (3)
87331980 **Open:** 07.00-24.00hrs ⛵
62 ⊖ 62F [BB]inc 🍽 28F ♂ 👫 🔲 🛏 🅿
🚲 ⚓ ✈ Metz A🚌 21 🚢 Fluvial
🚍 Metz 1km 🚌 3, 11 ap Place de
Pontiffroy or YH Ⓡ Grps

Millau (Assoc) 1 SE 26 rue Lucien Costes,
12100 Millau (Aveyron). 📞 (5)
65612774 **FAX** (5) 65612774 ⛵ 30
⊖ 49F 🍽 👫 🚍 Millau 1km

Montargis ☞ **Cepoy**

Montpellier (*see town plan on next page*)
ⒾⒷⓃ ⒸⒸ Rue des Ecoles Laïques,
34000 Montpellier (Hérault). 📞 (4)
67603222 **FAX** (4) 67603230 **Open:**
08.00-24.00hrs, 9.1-15.12 ⛵ 87 [BB]inc
🍽 👫 🔲 🛏 🅿 ✈ 10km A🚌 🚍
Montpellier 1km 🚌 2, 3, 5, 6, 7, 9,
16 ap Ursulines Ⓡ ● No Sleeping
Bags

Montreuil- Sur- Mer (Assoc) AJ
Verte/Country Hostel, "La Hulotte",

Citadelle, rue Carnot, 62170 Montreuil-Sur-Mer (Pas de Calais). ☎ (3) 21061083 **Open:** 1.2-30.9 **Shut:** Tues ⚡ 50 ☂ ♯♯♯ ⊡ Ⓟ 🚌 Montreuil 500m Ⓡ

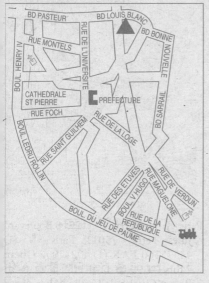

MONTPELLIER

Morzine / Avoriaz Holiday Campus, La Coutettaz, BP 74, 74110 Morzine (Haute-Savoie). ☎ (4) 50791486 **Open:** 21.12.96-26.4; 28.6-7.9; (Grps 21.12-7.9.98) ⚡ 76 ⬤ 62F ᵇᵇⁱⁿᶜ ✝️⍤ ♯♯♯ ⊡ ♒ Alt 1000m ✈ Genève 70km 🚌 Cluses 28km 🚏 Cluses/Morzine ap Office du Tourisme ⬤ Min age 12 years.

Mulhouse ③S ᴄᴄ 37 Rue de l'Illberg, 68200 Mulhouse - Dornach (Haut-Rhin). (near Université, Parc des Sports) ☎ (3) 89426328 **FAX** (3) 89597495 **Open:** 07.00-23.00hrs Wi (24hrs Su) **Shut:** Christmas + New Year ⚡ 64 (+ 10 Su) ⬤ 46F ✝️⍤ ☂ ♯♯♯ ♿ 🏛 Ⓟ 🚲 ✈ Bâle 30km 🚌 Mulhouse 3km 🚏 1, 2 ap Héricourt or Salles des Sports Ⓡ

Munster (Assoc) ②E "Luttenbach", 102 rue de la Gare, 68140 Munster. ☎ (3) 89773420 ⚡ 30 ✝️⍤ (D Grps) ☂ ♯♯♯ ✈ Colmar 🚌 Luttenbach 200m 🚏 Munster

Nancy (Assoc) ④SW "Chateau de Remicourt", 149, Rue de Vandoeuvre, Villers les Nancy, 54600 Nancy ☎ (3) 83277367 **FAX** (3) 83414135 **Open:** 2.1-23.12 ⚡ 60 ᵇᵇⁱⁿᶜ ✝️⍤ ♯♯♯ ♿ 🎠 ⊡ 🏛 Ⓟ ✈ Metz/Nancy A 🚏 Navette Brabois 🚌 Nancy 3km 🚏 26, 16 or 4 ap St-Fiacre, Lycee Bio or Basch Ⓡ

NANTES (3 Hostels)

Nantes - Place de la Manu ɪʙɴ 2 Place de la Manu, 44000 Nantes (Loire-Atlantique). ☎ (2) 40292920 FAX (2) 40200894 Open: 09.00-12.00hrs, 14.00-23.00hrs, 30.6-15.9 ⚡ 73 ✝️⍤ ☂ ♯♯♯ ♿ ⊡ 🏛 ✈ Nantes 8km 🚌 Nantes 400m � 1 ap Manufacture

Nantes - Porte Neuve (Assoc) ①SE Résidence "Porte Neuve", 1 place Ste Elisabeth, 44042 Nantes Cedex 02 (Loire Atlantique). ☎ (2) 40206363 **FAX** (2) 40206979 ⚡ 36 ⬤ 70F ᵇᵇⁱⁿᶜ ✝️⍤ ☂ ♿ ⊡ ✈ Nantes 8km 🚌 Nantes 2.5km 🚏 40, 41 ap Viarme � Marchix ap YH

Nantes - Port Beaulieu (Assoc) FJT Port Beaulieu, 9 Bd Vincent Gache, 44200 Nantes (Loire Atlantique). ☎ (2) 40122400 **FAX** (2) 51820005 **Open:** 1.6-31.8 ⚡ 50 ⬤ 54F ✝️⍤ ☂ ♯♯♯ ♿ ⊡ ✈ Nantes A 🚏 🚌 Nantes 2km 🚏 24, 26, 28, 29, 31 ap Beaulieu Man � Place du Commerce ap Vincent Gache

NICE (2 Hostels)

Nice - AJ Nice ɪʙɴ Route Forestière du Mont Alban, 06300 Nice (Alpes-Maritimes). ☎ (4) 93892364 FAX (4) 92040310 Open: 07.00-10.00hrs, 17.00-24.00hrs ⚡ 56 ✝️⍤(B) ☂ ⊡ 🚌 Nice 4km 🚏 17, 14 ap YH

Nice - Summer Hostel ɪʙɴ "Les Colinettes", 3, Ave R.Schuman, 06000

Nice 📞 (4) 93865848 **FAX** (4) 92040310 **Open:** 24hrs, 4.7-27.8 🛏 240 ● 98F 🔒 ⚿ 🔲 🚌 Nice 1km 🚌 17 Parc Imperial ap Châteauneuf (AJ Nice, 📞 (4) 92040310)

Nimes 2NW IBN CC Chemin de la Cigale, 30900 Nîmes (Gard). 📞 (4) 66232504 **FAX** (4) 66238427 **Open:** 24hrs, 1.4-30.9 (07.30-23.30hrs, 1.10-31.3) 🛏 76 ● 63F BB inc 🍽 🔒 🏧 🅿 ⚲ ✈ 15km A🚌 🚌 Nimes 3.5km 🚌 2 Ales-Villeverte ap Stade ● Pont du Gard by bike or bike+canoe from YH.

Nouméa 51 bis rue Olry, BP 767, Nouméa (New Caledonia). 📞 (687) 275879 **FAX** (687) 254817 🛏 88 ● 1000-2600 CFP 🔒 🚻 🔲 🅿 ✈ Nouméa 50km A🚌 SCEA ap YH

Oinville AJ Verte/Country Hostel "Relais Randonnée" 10 bis rue de Gournay, Oinville- sur- Montcient, 78250 Meulan (Yvelines). 📞 (1) 34753391 **Open:** 24hrs, 1.7-31.8 + weekends 🛏 19 ● 35F 🔒 🔲 🚌 Meulan Hardricourt 5km

Paimpol CC Château de Kerraoul, 22500 Paimpol (Côtes-d'Armor). 📞 (2) 96208360 **FAX** (2) 96209646 🛏 80 🍽 🔒 🚻 ⚲ 🚌 Paimpol 1.5km

PARIS (6 Hostels)

Paris - Cité des Sciences IBN 24, Rue des Sept Arpents, 93310 Le Pré St Gervais. 📞 (1) 48432411 **FAX** (1) 48432682 **Open:** 24hrs 🛏 125 ● 114F (95F Wi) BB inc 🔒 🚻 ⚿ 🔲 🏧 ⚲ ✈ Charles de Gaulle/Orly 🚌 Austerlitz/Gare de l'Est/Gare du Nord 🚌 PC 200m ap Porte de Pantin U Line 5 Hoche 200m

Paris - Le d'Artagnan 3NW IBN CC 80 rue Vitruve, 75020 Paris. 📞 (1) 40323456 **FAX** (1) 40323455 **Shut:** rooms 10.00-14.00hrs 🛏 428 ● 114F

BB inc 🍽 🚻 ⚿ 🔲 ✈ Charles de Gaulle 30km A🚌 351 🚌 Eurolines terminal 1km 🚌 351 ap rue Vitruve U Line 3 Porte de Bagnolet 500m

PARIS - Le D'Artagnan

Paris - Jules Ferry 2NE CC 8 Boulevard Jules Ferry, 75011 Paris. 📞 (1) 43575560 **FAX** (1) 40217992 **Open:** 24hrs 🛏 99 ● 114F BB inc 🍽 🏧 ⚲ ✈ Roissy Charles de Gaulle 45km A🚌 350 🚌 96, 75 U République

PARIS - Jules Ferry

Paris - Clichy IBN "Leo Lagrange", 107 Rue Martre, 92110 Clichy 📞 (1) 41272690 **FAX** (1) 42705263 🛏 338 ● 114F BB inc 🍽 🔒 🚻 ⚿ 🔲 🏧 🅿 ✈ Paris/Orly or Roissy A🚌 Orlybus or Roissybus 🚌 Paris/Saint Lazare or

Montparnasse Ⓤ Mairie de Clichy line 3 ®

Paris - Arpajon 3 rue Marcel Duhamel, 91290 Arpajon (Essonne). ✆ (1) 64902885 ⌗ 36 ⬤ 45F ♂ ⊡ ⌂ Ⓟ ✈ Orly Ⓤ RER/C4 Direction Dourdan-first 4 cars/Interrail-Eurail free; Arpajon 400m ®

Paris - Relais Européen (Assoc) Athismons Relais Européen de la Jeunesse, 52 ave Robert Schumann, 91200 Athis Mons (Essonne). ✆ (1) 69848139 **FAX** (1) 69847848 ⌗ 130 ⬤ 89-96F ᴮᴮⁱⁿᶜ ⦿(B D) ♦♦♦ ⊡ 👥 Athis Mons 500m Ⓤ RER/C4 or C6 Gill-Cime

Parthenay (Assoc) ⊡0.5S⊡ 16, Rue Blaise Pascal, 79200 Parthenay ✆ (5) 49952632 **FAX** (5) 49946485 ⌗ 105 ⦿(B) ♂ ♦♦♦ ♿ ✈ Poitiers/Nantes 👥 Parthenay 1km

Pau- Gelos (Assoc) Logis des Jeunes, Base de Plein Air, 64110 Gelos. ✆ (5) 59065302 ⌗ 50 ⬤ 59F ⦿(L) ♂ ⊡ ✈ Pau Pyrénées 👥 Pau 2.5km 🚌 1 ap Mairie de Gelos ®

Perigueux (Assoc) FJT Résidense Lakanal, 24000 Perigueux (Dordogne). ✆ (5) 53535205, (5) 53092277 **FAX** (5) 53543746 ⌗ 12 ⬤ 65F ᴮᴮⁱⁿᶜ ⦿ ♦♦♦ ⊡ 👥 Perigueux 1km 🚌 5 ap Gare Routière- Place Francheville ®

Perpignan Parc de la Pépinière, Av de Grande- Bretagne, 66000 Perpignan (Pyrénées- Orientales): situated behind Police Station. ✆ (4) 68346332 **FAX** (4) 68511602 **Open:** 20.1-20.12 ⌗ 49 ᴮᴮⁱⁿᶜ ♂ ♦♦♦ 👥 Perpignan 300m

Plouguernevel (Assoc) ⊡3N⊡ AJ Verte/Country Hostel, Centre de Vacances de Kermarc'h, Plouguernevel, 22110 Rostrenen. ✆ (2) 96291095 ⌗

25 ⬤ 40F ♂ ♦♦♦ ⊡ ✈ St Brieuc 👥 St Brieuc 🚌 ap Rostrenen ®

Poitiers ⟦IBN⟧ ⟦CC⟧ 1 Allée Roger Tagault, 86000 Poitiers (Vienne). ✆ (5) 49580305 **FAX** (5) 49372585 **Open:** 08.00-10.00hrs, 18.00-23.00hrs, 2.1-23.12 ⌗ 131 ⦿ ♦♦♦ ♿ Ⓟ 👥 Poitiers 3km 🚌 1, 3 ap Cap Sud ®

Pontarlier 2 rue Jouffroy, 25302 Pontarlier (Doubs). ✆ (3) 81390657 **FAX** (3) 81392434 **Open:** 26.12.96-15.11 ⌗ 72 ⦿ ♂ ♦♦♦ ⚲ Alt 840m 👥 Pontarlier 500m

Pontivy Ile des Récollets, 56300 Pontivy (Morbihan). ✆ (2) 97255827 **FAX** (2) 97257648 **Open:** 08.00-12.00hrs, 17.30-22.00hrs ⌗ 65 ⦿ ♂ ♦♦♦ ⊡ Ⓟ ⛃ ✈ Lorient 50km ⛴ Lorient 50km 👥 Pontivy 1.5km

Pontorson (Assoc) Centre Duguesclin, 21 rue Patton, 50170 Pontorson (Manche). ✆ (2) 33600018 **FAX** (2) 33602581 **Open:** 1.6-30.9 ⌗ 50 ⬤ 40F (+ 1F visitors tax) ♂ ♦♦♦ ♿ ⛃ 👥 Pontorson 1km ® (Mairie de Pontorson, 50 170 Pontorson)

Puicheric 2 rue Marcellin Albert, 11700 Puicheric. ✆ (4) 68437381 **FAX** (4) 68437184 **Open:** 07.00-01.00hrs ⌗ 17 ⬤ 46F ⦿ ♦♦♦ ⌖ ⊡ ⌂ Ⓟ ◭ ✈ Toulouse 👥 Lezignan Corbieres 12km 🚌 from Carcassonne 23km ap Puicheric ®

Quiberon "Les Filets Bleus", 45 rue du Roch Priol, 56170 Quiberon (Morbihan). ✆ (2) 97501554 **Open:** 08.30-22.00hrs, 1.5-30.9 ⌗ 30 ⦿ ♂ ⌂ Ⓟ ⛃ ◭ ✈ Lorient 👥 Quiberon 1.5km 🚌 23, 24 ®

Quimper (Assoc) Auberge de Jeunesse, 6 ave des Oiseaux, 29000 Quimper (Finistère). ✆ (2) 98649797 **FAX** (2) 98553837 **Open:** 1.2-30.11 ⌗ 50 ⦿ (B+D Grps) ♂ ✈ Pluguffan Quimper

W Quimper 2km **W** 1 ap Chaptal **R**

Redon (Assoc) Mapar, 2, Rue Chantebel, BP 101, 35603 Redon Cedex (Ille et Vilaine). ✆ (2) 99721439 **FAX** (2) 99721653 **Open:** 1.6-31.8 ✉ 20 ● 48F ⑧ ✆ ⅲ ☒ ⅏ ⏢ ✈ Rennes **W** Redon **R**

Reims (Assoc) Centre International de Séjour, Parc Léo- Lagrange, 51100 Reims (Marne). ✆ (3) 26405260 **FAX** (3) 26473570 **Open:** 2.1-23.12 ✉ 63 (+ 10 Su) ⑧ ✆ ⅲ ☒ ⏢ ⅙ **W** Reims 1.5km **W** M, N, B, E ap Colin or H ap Pont de Gaulle **R**

Reims ☞ **Verzy**

Rennes ⟨2S⟩ ⟨IBN⟩ ⟨CC⟩ Centre International de Séjour, Auberge de Jeunesse, 10-12 Canal Saint- Martin, 35700 Rennes (Ille-et-Vilaine). ✆ (2) 99332233 **FAX** (2) 99590621 ✉ 100 ⟨BB⟩inc ⑧ ✆ ⅲ ⅙ ☒ ⅏ ⏢ ✈ 3km A **W** 57+20 **W** Rennes 3km **W** 20, Sat/Sun 18, 1 ap St Malo (Su **W** 2) ap Coëtlogon or St Malo

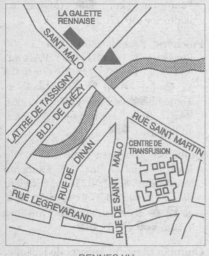

LA GALETTE RENNAISE

SAINT MALO

LATTRE DE TASSIGNY

BLD. DE CHEZY

RUE DE DINAN

RUE SAINT MARTIN

RUE DE SAINT MALO

CENTRE DE TRANSFUSION

RUE LEGREVARAND

RENNES YH

Roanne AJ "Centre Jeunesse P Bérégovoy", 4 Rue Fontenille, 42300 Roanne (Loire). ✆ (4) 77725211 **FAX** (4) 77706628 ✉ 60 ⟨BB⟩inc ⑧ ✆ ⅲ ⅙ ☒ ⅏ ⏢ ✈ Lyon Satolas **W** Roanne 800m **W** 1, 10 ap Clemenceau

Rochefort-sur-Mer (Assoc) Auberge de Jeunesse OMJ, 20 rue de la République, 17300 Rochefort- sur- Mer. ✆ (5) 46997462, (5) 46821040 **FAX** (5) 46992125 **Open:** 1.7-31.8 + all year on demand ✉ 40 ● 44F ⑧ ✆ ⅲ ☒ **W** Rochefort-sur-Mer 1km **R** (OMJ, 97 Rue de la République, 17300 Rochefort)

Rodez (Assoc) ⟨CC⟩ AJ/FJT "4 Saisons", 26 Bd des Capucines, Onet le Chateau, 12034 Rodez Cedex 9 (Aveyron). ✆ (5) 65423545 **FAX** (5) 65673797 ✉ 30 ● 83F + sheets ⟨BB⟩inc ⑧ ✆ ⅲ ⅙ ☒ ⏢ ✈ Rodez **W** Rodez 4km **W** 1, 3 ap Marché d'Oc or Rosiers Capucines **R**

Rodome (Assoc) AJ Verte/Country Hostel, Ferme Équestre, 11140 Rodome. ✆ (4) 68203222 **FAX** (4) 68207610 **Open:** 15.2-30.11 ✉ 26 ● 55F sheets Inc ⑧(B D) ✆ ⅲ ⅄ Alt 950m ✈ 90km **W** Quillan 31km **W** Espezel **R** (1.7-31.8)

Rouen (Assoc) ⟨5S⟩ 118 bd de l'Europe, 76100 Rouen. ✆ (2) 35720645 **Open:** 07.00-10.00hrs, 17.00-22.00hrs, (23.00hrs Su), 3.1-17.12 ✉ 96 ● 62F ⟨BB⟩inc ⑧ ✆ ⅲ ⏢ ✈ Rouen Boos - Vallee de Seine ⛴ Dieppe **W** Rouen 4km ⓤ Hôtel de Ville-Sotteville Europe 5km

Saintes 2 Place Geoffroy Martel, 17100 Saintes (Charente- Maritime). ✆ (5) 46921492 **FAX** (5) 46929782 **Open:** 07.00-12.00hrs, 17.30-23.00hrs, 15.1-15.12 ✉ 70 ● 66F ⟨BB⟩inc ⑧(L D) (48F) ⅲ ⅙ ⅏ ⏢ ⅙ ✈ Bordeaux ⛴ Royan **W** Saintes 2km **W** 1 Abbaye aux Dames ap Centre Commercial Leclerc

Saint- Barthelemy de Bellegarde (Assoc) AJ Verte/Country Hostel, "La

Chabrouillarde", 24 700 Saint Barthelemy de Bellegarde (Dordogne). ☎ (5) 53804598 ⇌ 30 ⊜ 43F ⑩ ☞ 7F ♙♿ 🗄 ⛪ 🄿 🚲 ✈ Bordeaux 🚢 Bordeaux 80km 🚎 Montpon (direct transfer to YH) 11km ⓡ

Saint- Brévin les Pins 1S IBN "La Pinède", Allée de la Jeunesse, 44250 St- Brévin (Loire Atlantique). ☎ (2) 40272527 FAX (2) 40644877 ⇌ 61 BBinc ⑩ ☞ ♙♙ 🗄 🚲 ✈ Nantes Atlantique 60km 🚎 St Nazaire 12km 🚎 P ap La Courance 1.5km or ligne 8 except Sun ap camping 150m ⓡ (Grps)

Saint- Brieuc Manoir de la Ville Guyomard, Les Villages, 22000 St- Brieuc (Côtes- d'Armor). ☎ (2) 96787070 FAX (2) 96782747 ⇌ 130 ⑩ ☞ ♙♙ ♿ 🗄 🚲 🚎 St Brieuc 3km 🚎 3 ap "Géant" or "Jean Moulin"

Saint-Etienne ☞ Les Echandes

Saint-Gaudens (Assoc) "Le Venasque", 3 Rue de la Résidence, 31804 Saint- Gaudens Cedex. ☎ (5) 61947273 FAX (5) 61956102 ⇌ 20 ⑩ ♙♙ 🗄 ⛪ 🄿 🚲 ✈ Toulouse 🚎 Saint-Gaudens 1km

Saint-Guen AJ Verte/Country Hostel, Bourg de St Guen, 22530 Mur de Bretagne (Côtes d'Armor). ☎ (2) 96285434 (Wi:(2) 96285510) FAX (2) 96260156 Open: 1.4-31.10 ⇌ 40 ⑩ (B D) ☞ 🚎 Loudéac 18km 🚎 Loudéac SNCF ap Saint- Guen ⬤ YH can host horses

Saint- Junien 13 rue de St- Amand, 87200 St-Junien (Haute-Vienne). ☎ (5) 55022279 Open: 08.00-20.00hrs ⇌ 50 ☞ ♙♙ 🗄 ⛪ 🄿 🚂 St-Junien 1km ⓡ

Saint- Malo (Assoc) 2E 37 Av du RP Umbricht, BP 108, 35407 St- Malo Cedex (Bretagne). ☎ (2) 99402980 FAX (2) 99402902 Open: 24hrs ⇌ 150 ⊜ 67F-109F (+ 5F 1.6-31.8) BBinc ⑩ (38F) ☞ ♙♙ ♿ 🗄 ⛪ 🚲 🚢 2km 🚎 St-Malo 2km 🚎 1, 2, 5 ap YH

Saint- Martin des Olmes (Assoc) Auberge de Jeunesse, St Martin des Olmes, 63600 Ambert (Puy de Dome). ☎ (4) 73820138 Open: 15.2-15.11 (Grps 1.1-31.12) ⇌ 50 ⑩ ☞ ♙♙ 🗄 🄿 🚲 🚎 Ambert 6km 🚎 call YH

Saint-Mihiel 12 rue sur Meuse, 55300 St- Mihiel (Meuse). ☎ (3) 29891506 Open: 1.4-31.10 (Grps 1.1-31.12) ⇌ 66 ⑩ (B D) ☞ ♙♙ 🚎 Commercy 19km 🚎 ap St-Mihiel

Saint- Pierre de Maillé Grand Rue, 86260 Saint- Pierre de Maillé. ☎ (5) 49489225 Open: 1.4-30.9 (1.10-30.3.98 Grps) ⇌ 35 ⑩ (B L) ☞ ♙♙ 🚲 🚎 Poitiers/Chatellerault 30km ⓡ (Grps)

Saint-Raphaël ☞ Fréjus

Salies- de- Béarn AJ Verte/Country Hostel, Route du Padu, Stade Al Cartero, 64270 Salies- de- Béarn (Pyrénées- Atlantiques). ☎ (5) 59382966 ⇌ 20 ☞ 🗄 🚎 Puyoo 7km 🚎 Pau/Biarritz ap Salies ⓡ ⬤ No heating in Wi

Saverne Château des Rohan, 67700 Saverne (Bas- Rhin). ☎ (3) 88911484 FAX (3) 88711597 Open: 15.1-15.12 ⇌ 88 ⑩ ♙♙ 🏠 🚎 Saverne 500m

Savines-le-Lac "Les Chaumettes", 05160 Savines- le- Lac (Hautes- Alpes). ☎ (4) 92442016 FAX (4) 92442454 Open: 1.5-30.9 ⇌ 86 ⊜ 47F ⑩ (48F) ☞ ♙♙ 🚲 ⛰ 🚎 Embrun 10km ⓡ

Seez "La Verdache", Seez, 73700 Bourg- St- Maurice (Savoie). ☎ (4) 79410193 FAX (4) 79410336 Open: 1.1-30.9; 21-31.12 (Grps 1.1-31.12) ⇌ 64 ⑩ ⛰ Alt 900m 🚲 🚎 Bourg-St-Maurice

4km 🚌 Martin ap Longefoy **R**
(15.12-15.4)

Serre-Chevalier/Le Bez Le Bez, 05240
La Salle-les-Alpes (Hautes-Alpes). ☎ (4)
92247454 **FAX** (4) 92248339 **Open:**
24hrs 🛏 127 (+ 20 Su) 🍴 🚿 (Su only)
👪 ♿ 🅿 ⚓ Alt 1410m 🚲 🚂 Briançon
8km 🚌 Rignon ap Villeneuve la Salle
U **R** (Wi)

Sète **IBN** **CC** "Villa Salis", rue du
Général Revest, 34200 Sète (Hérault):
inaccessible to buses ☎ (4) 67534668
FAX (4) 67513401 **Open:** 1.2-15.12
🛏 80 **BB** inc 🍴 👪 🅿 ⚓ ✈ Montpellier
25km ⛴ Sète 🚌 Sète 1.5km

Spontour AJ Verte/Country Hostel,
Auberge des Barrages, Spontour- de-
Soursac, 19550 Lapleau (Corréze). ☎ (5)
55275509 **Open:** 1.6-15.9 🛏 12 🚿 👪
🚂 Tulle 50km or Mauriac 18km 🚌
Tulle 50km ap Spontour **R**

STRASBOURG (2 Hostels)

Strasbourg - Parc du Rhin (*see town plan
on next page*) **3E** **IBN** **CC** Centre
International de Rencontres du Parc du
Rhin, rue des Cavaliers, BP 58, 67017
Strasbourg Cedex (Bas-Rhin): 1km from
German frontier. ☎ (3) 88455420 **FAX**
(3) 88455421 **Open:** 07.00-01.00hrs,
1.1-30.11 (see also "René Cassin") 🛏
221 ⊖ 96F **BB** inc 🍴 👪 ♿ 🅿 ⚓ ✈
Entzheim 15km 🚂 Strasbourg 4km
🚌 21, 2 ap Parc du Rhin

Strasbourg - René Cassin **2 SW** **IBN** 9
rue de l'Auberge de Jeunesse, Montagne
Verte, 67200 Strasbourg (Bas-Rhin). ☎
(3) 88302646 **FAX** (3) 88303516
Open: 3.2-31.12 (see also "Parc du
Rhin") 🛏 280 ⊖ 69F **BB** inc 🍴 49F 🚿
👪 ♿ 🅿 ✈ Entzheim 8km 🚂
Strasbourg 2km 🚌 3, 23 ap YH

Tarascon 31 Boulevard Gambetta,
13150 Tarascon (Bouches-du-Rhône).
☎ (4) 90910408 **FAX** (4) 90915417

Open: 07.00-10.00hrs, 17.30-23.00hrs,
1.3-15.12 🛏 65 ⊖ 46F 🍴(B) 🚿 👪 ♿
🔲 ♻ 🅿 🚲 🚂 Tarascon 500m

Tarbes (Assoc) AJ Internationale, 88
Rue Alsace Lorraine, 65000 Tarbes. ☎
(5) 62389120 **FAX** (5) 62376981
Open: 24hrs 🛏 58 ⊖ 48F 🍴(L D) 38F
🚿 👪 ♿ 🔲 ♻ 🅿 ✈ (TOL) Tarbes Ossun
Lourdes 🚂 Tarbes 2km 🚌 1 ap FJT

Théoule-sur-Mer ☞ **Le Trayas**

Thionville **CC** "Salvador Allende", 3
Place de la Gare, 57100 Thionville ☎
(3) 82563214, (3) 82561606 **Open:**
08.00-10.00hrs, 17.00-22.00hrs 🛏 60
⊖ 48F 🚿 👪 🎫 🔲 ♻ 🅿 🚲 ✈ ✈ Nancy
🚂 at 2 minutes 🚌 at 2 minutes
ap Thionville

Thouars F.J.T. "Hector Etoubleau", 5
Boulevard du 8 Mai, BP 77, 79102
Thouars ☎ (5) 49662240 **FAX** (5)
49661074 🛏 19 +16 in Su ⊖ 50F 🍴
👪 ♿ ♻ 🅿 🚂 Thouars

Tignes **2 SE** "Les Clarines" Les Boisses,
73320 Tignes. ☎ (4) 79063507 or AJ
Seez (4) 79410193 **FAX** (4) 79410336
Open: 1.1-1.5; 29.6-31.12 🛏 66 🍴
👪 ⚓ Alt 1810m ✈ Lyon- Genève
200km A🚌 Bourg St Maurice 🚂
Bourg St Maurice 22km 🚌 Martin
ap Les Boisses

STRASBOURG - René Cassin

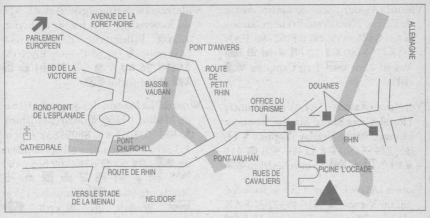

STRASBOURG - Parc du Rhin

Toulouse 3E 125 Ave Jean Rieux, 31500 Toulouse (Haute- Garonne). ☎ (5) 61804993 **FAX** (5) 61205066 **Open:** 08.00-10.00hrs, 17.00-23.00hrs, 22.1-30.12 ⊠ 54 ⑩(B) ☞ ✈ Toulouse A ♨♨♨ Toulouse 3km ♨♨♨ 22 ap Armand Leygues

Tours 4SE IBN Parc de Grandmont, 37200 Tours (Indre- et- Loire). ☎ (2) 47251445 FAX (2) 47482659 ⊠ 170 ⑩ ☞ ♦♦♦ ♿ ▤ 📖 🅿 ✈ Tours 5km ♨♨♨ Tours 3km ♨♨♨ 1 Joué- Blotterie or 6 Chambray II ap AJ; from 22.00hrs Bleu de nuit direction Joué Centre ℝ (☎ YH)

Trébeurden Le Toëno, 22560 Trébeurden (Côtes- d'Armor). ☎ (2) 96235222 **FAX** (2) 96154434 ⊠ 56 ⊜ 45F ⑩ (Su) ☞ ♦♦♦ ▤ 🅿 ⛵ ⚓ 🚢 Roscoff 50km ♨♨♨ Lannion 10km ♨♨♨ Verts ap YH

Troyes- Rosières 5SW Chemin Ste Scholastique 10430, Rosières (Aube). ☎ (3) 25820065, (3) 25490738 **FAX** (3) 25729378 ⊠ 104 ⑩ ☞ ♦♦♦ ♿ 📖 🅿 ⛟ ♨♨♨ Troyes 5km ♨♨♨ 6B ap Terminus ℝ

Unieux ☞ Les Echandes

Valence (Assoc) CC Vacanciel l'Epervière, Chemin de l'Epervière,

26000 Valence (Drome). ☎ (4) 75423200 **FAX** (4) 75562067 ⊠ 48 ⊜ 48F ⑩ ♦♦♦ ♿ ▤ ♨♨♨ Valence ♨♨♨ 1 ap Valensolles

Vénissieux ☞ Lyon- Vénissieux

Ventron AJ Verte/Country Hostel, "Les Roches", Lieudit Fondronfaing, 88310 Ventron (Vosges). ☎ (3) 29241956 **Open:** 17.00-20.00hrs ⊠ 36 ⊜ 40F ☞ ♦♦♦ 🅿 ♨♨♨ Kruth 10km ♨♨♨ Cornimont 7km ℝ

Verdun IBN AJ Centre Mondial de la Paix, Place Monseigneur Ginisty, 55100 Verdun ☎ (3) 29862828 FAX (3) 29862882 Open: 08.00-12.00hrs, 17.00-23.00hrs ⊠ 69 ⊜ 67F BB inc ⑩(B D) ♦♦♦ ♿ 🏠 📖 🅿 ⚓ ✈ Nancy ♨♨♨ Verdun 1km ♨♨♨ ap Centre Mondial de la Paix.

Vernon (Assoc) 28 Av de l'Ile-de-France, 27200 Vernon (Eure). ☎ (2) 32516648 **FAX** (2) 32212341 **Open:** 1.4-30.9 ⊠ 24 ⑩(B) ☞ ♦♦♦ ♿ ▤ ♨♨♨ Vernon 2km ♨♨♨ ap Folenrue ℝ (♦♦♦)

Verzy 16 Rue du Bassin, 51380 Verzy (Marne). ☎ (3) 26979010 **Open:** Mon- Sat ⊠ 46 ⑩(B D) ☞ ♿ 📖 ♨♨♨ Reims 20km ♨♨♨ ap Beaumont-sur-Vesle

Vesoul (Assoc) Zone de Loisirs du Lac de Vaivre, 70000 Vesoul (Haute-Sâone). 📞 (3) 84764855, (3) 84762286 **FAX** (3) 84756480 ⊯ 72 ⏏️ ☂ ⛷ 🚻 🔟 🚍 Vesoul 2km 🚌 1 ap Camping **R** (🚻)

Vézelay (Assoc) AJ Verte/Country Hostel, Croix Sainte-Marthe, Route de l'Etang, 89450 Vézelay (Yonne). 📞 (3) 86332418 (Su) ⊯ 42 (10 Wi) ⛔ 45F ☂ 🚻 ♿ 🅿 🚲 🚌 Sermizelles 9km **R**

Vienne (Assoc) Isère, 11 Quai Riondet, 38200 Vienne. 📞 (4) 74532197 **FAX** (4) 74319893 **Shut:** Sun 15.9-15.5 ⊯ 50 ⏏️ ☂ 🚻 🚌 Vienne 500m

Vierzon Place de la République, 18100 Vierzon (Cher). 📞 (2) 48753062 **FAX** (2) 48711903 **Open:** 3.1-22.12 ⊯ 80 ⏏️ ☂ 🚻 🔟 🚍 🅿 🚲 🚌 Vierzon 500m 🚌 Centre ville ap Forum République

Villefranche de Rouergue (Assoc) FJT du Rouergue, 13 rue Emilie de Rodat, 12200 Villefranche de Rouergue (Aveyron). 📞 (5) 65450968 **FAX** (5) 65456226 ⊯ 8 ⛔ 49F ⏏️ 🚻 🚍 🅿 🚌 Villefranche **R**

Woerth "La Maison des Soeurs" 10 rue du Moulin, 67360 Woerth (Bas-Rhin). 📞 88540330 **FAX** 88095832 **Open:** 1.3-30.11 (weekends + school holidays on **R**) ⊯ 60 ⛔ 63F (46F bed only) 🆎inc ⏏️ ☂ 🚻 🏠 🔟 🚍 🅿 🚲 ✈️ Strasbourg 60km 🚌 Haguenau 15km 🚌 Woerth ap Woerth **R** (1.12-28.2)

Yvetot AJ Verte/Country Hostel, Auberge de Jeunesse, 4 rue de la Briqueterie "Camping Municipal", 76190 Yvetot (Seine Maritime). 📞 (2) 35953701 **Open:** 19.4-1.11 ⊯ 8 ☂ 🚻 🚌 Yvetot 700m **R**

Les normes seront contrôlées par Hostelling International et par vous, les utilisateurs. Si vous n'êtes pas satisfaits, faites-le nous savoir et nous vous promettons que nous examinerons le problème en question et si le cas l'exige, nous nous engageons à prendre les mesures appropriées. Ce guide contient des formulaires spéciaux pour vous aider à nous contacter à ce sujet.

GERMANY
ALLEMAGNE
DEUTSCHLAND
ALEMANIA

ASSURED STANDARD

Deutsches Jugendherbergswerk,
Hauptverband, Postfach 1455,
32704 Detmold, Germany.

☎ (49) (5231) 74010
FAX (49) (5231) 740149

Office Hours: Monday-Thursday
                 09.00-12.00; 14.00-16.30h;
                 Fri 09.00-12.00; 14.00-14.30h.

Travel Section: c/o Deutsches Jugendherbergswerk,
Hauptverband,
Postfach 1455,
32704 Detmold,
Germany.

IBN Booking Centres for outward bookings:
- Detmold - DJH, *via National Office above.*
- Berlin - Brandenburg Regional Office, Templehof Ufer 32.
- Düsseldorf - Rheinland Reg Office, Düsseldorfer Str 1.
- Hamburg - Nordmark Reg Office, Reinnbalnstrasse 100.

Capital:	Berlin
Language:	German
Currency:	DM (Deutsche Mark)
Population:	81,817,499
Size:	356,978 sq km

GERMANY - NORTH WEST

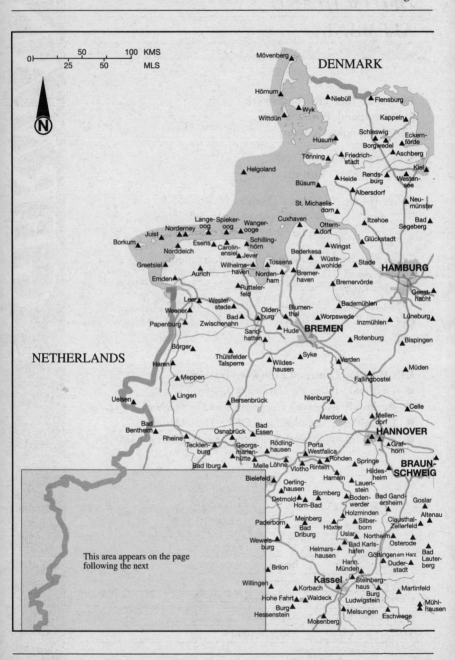

0 | 50 | 100 KMS
25 | 50 | MLS

N

DENMARK

Mövenberg

Hörnum
Wyk
Niebüll
Flensburg

Wittdün
Kappeln

Schleswig
Eckern-
förde

Husum
Borgwedel
Aschberg

Tönning
Friedrich-
stadt
Kiel

Helgoland
Rends-
burg
Westen-
see

Büsum
Heide

Albersdorf
Neu-
münster

St. Michaelis-
dorn

Cuxhaven
Itzehoe
Bad
Segeberg

Lange-Spieker-
oog oog
Wanger-
ooge
Ottern-
dorf
Glückstadt

Norderney
Esens
Schilling-
hörn
Bederkesa
Wingst

Borkum
Juist
Carolin-
ensiel
Jever
Wüste-
wohlde
Stade

Norddeich
Tossens
HAMBURG

Greetsiel
Wilhelms-
haven
Norden-
ham
Bremer-
haven
Bremervörde
Geest-
hacht

Emden
Aurich
Ruttteler-
feld

Leer
Wester-
stede
Bademühlen

Weener
Olden-
burg
Blumen-
thal
Lüneburg

Papenburg
Zwischenahn
Bad
Worpswede
Inzmühlen

Sand-
hatten
Hude
BREMEN
Rotenburg
Bispingen

Börger
Thülsfelder
Talsperre
Wildes-
hausen
Syke
Verden
Müden

Haren
Meppen
Nienburg
Fallingbostel

Uelsen
Lingen
Bersenbrück
Mardorf
Celle

NETHERLANDS

Bad
Bentheim
Rheine
Osnabrück
Bad
Essen
Mellen-
dorf
HANNOVER

Tecklen-
burg
Georgs-
marien-
hütte
Rödling-
hausen
Porta
Westfalica
Rohden
Springe
Graf-
horn

Bad Iburg
Melle
Löhne
Vlotho
Rinteln
Hildes-
heim
BRAUN-
SCHWEIG

Bielefeld
Oerling-
hausen
Hameln
Lauen-
stein

Detmold
Blomberg
Boden-
werder
Bad Gand-
ersheim
Goslar

Horn-Bad
Silber-
born
Clausthal-
Zellerfeld
Altenau

Paderborn
Meinberg
Bad
Driburg
Höxter
Holzminden
Northeim
Osterode

Wewels-
burg
Uslar
Bad Karls-
hafen
Göttingen am Harz
Bad
Lauter-
berg

Helmars-
hausen
Harn.
Münden
Duder-
stadt

Brilon
Steinberg-
haus
Martinfeld

Willingen
Kassel
Korbach
Burg
Ludwigstein

Hohe Fahrt
Waldeck
Melsungen
Mühl-
hausen

Burg
Hessenstein
Mosenberg
Eschwege

This area appears on the page
following the next

GERMANY - NORTH EAST

POLAND

BRAUN-SCHWEIG

BERLIN

Schönberg
Kiel
Oldenburg
Burg
Malente
Lensahn
Plön
Schönwalde
Eutin
Kühlungsborn
Scharbeutz-Klingberg
Bad Segeberg
Travemünde
Beckerwitz
Bad Doberan
Lübeck
Dassow-Holm
Großenhof
Bad Oldesloe
Ratzeburg
Flessenow
Mölln
Schwerin

Ibenhorst
Zingst
Graal-Müritz
Barth
Stralsund
Prora
Binz
Warnemünde
Ribnitz-Damgarten
S.-Devin
Rostock
Murchin
Heringsdorf
Demmin
Teterow
Ueckermünde-Bellin
Dahmen
Waren/Müritz
Neubrandenburg
Burg Stargard
Plau
Zielow
Mirow
Feldberg
Prebelow

Geesthacht
Lauenburg
Lüneburg
Hitzacker
Grabow

Uelzen

Hankensbüttel

Wandlitz
Liepnitzsee
Gardelegen
Milow
Brieselang
Ernst Reuter JGH
Buckow
Münchehöfe
Wolfsburg
Brandenburg
Wannsee
Braunsdorf
Haldensleben
Bad Saarow
Lange-leben
Klausdorf
Klein-Köris
Bremsdorfer Mühle
Schöningen
Gommern
Köthener See
Chossewitz
Raben
Goslar
Lübben/Spreewald
Bad Harzburg
Lutherstadt Wittenberg
Altenau
Torfhaus
Dessau
Burg
Cottbus
St. Andreasberg
Thale
Bernburg
Radis
Braunlage
Meisdorf
Bad Lauterberg
Bagenz
Bad Sachsa
Nordhausen
Gorenzen
Halle
Bad Frankenhausen
Heldrungen
Mühlhausen
Naumburg
Eckartsberga
Bad Kösen

This area appears on the page
following the next

GERMANY - SOUTH WEST

This area appears on the page following the next

FRANCE

SWITZERLAND

Willingen
Kassel
Korbach
Steinberg-haus
Martinfeld
Hohe Fahrt
Waldeck
Burg Ludwigstein
Mühl-hausen
Burg Hessen-stein
Mosenberg
Melsungen
Eschwege
Rotenburg a.d. Fulda
Eisenach
Marburg
Bad Hersfeld
Insels-berg
Rurberg
Nideggen
Bonn
Bad Salzungen
Brotte-rode
Monschau
Gemünd
Bad Münster-eifel
Bad Honnef
Bad Marien-berg
Wetzlar
Lauterbach
Fulda
Hilders
Ahrweiler
Bad Neuenahr-
Hellenthal
Blanken-heim
Altenahr
Montabaur
Weilburg
Gießen
Laubach
Ober-bernhards
Dahlem
Koblenz
Dietz
Hoherods-kopf
Gersfeld
Bischofsheim
Prüm
Gerolstein
Mayen
Limburg
a.d. Lahn
Grävenwiesbach
Büdingen
Daun
Bad Ems
Bad Homburg
Manderscheid
Broden-bach
St. Goar
Ober-reifenberg
Gelnhausen
Cochem
Oberwesel
Wiesbaden
FRANK-FURT
Linsen-gericht
Königs-berg
Traben-Trabach
Bacharach
Schweinfurt
Bollendorf
Bernkastel-Kues
Bingen
Rüdes-heim
Mainz
Aschaf-fenburg
Löhr am Main
Retzstadt
Trier
Morbach
Sargen-roth
Bad Kreuznach
Darmstadt
Rothenfels
Ebrach
Hermes-keil
Idar-Oberstein
Breuberg
Würzburg
Saarburg
Weis-kirchen
Burg Lichtenberg
Steinbach
Worms
Zwingenberg
Wertheim
Kitzingen
Dreisbach
Tholey
Wolfstein
Altleiningen
Heppenheim
Erbach
Amorbach
Tauber-bischof-sheim
Ochsenfurt
Hochspeyer
Weinheim
Walldürn
Igersheim
Weikersheim
St. Ingbert
Homburg
Mannheim
Heidel-berg
Eberbach
Creglingen
Saarbrücken
Merzalben
Neustadt a.d. Weinstraße
Dilsberg
Mosbach
Rothenburg ob der Tauber
Dahn
Speyer
Bad Wimpfen
Kirchberg
Feucht-wangen
Bad Berg-zabern
Heilbronn
Schwäbisch Hall
Rechen-berg
Dinkelsbühl
Karlsruhe
Murrhardt
Ellwangen
Pforzheim
Ludwigs-burg
Schwäbisch
Baden-Baden
Bad Herrenalb
Calw
STUTTGART
Gmünd
Aalen
Nördlingen
Herrenwies
Forbach
Esslingen
Hohen-staufen
Königsbronn
Donauwörth
Kehl
Sohlberg
Heidenheim
Ortenberg
Zuflucht
Freuden-stadt
Dornstetten-Hallwangen
Tübingen
Bad Urach
Ulm
Günzburg
Alpirsbach
Erpfingen
Blaubeuren
Triberg
Rottweil
Balingen
Lochen
Breisach
Freiburg
Villingen
Burg Wildenstein
Sigmaringen
Biberach
Memmingen
Todtnau-berg
Titisee-Neustädt
Ottobeuren
Wieden
Feldberg
Menzen-schwand
Bonndorf
Schluchsee
Seebrugg
Singen
Über-lingen
Ravensburg
Isny
Kempten
Platzhof
Konstanz
Friedrichs-hafen
Lörrach
Lindau
Füssen
Kornau

GERMANY - SOUTH EAST

Bad Franken-hausen
Heldrungen
Mühlhausen
Eckartsberga
Naumburg
Bad Sulza
Bad Kösen
Kretzschau
Eisenach
Erfurt
Weimar
Eisenberg
Insels-berg
Friedrichs-roda
Tambach-Dietharz
Bad Blankenburg
Leuchten-burg
Brotte-rode
Gräfen-roda
Ilmenau
Schwarz-burg
Plothen
Langen-wetzendorf
Katzhütte
Neiden-berga
Fröbersgrün
Neuhaus am Rennweg
Schönbrunn
Taltitz

This area appears on the page following the next

Coburg
Kronach
Hof
Lichtenfels
Wirsberg
Hohenberg
Königs-berg
Kulmbach
Wunsiedel
Bamberg
Bayreuth
Marktredwitz
Ebrach
Streitberg
Potten-stein
Tannenlohe
Gößwein-stein
Erlangen
Hartenstein

CZECH REPUBLIK

NÜRNBERG
Leinburg/Weißenbrunn
Amberg
Trausnitz
Waldmünchen
Wernfels
Furth im Wald
Lam
Bayerisch Eisenstein
Am Kleinen Arber
Nördlingen
Eichstätt
Ihrlerstein
Regensburg
Maibrunn
Zwiesel
Frauenau
Waldhäuser/Neuschönau
Donauwörth
Ingolstadt
Straubing
Bischofs-mais
Mauth
Haidmühle
Saldenburg
Rosen-bergergut
Landshut
Passau
Augsburg

MÜNCHEN
Mühldorf
Ebersberg
Burghausen
Wörthsee
JGH
Pullach
Hemhof
Traunstein
Prien
Benedikt-beuren
Schliersee/Josephstal
Bergen
Ober-ammergau
Kochel
Lenggries
Strub/Berchtesgaden
Füssen
Urfeld/Walchensee
Scharling/Kreuth
Bayerischzell/Sudelfeld
Garmisch-Partenkirchen
Mittenwald

AUSTRIA

N

0   50   100 KMS
    25   50   MLS

GERMANY - WEST BORDER

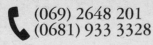
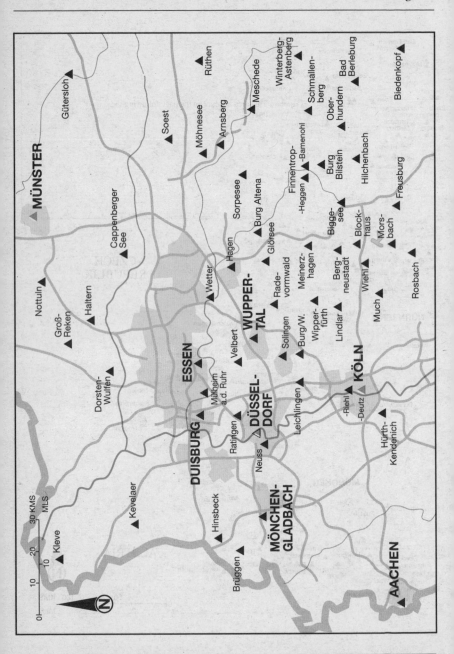

GERMANY - EAST BORDER

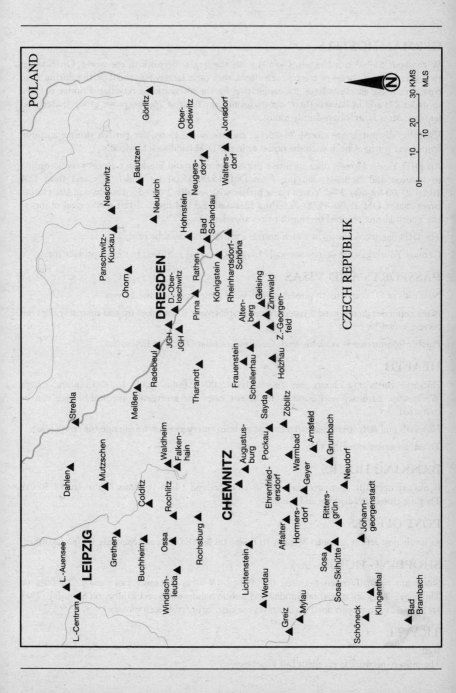

POLAND

Görlitz
Ober- odewitz
Jonsdorf
Bautzen
Neschwitz
Neukirch
Neugers- dorf
Walters- dorf
Hohnstein
Panschwitz- Kuckau
Ohorn
Bad Schandau
Schöna
DRESDEN
D.-Ober- loschwitz
Rathen
Königstein
Rheinhardsdorf-
Pirna
Geising
Altenberg
Zinnwald
Z.-Georgen- feld
JGH
JGH
Radebeul
Tharandt
Frauenstein
Schellerhau
Holzhau
Meißen
Strehla
Waldheim
Falken- hain
Sayda
Zöblitz
Warmbad
Arnsfeld
Augustus- burg
Pockau
Grumbach
CHEMNITZ
Ehrenfried- ersdorf
Geyer
Neudorf
Mutzschen
Dahlen
Colditz
Rochlitz
Rochsburg
Hormers- dorf
Ritters- grün
Johann- georgenstadt
Grethen
Buchheim
Ossa
Affalter
LEIPZIG
L.-Auensee
Windisch- leuba
Lichtenstein
Werdau
Sosa
Sosa-Skihütte
L.-Centrum
Greiz
Mylau
Schöneck
Klingenthal
Bad Brambach

CZECH REPUBLIK

N

30 KMS
20
10
0
10
20
30
MLS

ENGLISH

GERMAN HOSTELS

With about 617 Youth Hostels, Germany has the largest network in the world. Often larger than average, and always of the best standards, they cater largely for school parties during term time, but make excellent bases for exploration for the international traveller. Priority is given to under 27s and in Bavaria there is a maximum age limit of 26, except for group leaders and families. Most hostels have family rooms.

Virtually all hostels are closed 24-26.12, and many are closed for periods during autumn, winter and spring. Check with the hostel or in the DJH handbook for details.

All DJH Youth Hostels offer inclusive prices (overnight and breakfast). Prices vary according to location and facilities, ranging from DM 16.00-25.00 for under 27's and from DM 18.00-27.00 for over 27's. Youth guest houses with usually 2-4 bedded rooms and late closing times charge DM 25.00-45.00 including breakfast and bed linen. If you stay several nights at the Youth Hostel reduced overnight prices are offered.

The DJH handbook shows in which hostels a visitors' tax must be paid.

German Youth Hostels do not normally have self-catering facilities, but most provide meals.

PASSPORTS AND VISAS

Nationals of EC countries in possession of a valid passport do not need a visa.

Many countries do not need a visa provided employment is not taken up and their stay does not exceed 3 months.

Further information is available from German Consular Offices or Embassies.

HEALTH

Doctors' consulting hours are normally 10.00-12.00hrs and 16.00-18.00hrs except Wednesday, Saturday and Sunday. In urgent cases the emergency medical service can be contacted.

Hospitals and outpatients' departments provide an emergency service outside the above hours.

To call an ambulance dial 110.

BANKING HOURS

Banks are normally open weekdays 08.30-13.00hrs and 14.30-16.00hrs (Thursday 17.30hrs). They are closed on Saturday and Sunday.

POST OFFICES

As a rule post offices are open Monday to Friday 08.00-18.00hrs and Saturday 08.00-12.00hrs.

SHOPPING HOURS

Shops are normally open between 09.00 and 18.30hrs (in some cases until 20.30hrs on Thursday). They are closed on Sunday and public holidays and at 14.00hrs on Saturday. They are allowed to stay open until 16.00hrs on the first Saturday of each month.

TRAVEL

Rail
The railway network is excellent but expensive.

Bus

Bus lines operated by the railways offer free travel to holders of Eurail and Inter-Rail cards.

Driving

Germany boasts a highly efficient toll-free motorway system. There is a recommended speed limit of 130kmph on motorways and motorway-type arterial roads.

PUBLIC HOLIDAYS

New Year, 1 January; The Feast of the Three Kings (Baden-Württemberg, Bavaria and Saxony), 6 January; Good Friday, 28 March; Easter, 30/31 March; May Day, 1 May; Ascension of Christ, 8 May; Whitsun, 18/19 May; Feast of Corpus Christi (Baden-Württemberg, Bavaria, Hessen, North Rhine Westphalia, Rheinland-Pfalz, Saarland and Thüringen), 29 June; Festival of Peace (Augsburg town borough), 8 August; Assumption (Bavaria and Saarland), 15 August; German Unity Day, 3 October; Reformation Day (Brandenburg, Mecklenberg-Vorpommern, Saxony and Thüringen), 31 October; All Saints' Day (Baden-Württemberg, Bavaria, North Rhine Westphalia, Rheinland-Pfalz, Saarland and Thüringen), 1 November; Day of prayer and repentance (Sachsen), 19 November; Christmas, 25/26 December.

TELEPHONE INFORMATION

International Code	Country Code	Main City Area Codes	
00	49	Berlin	30
		Dresden	351
		Frankfurt/Main	69
		Hamburg	40
		Cologne	221
		Munich	89

When phoning within Germany, remember to put a "0" (zero) before the area code.

FRANÇAIS

AUBERGES DE JEUNESSE ALLEMANDES

Avec environ 617 auberges de jeunesse, l'Allemagne a le réseau le plus étendu dans le monde. Souvent plus grandes que la normale, et toujours de très haute qualité, elles reçoivent fréquemment des groupes d'écoliers pendant l'année scolaire, mais constituent une base excellente pour le voyageur international. Priorité est donnée aux moins de 27 ans et, en Bavière, l'âge limite supérieur est 26 ans, sauf en ce qui concerne les leaders de groupes et les familles. La plupart des auberges ont des chambres familiales.

Pratiquement toutes les auberges sont fermées du 24 au 26 décembre et beaucoup d'entre elles ferment pendant certaines périodes en automne, en hiver et au printemps. Vérifiez auprès de l'auberge en question ou dans le guide DJH.

Toutes les auberges de jeunesse de DJH offrent un prix tout compris (nuitée et petit déjeuner). Les prix varient selon les endroits et les services offerts et vont de DM 16,00-25,00 pour les moins de 27 ans et de DM 18,00-27,00 pour les plus de 27 ans. Une nuit dans un centre d'hébergement vous coûtera DM 25,00-45,00 petit déjeuner et linge compris. Si vous restez plusieurs jours à l'auberge de jeunesse on vous offre des reductions de prix.

Seule le guide DJH indique les AJ dans lesquelles il y a une taxe visiteur à payer.

Les auberges de jeunesse allemandes n'ont en principe pas de cuisine pour les voyageurs mais la plupart servent des repas.

PASSEPORTS ET VISAS

Les citoyens des pays de la CE munis d'un passeport valide n'ont pas besoin de visa.

Les ressortissants de nombreux pays n'ont pas besoin de visa s'ils s'engagent à ne pas prendre d'emploi et à ne pas séjourner plus de 3 mois.

De plus amples renseignements peuvent être obtenus auprès des bureaux du Consulat allemand ou des Ambassades.

SOINS MEDICAUX

Les médecins consultent normalement entre 10h et 12h et 16h et 18h sauf le mercredi, le samedi et le dimanche. En cas d'urgence, contacter le service des urgences.

Les hôpitaux et les services de consultations externes assurent un service d'urgences en dehors des heures mentionnées ci-dessus.

Pour appeler une ambulance, faites le 110.

HEURES D'OUVERTURE DES BANQUES

Les banques sont normalement ouvertes en semaine de 8h30 à 13h et de 14h30 à 16h (17h30 le jeudi). Elles sont fermées le samedi et le dimanche.

BUREAUX DE POSTE

Les bureaux de poste sont en principe ouverts du lundi au vendredi de 8h à 18h, et le samedi de 8h à 12h.

HEURES D'OUVERTURE DES MAGASINS

Les magasins sont en général ouverts entre 9h et 18h30 (quelquefois jusqu'à 20h30 le jeudi). Ils sont fermés le dimanche et les jours fériés et à 14h le samedi. Ils ont le droit de rester ouverts jusqu'à 16h le premier samedi du mois.

DEPLACEMENTS

Trains
Le réseau ferroviaire est excellent mais cher.

Autobus
Les services d'autobus gérés par les chemins de fer offrent des voyages gratuits aux personnes munies de cartes Eurail et Inter-Rail.

Automobiles
L'Allemagne est fière de son excellent réseau autoroutier sans péage. La limite de vitesse conseillée est de 130 km/h sur les autoroutes et les grandes artères du genre autoroute.

JOURS FERIES

Jour de l'An, 1 janvier; Épiphanie (Bade-Wurtemberg, Bavière et Saxe), 6 janvier; Vendredi saint, 28 mars; Pâques, 30/31 mars; Premier mai, 1 mai; L'Ascension, 8 mai; La Pentecôte, 18/19 mai; La Fête-Dieu (Bade-Wurtemberg, Bavière, Hesse, Rhénanie-du-Nord Westphalie, Rhénanie-Palatinat, Sarre et Thuringe), 29 juin; Festival de la Paix (Augsbourg), 8 août; L'Assomption (Bavière et Sarre), 15 août; Jour d'Unité de l'Allemagne, 3 octobre; La Réforme (Brandebourg, Mecklembourg-Poméramie-occidentale, Saxe et Thuringe), 31 octobre; La Toussaint (Bade-Wurtemberg, Bavière, Rhénanie-du-Nord Westphalie, Rhénanie-Palatinat, Sarre et Thuringe), 1 novembre; Jour de repentance et de prière (Sachsen), 19 novembre; Noël, 25/26 decembre.

TELEPHONE

Indicatif International	Indicatif du Pays	Indicatifs régionaux des Villes principales
00	49	Berlin 30
		Dresden 351
		Frankfurt/Main 69
		Hamburg 40
		Cologne 221
		Munich 89

En téléphonant en Allemagne, n'oubliez pas d'ajouter un '0' (zéro) devant l'indicatif régional.

DEUTSCH

DEUTSCHE JUGENDHERBERGEN

Mit etwa 617 Jugendherbergen hat Deutschland das größte Herbergsnetz der Welt. Die Herbergen sind oft überdurchschnittlich groß und immer von allerbestem Niveau. Während der Schulzeit werden sie hauptsächlich von Schulgruppen benutzt. Sie sind aber auch für international Reisende ein hervorragendes Quartier zum näheren Kennenlernen der Umgebung. Junge Leute unter 27 Jahren werden bevorzugt aufgenommen, und in Bayern beträgt die obere Altersgrenze, außer bei Gruppenleitern und Familien, 26 Jahre. Die meisten Herbergen haben Familienzimmer.

Fast alle Herbergen sind vom 24. bis 26.12. und viele sind auch im Herbst, Winter und Frühling zu bestimmten Zeiten geschlossen. Erkundigen Sie sich bei der betreffenden Herberge. Nähere Einzelheiten können auch dem DJH-Handbuch entnommen werden.

Alle Jugendherbergen des DJH bieten Übernachtung und Frühstück zu Inklusivpreisen an. Die Preise hängen von der Lage der Jugendherberge und der Ausstattung ab und liegen zwischen DM 16,00 und DM 25,00 für Junioren unter 27 Jahren und zwischen DM 18,00 und DM 27,00 für Senioren ab 27 Jahre. In Jugendgästehäusern (in der Regel 2-4-Bettzimmer und späte Schließzeiten) kostet die Übernachtung einschließlich Frühstück und Bettwäsche zwischen DM 25,00 und DM 45,00. Bei mehrtägigen Aufenthalten in JH besteht die Möglichkeit von Preisnachlässen.

Nur aus dem DJH-Handbuch ist ersichtlich, in welchen JH Kurtaxe bezahlt werden muß.

In deutschen Jugendherbergen gibt es gewöhnlich keine Einrichtungen für Selbstversorger. In den meisten werden aber Mahlzeiten geboten.

PÄSSE UND VISA

Staatsangehörige von EU-Ländern, die im Besitz eines gültigen Reisepasses sind, brauchen kein Visum.

Reisende aus vielen Ländern brauchen kein Visum, sofern sie in Deutschland keine Arbeit annehmen und sich nicht länger als 3 Monate im Land aufhalten.

Weitere Auskunft erteilen die deutschen Konsulate oder Botschaften.

GESUNDHEIT

Normale Sprechstundenzeit der Ärzte: 10.00-12.00 Uhr und 16.00-18.00 Uhr, außer mittwochs, samstags und sonntags. In dringenden Fällen kann man sich an den Notarzt wenden.

Krankenhäuser und ambulante Abteilungen bieten außerhalb der obigen Zeiten einen Notdienst.

Ein Krankenwagen wird über die Nr 110 gerufen.

GESCHÄFTSSTUNDEN DER BANKEN

Die Banken sind gewöhnlich werktags von 08.30-13.00 Uhr und von 14.30-16.00 Uhr (donnerstags 17.30 Uhr) geöffnet. Samstags und sonntags sind sie geschlossen.

POSTÄMTER

Postämter sind in der Regel montags bis freitags von 08.00-18.00 Uhr und samstags von 08.00-12.00 Uhr geöffnet.

LADENÖFFNUNGSZEITEN

Die Geschäfte sind im allgemeinen von 09.00 bis 18.30 Uhr (in gewissen Fällen donnerstags bis 20.30 Uhr) geöffnet. An Sonn- und Feiertagen sind sie geschlossen, und samstags schließen sie um 14.00 Uhr. Am ersten Samstag jedes Monats dürfen sie bis 16.00 Uhr geöffnet sein.

REISEN

Eisenbahn
Das Eisenbahnnetz ist ausgezeichnet, aber das Eisenbahnfahren ist teuer.

Busse
Wer im Besitz einer Eurail- oder Inter-Rail-Karte ist, kann die von der Eisenbahn betriebenen Busse kostenlos benutzen.

Autofahren
Deutschland ist stolz auf sein überaus leistungsfähiges, gebührenfreies Autobahnnetz. Für Autobahnen und autobahnartige Bundesstraßen wird ein Tempolimit von 130 km/h empfohlen.

FEIERTAGE

Neujahr, 1. Januar; Erscheinungsfest/Heilige Drei Könige (Baden-Württemberg, Bayern und Sachsen-Anhalt), 6. Januar; Karfreitag, 28. März; Ostern, 30./31. März; Maifeiertag, 1. Mai; Christi Himmelfahrt, 8. Mai; Pfingsten, 18./19. Mai; Fronleichnam (Baden-Württemberg, Bayern, Hessen, Nordrhein-Westfalen, Rheinland-Pfalz, Saarland und Thüringen), 29. Juni; Friedensfest (Stadtskreis Augsburg), 8. August; Mariä Himmelfahrt (Bayern und Saarland), 15. August; Tag der deutschen Einheit, 3. Oktober; Reformationstag, (Brandenburg, Mecklenburg-Vorpommern, Sachsen, Sachsen-Anhalt und Thüringen) 31. Oktober; Allerheiligen, (Baden-Württemberg, Bayern, Nordrhein-Westfalen, Rheinland-Pfalz, Saarland und Thüringen) 1. November; Buß- und Bettag (Sachsen), 19. November; Weihnachten, 25./26. Dezember

FERNSPRECHINFORMATIONEN

Internationale Kennzahl	Landes- Kennzahl	größere Städte - Ortsnetzkennzahlen	
00	49	Berlin	30
		Dresden	351
		Frankfurt/Main	69
		Hamburg	40
		Köln	221
		München	89

Wenn innerhalb Deutschlands telefoniert wird, ist vor der Ortsnetzkennzahl eine '0' (Null) zu wählen.

ESPAÑOL

ALBERGUES DE JUVENTUD ALEMANES

Con unos 617 albergues juveniles, Alemania tiene la mayor red del mundo. Con frecuencia los albergues son mayores que la media y del más alto nivel, sirven en gran medida a grupos escolares durante el curso lectivo, pero resultan una excelente base para la exploración por parte del turista internacional. Se da prioridad a los menores de 27 años y en Bavaria existe un límite de edad de 26 años, salvo para responsables de grupo y familias. La mayor parte de los albergues ofrecen habitaciones familiares.

Prácticamente todos los albergues cierran del 24 al 26 de diciembre y muchos están cerrados durante determinados períodos del otoño, invierno y primavera. Consultar con el albergue deseado o la guía DJH para más información.

Todos los albergues de DJH ofrecen precios contodo incluido (alojamiento y desayuno). Los precios varían según la ubicación y los servicios ofrecidos, desde DM 16,00 a DM 25,00 para menores de 27 años y desde DM 18,00 a DM 27,00 para mayores de 27 años. En centros de alojamiento (por regla general habitaciones de 2 a 4 camas y cierran más tarde) se paga desde DM 25,00 a DM 45,00 incluyendo desayuno y ropa de cama. Se puede ofrecir precios especiales para un alojamiento de algunos días en un albergue.

Sólo la guía de DJH indica los albergues en los cuales se debe pagar un impuesto de huésped.

Los albergues de juventud alemanes no disponen normalmente de cocina para huéspedes, pero sí sirven comidas.

PASAPORTES Y VISADOS

Los ciudadanos de países de la CE en posesión de un pasaporte válido no necesitan visado.

Muchos países no necesitan visado siempre que no tomen empleo y su estancia no supere los 3 meses.

Para más información, consultar a las oficinas consulares o embajadas alemanas.

SANIDAD

El horario de consulta médica suele ser de 10.00 a 12.00 horas y de 16.00 a 18.00 horas excepto el miércoles, sábado y domingo. En caso de urgencia se puede acudir al servicio médico de urgencias.

Los hospitales y las consultas para pacientes externos ofrecen un servicio de urgencias fuera de las horas anteriormente indicadas.

Para llamar a una ambulancia marcar 110.

HORARIO DE BANCOS

Los bancos suelen abrir los días laborables de 08.30 a 13.00 horas y de 14.30 a 16.00 horas (jueves 17.30 horas), y cierran los sábados y domingos.

CASAS DE CORREO

Por lo general las casas de correo abren de lunes a viernes de 08.00 a 18.00 horas y los sábados de 08.00 a 12.00 horas.

HORARIO COMERCIAL

Las tiendas abren normalmente de 09.00 a 18.30 horas (en algunos casos hasta las 20.30 horas los jueves). Cierran los domingos y festivos y a las 14.00 horas los sábados, si bien pueden estar abiertas hasta las 16.00 horas el primer sábado de cada mes.

DESPLAZAMIENTOS

Tren
La red ferroviaria es excelente pero cara.

Autobús
Las líneas de autobús operadas por la compañía ferroviaria ofrecen transporte gratuito a los titulares de tarjetas Eurail e Inter-Rail.

Coche
Alemania se enorgullece de su excelente sistema de autopistas sin peaje. El límite de velocidad recomendado para autopistas y carreteras principales tipo autopista es de 130 km/h.

DIAS FESTIVOS

Año Nuevo, 1 de enero; Epifanía (Baden-Württemberg, Baviera y Sajonia), 6 de enero; Viernes Santo, 28 de marzo; Semana Santa, 30/31 de marzo; Día del Trabajador, 1 de mayo; La Ascensión, 8 de mayo; Pentecostés, 18/19 mayo; Corpus Christi (Baden-Württemberg, Baviera, Hessen, Westfalen del Norte del Rino, Rheinland-Pfalz, Sarre y Thüringen), 29 de junio; Festival de la Paz (Baviera y Sarre), 8 de agosto; Día de la Unidad Alemana, 3 de octubre; Día de la Reforma (Brandenburg, Mecklenberg-Vorpommen, Sajonia y Thüringen), 31 de octubre; Día de Todos Los Santos (Baden-Württemberg, Baviera, Westfalen del Norte del Rino, Rheinland-Pfalz, Saare y Thüringen), 1 de noviembre; Día de Oración y Arrepentimiento (Sachsen), 19 de noviembre; Navidad, 25/26 de diciembre.

INFORMACION TELEFONICA

Código Internacional	Código Nacional	Indicativo de área de las Ciudades principales	
00	49	Berlin	30
		Dresden	351
		Frankfurt/Main	69
		Hamburg	40
		Colonia	221
		Munich	89

Al llamar en Alemania hay que marcar '0' (cero) antes del indicativo de área.

DISCOUNTS AND CONCESSIONS

Concessions are available at places near all Youth Hostels, especially for ski-lifts, swimming pools, sports facilities, ferries, sightseeing tours, boat trips, attractions etc.

Hostels in this country may also display this symbol.

Les auberges de ce pays pourront également afficher ce symbole.

Jugendherbergen in diesem Land können auch dieses Symbol zeigen.

Es posible que los albergues de este país exhiban además este símbolo.

Aachen ▲ 5SW "Colynshof", Maria-Theresia-Allee 260, 52074 Aachen. ☎ (241) 71101 **FAX** (241) 708219 ⤳ 170 ● DM 25,00 BBinc ⑩ P ꘯ 2km ⛺ 2, 12

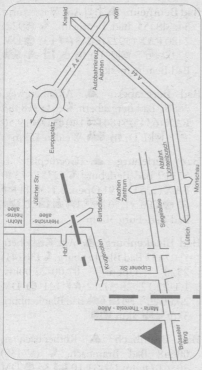

AACHEN

Aalen ▲ "Schubart- Jugendherberge", Stadionweg 8, 73430 Aalen. ☎ (7361) 49203 **FAX** (7361) 44682 ⤳ 118 ● DM 20,00 BBinc ⑩(L D) ꘯꘯ ꘯ Aalen 3km ⛺ 500m ap Waldfriedhof or Fachhochschule

Affalter ▲ Weg zur Jugendherberge 4, 08294 Affalter. ☎ (37751) 33940 **Open:** Mon- Fri 07.00-09.00hrs, 15.00-19.00hrs ⤳ 35 ● DM 20,00 BBinc ⑩ P ꘯ ꘯ Lößnitz, upper station 1.5km ⛺ Aue-Zwönitz T-363 800m ap Niederer Gasthof Affalter

Albersdorf ▲ Bahnhofstraße 19, 25767 Albersdorf. ☎ (4835) 642 **FAX** (4835) 8462 ⤳ 88 ● DM 20,00 BBinc ⑩ P ꘯ Albersdorf 500m

Alpirsbach ▲ Reinerzauer Steige 80, 72275 Alpirsbach. ☎ (7444) 2477 **FAX** (7444) 1304 ⤳ 124 ● DM 22,00 BBinc ⑩(L D) ꘯ Alpirsbach 2km

Altena ▲ "Burg Altena", Fritz-Thomee-Straße 80, 58762 Altena. ☎ (2352) 23522 **FAX** (2352) 26330 **Open:** 1.1-9.2; 8.3-31.12 ⤳ 38 ● DM 20,00 BBinc ⑩ ꘯ ꘯ P ꘯ Altena 1km

Altenahr ▲ Langfigtal 8, 53505 Altenahr. ☎ (2643) 1880 **FAX** (2643) 8136 ⤳ 98 ● DM 19,50 BBinc ⑩(L D) ✈ Köln/Bonn 50km ꘯ Altenahr 2km

Altenau ▲ 0.5SE Auf der Rose 11, 38707 Altenau. ☎ (5328) 361 **FAX** (5328) 8276 ⤳ 168 ● DM 20,00 BBinc ⑩ ꘯꘯ ꘯ P ꘯ ꘯ Goslar 22km ⛺ Goslar 22km

Altenberg ▲ Dresdener Str 70, 01773 Altenberg. ☎ (35056) 32318 **Open:** 08.00-10.00hrs, 16.00-18.00hrs ⤳ 114 ● DM 22,00 BBinc ⑩ ꘯꘯ ꘯ P ꘯ Alt 900m ⛴ Dresden/Heidenau-Altenburg ꘯ Altenburg 1km ⛺ 200m ap "Abzweig nach Schellerhau"

Altglashütten ▲ "Turnerheim", Am Sommerberg 26, 79868 Feldberg. ☎ (7655) 206 **FAX** (7655) 1627 ⤳ 89 BBinc ⑩ P ꘯ ꘯ Altglashütten 1.5km

Altleiningen ▲ "Jugendburg", 67317 Altleiningen. ☎ (6356) 1580 **FAX** (6356) 6364 ⤳ 153 ● DM 19,50 BBinc ⑩(L D) ꘯ ꘯ Grünstadt 10km

Am Kleinen Arber ☞ **Bodenmais**

Amberg ▲ Fronfestgasse 22, 92224 Amberg (Bavaria). ☎ (9621) 10369 **Open:** 4.1-23.12 ⤳ 38 ● DM 16,50 BBinc ꘯꘯ ꘯ 1.5km ⛺ 200m

Amorbach ▲ Kniebreche 4, 63916 Amorbach (Bavaria). ☏ (9373) 1366 **FAX** (9373) 7140 **Open:** 1.2-30.11 ✆ 93 ● DM 18,00 ⒝Ⓑinc ⦿ ♦♦♦ 🚃 1km

Annweiler ▲ Turnerweg 60, 76855 Annweiler. ☏ (6346) 8438 **FAX** (6346) 1623 ✆ 110 ⒝Ⓑinc ⦿ ♦♦♦ 🚃 Annweiler 1.5km

Arnsberg ▲ Rumbecker Höhe 1, 59821 Arnsberg. ☏ (2931) 10627 **FAX** (2931) 13589 **Open:** 3.1-21.12 ✆ 138 ● DM 20,00 ⒝Ⓑinc ⦿ 🍴 🅿 🚃 Arnsberg 2km 🚌 Wolfsschlucht 200m

Aschaffenburg ▲ Beckerstraße 47, 63739 Aschaffenburg (Bavaria). ☏ (6021) 930763 **FAX** (6021) 970694 **Open:** 21.1-19.12 ✆ 114 ● DM 18,00 ⒝Ⓑinc ⦿ ♦♦♦ 🚃 2.5km 🚌 300m

Ascheffel- Aschberg ▲ 24358 Ascheffel. ☏ (4353) 307 **FAX** (4353) 815 **Open:** 28.3-31.10 ✆ 38 ● DM 18,00 ⒝Ⓑinc ⦿(L D) 🅿 🚃 Owschlag, Eckernförde 🚌 2km

Augsburg ▲ Beim Pfaffenkeller 3, 86152 Augsburg (Bavaria). ☏ (821) 33909 **FAX** (821) 151149 **Open:** 13.1-20.12 ✆ 124 ● DM 20,00 ⒝Ⓑinc ⦿ ♦♦♦ 🚃 2km 🚌 2, 300m

Augustusburg ▲ 'Schloss Augustusburg', 09573 Augustusburg. ☏ (37291) 20256 **Open:** 06.30-22.00hrs ✆ 114 ● DM 20,00 ⒝Ⓑinc ⦿ 🎰 🍴 🅿 🚃 Erdmannsdorf + cable car to Augustusburg/Schloß 400m 🚌 Augustusburg T- 245 500m ap Schloßberg

Aurich ▲ 1SW Am Ellernfeld, 26603 Aurich. ☏ (4941) 2827 **FAX** (4941) 67482 **Open:** 16.1-14.12 ✆ 90 ● DM 22,00 ⒝Ⓑinc ⦿(L D) ♦♦♦ ♿ 🅿 🚲 🚃 Ostertorplatz 2km

Bacharach ▲ "Jugendburg Stahleck", 55422 Bacharach. ☏ (6743) 1266 **FAX** (6743) 2684 ✆ 207 ● DM 22,50 ⒝Ⓑinc ⦿(L D) ♦♦♦ ✈ Frankfurt/Main 80km 🚃 Bacharach 1km

Bad Bentheim ▲ 1E Am Wasserturm 34, 48455 Bad Bentheim. ☏ (5922) 2480 **FAX** (5922) 6043 ✆ 122 ● DM 22,00 ⒝Ⓑinc ⦿(L D) ♦♦♦ ♿ 🅿 🚲 🚃 Bad Bentheim 2km

Bad Bergzabern ▲ Altenbergweg, 76887 Bad Bergzabern. ☏ (6343) 8383 **FAX** (6343) 5184 ✆ 140 ● DM 19,50 ⒝Ⓑinc ⦿(L D) ♦♦♦ 🚃 Weiden 15km

Bad Berleburg ▲ Goetheplatz 1, 57319 Bad Berleburg ☏ (2751) 7340 **FAX** (2751) 2791 **Open:** 2.1-30.11 ✆ 60 ● DM 21,50 ⒝Ⓑinc ⦿ 🎰 🅿 🎣 🚃 Bad Berleburg 500m

Bad Blankenburg ▲ Am Kesselberg 1, 07422 Bad Blankenburg. ☏ (36741) 2528 **Open:** 07.00-22.00hrs, 1.1-22.12; 28-31.12 ✆ 141 ● DM 20,00 ⒝Ⓑinc ⦿ 🅿 🚃 Bad Blankenburg 3km 🚌 3km Ⓡ

Bad Brambach ▲ Röthenbach 4, 08648 Bad Brambach. ☏ (37438) 20541 **Open:** 1.2-31.10 ✆ 34 ● DM 20,00 ⦿(D) ♦♦♦ 🅿 ⛴ Bad Brambach 🚃 Bad Brambach HBf 2.5km

Bad Doberan ▲ Tempelberg, 18209 Bad Doberan. ☏ (38203) 2439 **FAX** (38203) 2439 **Open:** 08.00-09.00hrs, 15.00-22.00hrs, 11.1-31.10 ✆ 124 ● DM 19,00 ⒝Ⓑinc ⦿ 🚃 Bad Doberan 1km 🚌 Rostock Hbf- Bad Doberan 500m Ⓡ

Bad Driburg ▲ "Osning- JH", Schirrmannweg 1, 33014 Bad Driburg. ☏ (5253) 2570 **FAX** (5253) 3882 **Open:** 7.1-19.12 ✆ 124 ● DM 21,00 ⒝Ⓑinc ⦿ 🎰 🅿 🎣 🚃 Bad Driburg 2.5km 🚌 438 800m ap Friedhof-Langestraße

Bad Dürkheim ▲ St Christophorus Haus, Schillerstr 151, 67098 Bad Dürkheim. ☎ (6322) 63151 **FAX** (6322) 62442 🚲 16 ᴮᴮⁱⁿᶜ ⅲ 🚆 Bad Dürkeim 1km

Bad Ems ⛪ Alte Kemmenauer Str 41, 56130 Bad Ems. ☎ (2603) 2680 **FAX** (2603) 50384 🚲 121 ● DM 25,10 ᴮᴮⁱⁿᶜ ⅳ(L D) ⅲ 🚆 Bad Ems 2.5km

Bad Endorf- Hemhof ▲ Rankhamer Weg ll, 83093 Bad Endorf (Bavaria). ☎ (8053) 509 **FAX** (8053) 3292 **Open:** 1.2-30.11 🚲 40 ● DM 16,50 ᴮᴮⁱⁿᶜ ⅳ(D) ⅲ 🚆 3km

Bad Essen ▲ Schledehauser Str 81, 49152 Bad Essen. ☎ (5472) 2123 **FAX** (5472) 6233 🚲 140 ● DM 22,00 ᴮᴮⁱⁿᶜ ⅳ(L D) ⅲ 🚲 🅿 🚴 🚆 Bohmte 7km

Bad Frankenhausen ▲ Bahnhofstr. 6, 06567 Bad Frankenhausen ☎ (34671) 2018 **FAX** (34671) 2018 **Open:** 06.00-22.00hrs, 1.1-20.12; 29-31.12 🚲 120 ● DM 20,00 ᴮᴮⁱⁿᶜ ⅳ ⅲ 🚆 Bad Frankenhausen 500m 🚌 800m ⓡ (Grps)

Bad Freienwalde ▲ 2W Hammerthal 3, 16259 Bad Freienwalde ☎ /**FAX** (3344) 3875 **Open:** 07.30-22.00hrs, 1.1-30.11 🚲 57 ● DM 20,00 ᴮᴮⁱⁿᶜ ⅳ(B D) ⅲ ✈ Berlin 55km 🚆 Bad Freienwalde 3km ⓡ 1.11-31.03, on inquiry

Bad Gandersheim ▲ Am Kantorberg 17, 37581 Bad Gandersheim. ☎ (5382) 2967 **FAX** (5382) 8368 🚲 91 ● DM 20,00 ᴮᴮⁱⁿᶜ ⅳ ⅲ 🚲 🅿 🚆 24 min

Bad Herrenalb ▲ "Ev Ferienheim", Aschenhüttenweg 44, 76332 Bad Herrenalb. ☎ (7083) 2430 **FAX** (7083) 51031 🚲 102 ᴮᴮⁱⁿᶜ ⅳ ⅲ 🚲 🅿 🚆 Karlsruhe 🚌 A 4km ap Bad Herrenalb ⓡ (Erika Wettach, Links der Alb 23, 76199 Karlsruhe, ☎ (721) 881465, **FAX** (721) 881430)

Bad Hersfeld ▲ 2N Wehneberger Str 29, 36251 Bad Hersfeld. ☎ (6621) 2403 **FAX** (6621) 14429 **Open:** 1.1-23.12; 27-31.12 🚲 121 ● DM 20,50 ᴮᴮⁱⁿᶜ ⅳ ⅲ 🅿 🚆 Bad Hersfeld 2.5km

Bad Homburg ▲ 0.5SW Meiereiberg 1, 61348 Bad Homburg. ☎ (6172) 23950 **FAX** (6172) 22312 **Open:** 1.1-23.12; 27-31.12 🚲 99 ● DM 21,00 ᴮᴮⁱⁿᶜ ⅳ ⅲ 🅿 ⛵ 🚆 Bad Homburg 2km 🚌 S5 1.5km ap Bad Homburg Bahnhof

Bad Honnef ▲ Selhoferstr 106, 53604 Bad Honnef. ☎ (2224) 71300 **FAX** (2224) 79226 🚲 210 ● DM 25,00 ᴮᴮⁱⁿᶜ ⅳ ⅾ ⅲ 🅿 🚆 Bad Honnef 3km

Bad Iburg ▲ 1.5N Offenes Holz, 49186 Bad Iburg. ☎ (5403) 74220 **FAX** (5403) 9770 🚲 142 ● DM 22,00 ᴮᴮⁱⁿᶜ ⅳ(L D) ⅲ 🚲 🅿 🚴 🚆 Bad Iburg 2km 🚌 2km ap Offenes Holz

Bad Karlshafen ▲ 0.5N Winnefelder Str 7, 34385 Bad Karlshafen. ☎ (5672) 338 **FAX** (5672) 8361 **Open:** 1.1-23.12; 27-31.12 🚲 140 ● DM 20,50 ᴮᴮⁱⁿᶜ ⅳ ⅲ 🅿 ⛵ 🚆 Bad Karlshafen 250m

Bad Kösen ▲ Bergstr 3, 06628 Bad Kösen. ☎ (34463) 27597 **Open:** 06.00-22.00hrs, 11.1-14.12 🚲 119 ● DM 18,00 ᴮᴮⁱⁿᶜ ⅳ ⅲ ⅾ 🚲 🅿 ⛵ 🚆 Bad Kösen 2km

Bad Kreuznach ⛪ ⒸⒸ Auf dem Kuhberg, 55543 Bad Kreuznach. ☎ (671) 62855 **FAX** (671) 75351 🚲 136 ● DM 25,10 ᴮᴮⁱⁿᶜ ⅳ(L D) ⅲ ⅾ ✈ Frankfurt/Main 80km 🚆 Bad Kreuznach 5km 🚌 4 500m

Bad Lausick ▲ Herbergsweg 2, 04651/Ortsteil Buchheim. ☎ (34345) 22657 **Open:** 06.00-22.00hrs 🚲 140 ● DM 22,00 ᴮᴮⁱⁿᶜ ⅳ ⅲ 🅿 🧗 🚆 Bad Lausick 2km 🚌 Leipzig-Mittweida T-671 200m ap Buchheim

Bad Lauterberg ▲ Flösswehrtal 25, 37431 Bad Lauterberg. ✆ (5524) 3738 **FAX** (5524) 5708 ✈ 131 ⬤ DM 20,00 BBinc 🍴 ♔ 🖕 🅿 🛉 ⛟ 40 min 🚌 5 min

Bad Marienberg ▲ Erlenweg 4, 56470 Bad Marienberg. ✆ (2661) 5008 **FAX** (2661) 61898 ✈ 121 ⬤ DM 19,50 BBinc 🍴(L D) 🛉 Alt 400m ⛟ Erbach 6km

Bad Mergentheim ☞ **Igersheim**

Bad Münstereifel- Rodert ▲ Herbergsweg 15, 53902 Bad Münstereifel- Rodert. ✆ (2253) 7438 **FAX** (2253) 7483 **Open:** 6.1-21.12 ✈ 164 ⬤ DM 25,00 BBinc 🍴 ♔ ♔ ♿ 🅿 ⛟ Bad Münstereifel 2km

Bad Neuenahr- Ahrweiler ⚠ 🆔 "Jugendgästehaus" St Pius-Str 7, 53474 Bad Neuenahr- Ahrweiler. ✆ (2641) 34924 **FAX** (2641) 31574 ✈ 140 ⬤ DM 26,30 BBinc 🍴(L D) ♔ ♿ ✈ Köln/Bonn 70km ⛟ Ahrweiler 2km

Bad Oldesloe ▲ Konrad- Adenauer- Ring 2, 23843 Bad Oldesloe. ✆ (4531) 5945 **FAX** (4531) 67574 **Open:** 6.1-30.11 ✈ 125 ⬤ DM 20,00 BBinc 🍴(L D) 🅿 🚲 ⚓ ⛟ Bad Oldesloe 1.5km 🚌 100m

Bad Sachsa ▲ Jugendherbergsstr 9-11, 37441 Bad Sachsa. ✆ (5523) 8800 **FAX** (5523) 7163 ✈ 121 ⬤ DM 20,00 BBinc 🍴 ♔ 🅿 🛉 ⛟ 20 min

Bad Salzungen J.H. ▲ Bad Salzungen, Kaltenborner- Str- 70, 36433 Bad Salzungen. ✆ (3695) 622208 **Open:** 07.00-22.00hrs **Shut:** 24-27.12 ✈ 60 ⬤ DM 18,00 BBinc 🍴 ♔ 🅿 ⛟ Bad Salzungen 1.5km 🅡

Bad Schandau-Ostrau ▲ Dorfstr 14, 01814 Bad Schandau- Ostrau. ✆ (35022) 42408 **FAX** (35022) 42408 **Open:** 07.00-22.00hrs ✈ 101 ⬤ DM 22,00 🍴 ♔ 🖕 ⛟ Dresden- Schöna 245 ap Bad Schandau 10km 🚌 Bad Schandau, Elbkai 200m ap "Ostrauer Scheibe"

Bad Segeberg ▲ Kastanienweg 1, 23795 Bad Segeberg. ✆ (4551) 2531 **FAX** (4551) 4518 ✈ 152 ⬤ DM 20,00 BBinc 🍴(L D) 🅿 ⛟ Bad Segeberg 300m

Bad Sulza ▲ August- Bebel- Str 27, 99518 Bad Sulza. ✆ (36461) 20567 **FAX** (36461) 20567 **Open:** 07.00-22.00hrs, 1.1-22.12; 28-31.12 ✈ 74 ⬤ DM 18,00 BBinc 🍴 ♔ ▣ 🅿 ⛟ Bad Sulza 1km 🚌 1km 🅡

Bad Urach ▲ Burgstr 45, 72574 Bad Urach. ✆ (7125) 8025 **FAX** (7125) 40358 ✈ 123 ⬤ DM 20,00 BBinc 🍴(L D) ♔ 🅿 🚌 300m ap Krankenhaus

Bad Wimpfen ▲ Im Burgviertel 21-23, 74206 Bad Wimpfen. ✆ (7063) 7069 **FAX** (7063) 1484 ✈ 62 ⬤ DM 22,00 BBinc 🍴(L D) ♔ 🏠 ⛟ Bad Wimpfen 400m 🚌 400m ap Alte Kelter

Bad Zwischenahn ▲ Schirrmannweg 14, 26160 Bad Zwischenahn. ✆ (4403) 2393 **FAX** (4403) 64588 ✈ 115 ⬤ DM 20,00 BBinc 🍴(L D) 🖕 🅿 🚲 ⚓ ⛟ Bad Zwischenahn 3km

Baden-Baden ⚠ 2NW Werner-Dietz JH, Hardbergstr 34, 76532 Baden- Baden. ✆ (7221) 52223 **FAX** (7221) 60012 ✈ 151 ⬤ DM 22,00 BBinc 🍴 ♔ 🅿 ⛟ Baden-Baden 5km 🚌 1km ap Große Dollenstr

Balingen ▲ Schloßstr 5, 72336 Balingen. ✆ (7433) 20805 **FAX** (7433) 5911 **Open:** 2.3-30.11 ✈ 49 ⬤ DM 20,00 BBinc 🍴(L D) ♔ 🏠 ⛟ Balingen 1km 🚌 50m ap Volksbank

Balingen ☞ **Lochen**

Bamberg "Wolfsschucht" ▲ Oberer Leinritt 70, 96049 Bamberg (Bavaria). ☎ (951) 56002 **FAX** (951) 55211 **Open**: 1.2-14.12 ⊘ 84 ● DM 20,00 ⃞BB⃞inc ⟦❍⟧ ⃟⃟⃟ 🚌 6km 🚐 1 and 18, 200m

Barth ▲ Donnerberg, 18356 Barth. ☎ (38231) 2843 **FAX** (38231) 2090 **Open**: 08.00-09.00, 15.00-22.00hrs, 1.2-30.11 ⊘ 157 ● DM 17,00 ⃞BB⃞inc ⟦❍⟧(L D) ⃟⃟⃟ ⃟ 🅿 ⚓ 🚌 Barth 3km 🚐 3km Ⓡ

Bautzen ▲ Am Zwinger 1, 02625 Bautzen. ☎ (3591) 44045 **Open**: 07.00-09.00hrs, 15.00-22.00hrs ⊘ 50 ● DM 17,00 ⟦❍⟧(B L) ⃟⃟⃟ 🍴 🚌 Dresden-Görlitz 230 ap Bautzen 3km

Bayerisch-Eisenstein ▲ Brennesstr 23, 94252 Bayerisch-Eisenstein (Bavaria). ☎ (9925) 337 **FAX** (9925) 730 **Open**: 1.1-31.10; 26-31.12 ⊘ 166 ● DM 20,00 ⃞BB⃞inc ⟦❍⟧ 🍴 ⃟⃟⃟ ▣ ⤳ Alt 830m 🚌 2.5km

Bayreuth ▲ Universitätsstr 28, 95447 Bayreuth (Bavaria). ☎ (921) 251262 **FAX** (921) 512805 **Open**: 1.2-14.12 ⊘ 150 ● DM 20,00 ⃞BB⃞inc 🍴 ⃟⃟⃟ ▣ 🚌 5km 🚐 1km

Bayrischzell - Sudelfeld ▲ Unteres Sudelfeld 9, 83735 Bayrischzell (Bavaria). ☎ (8023) 675 **FAX** (8023) 274 **Open**: 1.1-31.10; 28-31.12 ⊘ 94 ● DM 22,00 ⃞BB⃞inc ⟦❍⟧(D) ⃟⃟⃟ ⤳ Alt 1200m 🚌 5km 🚐 500m

Beckerwitz ▲ Haus Nr 21, 23968 Beckerwitz. ☎ (38428) 362 **FAX** (38428) 362 **Open**: 08.00-09.00hrs, 15.00-22.00hrs, 28.12.96-31.10 ⊘ 106 ● DM 19,00 ⃞BB⃞inc ⟦❍⟧(L D) ⃟⃟⃟ 🍴 🅿 🚲 ⚓ 🚌 Wismar 8km 🚐 500m Ⓡ

Bederkesa ▲ ⃞1 W⃞ Margaretenweg 2, 27624 Bederkesa. ☎ (4745) 406 **FAX** (4745) 8058 **Open**: 1.4-31.10 ⊘ 70 ● DM 20,00 ⃞BB⃞inc ⟦❍⟧(L D) ⃟⃟⃟ 🚲 ⚓

🚌 Bremerhaven 25km 🚐 1829 Bremerhaven-Bederkesa 25km

BENEDIKTBEUERN (2 Hostels)

Benediktbeuern - "JH Don-Bosco" ⚠ Don- Bosco- Str 3, 83671 Benediktbeuern (Bavaria). ☎ (8857) 88350 **FAX** (8857) 88351 **Open**: 11.1-14.12 ⊘ 170 ● DM 22,00 ⃞BB⃞inc ⟦❍⟧(D) ⃟⃟⃟ 🚌 500m

Benediktbeuern - "JH für Mädchen" ▲ Bahnhofstr 58, 83671 Benediktbeuern (Bavaria). ☎ (8857) 9050 **Open**: 16.1-14.12 ⊘ 130 ● DM 20,00 ⃞BB⃞inc ⃟⃟⃟

Berchtesgaden ☞ **Strub**

Bergen ▲ Hochfellnstr 18, 83346 Bergen (Bavaria). ☎ (8662) 8246 **FAX** (8662) 5954 **Open**: 6.1-14.11 ⊘ 62 ● DM 20,00 ⃞BB⃞inc ⟦❍⟧(D) ▣ ⤳ Alt 560m 🚌 3km 🚐 100m

BERLIN (3 Hostels)
Address all Advance Bookings at least 14 days before departure (back from Berlin) to: D J H. Central Booking Service, Kluckstr. 3, 10785 Berlin ☎ (30) 2623024 **FAX** (30) 2629529

Berlin - JH Ernst Reuter (*see town plan on next page*) ⚠ ⃞18N⃞ Hermsdorfer Damm 48-50, 13467 Berlin. ☎ (30) 4041610 **FAX** (30) 4045972 ⊘ 111 ● DM 26,00 ⟦❍⟧ ✈ Tegel A🚐 128 🚌 Berlin- Friedrichstraße 11.5km 🚐 125 5m ap YH 🚋 (S-Bahn) S 25 Tegel 2km Ⓤ U 6 ALT-Tegel 2km Ⓡ

Berlin - JGH Berlin (*see town plan on next page*) ⚠ ⃞3 W⃞ Kluckstr. 3, 10785 Berlin. ☎ (30) 2611097 **FAX** (30) 2650383 ⊘ 364 ● DM 32,00 ⟦❍⟧ 🅿 ✈ Tegel A🚐 X09 🚌 Berlin-Zoologischer Garten 2km 🚐 129 Gedenkstätte Dt. Widerstand 30m ap YH 🚋 (S-Bahn) S 1, S 2, Potsdamer Platz 1km Ⓤ U 1 Kurfürstenstraße 0.5km, U 2 Bülowstrasse 1km Ⓡ

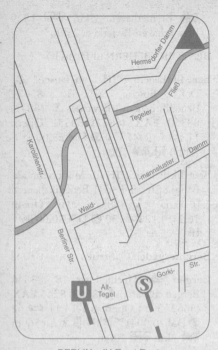

BERLIN - JH Ernst Reuter

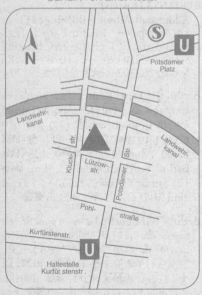

BERLIN - JGH (Kluckstraße)

Berlin - **JGH am Wannsee** ⛺ 25 SW
Badeweg 1, Ecke Kronprinzessinnenweg,
14129 Berlin. ☎ (30) 8032034 **FAX**

(30) 8035908 ✉ 264 ● DM 32,00 ✆
� & ⬛ 🅿 ⛵ ✈ Tegel 🚆 Berlin-
Wannsee 1.5km 🚌 118 Badeweg
30m 🚆 (S-Bahn) S1, S3, S7, Nikolassee
500m Ⓡ

BERLIN - YGH am Wannsee

Bernburg ▲ Krumbholzallee 2, 06406
Bernburg. ☎ (3471) 352027 **Open:**
06.00-22.00hrs (Reception from
15.00hrs) ✉ 67 ● DM 22,00 BB|inc ✆
♦♦♦ ⬛ 🚆 4km 🚌 city line 201

Bernkastel-Kues ▲ Jugendherbergsstr
1, 54470 Bernkastel- Kues. ☎ (6531)
2395 **FAX** (6531) 1529 ✉ 96 ● DM
20,50 BB|inc ✆(L D) ♦♦♦ 🚆 Wittlich
15km

Biberach ▲ Heusteige 40, 88400
Biberach. ☎ (7351) 21885 **FAX** (7351)
21315 ✉ 150 ● DM 22,00 BB|inc
✆(L D) ♦♦♦ 🅿 🚆 Biberach 1.5km

Biedenkopf ⛺ 0.5W "Haus der
Jugend", Am Freibad 15, 35216
Biedenkopf. ☎ (6461) 5100 **FAX**
(6461) 2425 **Open:** 1.1-23.12;
27-31.12 ✉ 207 ● DM 22,00 BB|inc

|⦿| ♦♦♦ 🅿 ⚡ ♿ ⚓ 🚻 Biedenkopf 2km
🚌 500m ap Kath. Kirche

Bielefeld ▲ Oetzer Weg 25, 33605
Bielefeld-Sieker. ℰ (521) 22227 **FAX**
(521) 25196 **Open:** 18.1-21.12 ✉ 164
⦿ DM 21,00 [BB]inc |⦿| ♣ 🅿 🚻
Bielefeld 6km 🚃 2, 2km ap Sieker

Biggesee ▲ Auf dem Mühlenberg,
57462 Olpe-Stade. ℰ (2761) 6775 **FAX**
(2761) 64714 ✉ 240 ⦿ DM 21,50
[BB]inc |⦿| ♣ 🅿 ⚓ 🚻 Eichhagen 1.5km

Bilstein ▲ "Jugendburg", Von-Gevore-
Weg 10, 57368 Lennestadt. ℰ (2721)
81217 **FAX** (2721) 83016 ✉ 226 ⦿
DM 21,50 [BB]inc |⦿| 🏨 ♣ 🅿 🚻
Altenhundem 5km 🚌 106 300m
ap Bilstein-Werth

Bingen-Bingerbrück ▲ Herterstr 51,
55411 Bingen-Bingerbrück. ℰ (6721)
32163 **FAX** (6721) 34012 ✉ 176 ⦿
DM 19,50 [BB]inc |⦿| ♦♦♦ ✈
Frankfurt/Main 60km 🚻 Bingen (Rh)
Hbf 800m

BINZ (2 Hostels)

Binz ▲ Strandpromenade 35, 18609
Ostseebad Binz/Rügen. ℰ (38393)
32597 **FAX** (38393) 32596 **Open:**
08.00-09.00hrs, 15.00-22.00hrs,
28.12.96-18.12 ✉ 143 ⦿ DM 24,00
[BB]inc |⦿|(L D) ♦♦♦ 🔲 ⚓ 🚻 Binz 500m
🚌 500m Ⓡ

Binz ▲ 18609 OT- Prora ℰ (38393)
32844 **FAX** (38393) 32845 **Open:**
29.12.96-30.11 ✉ 401 ⦿ DM 22,00
[BB]inc |⦿| ♦♦♦ 🔲 ♣ 🅿 ⚓ 🚻 Prora/Ost
200m Ⓡ

Bispingen ▲ Töpinger Str 42, 29646
Bispingen. ℰ (5194) 2375 **FAX** (5194)
7743 ✉ 108 ⦿ DM 20,00 [BB]inc |⦿| ♣
🅿 🚻 Soltau 18km

Blankenheim ▲ Burg 1, 53945
Blankenheim ℰ (2449) 1079 ✉ 158
⦿ DM 25,00 [BB]inc |⦿| ♦♦♦ 🏨 🅿

Blankenheim ▲ Burg 1, 53945
Blankenheim ℰ (2449) 1079 ✉ 158
⦿ DM 25,00 [BB]inc |⦿| ♦♦♦ 🏨 🅿

Blaubeuren ▲ Auf dem Rucken 69,
89143 Blaubeuren. ℰ (7344) 6444
FAX (7344) 21416 ✉ 126 ⦿ DM
22,00 [BB]inc |⦿|(L D) ♦♦♦ ▣ 🚻
Blaubeuren 700m 🚌 300m

Blockhaus ▲ 51580 Reichshof-
Eckenhagen. ℰ (2265) 8628 **FAX**
(2265) 9042 **Open:** 1.1-30.11;
28-31.12 ✉ 58 ⦿ DM 20,00 [BB]inc ♣
🅿 ⚡ 🚻 Gummersbach 18km 🚌
Eckenhagen 3km

Blomberg ▲ Ulmenallee 15, 32825
Blomberg. ℰ (5235) 7255 **FAX** (5235)
2130 ✉ 124 ⦿ DM 21,50 [BB]inc |⦿| ♣
🅿 🚻 Schieder 5km 🚌 Altenheim
700m

Bockswiese ☞ **Hahnenklee**

Bodenmais - Am Kleinen Arber ▲
94249 Bodenmais (Bavaria). ℰ (9924)
281 **FAX** (9924) 850 **Open:** 1.1-19.4;
21.5-31.10; 27-31.12 ✉ 81 ⦿ DM
22,00 [BB]inc |⦿|(D) ♦♦♦ ⚡ Alt 1330m 🚻
10km

Bodenwerder ▲ Richard-Schirrmann-
Weg, 37619 Bodenwerder. ℰ (5533)
2685 **FAX** (5533) 6203 ✉ 124 ⦿ DM
20,00 [BB]inc |⦿| ♦♦♦ ♿ ♣ 🅿 ⚓ 🚻
Hameln 25km

Bollendorf ⛺ Auf der Ritschlay 1,
54669 Bollendorf. ℰ (6526) 200 **FAX**
(6526) 1204 ✉ 156 ⦿ DM 25,10 [BB]inc
|⦿|(L D) ♦♦♦ ✈ Luxembourg 40km 🚻
Trier 20km

BONN (2 Hostels)

Bonn - **Bad Godesberg** (*see town plan on
next page*) ⛺ "Jugendgästehaus",
Horionstr 60, 53177 Bonn. ℰ (228)
317516 **FAX** (228) 314537 ✉ 90 ⦿
DM 37,00 [BB]inc |⦿| 🅿 🚻 Bonn-Bad
Godesberg 5km 🚌 615 Ⓤ 63,16

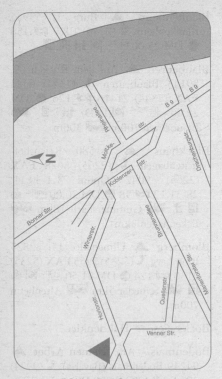

BONN - Bad Godesberg

Bonn - Venusberg ▲ YGH, Haager Weg 42, 53127 Bonn. ☎ (228) 289970, 281200 **FAX** (228) 2899714 ⚑ 249 ● DM 37,00 [BB]inc ¶⊙¶ ♦♦ & ⬛ ✈ Köln-Bonn 30km 🚌 6km 🚃 621

Bonndorf/Schw ▲ [1 W] Waldallee 27, 79848 Bonndorf. ☎ (7703) 359 **FAX** (7703) 1686 ⚑ 232 ● DM 20,00 [BB]inc ¶⊙¶ ♦♦ ⬛ ⬛ 🚂 🚌 Neustadt 25km 🚃 Bonndorf 1km ap Bonndorf-Bnf

Börger ▲ [1 NW] Herbergsweg 2, 26904 Börger. ☎ (5953) 228 **Open:** 1.4-31.10 ⚑ 62 ● DM 20,00 ¶⊙¶(L D) ♦♦ ♂

Borgwedel ▲ Kreisstr 17, 24857 Borgwedel. ☎ (4354) 219 **FAX** (4354) 1305 ⚑ 305 ● DM 20,00 [BB]inc ¶⊙¶(L D) ⬛ ⬛ ⬛ ◆ 🚂 Schleswig

Borkum ▲ [7 SE] Reedestr.2000, 26757 Borkum, (North Sea). ☎ (4922) 579

FAX (4922) 7124 ⚑ 500 [BB]inc ① ⬛ ♂ ◆ 🚢 Emden-Außenhaufen ⓡ

Born-Ibenhorst ▲ Im Darßer Wald, 18375 Born-Ibenhorst. ☎ (38234) 229 **FAX** (38234) 231 **Open:** 08.00-09.00hrs, 15.00-22.00hrs, 15.4-5.10 ⚑ 180 ● DM 16,50 [BB]inc ¶⊙¶(L D) ♦♦ ⬛ ⬛ ♂ 🚂 Ribnitz-Damgarten 20km 🚃 500m ap Ibenhorst ⓡ ● 150 spaces for tents

Brandenburg ▲ Hevellerstr 7, 14776 Brandenburg. ☎ (3381) 521040 **Open:** 07.00-11.30hrs, 15.00-21.30hrs, 1.1-15.12 ⚑ 80 ● DM 20,00 [BB]inc ¶⊙¶(D) ⬛ 🚂 Brandenburg 1.5km 🚃 300m

Braunlage ▲ Von- Langen- Str 28, 38700 Braunlage. ☎ (5520) 2238 **FAX** (5520) 1569 ⚑ 130 ● DM 20,00 [BB]inc ¶⊙¶ ♦♦ ⬛ ⬛ ✢ 🚂 Bad Harzburg 24km

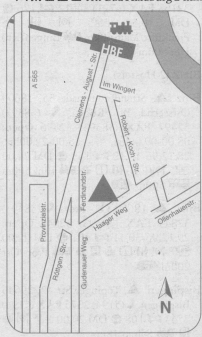

BONN - Venusberg

Braunsdorf ▲ Dorfstr 17, 15518 Braunsdorf. ☎ (33633) 635 **Open:**

07.00-22.00hrs ⚑ 43 ● DM 20,00 [BB]inc ⵾⊙⵾ ⵾⵾⵾ ⛵ ⚓ 🚋 Fürstenwalde 12km 🚐 3 daily - Braunsdorf

Breisach ⚠ Rheinuferstr 12, 79206 Breisach. 📞 (7667) 7665 **FAX** (7667) 1847 ⚑ 158 ● DM 22,00 [BB]inc ⵾⊙⵾ ⛁ 🅿 ⵯⵯ ⚓ 🚋 Breisach 1.5km 🚐 1.5km

Bremen ⚠ [1 NW] [IBN] YGH, Kalkstr 6, 28195 Bremen. 📞 (421) 171369 **FAX** (421) 171102 ⚑ 168 ● DM 22,00 [BB]inc ⵾⊙⵾(L D) ⵾⵾⵾ ⛙ ⛪ 🅿 ⵯⵯ ⚓ ✈ Bremen 5km 🚋 Bremen 3km 🚐 26 200m ap Brill 🚊 6 200m ap Brill

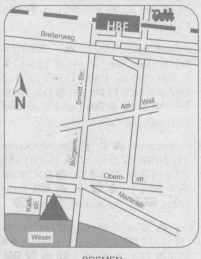

BREMEN

Bremen- Blumenthal ▲ Bgm-Dehnkamp-Str 22, 28777 Bremen. 📞 (421) 601005 **FAX** (421) 6090795 **Open:** 1.3-31.10 ⚑ 54 ● DM 20,00 [BB]inc ⵾⊙⵾(L D) 🅿 ⚓ ✈ Bremen 30km 🚋 Bremen- Vegesack 6km 🚐 70, 71 2km ap Fähre Blumenthal

Bremerhaven ⚠ YH + YGH Gausstr 54-56, 27580 Bremerhaven. 📞 (471) 85652 **FAX** (471) 87426 **Open:** 16.1-19.12 ⚑ 58 YGH; 82 YH ● DM 26,50 YGH; DM 22,00 YH [BB]inc ⵾⊙⵾(L D) ⵯⵯ ⚓ 🚢 Bremerhaven 🚐 2,6 300m ap Gesundheitsamt

Bremervörde ▲ Feldstr 9, 27432 Bremervörde. 📞 (4761) 1275 **FAX** (4761) 70701 ⚑ 122 ● DM 20,00 [BB]inc ⵾⊙⵾(L D) ⵾⵾⵾ ⛙ 🅿 ⵯⵯ 🚋 Bremervörde 3km 🚐 3km ap Waldstr.

Bremsdorfer Mühle ▲ 15890 Bremsdorf. 📞 (33654) 272 **FAX** (33654) 272 **Open:** 07.00-22.00hrs, 1.11-28.2 on inquiry ⚑ 160 ● DM 20,00 [BB]inc ⵾⊙⵾ ⵾⵾⵾ 🚋 Eisenhüttenstadt 15Km/Grunow 8km

Breuberg, Burg ⚠ [3E] 64747 Breuberg. 📞 (6165) 3403 **FAX** (6165) 6469 **Open:** 1.1-23.12; 27-31.12 ⚑ 129 ● DM 22,00 [BB]inc 🏠 🅿 🚋 Höchst/Odenwald 7km 🚐 Höchst to Breuberg 1.5km ap Neustadt Marktplatz

Brieselang ▲ Am Wald 24, 14656 Brieselang. 📞 (33232) 39408 **FAX** (33232) 39408 **Open:** 07.00-12.00hrs, 15.00-22.00hrs ⚑ 71 ● DM 18,00 [BB]inc ⵾⊙⵾(B D) ⛁ ✈ Tegel 20km 🚋 Brieselang 1km Ⓡ

Brilon ▲ Am Hölsterloh 3, 59929 Brilon. 📞 (2961) 2281 **FAX** (2961) 51731 **Open:** 16.1-14.12 ⚑ 151 ● DM 21,50 [BB]inc ⵾⊙⵾ ⛙ 🅿 🚋 Brilon-Wald 6km 🚐 482 150m ap YH

Brodenbach ▲ Moorkamp 7, 56332 Brodenbach. 📞 (2605) 3389 **FAX** (2605) 4244 ⚑ 135 ● DM 19,50 [BB]inc ⵾⊙⵾(L D) ⵾⵾⵾ 🚋 Löf 3km

Brotterode ▲ Am Zainhammer 4, 98599 Brotterode. 📞 (36840) 32125 **FAX** (36840) 32125 **Open:** 07.00-22.00hrs, 1.1-23.12; 28-31.12 ⚑ 65 ● DM 18,00 [BB]inc ⵾⊙⵾ ⵾⵾⵾ ⚓ 🚐 Mause 500m Ⓡ

Brüggen ▲ Auf dem Eggenberg 1, 41379 Brüggen. 📞 (2163) 5161 **FAX** (2163) 59967 ⚑ 134 ⵾⊙⵾ ⵷ ⵾⵾⵾ 🅿 🚋

Mönchengladbach 10km 🚐 074 ap Viersen

Buchheim ☞ **Bad Lausick**

Buckow ▲ ⬜1.5S⬜ Berliner Str 36, 15377 Buckow. ☏ (33433) 286 **FAX** (33433) 286 **Open:** 06.00-22.00hrs, 1.2-15.12 🛏 98 ⊖ DM 22,00 ⬜BB⬜inc ⚹ ⁘ ✈ Schönefeld 50km 🚊 Buckow 2km 🚐 10m ⓡ (1.5-30.6: 3 weeks)

Büdingen ▲ ⬜2NE⬜ Jugendherberge 1, 63654 Büdingen. ☏ (6042) 3697 **FAX** (6042) 68178 **Open:** 1.1-23.12; 27-31.12 🛏 121 ⊖ DM 23,50 ⬜BB⬜inc ⚹ ⁘ 🅿 ⚑ 🚊 Büdingen 4km

Burg auf Fehmarn ▲ Mathildenstr 34, 23769 Burg auf Fehmarn. ☏ (4371) 2150 **FAX** (4371) 6680 🛏 175 ⊖ DM 20,00 ⬜BB⬜inc ⚹(L D) ① 🅿 ♿ ⚑ ⛴ Puttgarden 🚊 Puttgarden 🚐 Burg 1.5km

Burg an der Wupper ▲ An der Jugendherberge 7-11, 42659 Solingen. ☏ (212) 41025 **FAX** (212) 49449 🛏 118 ⊖ DM 24,00 ⬜BB⬜inc ⚹ ⁘ 🅿 🚊 Solingen 3km 🚐 683, 266 ap Solingen Central Station

Burg/Spreewald ▲ JH 'Friedrich-Ludwig- Jahn', Jugendherbergsweg 8, 03096 Burg/Spreewald. ☏ (35603) 225 **FAX** (35603) 225 **Open:** 07.00-11.00hrs, 13.00-16.00hrs, 18.00-21.00hrs, 3.1-15.12 🛏 164 ⊖ DM 22,00 ⬜BB⬜inc ⚹ ⁘ ⚑ 🚊 Cottbus 22km 🚐 Burg/Bleske 1.2km ⓡ (1.7-31.8: 5 weeks)

Burg Stargard ▲ Dewitzer Chausse, 17094 Burg Stargard. ☏ (39603) 20207 **FAX** (39603) 20207 **Open:** 08.00-09.00hrs, 15.00-22.00hrs, 2.2-30.11 🛏 126 ⊖ DM 19,00 ⬜BB⬜inc ⚹(L D) ⁘ 🅿 🚊 Burg Stargard 1.4km 🚐 500m ap Markt ⓡ

Burg Wildenstein ☞ **Wildenstein**

Burghausen ▲ ⬜0.5S⬜ Kapuzinergasse 235, 84489 Burghausen (Bavaria) ☏ (8677) 4187 **FAX** (8677) 911318 **Open:** 1.2-30.11 🛏 110 ⊖ DM 20,00 ⬜BB⬜inc ⚹(L D) ⚐ ⁘ ♿ ⚑ 🅿 🚊 Burghausen 3.5km 🚐 To city centre + 🚊 ap YH

Büsum ▲ Dr Martin-Bahr-Str 1, 25761 Büsum. ☏ (4834) 2436 **FAX** (4834) 4742 **Open:** 1.2-22.12 🛏 206 ⊖ DM 20,00 ⬜BB⬜inc ⚹(L D) 🅿 ♿ 🚊 Büsum 1km

Calw ▲ Im Zwinger 4, 75365 Calw. ☏ (7051) 12614 **FAX** (7051) 77009 🛏 62 ⊖ DM 20,00 ⬜BB⬜inc ⚹(L D) 🎏 🚊 Calw 600m 🚐 600m

Cappenberger See ▲ Richard-Schirrmann-Weg 7, 44534 Lünen. ☏ (2306) 53546 **FAX** (2306) 73000 **Open:** 9.1-26.12 🛏 120 ⊖ DM 20,00 ⬜BB⬜inc ⚹ ⚑ 🅿 ⚑ 🚊 Lünen 4km 🚐 113 700m ap Cappenberger See

Carolinensiel ▲ ⬜0.5W⬜ Herbergsmense 13, 26409 Wittmund. ☏ (4464) 252 **FAX** (4464) 655 🛏 123 ⊖ DM 20,00 ⬜BB⬜inc ⚹(L D) ⚑ 🅿 ♿ ⚑ 🚊 Jever 18km 🚐 Carolinensiel 500m ⓡ

Celle ▲ Weghausstr 2, 29223 Celle. ☏ (5141) 53208 **FAX** (5141) 53005 🛏 128 ⊖ DM 20,00 ⬜BB⬜inc ⚹ ⚑ 🅿 🚊 20 min 🚐 100m

Chemnitz (*see town plan on next page*) ▲ Augustusburger Str 369, 09127 Chemnitz. ☏ (371) 71331 **FAX** (371) 71331 **Open:** 07.00-22.00hrs 🛏 114 Su (58 Wi) ⊖ DM 17,00 - 22,00 ⬜BB⬜inc ⚹ ⁘ 🅿 🚊 Chemnitz Central 5km 🚐 Chemnitz- Augustusburg T-245 200m ap "Walter-Klippel-Str" 🚃 from central stop Line 1 or 6 1.5km ap "Pappelhain"

Chossewitz ▲ Dorfstr 29, 15848 Chossewitz. ☏ (33673) 5757 **FAX** (33673) 5757 **Open:** 07.00-22.00hrs,

6.1-14.12 ⌘ 58 ⊜ DM 22,00 ᴮᴮⁱⁿᶜ ¶◯|
♦♦♦ ⚓ � Beeskow or Eisenhüttenstadt
20km 🚌 3km Ⓡ (1.5-30.8: 2 weeks
in advance)

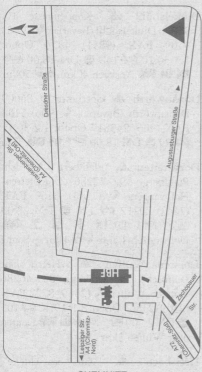

CHEMNITZ

Clausthal-Zellerfeld ▲ Altenauer Str
55, 38678 Clausthal-Zellerfeld. ✆
(5323) 84293 **FAX** (5323) 83827 ⌘
122 ⊜ DM 20,00 ᴮᴮⁱⁿᶜ ¶◯| 🎂 🅿 ⚲ �
Goslar 20km

Coburg ▲ Parkstr 2, 96450 Coburg
(Bavaria). ✆ (9561) 15330 **FAX** (9561)
28653 **Open:** 1.2-30.11 ⌘ 145 ⊜ DM
22,00 ᴮᴮⁱⁿᶜ ¶◯| ♦♦♦ 🏠 � 3km 🚌 1,
5 or 6, 100m

Cochem ▲ Klottener Str 9, 56812
Cochem. ✆ (2671) 8633 **FAX** (2671)
8568 ⌘ 167 ⊜ DM 20,50 ᴮᴮⁱⁿᶜ ¶◯|
� Cochem 150m

Colditz ▲ Haingasse 42, 04680 Colditz.
✆ (34381) 43335 **Open:**

07.00-22.00hrs ⌘ 32 ⊜ DM 17,00
ᴮᴮⁱⁿᶜ ¶◯| ♦♦♦ 🅿 � Colditz 1km 🚌
Leipzig-Colditz S-472 or S-931 500m
ap Sportplatz

Cologne ☞ **Köln**

Cottbus ▲ Klosterplatz 2/3, 03046
Cottbus. ✆ (355) 22558 **FAX** (355)
23798 ⌘ 43 ⊜ DM 22,00 ᴮᴮⁱⁿᶜ
¶◯|(B D) ⚲ ♦♦♦ 🏠 � Cottbus 2km

Creglingen ▲ Erdbacher Str 30, 97993
Creglingen. ✆ (7933) 336 **FAX** (7933)
1326 ⌘ 144 ⊜ DM 20,00 ᴮᴮⁱⁿᶜ
¶◯|(L D) ♦♦♦ ♿ � Weikersheim 12km,
Rothenburg o.d. Tauber 18km 🚌
1km ap Schulzentrum

Cuxhaven-Duhnen ▲ Schlensenweg 2,
27476 Cuxhaven. ✆ (4721) 48552
FAX (4721) 45794 **Open:** 25.1-14.12
⌘ 277 ⊜ DM 22,00 ᴮᴮⁱⁿᶜ ¶◯|(L D) 🅿
� Cuxhaven 6km 🚌 1, 21 to
Döse/Duhnen 500m ap Seelust

Dahlen ▲ Belgernsche Str 25, 04774
Dahlen. ✆ (34361) 51355 **FAX**
(34361) 51355 **Open:** 06.00-22.00hrs
⌘ 125 Su, 80 Wi ⊜ DM 22,00 ᴮᴮⁱⁿᶜ
¶◯| ⚲ ♦♦♦ 🅿 � Dahlen 3km 🚌
Oschatz or Torgau - Dahlen 1.5km
ap Terminus

Dahmen ▲ Dorfstr 14, 17166 Dahmen.
✆ (39933) 552 **FAX** (39933) 552
Open: 08.00-09.00hrs, 15.00-22.00hrs,
28.12.96-18.12 ⌘ 163 ⊜ DM 19,00
ᴮᴮⁱⁿᶜ ¶◯| ♦♦♦ 🖥 🎂 🅿 🚲 ⚓ � Teterow
20km 🚌 200m Ⓡ

Dahn ▲ Am Wachtfelsen 1, 66994
Dahn. ✆ (6391) 1769 **FAX** (6391)
5122 ⌘ 108 ⊜ DM 21,50 ᴮᴮⁱⁿᶜ
¶◯|(L D) ♦♦♦ � Hintherweidental 7km

Darmstadt *(see town plan on next page)* ▲ 0.8E
"Am grossen Woog", Landgraf-Georg-
Str 119, 64287 Darmstadt. ✆ (6151)
45293 **FAX** (6151) 422535 **Open:**
1.1-23.12; 27-31.12 ⌘ 122 ⊜ DM
23,50 ᴮᴮⁱⁿᶜ ¶◯| 🅿 ⚓ � Darmstadt
3km 🚌 D 10m ap Woog/Beckstraße

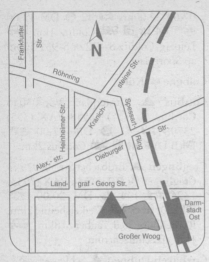

DARMSTADT

Dassow-Holm ▲ An der B 105, 23942 Dassow. ☎ (38826) 614 **FAX** (38826) 614 **Open:** 08.00-09.00hrs, 15.00-22.00hrs, 3.3-18.12 ✉ 122 ⬤ DM 19,00 [BB]inc ⦿| ♦♦♦ 🄿 ☥ 🚂 Grevesmühlen 🚌 100m **ℝ**

Daun ⛺ Am Dreesberg, 54550 Daun. ☎ (6592) 2884 **FAX** (6592) 1506 ✉ 147 ⬤ DM 25,10 [BB]inc ⦿|(L D) ♦♦♦ ⚲ 🚂 Gerolstein 20km

Demmin ▲ R-Breitscheid-Str, 17109 Demmin. ☎ (3998) 223388 **FAX** (3998) 223388 **Open:** 08.00-09.00hrs, 15.00-22.00hrs, 11.1-18.12 ✉ 32 ⬤ DM 15,50 [BB]inc ♂ 🅱 🄾 🚂 Demmin 1km 🚌 1km **ℝ**

Dessau ▲ Waldkaterweg 11, 06846 Dessau. ☎ (340) 619452 **FAX** (340) 619452 **Open:** 07.00-10.00hrs, 17.00-22.00hrs, 1.1-23.12; 27-31.12 ✉ 62 ⬤ DM 20,00 [BB]inc ⦿| ♦♦♦ 🄿 🚂 Dessau 2km 🚌 200m

Detmold ▲ Schirrmann-str 49, 32756 Detmold. ☎ (5231) 24739 **FAX** (5231) 28927 **Open:** 16.1-13.12 ✉ 111 ⬤ DM 21,00 [BB]inc ⦿| 🏛 🄿 🚂 Detmold 3km

Diez ▲ Schlossberg 8, 65582 Diez. ☎ (6432) 2481 **FAX** (6432) 4504 ✉ 91 ⬤ DM 20,50 [BB]inc ⦿|(L D) ♦♦♦ 🅱 🚂 Diez 2km

Dinkelsbühl ▲ Koppengasse 10, 91550 Dinkelsbühl (Bavaria). ☎ (9851) 9509 **FAX** (9851) 4874 **Open:** 1.3-30.10 ✉ 148 ⬤ DM 18,00 [BB]inc ⦿| ♦♦♦ 🚂 Ansbach 40km 🚌 500m

Donauwörth ▲ Goethestr 10, 86609 Donauwörth (Bavaria). ☎ (906) 5158 **FAX** (906) 243817 **Open:** 1.2-30.11 ✉ 89 ⬤ DM 18,00 [BB]inc ♦♦♦ 🚂 3km

Dornstetten ▲ "Pfahlberg", Auf dem Pfahlberg 39, 72280 Dornstetten-Hallwangen. ☎ (7443) 6469 **FAX** (7443) 20212 ✉ 126 ⬤ DM 22,00 [BB]inc ⦿|(L D) ♦♦♦ ♿ 🄿 ☥ 🚂 Dornstetten 4.5km 🚌 1km ap Sonne

Dorsten- Wulfen ▲ "Herrlichkeit Lembeck", Im Schöning 83, 46286 Dorsten-Wulfen. ☎ (2369) 8722 **FAX** (2369) 23867 **Open:** 8.1-19.12 ✉ 105 ⬤ DM 21,00 [BB]inc ⦿| 🏛 🄿 🚂 Deuten oder Wulfen 3km

Dreisbach ▲ "Zur Saarschleife", Herbergstr 1, 66693 Mettlach. ☎ (6868) 270 **FAX** (6868) 556 ✉ 133 ⬤ DM 19,50 [BB]inc ⦿| 🚂 Merzig 6km

DRESDEN (4 Hostels)

Dresden - Hübnerstr ⛺ Hübnerstr 11, 01069 Dresden. ☎ (351) 4710667 **FAX** (351) 4728959 **Open:** 07.00-22.00hrs ✉ 75 ⬤ DM 22,00 ⦿| 🄾 🏛 ✈ Dresden- Klotzsche 8km ⛴ 🚂 Dresden Central 1.2km 🚌 61 or 93 500m ap Nürnberger Platz 🚃 5 or 11 500m ap Nürnberger Platz

Dresden - Oberloschwitz ▲ Sierksstr 33, 01326 Dresden. ☎ (351) 36672 **FAX** (351) 36672 **Open:** 07.00-22.00hrs, 7.1-20.12 ✉ 51 ⬤ DM 22,00 [BB]inc ⦿|(B L) 🄾 🏛 🄿 ✈

Dresden- Klotzsche 12km 🚢 🚊 8km 🚌 84, 150m ap Malerstraße 🚋 500m 🅡

Dresden - **Radebeul** 🔺 Weintraubenstr 12, 01445 Radebeul. 📞 (351) 8305207 **FAX** (351) 8305207 **Open:** 07.00-22.00hrs 🛏 82 🍽 DM 22,00 BBinc 🍴 ♨ 🅿 ⚓ ✈ Dresden-Klotzsche 6km 🚊 Radebeul-Weintraube 300m 🚋 5 800m ap "Goldene Weintraube"

Dresden - **JGH Dresden** 🔺 Maternistraße 22, 01067 Dresden 📞 (351) 492620 **FAX** (351) 4926299 🛏 450 🍽 DM 33,00 - 40,00 BBinc 🍴 (B D) 🚻 ♨ 🅿 🚲 ✈ Dresden 10km A🚌 Airport-Cityliner & S-bahn 12km 🚢 Dresden-City 2km 🚊 Dresden Central 800m 🚋 7, 8 200m 🅡 06.00-24.00hrs

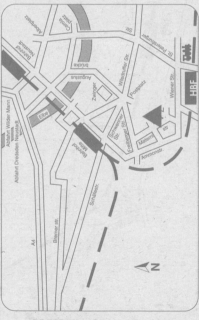

DRESDEN - JGH Maternistraße

Duderstadt 🔺 JGH, Mühlhauser Str 27, 37104 Duderstadt. 📞 (5527) 73001 **FAX** (5527) 73275 🛏 110 BBinc 🍴 🚻 ♿ ♨ 🅿 🚊 Göttingen 30km 🚌 5 min

Duisburg 🔺 Kalkweg 148E, 47279 Duisburg. 📞 (203) 724164 **FAX** (203) 720834 🛏 134 🍽 DM 25,00 BBinc 🍴 🖨 🅿 🚊 Duisburg 10km 🚌 934, 944

Düsseldorf 🔺 3W IBN Düsseldorfer Str 1, 40545 Düsseldorf. 📞 (211) 557310 **FAX** (211) 572513 🛏 280 🍽 DM 37,00 BBinc 🍴 🚿 🚻 ♿ ♨ 🅿 ✈ Düsseldorf 12km 🚊 Düsseldorf 6km 🚌 835

DÜSSELDORF

Eberbach/N 🔺 2SW "Neckartal", Richard- Schirrmann- Str 6, 69412 Eberbach. 📞 (6271) 2593 **FAX** (6271) 71393 🛏 127 🍽 DM 20,00 BBinc 🍴 🚻 🅿 🚊 Eberbach 2km

Ebersberg 🔺 Attenberger- Schillinger Str 1, 85560 Ebersberg (Bavaria). 📞 (8092) 22523 **FAX** (8092) 87623 **Open:** 1.2-30.11 🛏 54 🍽 DM 16,50 BBinc 🍴 (B D) 🚊 800m

Ebrach ▲ Horbachweg 7, 96157 Ebrach (Bavaria). ☎ (9553) 271 **FAX** (9553) 1657 **Open:** 1.2-30.11 ⇄ 76 ● DM 18,00 [BB]inc ⵀ⦿l ᵚᵚ Bamberg 35km ⛟ 500m

Eckernförde ▲ Sehestedter Str 27, 24340 Eckernförde. ☎ (4351) 2154 **FAX** (4351) 3604 **Open:** 11.1-9.12 ⇄ 177 ● DM 20,00 [BB]inc ⵀ⦿l(L D) ▣ ▣ ⊛ᵚᵚ Eckernförde 1.5km ⛟ 500m

Ehrenfriedersdorf ▲ Greifensteinstr 46, 09427 Ehrenfriedersdorf. ☎ (37346) 1253 **Open:** 07.00-22.00hrs, 1-31.12.96; 1.1-31.10 ⇄ 46 Su (32 Wi) ● DM 17,00 [BB]inc ⵀ⦿l ♂ ᵢᵢᵢ ▣ ⚓ Alt 500m ⛟ Annaberg-Thum T-432, Chemnitz-O'thal T-210 3km ap "Neumarkt"

Eichstätt ⛰ Reichenaustr 15, 85072 Eichstätt (Bavaria). ☎ (8421) 1980401 **FAX** (8421) 19804151 **Open:** 1.2-30.11 ⇄ 112 ● DM 22,00 [BB]inc ⵀ⦿l ᵢᵢᵢ ▣

EISENACH (2 Hostels)

"Artur Becker" ▲ Mariental 24, 99817 Eisenach. ☎ (3691) 203613 **FAX** (3691) 203613 **Open:** 07.00-23.00hrs, 1.1-22.12; 28-31.12 ⇄ 102 ● DM 23,00 ⵀ⦿l ᵢᵢᵢ ▣ ⚓ ᵚᵚ Eisenach 2km ⛟ 300m ⟨R⟩

Eisenach - **Bornstraße** ▲ Bornstraße 7, 99817 Eisenach. ☎ (3691) 732012 **Open:** 07.00-22.00hrs, 1.1-21.12; 28-31.12 ⇄ 65 ● DM 20,00 [BB]inc ⵀ⦿l ᵚᵚ Eisenach 1.5km ⛟ 3 400m ap Ernst-Abbe-Schule ⟨R⟩

Eisenberg ▲ JH "Froschmühle", Mühltal ☎ (36691) 43462 **Open:** 07.00-22.00hrs, 1.1-22.12; 28-31.12 ⇄ 105 ● DM 20,00 [BB]inc ᵢᵢᵢ ▣ ᵚᵚ Eisenberg/Rauda 6km ⛟ 4km ⟨R⟩

Ellwangen ▲ Schloß ob Ellwangen, 73479 Ellwangen. ☎ (7961) 53880 **FAX** (7961) 55331 ⇄ 57 [BB]inc ⵀ⦿l ᵢᵢᵢ ⛩ ᵚᵚ Ellwangen 4km ⛟ 1km

Emden ▲ An der Kesselschleuse 5, 26725 Emden. ☎ (4921) 23797 **FAX** (4921) 32161 **Open:** 1.2-30.11 ⇄ 90 ● DM 20,00 [BB]inc ⵀ⦿l(L D) ᵢᵢᵢ ▣ ⊛ ⚓ ᵚᵚ Emden 3km

Erbach ▲ ⟨1.5 NE⟩ Eulbacher Str 33, 64711 Erbach. ☎ (6062) 3515 **FAX** (6062) 62848 **Open:** 1.1-23.12; 27-31.12 ⇄ 158 ● DM 21,50 [BB]inc ⵀ⦿l ᵢᵢᵢ ▣ ᵚᵚ Erbach 2km ⛟ 500m ap Landratsamt

Erfurt ⛰ Hochheimerstr 12, 99094 Erfurt. ☎ (361) 5626705 **FAX** (361) 5626705 **Open:** 07.00-22.00hrs, 1.1-22.12; 28-31.12 ⇄ 200 ● DM 24,00 [BB]inc ⵀ⦿l ᵢᵢᵢ ✈ Erfurt 5km ᵚᵚ Erfurt 3km ⛟ 500m ⟨R⟩

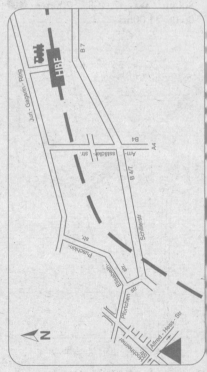

ERFURT

Erlangen ▲ Südliche Stadtmauerstr 35 91054 Erlangen (Bavaria). ☎ (9131) 862555 **FAX** (9131) 862119 **Open**

1.1-18.12 ⚡ 72 ● DM 18,00 [BB]inc
〒⦿(L) 🚃 900m 🚐 50m

Erpfingen ▲ Auf der Reute 1, 72820
Sonnenbühl. ☎ (7128) 1652 **FAX**
(7128) 3370 ⚡ 150 ● DM 22,00 [BB]inc
〒⦿(L D) 🚻 🗄 🅿 🛫 Alt 830m 🚲 🚃
Reutlingen 24km 🚐 800m
ap Marktpkatz **R**

Esborn ▲ Wacholderstr 11, 58300
Wetter. ☎ (2335) 7718 **FAX** (2335)
73519 Open: 18.1-22.12 ⚡ 57 ● DM
20,00 [BB]inc 〒⦿ 🚾 🅿 🚃 Wetter 9km
🚐 592 200m ap Am Sackern

Eschwege ▲ ⎣0.3NE⎦ "Haus der Jugend",
Fritz- Neuenroth- Weg 1, 37269
Eschwege. ☎ (5651) 60099 **FAX**
(5651) 70916 **Open:** 1.1-23.12;
27-31.12 ⚡ 182 ● DM 21,50 [BB]inc
〒⦿ 🚻 ♿ 🅿 ⛵ 🚃 Eschwege West
6km 🚐 1 1km ap Stadthalle

Esens- Bensersiel ⚠ ⎣1N⎦ Grashauser
Flage 2, 26427 Esens. ☎ (4971) 3717
FAX (4971) 659 **Open:** 1.2-31.12 ⚡
144 ● DM 24,00 [BB]inc 〒⦿(L D) 🚻 ♿
🚾 🅿 🚲 ⛵ 🚃 Esens 3km **R**

Essen-Werden ▲ ⎣8S⎦ Pastoratsberg 2,
45239 Essen-Werden. ☎ (201) 491163
FAX (201) 492505 ⚡ 130 ● DM
25,00 [BB]inc 〒⦿ 🅿 🚃 Essen 1.5km 🚐
179 🚆 S6

Esslingen ▲ Neuffenstr 65, 73734
Esslingen. ☎ (711) 381848 **FAX** (711)
388886 ⚡ 104 ● DM 20,00 [BB]inc
〒⦿(L D) 🚻 🅿 🚃 Esslingen 6km 🚐
500m ap Zollernplatz

Eutin ▲ Jahnhöhe 6, 23701 Eutin. ☎
(4521) 2109 **FAX** (4521) 74602 ⚡
190 ● DM 20,00 [BB]inc 〒⦿(L D) 🅿 🚲
⛵ 🚃 Eutin 1km

Falkenhain ▲ An der Talsperre
Kriebstein, 09648 Falkenhain. ☎
(3727) 2952 **FAX** (3727) 2952 **Open:**
06.00-22.00hrs, 30.4-4.10 ⚡ 220 ●

DM 20,00 [BB]inc 〒⦿ 🚻 🗄 🚾 🅿 ⛵ 🚃
Mittweida 8km 🚐 Mittweida-
Waldhein S- 919 1km ap Falkenhain
"Schmiede"

Fallingbostel ▲ Liethweg 1, 29683
Fallingbostel. ☎ (5162) 2274 **FAX**
(5162) 5704 ⚡ 92 ● DM 20,00 [BB]inc
〒⦿ 🚻 🚾 🅿 🚃 Fallingbostel 20 min

Feldberg ▲ Klinkecken 6, 17258
Feldberg. ☎ (39831) 20520 **FAX**
(39831) 20520 **Open:** 08.00-09.00hrs,
15.00-22.00hrs, 4.2-18.12 ⚡ 75 ●
DM 19,00 [BB]inc 〒⦿(L D) 🚻 🅿 🚲 ⛵
🚃 Feldberg 1.5km 🚐 1km **R**

Feldberg/Schw ▲ "Hebelhof",
Passhöhe 14, 79868 Feldberg. ☎ (7676)
221 **FAX** (7676) 1232 ⚡ 270 ● DM
22,00 [BB]inc 〒⦿(L D) 🚻 🅿 🛫 🚃 1.5km
🚐 7300 100m **R**

Finnentrop- Bamenohl ▲ "Jupp-
Schöttler- Jugendherberge",
Herbergsweg 1, 57413 Finnentrop-
Bamenohl. ☎ (2721) 7293 ⚡ 26 ●
DM 21,00 [BB]inc 〒⦿ 🚾 🅿 🚃
Finnentrop 1.8km 🚐 101 10m
ap Killeschlader Weg

Finnentrop- Heggen ▲ Ahauser Str
22-24, 57405 Finnentrop-Heggen. ☎
(2721) 50345 **FAX** (2721) 79460 ⚡
216 ● DM 21,50 [BB]inc 〒⦿ ♿ 🚾 🅿 🛫
⛵ 🚃 Finnentrop-Heggen 2km 🚐
800m ap Heggen-Ahauser-Str.

Flensburg ▲ ⎣4NE⎦ Fichtestr 16, 24943
Flensburg. ☎ (461) 37742 **FAX** (461)
312952 **Open:** 1.12.96-31.10 ⚡ 220
● DM 20,00 [BB]inc 〒⦿(L D) 🅿 🚃
Flensburg 4km 🚐 400m ap Stadion

Flessenow ▲ 19067 Flessenow. ☎
(3866) 435 **FAX** (3866) 435 **Open:**
08.00-09.00hrs, 15.00-22.00hrs,
3.3-30.11 ⚡ 123 ● DM 17,00 [BB]inc
〒⦿(L D) 🚻 🚾 🅿 🚲 ⛵ 🚃 Schwerin
🚐 300m **R**

FORBACH (2 Hostels)

Forbach - "Heinrich-Kastner-YH" ▲
[2E] Birket 1, Postfach 1175, 76594
Forbach. ✆ (7228) 2427 **FAX** (7228)
1551 ⇌ 84 ● DM 20,00 [BB]inc ⭫⭐ ⭐⭐⭐
🅿 ⭐ ⭐⭐ Forbach 5km

Forbach - Herrenwies ▲
Environmental Study Centre, "Franz-
Köbele-JH", OT Herrenwies, Haus Nr
33, 76596 Forbach. ✆ (7226) 257 **FAX**
(7226) 1318 ⇌ 139 ● DM 22,00 [BB]inc
⭭⭐ ⭐⭐ 🅿 ⭐ ⭐⭐ Bühl 20km 🚌 7115
100m

Frankfurt (*see town plan on next page*) ⚠
[1 SE] [IBN] "Haus der Jugend"
Deutscherrnufer 12, 60594 Frankfurt.
✆ (69) 619058 **FAX** (69) 618257
Open: 3.1-22.12 ⇌ 500 ● DM 24,00
[BB]inc ⭭⭐ ⭐⭐ ⭐ ⭐ ✈ Frankfurt 12km
A🚌 61 South, then tram 14 to Zoo,
stop "Frankensteiner Platz" Railway
Station ⭐⭐ Frankfurt 3km 🚃 16 to
stop "Textorstraße" 600m
ap Lokalbahnhof

Frauenau ▲ Hauptstr 29a, 94258
Frauenau (Bavaria). ✆ (9926) 735
Open: 1.1-30.11 ⇌ 24 ● DM 16,50
[BB]inc ♂ ⭐⭐ 500m

Frauenberg ☞ Haidmühle

Frauenstein ▲ Walkmühlenstr 13,
09623 Frauenstein. ✆ (37326) 1307
Open: 07.00-22.00hrs ⇌ 86 ● DM
20,00 [BB]inc ⭭⭐ ♂ ⭭⭐ ⭐ 🅿 ⭐ Alt 620m
⭐⭐ Nassau 6.5km 🚌 from Freiberg,
Dresden or Klingenberg R-363 500m
ap Frauenstein Markt

Freiburg ⚠ [6E] Kartäuserstr 151,
79104 Freiburg. ✆ (761) 67656 **FAX**
(761) 60367 ⇌ 391 ● DM 22,00 [BB]inc
⭭⭐ ⭭⭐ & 🔳 🅿 ⭐⭐ Freiburg 5km 🚃 1
1km ap Römerhof **R**

Freudenstadt ▲ Eugen-Nägele-Str 69,
72250 Freudenstadt. ✆ (7441) 7720
FAX (7441) 85788 ⇌ 132 ● DM

22,00 [BB]inc ⭭⭐(L D) ⭭⭐ 🔳 ⭐ ⭐⭐
Freudenstadt Hbf 2.5, Sbf 500m 🚌
200m ap Berufsschule

Freusburg ▲ "Jugendburg",
Burgstrasse 46, 57548 Kirchen-
Freusburg. ✆ (2741) 61094 **FAX**
(2741) 63135 ⇌ 212 ● DM 21,50
[BB]inc 🏰 ⚒ 🅿 ⭐⭐ Freusburg-Siedlung
1.5km 🚌 1km

FRIEDRICHRODA (2 Hostels)

Friedrichroda - Friedrichroda ▲
Herzogsweg 25, 99894 Friedrichroda.
✆ (3623) 304410 **FAX** (3623) 304410
Open: 07.00-22.00hrs, 1.1-22.12;
28-31.12 ⇌ 57 ● DM 17,00 [BB]inc ⭭⭐
⭐ ⭐⭐ Thüringer Waldbahn 500m
🚌 1km **R**

Friedrichroda - **Wanderhütten Heuberg**
▲ Herzogsweg 25, 99894
Friedrichroda. ✆ (3623) 304410 **FAX**
(3623) 304410 **Open:** 1.1-22.12;
28-31.12 ⇌ 37 ● DM 17,00 ⭭⭐(B L)
🅿 ⭐ ⭐⭐ Thüringer Waldbahn 5km
🚌 300m **R**

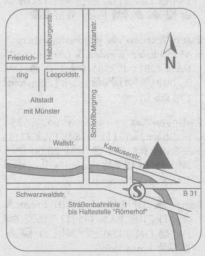

FREIBURG

Friedrichshafen ▲ [2E] "Graf-
Zeppelin-JH", Lindauer Str 3, 88046
Friedrichshafen. ✆ (7541) 72404 **FAX**

(7541) 74986 ⚑ 235 ⬤ DM 22,00
BB|inc ¶O¶(L D) ⬛ P 🚌 Friedrichschafen
3km 🚐 150m ap YH Ⓡ

(9973) 9254 **FAX** (9973) 2447 **Open:**
1.1-31.10; 27-31.12 ⚑ 128 ⬤ DM
20,00 BB|inc ¶O¶ ♦♦♦ ⚘ Alt 420m 🚌 3km

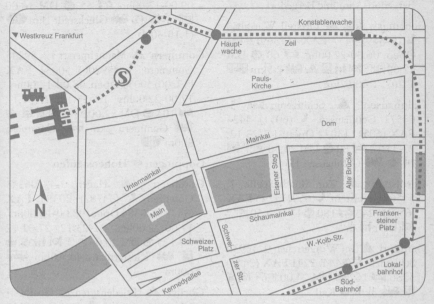

FRANKFURT

Friedrichstadt ▲ Ostdeutsche Str 1,
25840 Friedrichstadt. ☎ (4881) 7984
Open: 16.1-14.12 ⚑ 65 ⬤ DM 18,00
BB|inc ¶O¶(L D) P 🚌 Friedrichstadt
1km

Fröbersgrün ▲ Umweltstudienplatz,
Ortsstr 17, 08548 Fröbersgrün. ☎
(37431) 3256 **FAX** (37431) 3256
Open: 07.00-22.00hrs ⚑ 82 Su (42
Wi) ⬤ DM 20,00 BB|inc ¶O¶ ♦♦♦ ⬛ P ⚘
🚌 Plaun/Vogtl, upper station change
for Syrau 2.5km 🚐 from Plauen-
Fröbersgrün T-10 ap YH

Fulda ▲ 2SW Schirrmannstr 31, 36041
Fulda. ☎ (661) 73389 **FAX** (661)
74811 **Open:** 1.1-23.12; 27-31.12 ⚑
128 ⬤ DM 23,50 BB|inc ¶O¶ ♦♦♦ P ⚓
🚌 Fulda 3km 🚐 1B 100m ap
Stadion, 1A 400m ap Feuerwache

Furth im Wald ▲ Daberger Str 50,
93437 Furth im Wald (Bavaria). ☎

Füssen ▲ IBN Mariahilferstr 5, 87629
Füssen (Bavaria). ☎ (8362) 7754 **FAX**
(8362) 2770 **Open:** 1.1-14.11;
27-31.12 ⚑ 138 ⬤ DM 20,00 BB|inc
¶O¶(D) ♦♦♦ ⬛ ⚘ Alt 800m 🚌 12km

Gardelegen ▲ Waldschnibbe, Otto-
Reutter- Haus, 39638 Gardelegen. ☎
(3907) 712629 **FAX** (3907) 712629
Open: 07.00-13.00hrs, 17.00-22.00hrs,
1.1-23.12; 27-31.12 ⚑ 97 ⬤ DM
18,00 BB|inc ¶O¶ ♦♦♦ P ⚘ 🚐 3.5km
ap Bahnhof Gardelegen

Garmisch- Partenkirchen ▲ Jochstr
10, 82467 Garmisch- Partenkirchen
(Bavaria). ☎ (8821) 2980 **FAX** (8821)
58536 **Open:** 1.1-31.10; 27-31.12 ⚑
210 ⬤ DM 20,00 BB|inc ¶O¶(D) ♂ ♦♦♦ ⬛
⚘ Alt 700m 🚌 4km 🚐 3 and 4
300m

Geesthacht ▲ Berliner Str 117, 21502
Geesthacht. ☎ (4152) 2356 **FAX**

(4152) 77918 ✉ 123 ⊖ DM 20,00
BB|inc ⦿(L D) 🅿 🚐 Hamburg 🚌 31,
231 or 131 500m ap YH Ⓤ S21 to
Bergedorf/Aumühle Bergedorf

Gehringswalde ▲ Ortsteil Warmbad
☎ (37369) 9437 **FAX** (37369) 9437
Open: 06.00-22.00hrs ✉ 60 ⊖ DM
22,00 BB|inc ⦿ 🚻 🅿 🚲 🚐 2.5km 🚌
T 207, T 400 2km

Gelnhausen ▲ Schützengraben 5,
63571 Gelnhausen. ☎ (6051) 4424
FAX (6051) 13072 **Open:** 1.1-23.12;
27-31.12 ✉ 80 ⊖ DM 20,50 BB|inc ⦿
🚻 ⚓ 🚐 Gelnhausen 1km

Gerolstein ▲ Zur Büschkapelle 1,
54568 Gerolstein. ☎ (6591) 4745 **FAX**
(6591) 7243 ✉ 180 ⊖ DM 20,50 BB|inc
⦿(L D) 🚻 ♿

Gemünd ▲ Im Wingertchen 9, 53930
Schleiden. ☎ (2444) 2241 **FAX** (2444)
3386 ✉ 162 ⊖ DM 24,00 BB|inc ⦿ ☞
🅿 🚐 3km ⊷ Kall

Gersfeld ▲ 0.5 SE Jahnstr 6, 36129
Gersfeld. ☎ (6654) 340 **FAX** (6654)
7788 **Open:** 1.1-23.12; 27-31.12 ✉
107 ⊖ DM 20,50 BB|inc ⦿ 🚻 🅿 ⚲ Alt
600m 🚐 Gersfeld 1km

Geyer ▲ Anton-Günther-Weg 3, 09468
Geyer. ☎ (37346) 1364 **Open:**
08.00-20.00hrs ✉ 93 ⊖ DM 20,00
BB|inc ⦿ ☞ 🚻 🅿 ⚲ Alt 500m 🚐
Annaberg then 🚌 to Geyer 16km
🚌 O'thal- Geyer T- 436 1km, Bus
station T-151 Zwönitzer Str 600m Ⓡ

Gießen ▲ 3W Richard- Schirrmann-
Weg 53, 35398 Giessen. ☎ (641) 65879
FAX (641) 65879 **Open:** 1.1-23.12;
27-31.12 ✉ 91 ⊖ DM 20,50 BB|inc ⦿
🚻 🅿 ⚓ 🚐 Giessen 3km 🚌 4, 200m
ap Hardtallee

Glörsee ▲ 58339 Breckerfeld. ☎ (2338)
434 **FAX** (2338) 3674 **Open:**
16.1-12.12 ✉ 121 ⊖ DM 21,00 BB|inc
⦿ ⚒ 🅿 🚐 Dahlerbrück 3.5km 🚌
84 1.5km

Glückstadt ▲ Pentzstr 12, 25348
Glückstadt. ☎ (4124) 2259 **FAX**
(4124) 6494 **Open:** 1.5-30.9 **Shut:**
09.00-17.00hrs ✉ 45 ⊖ DM 18,00
BB|inc ⦿(L D) 🚐 Glückstadt 1km Ⓡ
(1.10-30.4)

Gommern ⚠ Manheimerstr 12, 39245
Gommern. ☎ (39200) 50031 **FAX**
(39200) 50031 **Open:** 08.00-12.00hrs,
17.00-22.00hrs, 1.1-23.12; 27-31.12
✉ 104 ⊖ DM 22,00 BB|inc ⦿ ⬛ 🅿 🚲
🚐 Gommern 2km 🚌 Gommern
200m Ⓡ

Göppingen ☞ Hohenstaufen

Gorenzen ▲ Hagen 2-4, 06343
Gorenzen. ☎ (34782) 20384 **FAX**
(34782) 20384 **Open:** 08.00-13.00hrs,
17.00-22.00hrs, 1.1-23.12; 27-31.12
✉ 125 ⊖ DM 20,00 BB|inc ⦿ 🚻 ♿ ⚒
🅿 🚐 Klostermansfeld 10km 🚌
600m

Görlitz ▲ "Friedensgrenze", Goethestr
17, 02826 Görlitz. ☎ (3581) 406510
Open: 07.00-10.00hrs, 15.00-19.00hrs
✉ 100 ⊖ DM 20,00 ⦿ 🚻 🚋 🅿 🚐
2km 🚌 230 1.5km 🚃 150m
ap Goethestr.

Goslar ▲ Rammelsberger Str 25, 38644
Goslar. ☎ (5321) 22240 **FAX** (5321)
41376 ✉ 168 ⊖ DM 20,00 BB|inc ⦿
🚻 ♿ ⚒ 🅿 🚐 25 min 🚌 C to
Theresienhof 10 min

Gößweinstein ▲ Etzdorferstr 6, 91327
Gößweinstein (Bavaria). ☎ (9242) 259
FAX (9242) 7135 **Open:** 16.1-14.11
✉ 129 ⊖ DM 20,00 BB|inc ⦿ 🚻 🚐
Ebermannstadt 15km

Göttingen (*see town plan on next page*) ⚠
Habichtsweg 2, 37075 Göttingen. ☎
(551) 57622 **FAX** (551) 43887 ✉ 150
⊖ DM 22,00 BB|inc ⦿ 🚻 ♿ ⚒ 🅿 🚐
Göttingen 3km 🚌 to Kornmarkt +
6 to YH 100m

Gotha ▲ Mozartstr. 1, Postfach 100246,
99852 Gotha ☎ (3621) 54008 **FAX**

(3621) 54008 **Open:** 07.00-22.00hrs, 1.1-20.12; 30-31.12 🛏 150 ⬤ DM 20,00 ⏣inc ⓨ ♦♦♦ 🏠 🅿 🚊 Central 400m 🚃 1,2,4 100m Ⓡ (Grps)

GÖTTINGEN

Graal-Müritz ▲ An der Jugendherberge 32, 18181 Ostseebad Graal-Müritz. ☎ (38206) 520 **FAX** (38206) 204 **Open:** 08.00-09.00hrs, 15.00-22.00hrs, 1.2-31.10 🛏 80 ⬤ DM 17,50 ⏣inc ⓨ(L D) ♦♦♦ 🅿 ♿ ⚓ 🚊 Graal-Müritz 500m 🚌 600m Ⓡ

Grabow ▲ Jugendherberge 01, 19300 Grabow. ☎ (38756) 27954 **FAX** (38756) 27954 **Open:** 08.00-09.00hrs, 15.00-22.00hrs, 10.1-20.12 🛏 48 ⬤ DM 17,50 ⏣inc ⓨ(D) ♦♦♦ 🚊 Grabow 1.8km Ⓡ

Gräfenroda ▲ "Olga Benario", Waldstr 134, 99330 Gräfenroda. ☎ (36205) 76290, 95562 **Open:** 07.00-22.00hrs,

1.1-22.12; 27-31.12 🛏 60 ⬤ DM 17,00 ⏣inc ⓨ(B D) ♦♦♦ 🅿 🎿 🚊 Dörrberg 600m 🚌 Dörrberg 352 400m Ⓡ

Grävenwiesbach ▲ 2.5NE "Richard-Schirrmann- JH", Hasselbornerstr 20, 61279 Grävenwiesbach. ☎ (6086) 520 **FAX** (6086) 970352 **Open:** 1.1-23.12; 27-31.12 🛏 150 ⬤ DM 21,50 ⏣inc ⓨ ♦♦♦ 🅿 🚊 Grävenwiesbach 2.5km 🚌 900m ap Rathaus

Greetsiel ▲ Kleinbahnstr 15, 26736 Krummhörn. ☎ (4926) 550 **FAX** (4926) 1473 **Open:** 1.4-31.10 🛏 64 ⬤ DM 20,00 ⏣inc ⓨ(L D) 🅿 ♿ ⚓ 🚊 Emden + Norden 20km 🚌 Emden + Norden 20km

Greiz ▲ Amselstieg 12, O7973 Greiz. ☎ (3661) 2176 **FAX** (3661) 2176 **Open:** 07.00-22.00hrs, 1.1-22.12; 28-31.12 🛏 92 ⬤ DM 20,00 ⏣inc ⓨ 🅿 🚊 Greiz 3km

Großenhof ▲ 23948 Großenhof. ☎ (3881) 4411 **FAX** (3881) 4411 **Open:** 08.00-09.00hrs, 15.00-22.00hrs, 1.2-18.12 🛏 152 ⬤ DM 15,50 ⏣inc ⓨ ♦♦♦ 🏠 🅿 ♿ 🚊 Grevesmühlen 8km 🚌 100m Ⓡ

Groß Reken ▲ Coesfelder Str 18, 48734 Groß Reken. ☎ (2864) 1023 **FAX** (2864) 2044 **Open:** 7.1-21.12 🛏 126 ⬤ DM 21,00 ⏣inc ⓨ 🎿 🅿 🚊 Maria Veen 3km 🚌 200m ap Hartmanns Höhe

Grumbach ▲ Jöhstädter Str 19, 09477 Grumbach. ☎ (37343) 2288 🛏 62 ⬤ DM 20,00 ⏣inc ⓨ 🚲 ♦♦♦ 🍴 🅿 🚉 🎿 🚊 to Annaberg 12km 🚌 from Annaberg T-430 towards Grumbach or Jöhstadt ap YH

Günzburg ▲ Schillerstr 12, 89312 Günzburg (Bavaria). ☎ (8221) 34487 **FAX** (8221) 31390 **Open:** 16.1-14.11 🛏 36 ⬤ DM 20,00 ⏣inc ⓨ(D) ♦♦♦ 🚊 2km 🚌 50m

Güstrow- Schabernack ▲
Jugendherberge Güstrow-Schabernack, Heidberg 33, 18273 Güstrow ☎ (381) 776670 **FAX** (381) 7698682 **Open:** 28.12.96-18.12 ⇄ 31 ● DM 20,00 ⟦BB⟧ⁱⁿᶜ 🅿 ⛰ 🚻 Güstrow 6km 🚌 1km

Gütersloh ⌂ "Haus der Jugend und des Sports", Wiesenstr 40, 33330 Gütersloh. ☎ (5241) 822181 **FAX** (5241) 822184 **Open:** 1.1-7.12 ⇄ 67 ⟦BB⟧ⁱⁿᶜ 🍴 ♿ 🏠 🅿 🚻 Gütersloh 2.5km 🚌 300m

Hagen ▲ Eppenhauser Str 65a, 58093 Hagen. ☎ (2331) 50254 **FAX** (2331) 588576 **Open:** 2.1-21.12 ⇄ 130 ● DM 21,00 ⟦BB⟧ⁱⁿᶜ 🍴 🏠 🅿 🚻 Hagen 3.5km 🚌 522 or 523 250m ap Emster Straße

Hahnenklee ▲ Hahnenkleer Str 13, 38644 Goslar - OT Hahnenklee-Bockswiese. ☎ (5325) 2256 **FAX** (5325) 3524 ⇄ 122 ● DM 20,00 ⟦BB⟧ⁱⁿᶜ 🍴 🏠 🅿 ⚓ 🚻 Goslar 10km

Haidmühle- Frauenberg ▲ Frauenberg 45, 94145 Haidmühle (Bavaria). ☎ (8556) 467 **FAX** (8556) 1021 **Open:** 1.1-31.10; 27-31.12 ⇄ 162 ● DM 20,00 ⟦BB⟧ⁱⁿᶜ 🍴(D) 👫 ☐ ⚓ Alt 880m 🚻 Passau 50km 🚌 300m

Haldensleben ▲ Bornsche Str 94, 39340 Haldensleben. ☎ (3904) 40386 **Open:** 07.00-22.00hrs, 1.1-22.12 ⇄ 40 ● DM 18,00 ⟦BB⟧ⁱⁿᶜ 🍴(B D) 👫 ☐ 🅿 🚲 🚻 Haldensleben 3km 🚌 50m Ⓡ

Halle (*see town plan on next page*) ⌂ August-Bebel-Str 48a, 06108 Halle. ☎ (345) 2024716 **FAX** (345) 2024716 **Open:** 07.00-10.00hrs, 17.00-23.00hrs, 1.1-23.12; 27-31.12 ⇄ 72 ● DM 22,00 ⟦BB⟧ⁱⁿᶜ 🍴 👫 ☐ 🅿 🚻 Halle 1.5km 🚌 1.5km 🚃 2, 7, 10

Hallwangen ☞ **Dornstetten**

Haltern ▲ "Emil- Zimmermann-JH", Stockwieser Damm 255, 45721

Haltern/Stausee. ☎ (2364) 2258 **FAX** (2364) 169604 ⇄ 138 ● DM 21,00 ⟦BB⟧ⁱⁿᶜ 🍴 🏠 🅿 🚻 Sythen 3km 🚌 1.5km ap Haus Niemen

HAMBURG (2 Hostels)

Hamburg - **Auf dem Stintfang** ⌂ ⟦2SW⟧ ⟦IBN⟧ Alfred-Wegener-Weg 5, 20459 Hamburg. ☎ (40) 313488 **FAX** (40) 315407 **Open:** 1.3-23.12 ⇄ 358 ● DM 24,00 ⟦BB⟧ⁱⁿᶜ 🍴(L D) ✈ 10km A 🚌 to Main Station ⟦U⟧ Landungsbrücken 50m Ⓡ

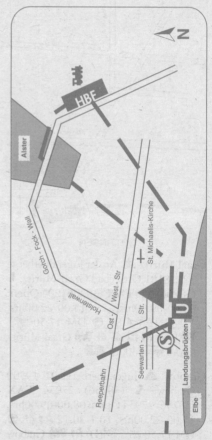

HAMBURG - "Auf dem Stintfang"

Hamburg - **Horner Rennbahn** ⌂ ⟦5E⟧ ⟦IBN⟧ JGH "Horner- Rennbahn", Rennbahnstr 100, 22111 Hamburg. ☎

(40) 6511671 **FAX** (40) 6556516
Open: 1.2-23.12 🛏 277 ● from DM
27,50 ᴮᴮⁱⁿᶜ ⑽(L D) ♿ 🅿 ✈ 10km
A🚌 38 to Tribünenweg 200m 🚋
Hamburg ⓤ U3 Horner Rennbahn
700m

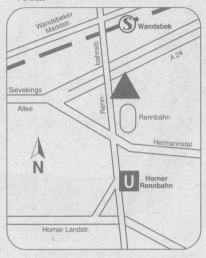

HAMBURG - Horner Rennbahn

HALLE

Hameln ▲ Fischbecker Str 33, 31785
Hameln. 📞 (5151) 3425 **FAX** (5151)
42316 🛏 106 ● DM 20,00 ᴮᴮⁱⁿᶜ ⑽
♿ 🍴 🅿 ⚲ 🚋 Hameln 25 min 🚌
2 to Wehler Weg 100m

Hamm ⚑ Jugendgästehaus
"Sylverberg", Ostenallee 101, 59071
Hamm. 📞 (2381) 83837 **FAX** (2381)
83837 **Open:** 1.2-23.12 🛏 56 ● DM
18,00 ᴮᴮⁱⁿᶜ ⑽ 🍴 🅿 🚋 Hamm 4km
🚌 1, 3 Knappenstraße 500m

Hankensbüttel ▲ Helmrichsweg 24,
29386 Hankensbüttel. 📞 (5832) 2500
FAX (5832) 6596 🛏 142 ● DM 20,00
ᴮᴮⁱⁿᶜ ⑽ 👫 ♿ 🍴 🅿 🚋 Celle 40km
🚌 from Wittingen + Celle 40km

HANNOVER (2 Hostels)

**Hannover - Ferdinand- Wilhelm-
Fricke-Weg** (*see town plan on next page*)
▲ ②ˢ Ferdinand-Wilhelm- Fricke-
Weg 1, 30169 Hannover. 📞 (511)
1317674 **FAX** (511) 18555 🛏 217 ●
DM 22,00 ᴮᴮⁱⁿᶜ ⑽ 🍴 🅿 ✈ Hannover
A🚌 to Hbf 🚋 Hannover 5km 🚈
3, 7 to Fischerhof station 1km

Hannover - Hermann- Bahlsen- Allee
▲ ④ᴺ Hermann- Bahlsen- Allee 8,
30665 Hannover. 📞 (511) 691493 🛏
82 ᴮᴮⁱⁿᶜ ⑽ 🅿 ✈ Hannover A🚌 to
Hbf 🚋 Hannover 30 min 🚈 3, 7 to
Spannhagenstr.

Hann.Münden ▲ Prof-Oelkers-Str 10,
34346 Hann.Münden. 📞 (5541) 8853
FAX (5541) 73439 🛏 135 ● DM
20,00 ᴮᴮⁱⁿᶜ ⑽ 👫 🍴 🅿 🚲 ⚲ 🚋
Hann.Münden 40 min

Hardter Wald ☞ Mönchengladbach

Haren/EMS ▲ "St Nikolaus- JH",
Nikolausweg 17, 49733 Haren (EMS).
📞 (5932) 2726 **Open:** 1.3-31.10 🛏 75
● DM 20,00 ᴮᴮⁱⁿᶜ ⑽(L D) 👫 🅿 🚲
⚲ 🚋 Haren 3km 🚌 Haren 3km

Hartenstein ▲ Salzlecke 10, 91235
Hartenstein (Bavaria). 📞 (9152) 1296

FAX (9152) 1328 **Open:** 1.2-30.11 🏠 68 ● DM 20,00 BB^inc 🍴 🚃 Velden 3km

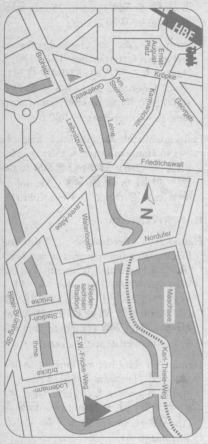

HANNOVER - Ferdinand - Wilhelm-Fricke-Weg

Hattingen ▲ Jugendbildungsstätte Welper, Falken- Freizeitwerk, Hüttenbauvereinigung Welper eV, Rathenaustrasse 59a, 45527 Hattingen- Welper. 📞 (2324) 60453 **FAX** (2324) 67588 **Open:** 1.1-23.12; 27-31.12 🏠 104 ● DM 34,00 BB^inc 🍴 ⛪ 🅿 🚃 Bochum 12km 🚌 Hüttenau 300m

Heide ▲ Poststr 4, 25746 Heide. 📞 (481) 71575 **FAX** (481) 72901 **Open:** 1.2-22.12 🏠 82 ● DM 20,00 BB^inc 🍴(L D) ♿ 🅿 🚃 Heide 1.5km

Heidelberg ▲ 4NW Tiergartenstr 5, 69120 Heidelberg. 📞 (6221) 412066 **FAX** (6221) 402559 🏠 440 ● DM 22,00 BB^inc 🍴 👫 📷 🅿 🚲 🚃 Heidelberg 4km 🚌 33 ap YH Ⓡ

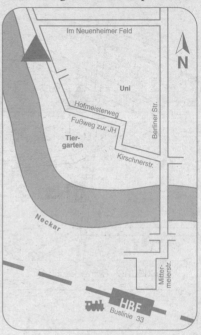

HEIDELBERG

Heidenheim ▲ Liststr 15, 89518 Heidenheim. 📞 (7321) 42045 **FAX** (7321) 949045 🏠 126 ● DM 22,00 BB^inc 🍴(L D) 👫 ♿ 🚃 Heidenheim 2.5km 🚌 500m ap Ratskeller

Heilbronn ▲ JH "Reinhardt", Schirrmannstr 9, 74074 Heilbronn. 📞 (7131) 172961 **FAX** (7131) 164345 🏠 128 ● DM 22,00 BB^inc 🍴(L D) 📷 🅿 🚲 🚃 Heilbronn 5km 🚌 1 200m ap Trappensee

Heldrungen ▲ JH "Wasserburg", Schloßstr. 13, 06577 Heldrungen 📞 (34673) 98136, 91224 **Open:** 07.00-22.00hrs, 1.1-22.12; 28-31.12 🏠 52 ● DM 18,00 BB^inc 🍴 👫 🏠 🅿 🚃 Heldrungen 2km 🚌 500m Ⓡ (Grps)

Helgoland ▲ "Haus der Jugend", Postfach 580, 27487 Helgoland. ☎ (4725) 341 **FAX** (4725) 7467 **Open:** 1.4-31.10 🛏 154 ⊖ DM 22,00 [BB]inc ¶⊙¶(L D) ① ⚓ Cuxhaven 800m

Hellenthal ▲ Platis 3, 53940 Hellenthal. ☎ (2482) 2238 **FAX** (2482) 2557 🛏 161 ⊖ DM 25,00 [BB]inc ¶⊙¶ ☞ ♔♚ ⅗ ⬚ ⬛ ⚘ ♿ 🚂 Kall 5km 🚌

Helmarshausen ⚠ [1 SE] JGH "Diemeltal", Gottsbürener Str 15, 34385 Bad Karlshafen-Helmarshausen. ☎ (5672) 1027 **FAX** (5672) 2976 **Open:** 1.1-23.12; 27-31.12 🛏 178 ⊖ DM 23,50 [BB]inc ¶⊙¶ ♔♚ ⬛ 🚂 Bad Karlshafen 4km 🚌 1.5km ap Helmarshausen Mitte

Hemhof ☞ **Bad Endorf**

Heppenheim ▲ [1.5 NE] JH "Starkenburg", 64646 Heppenheim. ☎ (6252) 77323 **FAX** (6252) 78185 **Open:** 1.1-23.12; 27-31.12 🛏 121 ⊖ DM 23,50 [BB]inc ¶⊙¶ ♔♚ ⚖ ⬛ 🚂 Heppenheim 3km

Heringsdorf ▲ Puschkinstr 7/9, 17424 Seebad Heringsdorf. ☎ (38378) 22325 **FAX** (38378) 32301 **Open:** 08.00-09.00hrs, 15.00-21.00hrs, 1.2-30.11 🛏 167 ⊖ DM 20,00 [BB]inc ¶⊙¶(L D) ♔♚ ① ⬛ ⚓ 🚂 Heringsdorf 1km 🚌 1km ⓡ

Hermeskeil ▲ Adolf- Kolping- Str 4, 54411 Hermeskeil. ☎ (6503) 3097 **FAX** (6503) 6146 🛏 105 ⊖ DM 25,10 [BB]inc ¶⊙¶(L D) ♔♚ ⚘

Herrenwies ☞ **Forbach**

Hertlingshausen ▲ Natur-freundehaus Rahnenhof, 67316 Hertlingshausen. ☎ (6356) 281 **FAX** (6356) 5614 🛏 48 [BB]inc ¶⊙¶ ♔♚

Hessenstein, Burg ▲ [12 S] 34516 Vöhl Ederbringhausen. ☎ (6455) 300 **FAX** (6455) 8771 **Open:** 1.1-23.12; 27-31.12 🛏 126 ⊖ DM 23,00 [BB]inc

¶⊙¶ ♔♚ ⚖ ⬛ 🚂 Frankenberg 12km 🚌 1.5km ap YH

Hilchenbach ▲ JH "Wilhelm-Münker", Wilhelm- Münker- Str 9, 57271 Hilchenbach. ☎ (2733) 4396 **FAX** (2733) 8085 **Open:** 1.2-31.12 🛏 86 ⊖ DM 21,00 [BB]inc ¶⊙¶ ⚖ ⬛ ⚘ 🚂 Hilchenbach 500m 🚌 75 200m ap Am Markt

Hilders ▲ [1.5 E] "Haus der Jugend", 36115 Hilders. ☎ (6681) 365 **FAX** (6681) 8429 **Open:** 1.1-23.12; 27-31.12 🛏 148 ⊖ DM 21,00 [BB]inc ¶⊙¶ ♔♚ ⬛ ⚘ Alt 600m ⚓ 🚂 Fulda 33km 🚌 5040 2km ap Marktplatz, 5033 2km ap Thüringer Str

Hildesheim (*see town plan on next page*) ▲ Schirrmannweg 4, 31139 Hildesheim. ☎ (5121) 42717 **FAX** (5121) 47847 🛏 104 ⊖ DM 20,00 [BB]inc ¶⊙¶ ♔♚ ⅗ ⚖ ⬛ 🚂 Hildesheim 8km 🚌 1, 4 1km

Hinsbeck ▲ "Vierlinden", Heide 1, 41334 Nettetal. ☎ (2153) 6492 **FAX** (2153) 89598 🛏 161 ⊖ DM 25,00 [BB]inc ¶⊙¶ ♔♚ ⬛ ♿ 🚂 15km 🚌 093 Kaldenkirchen

Hitzacker ▲ Wolfsschlucht 2 (An der Elbuferstrasse), 29456 Hitzacker. ☎ (5862) 244 **FAX** (5862) 7767 🛏 165 ⊖ DM 20,00 [BB]inc ¶⊙¶ ♔♚ ⅗ ⬚ ⚖ ⬛ 🚂 Hitzacker 40 min

Hochspeyer ▲ Trippstadter Strasse 150, 67691 Hochspeyer. ☎ (6305) 336 **FAX** (6305) 5152 🛏 148 ⊖ DM 25,10 [BB]inc ¶⊙¶(L D) ♔♚

Hof ▲ Beethovenstr 44, 95032 Hof (Bavaria). ☎ (9281) 93277 **FAX** (9281) 92016 **Open:** 16.1-30.11 🛏 91 ⊖ DM 20,00 [BB]inc ¶⊙¶ ⚘ ♔♚ ⬚ 🚂 2km 🚌 3 and 7 300m

Hohe Fahrt ▲ [4 SW] Am Edersee, 34516 Vöhl. ☎ (5635) 251 **FAX** (5635) 8142 **Open:** 1.1-23.12; 27.12-1.1.98 🛏 230

🚫 DM 22,00 [BB]inc 🍴 ♟️ 🅿️ ⛵ 🚆
Korbach 16km

HILDESHEIM

Hohenberg ▲ Auf der Burg, 95691 Hohenberg (Bavaria). 📞 (9233) 77260 **FAX** (9233) 772611 **Open:** 1.1-30.11; 27-31.12 ✉️ 137 🚫 DM 20,00 [BB]inc 🍴 ♟️ 👫 📮 🚆 Schirnding 3km 🚌 6, 100m

Hohenstaufen ▲ Schottengasse 45, 73037 Göppingen, Hohenstaufen. 📞 (7165) 438 **FAX** (7165) 1418 ✉️ 128 🚫 DM 22,00 [BB]inc 🍴(L D) 🚆 Schwäbisch Gmünd 12 km, Göppingen 8km 🚌 200m ap YH

Hoherodskopf ▲ [8NE] Haus der Jugend, 63679 Schotten. 📞 (6044) 2760 **FAX** (6044) 784 **Open:** 1.1-23.12; 27-31.12 ✉️ 120 🚫 DM 21,00 [BB]inc 👫 📮 🚶 Alt 702m 🚆 Nidda 24km 🚌 8km ap Schotten

Hohnstein ▲ Am Markt 1, 01848 Hohnstein. 📞 (35975) 202 **FAX** (35975) 203 **Open:** 06.30-22.00hrs ✉️ 210 🚫 DM 17,00 + 22,00 🍴 🏠 ♿ 📮 ✈️ Dresden 30km 🚆 Pirna 15km 🚌 237 Pirna-Sebnitz ⓡ (4 weeks)

Holzhau ▲ Ringelstr 6, 09623 Holzhau. 📞 (37327) 1322 **Open:** 07.00-22.00hrs, 27.12.96-29.11 ✉️ 44 🚫 DM 17,00 [BB]inc 🍴 ♟️ 👫 📮 🚶 Alt 510m 🚆 Holzhau 4km 🚌 Rechenberg-Bienenmühle-Holzhau T-531 1.5km ap "Teichhaus"

Holzminden ▲ Am Steinhof, 37603 Holzminden. 📞 (5531) 4411 **FAX** (5531) 120630 ✉️ 123 🚫 DM 20,00 [BB]inc 🍴 👫 📮 ⛵ 🚆 Holzminden 15 min

Homburg ▲ Sickinger Str 12, 66424 Homburg. 📞 (6841) 3679 **FAX** (6841) 120220 ✉️ 76 🚫 DM 19,50 [BB]inc 🍴(L D) 👫

Hormersdorf ▲ Am Greifenbachstauweiher, 09468 Geyer 📞 (37346) 1396 **FAX** (37346) 1396 ✉️ 204 🚫 DM 22,00 [BB]inc 🍴 👫 ♿ 📮 🚶 Alt 500m ⛵ 🚆 Annaberg 20km 🚌 Chemnitz-Annaberg-O'thal T-210 5km ap Ehrenfriedersdorf Markt

Horn- Bad Meinberg ▲ Jahnstr 36, Schließfach 1225, 32805 Horn- Bad Meinberg. 📞 (5234) 2534 **FAX** (5234) 69199 **Open:** 29.1-28.12 ✉️ 123 🚫 DM 21,00 [BB]inc 🍴 ♿ 📮 🚆 Horn-Bad Meinberg 2.5km 🚌 200m ap Jahnstr.

Hörnum ▲ Friesenplatz 2, 25997 Hörnum/Sylt. 📞 (4651) 880294 **FAX** (4651) 881392 **Open:** 16.1-30.11 ✉️ 169 🚫 DM 22,00 [BB]inc 🍴(L D) 🅛 📮 🚲 🚆 Westerland 16km 🚌 500m ap Hörnum-Nord

Höxter ▲ JH "Hoffmann- von-Fallersleben", An der Wilhelmshöhe 59, 37671 Höxter. 📞 (5271) 2233 **FAX**

(5271) 1237 **Open:** 4.1-21.12 ⚐ 124 ⊜ DM 20,00 ⒝inc 🍴 ⛪ 🅿 🚽 Höxter 2.5km

Hude ▲ Linteler Str 3, 27798 Hude. ☏ (4408) 414 **FAX** (4408) 60651 **Open:** 1.3-31.10 ⚐ 90 ⊜ DM 22,00 ⒝inc 🍴(L D) 🅿 🚽 Hude 3km

Hürth ▲ "Villehaus" Adolf- Dasbach- Weg 5, 50354 Hürth. ☏ (2233) 42463 ⚐ 70 ⊜ DM 24,00 ⒝inc 🍴 🚹🚺 🅿 🚽 Köln 25km 🚌 978

Husum ▲ Schobüller Str 34, 25813 Husum. ☏ (4841) 2714 **FAX** (4841) 81568 **Open:** 1.12.96-31.10 ⚐ 179 ⊜ DM 22,00 ⒝inc 🍴(L D) ♿ 🅿 🚽 Husum 3km 🚌 200m ap Westerkampweg

Idar- Oberstein ⚠ Alte Treibe 23, 55743 Idar-Oberstein. ☏ (6781) 24366 **FAX** (6781) 26712 ⚐ 128 ⊜ DM 25,10 ⒝inc 🍴(L D) 🚹🚺

Igersheim ▲ Erlenbachtalstr 44,97999 Igersheim ☏ (7931) 6373 **FAX** (7931) 52795 ⚐ 168 ⊜ DM 22,00 ⒝inc 🍴(L D) 🚹🚺 🅿 🚽 Bad Mergentheim 2km, Igersheim 1.5km 🚌 500m ap Solymar

Ihrlerstein- Kelheim ▲ Kornblumenweg 1, 93346 Ihrlerstein (Bavaria). ☏ (9441) 3309 **FAX** (9441) 21792 **Open:** 1.2-30.11 ⚐ 122 ⊜ DM 18,00 ⒝inc 🍴(D) 🚹🚺 🔲 🚽 Saal an der Donau 8km

Ilmenau ▲ Am Stollen 49, 98693 Ilmenau. ☏ (3677) 202413 **Open:** 07.00-22.00hrs, 1.1-22.12; 27-31.12 ⚐ 120 ⊜ DM 20,00 ⒝inc 🍴 🚹🚺 ♿ 🅿 🚅 🚽 Ilmenau 1km 🚌 500m Ⓡ

Ingolstadt ▲ Friedhofstr 4 1/2, 85049 Ingolstadt (Bavaria). ☏ (841) 34177 **FAX** (841) 910178 **Open:** 1.2-14.12 ⚐ 84 ⊜ DM 20,00 ⒝inc 🍴 🚹🚺 ♿ 🚽 3km 🚌 10, 250m

Inselsberg ▲ 98599 Brotterode ☏ (36259) 2329 **Open:** 07.00-22.00hrs, 1.1-22.12; 28-31.12 ⚐ 60 ⊜ DM 17,00 ⒝inc 🍴 🚅 Alt 916m 🚽 Tabarz 10km 🚌 1km ap Kleiner Inselsberg

Inzmühlen ▲ Wehlener Weg 10, 21256 Handeloh. ☏ (4188) 342 **FAX** (4188) 7858 **Open:** 1.2-22.12 ⚐ 166 ⊜ DM 20,00 ⒝inc 🍴(L D) 🅿 🚲 🚽 Handeloh 2km

Isny ▲ "Georg-Sulzberger-JH", Dekan-Marquardt-Str 18,88316 Isny. ☏ (7562) 2550 **FAX** (7562) 55547 ⚐ 130 ⊜ DM 22,00 ⒝inc 🍴(L D) 🅿 🚅 🚽 Leutkirch 17km, Kempten 27km 🚌 2km ap Marktplatz

Itzehoe ▲ Juliengardeweg 11-13, 25524 Itzehoe. ☏ (4821) 62270 **FAX** (4821) 5710 **Open:** 16.1-14.12 ⚐ 75 ⊜ DM 20,00 ⒝inc 🍴(L D) 📸 🅿 🚽 Itzehoe 2km 🚌 400m Ⓡ (1.11-31.3)

Jena "Am Herrenberge" ⚠ 3.5 W ⓒⓒ Jugendgästehaus "Am Herrenberge", Am Herrenberge 9, 07745 Jena. ☏ (3641) 6250 **FAX** (3641) 605554 **Open:** 1.1-31.12 ⚐ 100 ⊜ DM 33,50 ⒝inc 🍴 🚹🚺 ♿ 🔲 ⛪ 🅿 🚲 ✈ Erfurt 50km 🚽 Westbahnhof 2km 🚌 10,12,11,40 2km ap Mühlenstraße 1km 🚌 ap Mühlenstraße 2km Ⓡ

Jever ▲ Mooshütter Weg 12,26441 Jever. ☏ (4461)3590 **FAX** (4461)3565 **Open:** 1.4-31.10 ⚐ 50 ⊜ DM 18,00 ⒝inc 🍴(L D) 🚹🚺 🚲 🚽 Jever 1km

Johanngeorgenstadt ▲ Hospitalstr 5, 08349 Johanngeorgenstadt. ☏ (3773) 2194 **Open:** 06.00-22.00hrs ⚐ 45 ⊜ DM 20,00 ⒝inc 🍴 📸 🚹🚺 🔲 🅿 🚅 Alt 827m 🚽 Zwickau- Aue- Schwarzenberg- Johanngeorgenstadt 2km 🚌 Aue Schwarzenberg-Johanngeorgenstadt T-334 1km ap Markt

Jonsdorf ▲ Hainstr 14, 02796 Jonsdorf. ☏ (35844) 70220 **Open:**

07.00-09.00hrs, 15.00-20.00hrs ⌘ 69 ● DM 20,00 [BB]ⁱⁿᶜ �"⦿(B L) ⫙ ⌸ ⫿ ⚓ ⛟ Jonsdorf 1km 🚌 Zittau-Oybin 1km ap Jonsdorf station

Josefsthal ☞ **Schliersee**

Juist ▲ |1.5 W| Loogster Pad 20, 26571 Juist, (North Sea). ⚡ (4935) 92910 **FAX** (4935) 8294 **Open:** 1.1-31.10 ⌘ 294 ● (Full Board) ⦿ ⫙ ⊡ ⛙ ⚲ ⚓ ⛴ Norddeich ⓡ

Kandern ▲ "Platzhof", Auf der Scheideck, 79400 Kandern. ⚡ (7626) 484 **FAX** (7626) 6809 **Open:** 1.3-31.10 ⌘ 69 ● DM 18,00 [BB]ⁱⁿᶜ ⦿ ⫙ ⫿ ⛟ Steinen 10km 🚌 2km ap Schlächtenhaus

Kappeln ▲ Eckernförder Str 2, 24376 Kappeln. ⚡ (4642) 8550 **FAX** (4642) 81086 **Open:** 12.1-30.11 ⌘ 170 ● DM 20,00 [BB]ⁱⁿᶜ ⦿(L D) ⛴ ⫿ ⚲ 🚌 1.5km

Karlsruhe ▲ |4 NW| Moltkestr 24, 76133 Karlsruhe. ⚡ (721) 28248 **FAX** (721) 27647 ⌘ 164 ● DM 22,00 [BB]ⁱⁿᶜ ⦿ ⫙ ⫿ ⛟ Karlsruhe-Hbf 4km 🚊 3, 4 1km ap Europaplatz

Kassel (*see town plan on next page*) ⚠ |1.5 NW| "JH Am Tannenwäldchen", Schenkendorfstr 18, 34119 Kassel. ⚡ (561) 776455 **FAX** (561) 776832 **Open:** 2.1-23.12; 27-30.12 ⌘ 209 ● DM 24,00 [BB]ⁱⁿᶜ ⦿ ⫙ ⛴ ⫿ ⚓ ⛟ Kassel 1.5km 🚊 4, 6 400m ap Annastraße

Katzhütte ▲ Bahnhofstr 82, 98746 Katzhütte. ⚡ (36781) 37785 **Open:** 07.00-22.00hrs, 1.1-22.12; 28-31.12 ⌘ 60 ● DM 18,00 [BB]ⁱⁿᶜ ⦿ ⌲ ⛟ Katzhütte 300m 🚌 300m ⓡ

Kehl ▲ |1 SW| Altrheinweg 11, 77694 Kehl. ⚡ (7851) 2330 **FAX** (7851) 76608 ⌘ 122 ● DM 22,00 [BB]ⁱⁿᶜ ⦿ ⫙ ⫿ ⛟ Kehl 1km

Kelheim ☞ **Ihrlerstein**

Kempten ▲ Saarlandstr 1, 87437 Kempten (Bavaria). ⚡ (831) 73663 **FAX** (831) 770381 **Open:** 1.1-31.10; 28-31.12 ⌘ 123 ● DM 18,00 [BB]ⁱⁿᶜ ⌲ Alt 670m ⛟ 5km 🚌 800m

Kevelaer ▲ Am Michelsweg 11, 47626 Kevelaer. ⚡ (2832) 8267 **FAX** (2832) 899432 ⌘ 130 ● DM 24,00 [BB]ⁱⁿᶜ ⦿ ⚿ ⫿ ⛟ Kevelaer 1km 🚌

Kiel ⚠ |2 SE| |IBN| Johannesstr 1, 24143 Kiel. ⚡ (431) 731488 **FAX** (431) 735723 **Open:** 4.1-17.12 ⌘ 265 ● DM 24,00 [BB]ⁱⁿᶜ ⦿(L D) ⫿ ⛟ Kiel Main 3km 🚌 4 500m

KIEL

Kirchberg ▲ Gaggstatter Str 35, 74592 Kirchberg. ⚡ (7954) 230 **FAX** (7954) 1319 ⌘ 90 ● DM 20,00 [BB]ⁱⁿᶜ ⦿(L D) ⫿ ⛟ Crailsheim 12km, Schwäbisch Hall 25km 🚌 500m ap Frankenplatz

Klausdorf ▲ Am See 30, 15838 Klausdorf. ⚡ (33703) 634 **Open:** 07.00-22.00hrs, 1.4-31.10 ⌘ 65 ● DM 18,00 [BB]ⁱⁿᶜ ⦿(D) ⫙ ⛟ Zossen 6km 🚌 from Zossen 500m

Köris ▲ JH 'Köriser See', Am See 5, 15746 Gross Köris. ⚡ (33766) 62730 **FAX** (33766) 62730 **Open:**

07.00-09.00hrs, 11.00-19.00hrs, 6.1-19.12 🏠 80 ● DM 22,00 BBinc ¶Ol ♣ ✈ Schönefeld 30km 🚂 Gross-Köris 2.5km 🚌 200m Ⓡ

KASSEL

Kleve ▲ St Annaberg 2, 47533 Kleve Materborn. 📞 (2821) 23671 **FAX** (2821) 24778 🏠 122 ● DM 24,00 BBinc ¶Ol ♦♦♦ P 🚂 Kleve 4km 🚌 57

Klingenthal ▲ JH 'Aschberg', Grenzweg 22, 08248 Klingenthal. 📞 (37467) 22094 **FAX** (37467) 22094 **Open:** 06.30-23.00hrs 🏠 122 ● DM 20,00 - 22,00 BBinc ¶Ol ⚓ Alt 936m 🚂 Zwickau- Klingenthal 7km 🚌 Rodewisch-Auerbach-Klingenthal T-79 5km ap Gasthof "Stern"

Koblenz (*see town plan on next page*) ▲ 6NE CC 56077 Koblenz-Ehrenbreitstein, Festung, niedere Ostfront, rechte Rheinseite. 📞 (261) 73737 **FAX** (261) 702707 🏠 201 ● DM 22,50 BBinc ¶Ol(L D) ♦♦♦ ⚓

Kochel ▲ Badstr 2, 82431 Kochel (Bavaria). 📞 (8851) 5296 **FAX** (8851) 7019 **Open:** 1.2-31.10 🏠 31 ● DM 20,00 BBinc ¶Ol(D) 🚂 2km 🚌 1085, 1086 100m

KÖLN (2 Hostels)

Köln - Deutz ▲ 3E IBN CC Siegesstr 5a, 50679 Köln. 📞 (221) 814711 **FAX** (221) 884425 🏠 374 ● DM 30,00 BBinc ¶Ol ♦♦♦ ⚓ P ✈ 12km 🚂 Köln-Deutz 50m

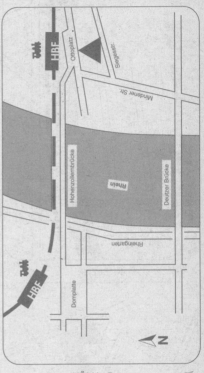

KÖLN - Deutz

Köln - Riehl (*see town plan on next page*) ▲ 6NE YGH "Jugendgästehaus", An der Schanz 14, 50735 Köln. 📞 (221) 767081 **FAX** (221) 761555 🏠 366 ● DM 37,00 BBinc ¶Ol ♦♦♦ ♿ ⚓ P ✈ 14km 🚂 Köln 3km U 16,18

Königerode JH **Wippra** ▲ Schiefergraben, 06493 Königerode 📞 (39484) 8310 🏠 80 ● DM 18,00 ¶Ol ♦♦♦ 🚌 Bushaltestelle 3.5km

Königsberg ▲ Schlossberg 10, 97486 Königsberg (Bavaria). 📞 (9525) 237 **FAX** (9525) 8114 **Open:** 7.1-5.11 🏠

89 ● DM 18,00 BB^inc ¶O¶(L) ♦♦♦ 🚂 1km

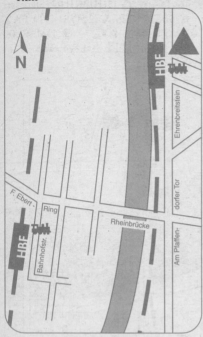

KOBLENZ

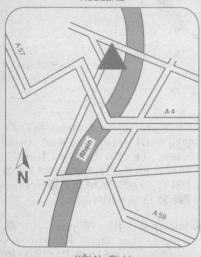

KÖLN - Riehl

Königsbronn ▲ Weilerweg 12, 89551 Königsbronn- Ochsenberg. ✆ (7328) 6600 **FAX** (7328) 7451 ⤢ 112 ● DM 22,00 BB^inc ¶O¶(L D) ♦♦♦ ♿ 🅿 🚲 🚂

Königsbronn 3km 🚌 300m ap 'Im Weiler' Ochsenberg

Konstanz ▲ 5NE "Otto- Möricke- Turm", Zur Allmannshöhe 18, 78464 Konstanz. ✆ (7531) 32260 **FAX** (7531) 31163 **Open:** 1.3-31.10 ⤢ 184 ● DM 20,00 BB^inc ¶O¶ ♦♦♦ 🅿 🚂 Konstanz 3km 🚌 4 400m ap YH

Korbach ⚠ 0.5W Enser Str 9, 34497 Korbach. ✆ (5631) 8360 **FAX** (5631) 4835 **Open:** 1.1-23.12; 27-31.12 ⤢ 98 ● DM 24,00 BB^inc ¶O¶ ♦♦♦ ♿ 🅿 🚲 ⛵ 🚂 Korbach 1km

Köthener See ▲ Dorfstr 20, 15748 Märkisch- Bucholz ✆ (33765) 80555 **FAX** (33765) 84870 **Open:** 07.00-22.00hrs, 1.1-9.11; 25.11-21.12; 28.12-31.12 ⤢ 110 ● DM 22,00 BB^inc ¶O¶ ♦♦♦ 🗑 ⛵ ✈ Schönefeld 45km 🚂 Oderin 6km 🚌 50m ⓡ (12 weeks)

Kretzschau ⚠ 06712 Kretzschau. ✆ (3441) 212678 **FAX** (3441) 212678 **Open:** 07.00-22.00hrs, 1.1-23.12; 27-31.12 ⤢ 203 ● DM 22,00 BB^inc ¶O¶ ♦♦♦ 🏛 🅿 ⛵ 🚂 Kretzschau 2km 🚌 1.5km

Kreuth- Scharling ⚠ Nördliche Hauptstr 91, 83708 Kreuth (Bavaria). ✆ (8029) 552 **FAX** (8029) 1060 **Open:** 1.1-31.10; 27-31.12 ⤢ 103 ● DM 22,00 BB^inc ¶O¶(B D) ♂ ♦♦♦ 🗑 ⚓ Alt 780m 🚂 Tegernsee 8km 🚌 100m

Kronach ▲ Festung 1, 96317 Kronach (Bavaria). ✆ (9261) 94412 **Open:** 1.4-31.10 ⤢ 106 ● DM 18,00 BB^inc ¶O¶ 🏚 🗑 🚂 2km

Kronenburg- Baasem ▲ 53949 Dahlem. ✆ (6557) 339 **FAX** (6557) 7350 ⤢ 130 ● DM 24,00 BB^inc ¶O¶ ♦♦♦ 🅿 🚂 Dahlem 🚌

Kühlungsborn ▲ Dünenstr 4, 18225 Ostseebad Kühlungsborn. ✆ (38293) 270 **FAX** (38293) 279 **Open:** 08.00-09.00hrs,   15.00-22.00hrs,

6.2-5.1.98 ✉ 124 ● DM 20,00 [BB]inc
{O|(L D) ♦♦♦ ⛟ P ⚓ ☲ Kühlungsborn
Ost 200m ☷ 200m ®

Kulmbach ▲ Mangersreutherstr 43,
95326 Kulmbach (Bavaria). ✆ (9221)
7243 **FAX** (9221) 7243 **Open:**
11.1-14.8; 11.9-21.12 ✉ 90 ● DM
20,00 [BB]inc {O| ♦♦♦ ☲ 4km

Lam ▲ Jugendherbergsweg 1, 93462
Lam (Bavaria). ✆ (9943) 1068 **FAX**
(9943) 2936 **Open:** 1.1-31.10;
27-31.12 ✉ 130 ● DM 20,00 [BB]inc
{O| ♦♦♦ ⚐ Alt 700m ☲ 2km

Landshut ⛰ Richard-Schirrmann-Weg
6, 84028 Landshut (Bavaria). ✆ (871)
23449 **FAX** (871) 274947 **Open:**
8.1-22.12 ✉ 100 ● DM 20,00-29,00
[BB]inc ⛍ ♦♦♦ ♿

Langeleben ▲ 33154 Königslutter. ✆
(5353) 8582 ✉ 150 [BB]inc {O| P ☲
Königsbutte 7km

Langenwetzendorf ▲ Greizerstr. (Am
Schwimmbad), 07957 Langenwetzendorf
✆ (36625) 20305 **Open:** 07.00-22.00hrs,
1.1-22.12; 28-31.12 ✉ 66 (Wi 50) ●
DM 17,00 [BB]inc {O| P ®

Langeoog ▲ [5E] Domäne Melkhörn,
26465 Langeoog, (North Sea). ✆ (4972)
276 **FAX** (4972) 6694 **Open:** 1.4-30.9
✉ 126 ● (Full Board) {O| ① ⛟ ♨ ⚓
☷ Esens 5km ☷ Esens-Bensersiel
5km ®

Laubach ▲ [2N] Felix-Klipstein-Weg
35, 35321 Laubach. ✆ (6405) 1376
FAX (6405) 7046 **Open:** 1.1-23.12;
27-31.12 ✉ 122 ● DM 21,50 [BB]inc
{O| P ⚓ ☲ Grünberg 6km ☷ 2km
ap Busbahnhof Laubach

Lauenburg ▲ Am Sportplatz 7, 21481
Lauenburg. ✆ (4153) 2598 **FAX** (4153)
2310 ✉ 131 ● DM 20,00 [BB]inc
{O|(L D) P ☲ Hamburg ☷ 31
400m ap Lauenburg

Lauterbach ▲ [4NE] Schlitzer Str 50,
36341 Lauterbach. ✆ (6641) 2181 **FAX**
(6641) 61200 **Open:** 1.1-23.12;
27-31.12 ✉ 172 ● DM 23,00 [BB]inc
{O| ♦♦♦ P ⚓ ☲ Lauterbach 2km

Leer ▲ Süderkreuzstr 7, 26789 Leer. ✆
(491) 2126 ✉ 94 ● DM 20,00 [BB]inc
{O| ♨ ⚓ ☲ Leer 2km

Leichlingen ▲ "Naturfreundehaus",
Am Block 4, 42799 Leichlingen. ✆
(2175) 2917 ✉ 43 ● DM 24,00 [BB]inc
{O| P ☲ Leichlingen

Leinburg-Weißenbrunn ▲ Badstr 15,
91227 Leinburg (Bavaria). ✆ (9187)
1529 **FAX** (9187) 5920 **Open:**
1.2-30.11 ✉ 70 ● DM 16,50 [BB]inc {O|
☲ Altdorf 6km ☷ 411, 500m

LEIPZIG (2 Hostels)

Leipzig - Centrum (*see town plan on next
page*) ▲ Käthe - Kollwitz-Str 64-66,
04109 Leipzig. ✆ (341) 470530 **FAX**
(341) 475888 **Open:** 06.00-23.00hrs
✉ 106 ● DM 22,00 {O| ♦♦♦ P ✈
Leipzig - Halle 25km A☷ Leipzig -
Central Station 3km ☲ Leipzig
Central - Plagwitz (Line 2) 150m ⛋ 2
Plagwitz 150m ap Marschnerstr ®

Leipzig - Auensee ▲ Gustav-Esche-Str
4, 04159 Leipzig. ✆ (341) 4611114
FAX (341) 4611114 **Open:**
07.00-21.00hrs, 15.1-21.12 ✉ 43 ●
DM 20,00 {O|(B D) ♦♦♦ ✈ Leipzig-Halle
25km A☷ Leipzig- Central Station
10km ☲ Leipzig Central - Rathaus
Wahren 800m ⛋ 10,11,28 to
Wahren/Schkeuditz 800m ap Rathaus
Wahren

Lenggries ▲ Jugendherbergsstr 10,
83661 Lenggries (Bavaria). ✆ (8042)
2424 **FAX** (8042) 4532 **Open:**
1.1-30.11; 27-31.12 ✉ 102 ● DM
20,00 [BB]inc {O|(B D) ⚐ Alt 650m ☲
2.5km

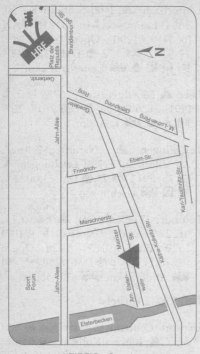

LEIPZIG - Centrum

Lensahn ▲ Sundstr 1, 23738 Lensahn.
☎ (4363) 2241 **Open:** 1.4-30.9 ⚑ 38
⊖ DM 18,00 BBinc ⵙⵙ(L D) 🚊
Lensahn 500m

Leuchtenburg ▲ 07768 Seitenroda. ☎
(36424) 23216 **Open:** 06.00-20.00hrs,
1.1-22.12; 28-31.12 ⚑ 122 ⊖ DM
16,00 BBinc ⵙⵙ ⵙⵙ 🏠 🅿 🚊 Kahla 4km
🚌 Seitenroda 500m

Lichtenfels ▲ Alte Coburger Str 43,
96215 Lichtenfels (Bavaria). ☎ (9571)
71039 **FAX** (9571) 71877 **Open:**
1.2-14.12 ⚑ 87 ⊖ DM 20,00 BBinc ⵙⵙ
ⵙⵙ 🚊 2km

Lichtenstein ▲ An der Jugendherberge
3, 09350 Lichtenstein. ☎ (37204) 2718
FAX (37204) 2718 **Open:**
06.00-22.00hrs ⚑ 105 Su; 60 Wi ⊖
DM 20,00 ⵙⵙ ⵙⵙ ⵙⵙ 🅿 🚊 St Egidien
8km 🚌 T 251, 670, 108 1km ap 🚊

Liepnitzsee ▲ Wandlitzer Str 6, 16359
Lanke/Ützdorf. ☎ (33397) 21659 **FAX**
(33397) 21659 **Open:** 07.00-15.00hrs,
17.30-22.00hrs, 1.2-16.11 ⚑ 39 ⊖
DM 22,00 BBinc ⵙⵙ ✈ Tegel/Berlin
50km 🚊 Wandlitz 4km 🚌 2km
Ⓡ (3 weeks in advance)

Limburg ▲ ⟦1.5S⟧ Auf dem
Guckucksberg, 65549 Limburg. ☎
(6431) 41493 **FAX** (6431) 43873
Open: 1.1-23.12; 27-31.12 ⚑ 162 ⊖
DM 21,00 BBinc ⵙⵙ ⵙⵙ 🅿 ⛵ 🚊
Limburg 1.5km 🚌 3, 4 300m
ap Hammersberg

Lindau ⛺ ⟦5NW⟧ Herbergsweg 11,
88131 Lindau (Bavaria). ☎ (8382) 5813
Open: 1997 ⚑ 250 ⊖ DM 25,50 BBinc
ⵙⵙ(B D) ⵙⵙ ⵙⵙ ♿ 🖨 🏠 🅿 🚲 ⛵ 🚊
2km 🚌 "Inselbus" 500m
ap "Schwimmbad" Ⓡ (**Shut:** DJH-
Landesver- band, Bayern. ☎(89)
92209832, **FAX**(89) 92209840)

Lindlar ▲ Jugendherberge 30, 51789
Lindlar. ☎ (2266) 5264 **FAX** (2266)
45517 ⚑ 174 ⊖ DM 24,00 BBinc ⵙⵙ
ⵙⵙ ⵙⵙ 🅿 🚊 Engelskirchen 10km 🚌
332

Lingen ⛺ Lengericher Str 62, 49811
Lingen. ☎ (591) 97306-0 **FAX** (591)
76954 ⚑ 152 ⊖ DM 24,00 BBinc ⵙⵙ
ⵙⵙ 🖨 🅿 🚲 ⛵ 🚊 Lingen 3km

Linsengericht ▲ ⟦6S⟧ "Haus der Jugend
Geislitz", 63589 Linsengericht. ☎
(6051) 72029 **FAX** (6051) 75694
Open: 1.1-23.12; 27-31.12 ⚑ 124 ⊖
DM 23,50 BBinc ⵙⵙ ⵙⵙ 🅿 🚊
Gelnhausen 6km 🚌 Buslinie 1km
ap YH

List ▲ JH Mövenberg, 25992 List/Sylt.
☎ (4651) 870397 **FAX** (4651) 871039
Open: 15.3-31.10 ⚑ 399 ⊖ DM
22,00 BBinc ⵙⵙ(L D) 🚻 🖨 🅿 🚊
Westerland 20km 🚌 500m ap List
Schule

Lochen ▲ Auf der Lochen 1, 72336 Balingen- Lochen, ☎ (7433) 37383 **FAX** (7433) 382296 🛏 100 ● DM 22,00 BBinc 🍴(L D) 👪 P Alt 936m 🚂 Balingen 11km 🚌 100m ap Lochen

Löhne- Gohfeld ▲ Naturfreundehaus "Carl Schreck", In den Tannen 63, 32584 Löhne. ☎ (5731) 81012 🛏 84 BBinc 🍴 ♿ P 🚂 Bad Oeynhausen 4km 🚌 406 1km ap Jöllenbeck

Lohr ▲ Brunnenwiesenweg 13, 97816 Lohr (Bavaria). ☎ (9352) 2444 **FAX** (9352) 70873 **Open:** 1.2-30.11 🛏 94 ● DM 22,00 BBinc 🍴 👪 🚂 1.8km 🚌 500m

Lörrach ▲ 3SE Steinenweg 40, 79540 Lörrach. ☎ (7621) 47040 **FAX** (7621) 18156 🛏 168 BBinc 🍴 👪 ♿ P 🚂 Lörrach 4km 🚌 7 200m ap YH

Lübben ▲ 2.5SE Zum Wendenfürsten 8, 15907 Lübben. ☎ (3546) 3046 **FAX** (3546) 3046 **Open:** 07.00-22.00hrs 🛏 122 ● DM 22,00 BBinc 🍴 ⛵ 🚂 Lübben 3.5km 🚌 1.5km R (1.9-30.1: 2 weeks in advance; 1.4-30.6: 3 days in advance)

LÜBECK (2 Hostels)
(see town plan on next page)

Lübeck ▲ 2NE Am Gertrudenkirchhof 4, 23568 Lübeck. ☎ (451) 33433 **FAX** (451) 34540 **Open:** ☎ Hostel for details 🛏 220 ● DM 22,00 BBinc 🍴(L D) P 🚂 Lübeck 3km 🚌 1,3,11,12 500m ap Gustav-Radbruch-Platz

Lübeck - **JGH** ▲ 1W Mengstr 33, 23552 Lübeck. ☎ (451) 7020399 **FAX** (451) 77012 🛏 72 ● from DM 26,50 BBinc 🚂 Lübeck 2km

Ludwigsburg JH + YGH ▲ Gemsenbergstr 21, 71640 Ludwigsburg. ☎ (7141) 51564 **FAX** (7141) 59440 🛏 72 + 48 ● DM 22,00 BBinc 🍴(L D) P 🚂 Ludwigsburg 2.5km 🚌 422 50m ap 'S Schlößlesfeld' Endstation

Ludwigstein ▲ "Jugendburg", 37214 Witzenhausen. ☎ (5542) 1812 **FAX** (5542) 3649 **Open:** 1.1-23.12; 27-31.12 🛏 174 BBinc 🍴 👪 P 🚂 Witzenhausen Nord 9km 🚌 Witzenhausen- Eschwege 1km ap Ludwigstein

Lüneburg ▲ Soltauer Str 133, 21335 Lüneburg. ☎ (4131) 41864 **FAX** (4131) 45747 🛏 107 ● DM 20,00 BBinc 🍴 P 🚂 Lüneburg 35 min 🚌 to Sande then Linie 1 to YH

Maibrunn ☞ **St Englmar**

Mainz ▲ 5SE CC YGH Otto-Brunfels-Schneise 4, 55130 Mainz. ☎ (6131) 85332 **FAX** (6131) 82422 🛏 174 ● DM 21,50-26,30 BBinc 🍴(L D) 👪

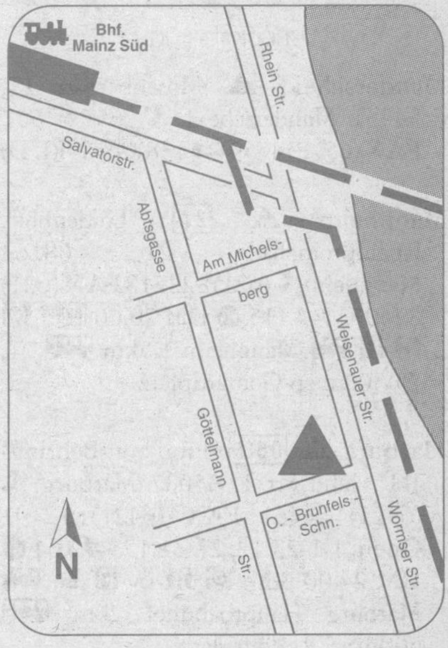

MAINZ

Malente ▲ Kellerseestr 48, 23714 Malente. ☎ (4523) 1723 **FAX** (4523) 2539 🛏 212 ● DM 20,00 BBinc 🍴(L D) P 🚲 🚂 Malente 3km 🚌 1.5km

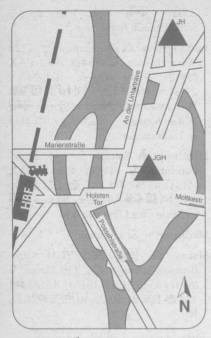

LÜBECK - JH, JGH

Manderscheid ▲ Mosenbergstr 17, 54531 Manderscheid. ☎ (6572) 557 **FAX** (6572) 4759 ⇌ 138 ⒝⒝inc ⓄⒾ(L D)

Mannheim ▲ 2W "Lindenhof", Rheinpromenade 21, 68163 Mannheim. ☎ (621) 822718 **FAX** (621) 824073 ⇌ 115 ⊖ DM 20,00 ⒝⒝inc ⓄⒾ ⫯⫯⫯ ⓟ ⊞⊞ Mannheim 1.5km ⊞⊞ 71, 75 300m ap Gontardplatz

Marburg ⚠ 0.5SE "Emil-von-Behring-JH", Jahn Str 1, 35037 Marburg. ☎ (6421) 23461 **FAX** (6421) 12191 **Open:** 1.1-23.12; 27-31.12 ⇌ 164 ⊖ DM 24,00 ⒝⒝inc ⓄⒾ ⫯⫯⫯ ⅁ ⓟ ⚓ ⊞⊞ Marburg Hauptbahnhof 2km ⊞⊞ 500m ap Rudolfsplatz

Mardorf ⚠ Warteweg 2, 31535 Neustadt-Mardorf. ☎ (5036) 457 **FAX** (5036) 1554 ⇌ 164 ⊖ DM 22,00 ⒝⒝inc ⓄⒾ ⫯⫯⫯ ⅁ ⓟ ⚓ ✈ Hannover 30km ⊞⊞ Neustadt 15km

Marktredwitz ▲ Wunsiedlerstr 29, 95615 Marktredwitz (Bavaria). ☎ (9231) 81082 **FAX** (9231) 87346 ⇌ 37 ⊖ DM 18,00 ⒝⒝inc ⓄⒾ(D) ⊞⊞ 3km

Mauth ▲ Jugendherbergsstr 11, 94151 Mauth (Bavaria). ☎ (8557) 289 **FAX** (8557) 1581 **Open:** 1.1-31.10; 27-31.12 ⇌ 96 ⊖ DM 20,00 ⒝⒝inc ⓄⒾ ⫯⫯⫯ ⊡ ⚓ Alt 820m ⊞⊞ Passau 50km ⊞⊞ Passau-Finsterau 200m

Mayen ▲ Am Knüppchen 5, 56727 Mayen. ☎ (2651) 2355 **FAX** (2651) 78378 ⇌ 130˙ ⊖ DM 20,50 ⒝⒝inc ⓄⒾ(L D) ⫯⫯⫯

Meinerzhagen ▲ Bergstr. 1, 58540 Meinerzhagen. ☎ (2354) 2280 **FAX** (2354) 14341 **Open:** 1.1-7.2; 1.3-1.11; 1-31.12 ⇌ 164 ⊖ DM 21,00 ⒝⒝inc ⓄⒾ ⅁ ⌨ ⓟ ⚓ ⊞⊞ Brügge 14km ⊞⊞ 58 2.5km ap Meinerzhagen Stadtsparkasse

Meisdorf ▲ Falkensteiner Weg 2B, 06463 Meisdorf. ☎ (34743) 8257 **Open:** 06.30-22.00hrs, 1.1-23.12; 27-31.12 ⇌ 108 ⊖ DM 20,00 ⒝⒝inc ⓄⒾ(B D) ⫯⫯⫯ ⊡ ⓟ ⚓ ⊞⊞ Meisdorf 6km ⊞⊞ 30m

Melle ▲ Fr-Ludwig-Jahn-Str 1, 49324 Melle. ☎ (5422) 2434 **FAX** (5422) 3988 ⇌ 67 ⊖ DM 22,00 ⒝⒝inc ⓄⒾ(L D) ⫯⫯⫯ ⓟ ⊞⊞ Melle 2km

Melsungen ▲ 1W Lindenbergstr 23, 34212 Melsungen. ☎ (5661) 2650 **FAX** (5661) 51928 **Open:** 1.1-23.12; 27-31.12 ⇌ 132 ⊖ DM 23,50 ⒝⒝inc ⓄⒾ ⫯⫯⫯ ⅁ ⓟ ⚓ ⊞⊞ Melsungen 1km

Memmingen ▲ Kempterstr 42, 87700 Memmingen (Bavaria). ☎ (8331) 494087 **FAX** (8331) 494087 **Open:** 1.3-31.11 ⇌ 70 ⊖ DM 18,00 ⒝⒝inc ⓄⒾ ⫯⫯⫯ ⊞⊞ 1.5km

Mendig ▲ "Laacherseehaus", Laacherseestr 17, 56743 Mendig. ☎

(2652) 4777 **FAX** (2652) 2282 ✉ 79 ❚❙❘ ☞

Menzenschwand ▲ OT Menzenschwand, Vorderdorfstr 10, 79837 St Blasien. ☎ (7675) 326 **FAX** (7675) 1435 ✉ 102 ● DM 20,00 BBinc ❚❙❘ ᴙ⛪ ℙ ⚓ ᴡ Seebrugg ᴡ 7321 ap Vorderdorf

Merzalben ▲ Tannenstr 20, 66978 Merzalben. ☎ (6395) 6271 **FAX** (6395) 7089 ✉ 110 ● DM 19,50 BBinc ❚❙❘(L D)

Meschede ▲ "Haus Dortmund", Warsteiner Straße, 59872 Meschede. ☎ (291) 6666 **FAX** (291) 1589 **Open:** 3.1-21.12 ✉ 100 ● DM 21,00 BBinc ❚❙❘ ᴥ ℙ ᴡ Meschede 5.5km

Milow ▲ Friedensstr 21, 14715 Milow. ☎ (3386) 280361 **FAX** (3386) 280361 **Open:** 07.00-22.00hrs, 1.2-15.12 ✉ 85 ● DM 22,00 BBinc ❚❙❘ ⚓ ᴡ Premnitz 2.5km ᴡ 500m Ⓡ (4 weeks)

Mirow ▲ Retzower Str, 17252 Mirow. ☎ (39833) 20726 **FAX** (39833) 22057 **Open:** 08.00-09.00hrs, 15.00-22.00hrs, 6.5-13.10 ✉ 100 ● DM 19,00 BBinc ❚❙❘(D) ☞ ᴙ ᴥ ℙ ⚓ ᴡ Mirow 2.7km ᴡ 500m ap Schleùse Ⓡ

Mittenwald ▲ Buckelwiesen 7, 82481 Mittenwald (Bavaria). ☎ (8823) 1701 **FAX** (8823) 2907 **Open:** 1.1-31.10; 28-31.12 ✉ 121 ● DM 20,00 BBinc ❚❙❘(D) ᴙ ⚓ Alt 1000m ᴡ 4km

Möhnesee ▲ Südufer 20, 59519 Körbecke- Möhnesee. ☎ (2924) 305 **FAX** (2924) 2788 ✉ 203 ● DM 21,00 BBinc ❚❙❘ ᴥ ℙ ⚓ ᴡ Soest 10km ᴡ 605 30m ap YH

Mölln ▲ Am Ziegelsee 2, 23879 Mölln. ☎ (4542) 2601 **FAX** (4542) 86718 **Open:** 27.1-14.12 ✉ 164 ● DM 20,00 BBinc ❚❙❘(L D) ℙ ⚓ ᴡ Mölln 2.5km ᴡ 1km

Mönchengladbach ▲ "Hardter Wald", Umweltstudienplatz, Brahmsstr 156, 41169 Mönchengladbach. ☎ (2161) 559512 **FAX** (2161) 556464 ✉ 131 ● DM 25,00 BBinc ❚❙❘ ᴡ 10km ᴡ 13, 23 Mönchengladbach 1.3km Ⓡ

MONSCHAU (2 Hostels)

Monschau - Burg ▲ Auf dem Schloss 4, 52156 Monschau. ☎ (2472) 2314 **FAX** (2472) 4391 ✉ 96 ● DM 24,00 BBinc ❚❙❘ ᴙ ᴡ Aachen 15km ᴡ

Monschau - Hagard ▲ Hargardsgasse 5, 52156 Monschau. ☎ (2472) 2180 **FAX** (2472) 4527 ✉ 148 ● DM 25,00 BBinc ❚❙❘ ☞ ᴙ ℙ ᴡ Aachen 12km ᴡ

Montabaur ⚠ Richard-Schirrmann-Str, 56410 Montabaur. ☎ (2602) 5121 **FAX** (2602) 180176 ✉ 136 ● DM 21,50 BBinc ❚❙❘(L D) ᴙ

Morbach ▲ Jugendherbergsstr 16, 54497 Morbach. ☎ (6533) 3389 **FAX** (6533) 2787 ✉ 83 ● DM 19,50 BBinc ❚❙❘(L D) ᴙ ⚓

Morsbach ▲ Obere Kirchstr 21, 51597 Morsbach. ☎ (2294) 8662 **FAX** (2294) 7807 ✉ 166 ● DM 24,00 BBinc ❚❙❘ ☞ ᴙ ℙ ᴡ 23km ᴡ Wissen/Sieg

Mosbach ▲ 3SW "Mutschlers Mühle", Beim Elzstadion (OT Neckarelz), 74821 Mosbach. ☎ (6261) 7191 **FAX** (6261) 61812 ✉ 149 ● DM 22,00 BBinc ❚❙❘ ᴙ ᴙ⛪ 🎱 ℙ ⚓ ᴡ Neckarelz 500m

Mosenberg ▲ 7S 34590 Wabern. ☎ (5681) 2691 **FAX** (5681) 60208 **Open:** 1.1-23.12; 27-31.12 ✉ 130 ● DM 22,50 BBinc ❚❙❘ ᴙ ℙ ᴡ Wabern 8km ᴡ Bahnbus Homburg 1.5km ap Berge

Much-Berghausen ▲ 53804 Much. ☎ (2245) 3828 **FAX** (2245) 5891 ✉ 192 ● DM 24,00 BBinc ❚❙❘ ᴙ ℙ ᴡ

Müden ⛺ Wiesenweg 32, 29328 Müden. ☎ (5053) 225 **FAX** (5053) 1021 🛏 156 ⊖ DM 20,00 ᴮᴮⁱⁿᶜ ¶◯ †‖† ♿ 🗄 ♨ 🅿 🚲 ⚓ 🚂 Celle 25km 🚐 Müden 500m

Mühldorf ▲ Friedr-Ludwig-Jahn-Str 19,84453 Mühldorf(Bavaria). ☎ (8631) 7370 **FAX** (8631) 7370 **Open:** 1.1-30.9; 1.11-31.12 🛏 58 ⊖ DM 16,50 ᴮᴮⁱⁿᶜ 🐕 🚂 1km 🚐 200m

Mühlhausen ⛺ Auf dem Tonberg 1, 99974 Mühlhausen. ☎ (3601) 813318 **FAX** (3601) 813318 **Open:** 07.00-22.00hrs, 1.1-21.12; 28-31.12 🛏 78 ⊖ DM 20,00 ᴮᴮⁱⁿᶜ ¶◯ †‖† ♿ ♨ 🅿 ⚓ 🚂 Mühlhausen 5km 🚐 6, 5 800m ap Blobach Ⓡ

Mülheim ▲ "JH Kahlenberg", Mendener Str 3, 45470 Mülheim. ☎ (208) 382191 **Shut:** Christmas + New Year 🛏 70 ⊖ DM 24,00 ᴮᴮⁱⁿᶜ ¶◯ †‖† 🚂 Mülheim 5km 🚐 151 🚃 110

Münchehofe ▲ Strasse der Jugend 2, 15374 Münchehofe. ☎ (33432) 8734 **FAX** (33432) 8734 **Open:** 06.00-22.00hrs 🛏 96 ⊖ DM 20,00 ᴮᴮⁱⁿᶜ ¶◯ †‖† ✈ Schönefeld 50km 🚂 Buckow 3km 🚐 100m

MÜNCHEN (2 Hostels)

München - Neuhausen JH ⛺ ⌊IBN⌋ Wendl- Dietrich Str 20, 80634 München (Bavaria). ☎ (89) 131156 **FAX** (89) 1678745 🛏 370 ⊖ DM 23,00-25,50 ᴮᴮⁱⁿᶜ ¶◯ Ⓤ 1 Rotkreuzplatz

München - Thalkirchen ⛺ ⌊IBN⌋ "JGH", Miesingstr 4, 81379 München (Bavaria). ☎ (89) 7236550, 7236560 **FAX** (89) 7242567 **Open:** 1.2-30.11 🛏 352 ⊖ DM 27,50-35,50 ᴮᴮⁱⁿᶜ ¶◯ †‖† ✈ München 🚂 10km Ⓤ 3 Thalkirchen 350m

MÜNCHEN - Neuhausen JH

MÜNCHEN - Thalkirchen

Münster- Aasee ⛰ 2W IBN "JGH", Bismarckallee 31, 48151 Münster. ☎ (251) 532470, 532477 FAX (251) 521271 ⟷ 208 ● 2 Bed DM 46,50; 4 Bed DM 37,50 BBinc ⚲ ♂ ♦♦♦ ♿ ◉ ⛲ 🅿 ⚲ ⛴ ⛴ Münster 3.5km 🚌 10, 34 500m ap Hoppendamm R

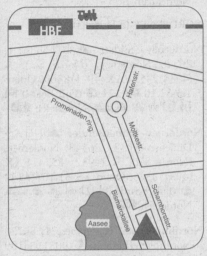

MÜNSTER

Murchin ▲ Jugendherberge Nr 1, 17390 Murchin. ☎ (3971) 210732 FAX (3971) 210732 Open: 08.00-09.00hrs, 15.00-22.00hrs, 28.12.96-18.12 ⟷ 50 ● DM 17,50 BBinc 🅿 ⚲ Anklam 7km 🚌 200m ap Zeltplatz R

Murrhardt ▲ "Eugen- Nägele- JH", Karnsberger Str 1, 71540 Murrhardt. ☎ (7192) 7501 FAX (7192) 29058 ⟷ 155 ● DM 22,00 BBinc ⚲(L D) ♦♦♦ ◉ 🅿 ⚲ Murrhardt 1km 🚌 1km

Mutzschen ▲ Str der Jugend 7, 04688 Mutzschen. ☎ (34385) 51241 Open: 07.00-20.00hrs, 15.2-30.11 ⟷ 100 ● DM 20,00 BBinc ⚲ ♦♦♦ 🕎 ♂ ⚲ Grimma 15km, Oschatz 18km 🚌 S-181 Grimma-Mutzsohen 300m

Mylau ▲ "Walderholung", OT Schneidenbach, 08491 Jägerhaus. ☎

(3765) 34584 FAX (3765) 64455 Open: 07.00-22.00hrs ⟷ 43 ● DM 20,00 BBinc ⚲(B L) ⚲ Reichenbach 10km 🚌 T 85 Reichenbach-Mylau-Lengenfeld 1.5km

Naumburg ⛰ JGH, Am Tennisplatz 9, 06618 Naumburg. ☎ (3445) 703422 FAX (3445) 703422 Open: 07.00-23.00hrs, 1.1-23.12; 27-31.12 ⟷ 204 ● DM 22,00 - 32,00 BBinc ⚲ 🅿 ⚲ Naumburg 2km 🚌 ap YH R

Neckargemünd- Dilsberg ▲ OT Dilsberg, Untere Str 1, 69151 Neckargemünd. ☎ (6223) 2133 FAX (6223) 74871 ⟷ 77 ● DM 20,00 BBinc ⚲ ♦♦♦ 🕎 🅿 ⚲ Neckargemünd 3km 🚌 80m

Neidenberga ▲ Schloß, 07338 Neidenberga. ☎ (36737) 22262 Open: 07.00-22.00hrs, 1.1-21.12; 28-31.12 ⟷ 50 ● DM 17,00 BBinc ⚲ 🕎 🅿 ⛴ 🚌 100m R

Neschwitz ▲ Kastanienallee 1, 02699 Neschwitz. ☎ (35933) 5370 Open: 06.00-09.00hrs, 17.00-22.00hrs, 1.4-31.10 ⟷ 38 ● DM 20,00 BBinc ⚲(B L) ♦♦♦ 🅿 ⚲ ⚲ Neschwitz 700m 🚌 Neschwitz 400m

Neubrandenburg ▲ Ihlenfelder Str 73, 17034 Neubrandenburg. ☎ (395) 4225801 FAX (395) 4225801 Open: 08.00-09.00hrs, 15.00-24.00hrs, 1.2-30.11 ⟷ 100 ● DM 19,00 BBinc ⚲(L D) ♦♦♦ ⚲ ⚲ Neubrandenburg 1.4km 🚌 7 50km ap YH R

Neudorf ▲ Vierenstr 26, 09465 Neudorf. ☎ (37342) 8282 Open: 06.00-22.00hrs, 2.1-31.7; 1.9-23.12 ⟷ 134 ● DM 20,00 BBinc ⚲ ♂ ♦♦♦ ◉ 🅿 🎣 Alt 750m ⚲ Vierenstraße 400m 🚌 T 428, T 436 800m ap Oberdorf

Neuhaus am Rennweg ▲ Apelsbergstr 54, 98724 Neuhaus. ☎

(3679) 722862 **Open:** 07.00-22.00hrs, 1.1-21.12; 28-31.12 ⚑ 80 ⊜ DM 18,00-22,00 ᴮᴮⁱⁿᶜ ᵗᵉᵘ ᶤᶤᶤ ⚒ 🚊 Ernstthal/Rennsteig 3km 🚌 1km ap Bus Station **R**

Neumünster ▲ Gartenstr. 32, 24534 Neumünster ✆ (4321) 43669 **FAX** (4321) 42418 **Open:** 27.1-14.12 ⚑ 210 ⊜ DM 20,00 ᴮᴮⁱⁿᶜ ᵗᵉᵘ(L D) ♿ 🅿 🚊 Neumünster 1km 🚌 62 200m ap Feuerwache/Gartenstr.

Neureichenau- Rosenbergergut ▲ 94089 Neureichenau (Bavaria). ✆ (8583) 1239 **FAX** (8583) 1566 **Open:** 1.1-14.12; 27-31.12 ⚑ 109 ⊜ DM 18,00 ᴮᴮⁱⁿᶜ ᵗᵉᵘ(B D) ᶤᶤᶤ ⚒ Alt 811m 🚊 Passau 48km 🚌 10m

Neuschönau- Waldhäuser ⛺ Herbergsweg 2, 94556 Neuschönau (Bavaria). ✆ (8553) 6000 **FAX** (8553) 829 **Open:** 1.1-31.10; 27-31.12 ⚑ 121 ⊜ DM 22,00 ᴮᴮⁱⁿᶜ ᵗᵉᵘ(L D) 🔌 ᶤᶤᶤ 🔟 ⚒ Alt 1000m 🚊 Grafenau 20km 🚌 86, 65 20m

Neuss- Uedesheim ▲ "Jugendhof", Macherscheiderstr 113, 41468 Neuss-Uedesheim. ✆ (2131) 39273 **FAX** (2131) 32078 ⚑ 77 ⊜ DM 24,00 ᴮᴮⁱⁿᶜ ᵗᵉᵘ 🔌 🅿 🚊 Neuss 15km 🚌 851

Neustadt/Schw ☞ **Titisee-Neustadt**

Nideggen ▲ Rather Str 27, 52385 Nideggen. ✆ (2427) 1226 **FAX** (2427) 8453 ⚑ 150 ⊜ DM 24,00 ᴮᴮⁱⁿᶜ ᵗᵉᵘ 🅿 🚊 Nideggen-Brück 3km 🚌 82

Niebüll ▲ Deezbülldeich 2, 25899 Niebüll-Deezbüll. ✆ (4661) 8762 **FAX** (4661) 20457 **Open:** 1.4-31.10 ⚑ 42 ⊜ DM 20,00 ᴮᴮⁱⁿᶜ ᵗᵉᵘ(L D) 🎰 🅿 🚊 Niebüll 2.5km **R** (1.11-31.3)

Norddeich ▲ Strandstr 1, 26506 Norden. ✆ (4931) 8064 **FAX** (4931) 81828 ⚑ 88 ⊜ DM 20,00 ᴮᴮⁱⁿᶜ

ᵗᵉᵘ(L D) ⚒ 🅿 🚲 ⚓ 🚊 Norddeich 2km

Nordenham ▲ Strandallee 12, 26954 Nordenham. ✆ (4731) 88262 **FAX** (4731) 88034 ⚑ 158 ⊜ DM 22,00 ᴮᴮⁱⁿᶜ ᵗᵉᵘ(L D) ᶤᶤᶤ ♿ ⚒ 🅿 ⚓ 🚊 Nordenham 1km

NORDERNEY (2 Hostels)

Norderney - Südstr ▲ |1E| Südstr 1, 26548 Norderney, (North Sea). ✆ (4932) 2451 **FAX** (4921) 83600 **Open:** 1.3-31.10 ⚑ 121 ⊜ (Full Board) ᵗᵉᵘ ᶤᶤᶤ 🔟 ⚒ 🚲 ⚓ 🚢 Norddeich **R**

Norderney- Dünensender ▲ |4E| Am Dünensender 3, 26548 Norderney, (North Sea). ✆ (4932) 2574 **FAX** (4921) 83266 **Open:** 1.3-31.10 ⚑ 142 ⊜ (Full Board) ᵗᵉᵘ 🔟 ⚒ 🚲 ⚓ 🚢 Norddeich **R**

Nördlingen ▲ Kaiserwiese 1, 86720 Nördlingen (Bavaria). ✆ (9081) 84109 **Open:** 1.3-31.10 ⚑ 80 ⊜ DM 18,00 ᴮᴮⁱⁿᶜ ᵗᵉᵘ ᶤᶤᶤ 🚊 1.5km

Nordhausen ▲ JH "Rothleimmühle", Parkallee 2, 99734 Nordhausen ✆ (3631) 2323 **FAX** (3631) 3507 **Open:** 31.1-30.11 ⚑ 71 ⊜ DM 22,00 ᴮᴮⁱⁿᶜ ᵗᵉᵘ ᶤᶤᶤ 🅿 🚊 Nordhausen 3km 🚌 200m 🚃 200m **R** (Grps)

Northeim ⛺ "Adolf- Galland-Jugendheim", Brauereistr 1, 37154 Northeim. ✆ (5551) 8672 ⚑ 100 ᴮᴮⁱⁿᶜ ᵗᵉᵘ 🅿 🚊 Northeim 2km

Nottuln ▲ "Annette- von- Droste-Hülshoff-JH", St Amand-Montrond-Str 6, 48301 Nottuln. ✆ (2502) 7878 **FAX** (2502) 9619 **Open:** 6.1-21.12 ⚑ 132 ⊜ DM 21,00 ᴮᴮⁱⁿᶜ ᵗᵉᵘ 🎰 ⚒ 🅿 🚊 Appelhülsen 5km 🚌 560, 561 600m ap Alter Kirchweg

Nürnberg ⛺ "Jugendgästehaus", Burg 2, 90403 Nürnberg (Bavaria). ✆ (911)

221024, 241352 **FAX** (911) 22040
Open: 1.1-23.12; 27-31.12 ⋈ 320 ●
DM 29,00 [BB]inc ⍾⍾⍾ ⍿⍿⍿ ⍾ ⌸ ⍾⍾ 2km
⍾⍾ 4, 9 700m

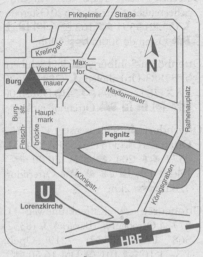

NÜRNBERG

Oberammergau ▲ Malensteinweg 10,
82487 Oberammergau (Bavaria). ☏
(8822) 4114 **FAX** (8822) 1695 **Open:**
1.1-31.10; 27-31.12 ⋈ 130 ● DM
20,00 [BB]inc ⍾⍾⍾ ⍿⍿⍿ ⍾ Alt 850m ⍾⍾
1.5km

Oberbernhards ▲ ⟨8NW⟩ Hauptstr 5,
36115 Hilders- Oberbernhards. ☏
(6657) 240 **FAX** (6657) 8896 **Open:**
1.1-23.12; 27-31.12 ⋈ 257 ● DM
23,50 [BB]inc ⍾⍾⍾ ⍿⍿⍿ ⍾ ⍾ Alt 630m ⍾⍾
Fulda 20km ⍾⍾ 5033 1.5km
ap Dörmbach

Oberbreitenau ☞ **Bischofsmais**

Oberhundem ▲ Wilhelm- Münker-
Weg 1, 57399 Kirchhundem. ☏ (2723)
72640 **FAX** (2723) 73597 **Open:**
1.1-14.11; 16-31.12 ⋈ 108 ● DM
21,00 [BB]inc ⍾⍾⍾ ⍾ ⍾ ⍾ ⍾⍾ Lennestadt-
Altenhundem 12km ⍾⍾ 109 200m
ap Wilhelm Münker

Oberoderwitz ▲ Zur Lindenallee 5,
02744 Oberoderwitz. ☏ (35842) 26544

Open: 07.00-09.00hrs, 14.00-20.00hrs
⋈ 138 Su, 66 Wi ● DM 20,00 - 22,00
⍾⍾⍾ ⍿⍿⍿ ⌸ ⍾⍾ Oberoderwitz 1.5km ⍾⍾
R 300 Dresden- Zittau 1km
ap Oberoderwitz, Landmannsheim

Oberreifenberg ▲ ⟨3SW⟩ Limesstr 14,
61389 Schmitten. ☏ (6082) 2440 **FAX**
(6082) 3305 **Open:** 1.1-23.12;
27-31.12 ⋈ 248 ● DM 22,00 [BB]inc
⍾⍾⍾ ⍿ ⍾ Alt 660m ⍾⍾ Bad Homburg
32km ⍾⍾ 1km ap Oberreifenberg-
Siedlung

Oberstdorf- Kornau ▲ Haus Nr 8,
87561 Oberstdorf Kornau (Bavaria). ☏
(8322) 2225 **FAX** (8322) 80446 **Open:**
1.1-31.10; 28-31.12 ⋈ 192 ● DM
22,00 [BB]inc ⍾⍾⍾(D) ⍿⍿⍿ ⍿ ⍾ Alt 950m
⍾⍾ 3.5km ⍾⍾ 300m

Oberwesel ▲ ⟨CC⟩ "Jugendgästehaus",
Auf dem Schönberg, 55430 Oberwesel.
☏ (6744) 93330 **FAX** (6744) 7446 ⋈
179 ● DM 26,80 [BB]inc ⍾⍾⍾(L D) ⍿⍿⍿

Ochsenfurt ▲ Hauptstr 1, 97199
Ochsenfurt (Bavaria). ☏ (9331) 80620
Open: 1.4-31.10 ⋈ 30 ● DM 16,50
[BB]inc ⍾⍾⍾ ⍿ ⍿⍿⍿ ⍾ ⍾⍾ 2km ⍾⍾ 100m

Oelsnitz Talsperre Pirk ▲ Dobenecker
Weg 27, 08606 Oelsnitz (Vogtland),
Ortsteil Taltitz; ☏ (37421) 23019 **FAX**
(37421) 20202 **Open:** 07.00-22.00hrs
⋈ 80 Su (68 Wi) ● DM 20,00 [BB]inc
⍾⍾⍾ ⍿⍿⍿ ⌸ ⍾ ⍾ ⍾ ⍾⍾ Chemnitz-
Plauen- Oelsnitz 5km ⍾⍾ T39
Oelsnitz- Taltitz or T11 Hof- Plauen
1.5km ap Taltitz-Siedlung

Oerlinghausen ▲ Auf dem Berge 11,
33813 Oerlinghausen. ☏ (5202) 2053
FAX (5202) 15456 **Open:** 1.1-14.12
⋈ 127 ● DM 21,00 [BB]inc ⍾⍾⍾ ⍾ ⍾
⍾⍾ Oerlinghausen 3km ⍾⍾ 369, 931
600m ap Marktplatz

Ohorn ▲ Schleißbergstr 39, 01896
Ohorn. ☏ (35955) 72762 **Open:**
07.00-22.00hrs ⋈ 44 ● DM 20,00

[BB]inc ¶⊙|(B L) ♦†♦ 🅿 ✈ Dresden-Klotzsche 35km 🚊 Dresden/Arnsdorf - Lubbenau 4km 🚌 Ohorn-Pflegeheim 1km

Oldenburg/Holstein ▲ Göhlerstr 58a, 23758 Oldenburg. ☎ (4361) 7670 **FAX** (4361) 60731 ⛱ 84 ⊜ DM 20,00 [BB]inc ¶⊙|(L D) 🅿 🚊 Oldenburg/Holst 1.5km 🚌 100m

Oldenburg/Oldenburg ▲ [1 NE] Alexander Str 65, 26121 Oldenburg. ☎ (441) 87135 ⛱ 90 ⊜ DM 22,00 [BB]inc ¶⊙|(L D) ♦†♦ 🅿 ☀ 🚊 Oldenburg 2km

Ortenberg ▲ Burgweg 21/Schloss, 77799 Ortenberg. ☎ (781) 31749 **FAX** (781) 9481031 ⛱ 148 ⊜ DM 22,00 [BB]inc ¶⊙| ♦†♦ 🏠 🅿 🚊 Offenburg 5km 🚌 7160, 7134, 2km ap Ortenberg-Bahnhof

Osnabrück ⚠ [2 S] YGH, Iburger Str 183A, 49082 Osnabrück. ☎ (541) 54284 **FAX** (541) 54294 ⛱ 145 ⊜ DM 21,00 [BB]inc ¶⊙|(L D) ♦†♦ ☀ ⚒ 🅿 ☀ 🚊 Osnabrück 🚌 13,15,62,83,8 300m

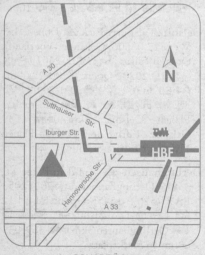

OSNABRÜCK

Ossa ▲ Dorfstr 69, 04643 Ossa. ☎ (34346) 60587 **Open:** 07.00-22.00hrs

⛱ 52 ⊜ DM 20,00 [BB]inc ¶⊙| ♂ ♦†♦ 🅿 🚊 Geithain 5km 🚌 Geithain-Ossa (Mon-Fri) 50m

Osterode ▲ "Haus der Jugend", Scheerenberger Str 34, 37520 Osterode. ☎ (5522) 5595 ⛱ 162 [BB]inc ¶⊙| 🅿 ✈ 🚊 Osterode 500m 🚌 500m

Ottenhöfen-Sohlberg ▲ [5 S] Sohlberg 5, 77883 Ottenhöfen. ☎ (7842) 2629 **FAX** (7842) 30008 ⛱ 74 ⊜ DM 20,00 [BB]inc ¶⊙| ♦†♦ 🅿 🚊 Ottenhöfen 6km

Otterndorf ▲ Schleusenstr 147, 21762 Otterndorf. ☎ (4751) 3165 **FAX** (4751) 4577 ⛱ 204 ⊜ DM 20,00 [BB]inc ¶⊙|(L D) ♿ 🅿 ☀ ⛵ 🚊 Otterndorf 3.5km 🚌 2km

Ottobeuren ▲ Kaltenbrunnweg 11, 87724 Ottobeuren (Bavaria). ☎ (8332) 368 **FAX** (8332) 7219 **Open:** 1.3-31.10 ⛱ 101 ⊜ DM 16,50 [BB]inc ¶⊙|

Paderborn ▲ "Heiersburg", Meinwerkstr 16, 33098 Paderborn. ☎ (5251) 22055 **FAX** (5251) 280017 **Open:** 13.1-7.12 ⛱ 108 ⊜ DM 21,00 [BB]inc ¶⊙| 🏠 ⚒ 🅿 ⛵ 🚊 Paderborn 1.5km 🚌 2, 5 150m ap Detmolder Tor, Maspernplatz ®

Panschwitz-Kuckau ▲ Cisinskistr 1, 01920 Panschwitz-Kuckau. ☎ (35796) 96357 **Open:** 07.00-09.00, 15.00-20.00hrs ⛱ 60 ⊜ DM 20,00 [BB]inc ¶⊙| ♦†♦ ☐ 🅿 🚌 R 102 Bautzen-Kamenz 200m ap P-Kuckau

Papenburg ▲ Kirchstr 38-40, 26871 Papenburg. ☎ (4961) 2793 **Open:** 1.3-31.10 ⛱ 78 ⊜ DM 20,00 [BB]inc ¶⊙|(L D) ♦†♦ 🅿 ☀ ⛵ 🚊 Papenburg 2km

Passau ▲ Veste Oberhaus 125, 94034 Passau (Bavaria). ☎ (851) 41351 **FAX** (851) 43709 ⛱ 50 ⊜ DM 16,50 [BB]inc ¶⊙|(D) ♦†♦ 🏠 🚊 2.5km 🚌 1,2,3,9, 250m

Pforzheim ▲ ⬛3SW "Burg Rabeneck", OT Dillweissenstein, Kräheneckstr 4, 75180 Pforzheim. ☎ (721) 962100 **FAX** (721) 613470 **Open:** 4.97 ☎/**FAX** for information ✉ 96 ⊖ DM 22,00 BBinc 🚻 3km 🚌 ap "Papierfabrik" 300m

Pirna- Copitz ▲ Birkwitzer Str 51, 01796 Pirna-Copitz. ☎ (3501) 527316 **Open:** 07.00-09.00hrs, 15.00-19.00hrs ✉ 170 ⊖ DM 22,00 BBinc 🍽(B L) 🚻 🍺 🚲 ⛴ ✈ Dresden-Klotzsche 20km 🚻 5km 🚌 150m ap Fahrzeugelektrik

Plau am See ▲ Meyenburger Chaussee 1a, 19395 Plau am See. ☎ (38735) 345 **FAX** (38735) 345 **Open:** 08.00-09.00hrs, 15.00-22.00hrs, 1.2-30.11 ✉ 128 ⊖ DM 19,00 BBinc 🍽(L D) 🚻 🍺 🅿 🚲 ⛴ 🚻 Plau 1km 🚌 500m ap Töpferstr. Ⓡ

Plauen HJ ▲ Zum Reusaer Waldhaus, 08529 Plauen ☎ (3741) 431881 **FAX** (3741) 431881 ✉ 65 ⊖ DM 22,00 BBinc 🚻 ⛴ 8km 🚻 8km 🚃 Nr 4, 8km

Plön ▲ Ascheberger Str 67, 24306 Plön. ☎ (4522) 2576 **FAX** (4522) 2166 **Open:** 15.1-15.12 ✉ 222 ⊖ DM 20,00 BBinc 🍽(L D) 🅿 🚻 Plön 2.5km 🚌 500m

Plothen ▲ "Am Hausteich", 07907 Plothen. ☎ (36648) 22329 **FAX** (36648) 22001 **Open:** 1.1-22.12; 29-31.12 ✉ 193 (20, 1.11-31.3) ⊖ DM 18,00 BBinc 🍽 🚻 🅿 🚲 ⛴ 🚻 4km 🚌 4km Ⓡ

Pockau ▲ Siedlungsstr 34, 09509 Pockau. ☎ (37367) 9589 **Open:** 06.00-22.00hrs, 1.1-22.12, 27-31.12 ✉ 44 ⊖ DM 17,00 BBinc 🍽 🍺 🚻 🅿 🚻 1km 🚌 T 245, T 492, T 400 600m

Porta Westfalica ▲ Kirchsiek 30, 32457 Porta Westfalica-Hausberge. ☎ (571) 70250 **FAX** (571) 7100047 ✉ 95 ⊖ DM 20,00 BBinc 🍽 🍺 🅿 🚻 Hausberge 800m 🚌 408 500m ap Unter der Schalksburg

Pottenstein ▲ Jugendherbergsstr 20, 91278 Pottenstein (Bavaria). ☎ (9243) 1224 **FAX** (9243) 7370 **Open:** 1.2-30.11 ✉ 159 ⊖ DM 20,00 BBinc 🍽 🍺 🚻 🚲 🆒 🚻 Pegnitz 17km 🚌 2km

Prebelow ▲ Prebelow 02, 16831 Zechlinerhü TTE ☎ (33921) 70222 **FAX** (33921) 70222 **Open:** 06.00-22.00hrs ✉ 54 ⊖ DM 20,00 BBinc 🍽 🚻 ⛴ 🚻 Rheinsberg 10km 🚌 Neustrelitz/Grosszerlang 100m ap Prebelow Ⓡ (6 weeks)

Prien ⚿ Carl- Braun- Str. 66, 83209 Prien (Bavaria). ☎ (8051) 2972 **FAX** (8051) 63485 **Open:** 1.2-30.11 ✉ 130 ⊖ DM 22,00 BBinc 🍽(D) 🚻 🚻 2km

Prüm ▲ Pferdemarkt, 54595 Prüm. ☎ (6551) 2500 **FAX** (6551) 70030 ✉ 74 ⊖ DM 20,50 BBinc 🍽(L D) 🚻 ⮕ Alt 500-800m

Pullach ⚿ "Burg Schwaneck", Burgweg 4-6, 82049 Pullach (Bavaria). ☎ (89) 7930643, 7930644 **FAX** (89) 7937922 **Open:** 6.1-21.12 ✉ 130 ⊖ DM 22,00 BBinc 🍽(D) 🚻 2km

Raben ▲ JH 'Burg Rabenstein', 14823 Raben, Burg. ☎ (33848) 221 **Open:** 06.30-22.00hrs, 1.1-24.11; 27-31.12 ✉ 52 ⊖ DM 20,00 BBinc 🍽(B D) 🏤 🚻 Belzig 16km Ⓡ (6 weeks)

Radebeul ☞ Dresden

Radevormwald ▲ Telegrafenstr 50, 42477 Radevormwald. ☎ (2195) 1063 **FAX** (2195) 6323 ✉ 97 ⊖ DM 24,00 BBinc 🍽 🅿 🚌 Wuppertal 30km

Radis ⚿ Bahnhofstr 18, 06773 Radis. ☎ (34953) 39288 **FAX** (34953) 39288 **Open:** 07.00-22.00hrs, 1.1-23.12;

27-31.12 ⚑ 104 ● DM 22,00 BB^inc
†⊙† ⋔⋔ ⊞ ▣ ▣ 🚂 Radis 700m 🚌
300m

Rathen ▲ Niederrathen B3, 01824
Kurort Rathen. ☎ (35024) 70425
Open: 07.00-19.00hrs ⚑ 32 ● DM
17,00 BB^inc ☝ 🚂 3km 🚌 2.1km ⓡ
(30 days: Anmeldung über JH Pirna-
Copitz ☎ (3501) 527316)

Ratingen ▲ Götschenbeck 8, 40882
Ratingen. ☎ (2102) 22997 **FAX** (2102)
27846 ⚑ 116 ● DM 24,00 BB^inc †⊙†
⋔⋔ ▣ 🚌 750

Ratzeburg ▲ Fischerstr 20, 23909
Ratzeburg. ☎ (4541) 3707 **FAX** (4541)
84780 ⚑ 146 ● DM 20,00 BB^inc
†⊙† (L D) ▣ 🚂 Ratzburg 3km 🚌
500m ap Marktplatz

Ravensburg ▲ "Veitsburg", 88212
Ravensburg. ☎ (751) 25363 **FAX** (751)
13769 ⚑ 109 ● DM 22,00 BB^inc
†⊙† (L D) ⅃ 🚂 ⊞ ▣ 🚂 Ravensburg
3km

Rechenberg ▲ "Schloss" Zum Schloss
1, 74597 Stimpfach- Rechenberg. ☎
(7967) 372 **FAX** (7967) 8985 ⚑ 108
● DM 20,00 BB^inc †⊙† (L D) ⋔⋔ ⊞ 🚂
Crailsheim 12km 🚌 300m
ap Rechenberg

Regensburg ▲ Wöhrdstr 60, 93059
Regensburg (Bavaria). ☎ (941) 57402
FAX (941) 52411 ⚑ 203 ● DM 22,00
BB^inc †⊙† (D) ⋔⋔ ⊞ 🚂 3km 🚌 17, 20m

Rendsburg ▲ Rotenhöfer Weg 48,
24768 Rendsburg. ☎ (4331) 71205
FAX (4331) 75521 **Open:** 1.2-22.12
⚑ 146 ● DM 20,00 BB^inc †⊙† (L D) ⅃
▣ 🚂 Rendsburg 2.5km 🚌 Stadtbus
100m ap YH

Rheine ▲ Mühlenstr 75, 48431 Rheine.
☎ (5971) 2407 **FAX** (5971) 13526
Open: 1.1-28.2; 22.3-31.12 ⚑ 53 ●

DM 21,00 BB^inc †⊙† ⅃ 🏠 ▣ 🚂 Rheine
1km 🚌 150m ap Amtsgericht

Ribnitz Damgarten ▲ Am
Wasserwerk, 18311 Ribnitz-
Damgarten ☎ (3821) 812311 **FAX**
(3821) 812311 ⚑ 24 ● DM 20,00
BB^inc †⊙† 🏠 ⚓ 🚂 Ribnitz-Damgarten
500m

Rinteln ▲ Am Bären 1, 31737 Rinteln.
☎ (5751) 2405 **FAX** (5751) 44630 ⚑
96 ● DM 20,00 BB^inc †⊙† ⋔⋔ ⅃ 🏠 ▣
⚓ 🚂 Rinteln 3km

Rittersgrün ▲ Zur Jugendherberg 2,
08355 Rittersgrün. ☎ (37757) 7260
Open: 06.00-22.00hrs, 1.1-22.12;
27-31.12 ⚑ 40 ● DM 20,00 BB^inc
†⊙† (B L) ⊞ ▣ 🚂 Antonsthal 3km 🚌
T 330 800m ap Arnoldshammer

Rochlitz ▲ "Schweizerhaus", Zaßnitzer
Weg 1, 09306 Rochlitz. ☎ (3737)
42131 **Open:** 06.00-23.00hrs ⚑ 49 ●
DM 17,00 BB^inc †⊙† ⋔⋔ ⊞ ▣ 🚲 🚂
Leipzig; Chemnitz to Rochlitz 2.5km
🚌 Mitlweida- Rochlitz T- 685 1km
ap "Clemens-Pfau-Platz"

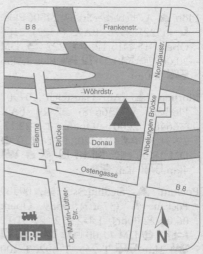

REGENSBURG

Rochsburg ▲ 'Schloss Rochsburg',
Schlossstr 1, 09322 Rochsburg. ☎

(37383) 6503 **Open:** 07.00-22.00hrs
�︎ 70 ● DM 17,00 BB|inc ⑂ ♙♙ 🏠 ℗
🚋 Leipzig- Glauchau 1km 🚌
Rochlitz-Penig 4km ap Lunzenau

Rödinghausen ▲ Jugendheim des
Kreises Herford, Zum Nonnenstein 21,
32289 Rödinghausen. ☎ (5746) 8173
Open: 1.1-19.12; 27-31.12 🚄 80 BB|inc
⑂ ⚒ ℗ 🚋 Bünde 15km 🚌 500m
ap ap Rödinghausen Kirche

Rosbach ▲ Herbergsstr 19, 51570
Windeck- Rosbach. ☎ (2292) 5042
FAX (2292) 6569 🚄 200 ● DM 25,00
BB|inc ⑂ ♂ ♙♙ ℗ 🚋 Köln 40km

Rosenbergergut ☞ **Neureichenau**

Rostock 🔺 JGS 'Traditionsschiff', PF
48, 18106 Rostock, Schmarl- Dorf. ☎
(381) 716224 **FAX** (381) 714014
Open: 08.00-09.00hrs, 15.00-24.00hrs
🚄 85 ● DM 26,00 BB|inc ⑂(L D) ♙♙
🏠 ⚒ ℗ ♦ 🚋 Rostock 1.8km 🚋
Lütten Klein **R**

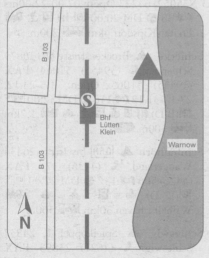

ROSTOCK - Schmarl

Rostock- Warnemünde ▲ Parkstraße
46, 18119 Rostock Warnemünde. ☎
(381) 5481700 **FAX** (381) 54817023
Open: 08.00-09.00hrs, 15.00-24.00hrs,
13.1-15.12 🚄 74 ● DM 19,00 BB|inc

⑂(D) ♙♙ ℗ ♂ ♦ 🚢 🚋
Warnemünde 1km 🚌 50m **R**

Rotenburg/Wümme ▲ 1 SW Verdener
Str 104, 27356 Rotenburg. ☎ (4261)
83041 **FAX** (4261) 84233 🚄 224 ●
DM 24,00 BB|inc ⑂(L D) ♙♙ 🗑 ⚒ ℗ ♦
🚋 3km 🚌 3km **R**

Rotenburg/Fulda ▲ 0.5N Obertor 17,
36199 Rotenburg. ☎ (6623) 2792 **FAX**
(6623) 43177 **Open:** 1.1-23.12;
27-31.12 🚄 125 ● DM 23,00 BB|inc
⑂ ♙♙ ♂ ♦ 🚋 Rotenburg 2km

Rothenburg/Tauber 🔺 IBN
Mühlacker 1, 91541 Rothenburg
(Bavaria). ☎ (9861) 94160 **FAX** (9861)
941620 **Open:** 3.1-14.12 🚄 180 ●
DM 22,00 BB|inc ⑂ ♙♙ 🚋 2km

Rothenfels ▲ 97851 Rothenfels
(Bavaria). ☎ (9393) 99999 **Open:**
6.1-20.3; 1.4-14.12 🚄 168 ● DM
20,00 BB|inc ⑂ 🏠 🚋 Lohr 16.5km 🚌
8051, 500m

Rottweil ▲ Lorenzgasse 8, 78628
Rottweil. ☎ (741) 7664 **Open:**
16.3-14.11 🚄 62 ● DM 20,00 BB|inc
⑂(L D) 🚋 Rottweil 2km 🚌 200m
ap Obere Hauptstraße

Rudenberg ☞ **Titisee-Neustadt**

Rüdesheim ▲ 1.5E Am Kreuzberg,
65385 Rüdesheim. ☎ (6722) 2711
FAX (6722) 48284 **Open:** 1.1-23.12;
27-31.12 🚄 205 ● DM 21,00 BB|inc
⑂ ♙♙ ℗ ♦ 🚋 Rüdesheim 2km

Rurberg ▲ Kesternicher Str, 52152
Simmerath- Rurberg. ☎ (2473) 2200
FAX (2473) 4911 🚄 174 ● DM 25,00
BB|inc ⑂ ♂ ♙♙ ℗ 🚋 Aachen 20km 🚌

Rüthen ▲ Am Rabenknapp 4, 59602
Rüthen. ☎ (2952) 483 **FAX** (2952)
2717 **Open:** 29.1-28.12 🚄 121 ● DM
21,00 BB|inc ⑂ ⚒ ℗ 🚋 Lippstadt
25km 🚌 562 3km ap Rüthen Markt

Ruttelerfeld ▲ Zollweg 27, 26340 Zetel. ☎ (4452) 416 **FAX** (4452) 8230 ⬛ 111 ⬤ DM 20,00 ⃞ᴮᴮⁱⁿᶜ ⃞⃝ ⬛ ⃝

Saarbrücken ⌂ ⃞4NE⃞ Meerwiesertalweg 31, 66123 Saarbrücken. ☎ (681) 33040 **FAX** (681) 374911 ⬛ 180 ⬤ DM 26,30 ⃞ᴮᴮⁱⁿᶜ ⃝(L D) ⃝⃝ ⃝

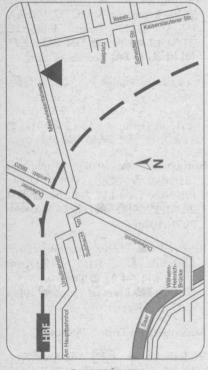

SAARBRÜCKEN

Saarburg ▲ Bottelter Str 8, 54439 Saarburg. ☎ (6581) 2555 **FAX** (6581) 1082 ⬛ 103 ⬤ DM 20,50 ⃞ᴮᴮⁱⁿᶜ ⃝(L D) ⃝⃝

Saldenburg ▲ Ritter- Tuschl- Str 20, 94163 Saldenburg (Bavaria). ☎ (8504) 1655 **FAX** (8504) 4449 **Open:** 1.1-31.10; 27-31.12 ⬛ 150 ⬤ DM 20,00 ⃞ᴮᴮⁱⁿᶜ ⃝ ⃝⃝ ⃝ ⃝ Passau 36km

Sandhatten ▲ ⃞1.5NW⃞ Wöschenweg 28, 26209 Hatten. ☎ (4482) 330 **FAX**

(4482) 8498 ⬛ 134 ⬤ DM 20,00 ⃞ᴮᴮⁱⁿᶜ ⃝(L D) ⃝⃝ ⃝ ⬛ ⃝ ⃝ Sandkrug 7km

Sargenroth ▲ Kirchweg 1, 55471 Sargenroth. ☎ (6761) 2500 **FAX** (6761) 6378 ⬛ 137 ⬤ DM 21,50 ⃝(L D) ⃝⃝ ⃝

Sayda ⌂ Mortelgrund 8, 09619 Sayda. ☎ (37365) 1277 **FAX** (37365) 1277 **Open:** 07.00-23.00hrs ⬛ 140 ⬤ DM 23,50 ⃞ᴮᴮⁱⁿᶜ ⃝ ⃝⃝ ⃝ ⬛ ⃝ ⃝ ⃝ Chemnitz- Heidersdorf 2.5km ⃝ T 508, T 458, T 534 2.5km ap Sayda-Markt

Scharbeutz-Klingberg ▲ Uhlenflucht 30, 23684 Scharbeutz. ☎ (4524) 428 **FAX** (4524) 1637 **Open:** 21.1-14.12 ⬛ 236 ⃞ᴮᴮⁱⁿᶜ ⃝(L D) ⬛ ⃝ Scharbeutz 5km ⃝ 300m

Scharling ☞ **Kreuth**

Schellerhau ▲ "Rotwasserhütte", Hauptstr 115, 01776 Schellerhau. ☎ (35052) 64227 **Open:** 07.00-22.00hrs ⬛ 38 ⬤ DM 20,00 ⃝ ⃝⃝ ⬛ ⃝ ⃝ Freital-Kipsdorf 4km ⃝ 200m

Schierke ▲ Brockenstrasse 50, 38879 Schierke. ☎ (39455) 51064 **FAX** (39455) 51065 **Open:** 1.3-23.12; 27.12-31.12 ⬛ 110 ⬤ DM 32,00 ⃞ᴮᴮⁱⁿᶜ ⃝(B D) ⃝⃝ ⃝ ⃝ ⬛ ⃝ ⃝ ⃝ 1.2km ⃝ 300m ⃝R⃝ ⃝

Schillighörn ▲ ⃞0.5N⃞ Inselstr 6, 26434 Wangerland. ☎ (4426) 371 **FAX** (4426) 506 ⬛ 132 ⬤ DM 22,00 ⃞ᴮᴮⁱⁿᶜ ⃝(L D) ⃝ ⬛ ⃝ ⃝ ⃝ Wilhelmshaven 30km ⃝ 500m

Schleswig ▲ Spielkoppel 1, 24837 Schleswig. ☎ (4621) 23893 **FAX** (4621) 20796 **Open:** 16.1-14.12 ⬛ 122 ⬤ DM 20,00 ⃞ᴮᴮⁱⁿᶜ ⃝(L D) ⬛ ⃝ ⃝ ⃝ Schleswig 1.5km ⃝ 1km

Schliersee-Josefsthal ▲ Josefstaler Str 19, 83727 Schliersee (Bavaria). ☎ (8026) 71068 **FAX** (8026) 71610

Open: 1.1-31.10; 27-31.12 ⚲ 97 ●
DM 20,00 ᴮᴮⁱⁿᶜ ꛬ(D) ♦♦♦ ⚥ Alt 820m
🚊 Fischhausen-Neuhaus 1.8km 🚌
9,5,6,2 30m

SCHLUCHSEE (2 Hostels)

Schluchsee - **Im Wolfsgrund** ▲ 1 NE
Im Wolfsgrund 28, 79859 Schluchsee.
✆ (7656) 329 **FAX** (7656) 9237
133 ● DM 22,00 ᴮᴮⁱⁿᶜ ꛬ ♦♦♦ 🔲 P ⚥
🚊 Schluchsee 500m 🚌 1.5km

Schluchsee - **Seebrugg** ▲ 3 SW Haus 9,
79859 Schluchsee, (OT Seebrugg). ✆
(7656) 494 **FAX** (7656) 1889 ⚲ 138
● DM 22,00 ᴮᴮⁱⁿᶜ ꛬ ♦♦♦ P ⚥ 🚊
500m 🚌 500m

Schmallenberg ▲ Im Lenninghof 20,
57392 Schmallenberg. ✆ (2972) 6098
FAX (2972) 4918 **Open:** 1.1-1.11;
1-31.12 ⚲ 128 ● DM 21,50 ᴮᴮⁱⁿᶜ ꛬ
🏛 P ⚥ 🚊 Altenhundem 18km 🚌
1.5km ap Kirche

Schnett ▲ "Auf dem Simmersberg",
98666 Schnett ✆ (36874) 532 **FAX**
(36874) 532 **Open:** 07.00-20.00hrs,
1.1-22.12; 28-31.12 ⚲ 61 ● DM
18,00 ᴮᴮⁱⁿᶜ ꛬ ♦♦♦ P ⚥ Alt 784m A🚌
Suhl 35km 🚊 Schleusingen 15km
🚌 Schnett 1.5km Ⓡ (Grps)

Schönberg ▲ Stakendorfer Weg 1,
24217 Schönberg. ✆ (4344) 2974 **FAX**
(4344) 4484 ⚲ 233 ● DM 20,00 ᴮᴮⁱⁿᶜ
ꛬ(L D) ♦♦♦ ♿ P ♂ 🚊 Kiel 23km
🚌 1km

Schönbrunn/Ebersdorf ▲ Nr
102(Bellevue), 07368 Schönbrunn/
Ebersdorf ✆ (36651) 87064, 30219
FAX (36651) 30219 **Open:**
07.00-20.00hrs, 1.1-22.12; 28-31.12
⚲ 72 ● DM 17,00 ᴮᴮⁱⁿᶜ ꛬ ♦♦♦ P 🚊
Schönbrunn 4.5km 🚌 2km Ⓡ

Schöneck ▲ Am Stadtpark 52, 08261
Schöneck. ✆ (37464) 8106 **FAX**
(37464) 8107 **Open:** 07.00-22.00hrs

⚲ 52 ● DM 22,00 ᴮᴮⁱⁿᶜ ꛬ ♦♦♦ 🔲 P
⚥ Alt 700m 🚊 Zwickau- Adorf-
Klingenthal 15km 🚌 T 29, T 38, T
354 300m ap Markt

Schöningen am Elm ▲ Richard-
Schirrmann-Str 6a, 38364 Schöningen
am Elm. ✆ (5352) 3898 **FAX** (5352)
3752 ⚲ 92 ● DM 20,00 ᴮᴮⁱⁿᶜ ꛬ ♦♦♦
🏛 P 🚊 Schöningen 45 min

Schönwalde ▲ Am Ruhsal 1, 23744
Schönwalde am Bungsberg. ✆ (4528)
206 **FAX** (4528) 9732 **Open:**
1.4-31.10 ⚲ 61 ● DM 18,00 ᴮᴮⁱⁿᶜ
ꛬ(L D) 🏛 ♂ 🚊 Neustadt, Eutin
12km 🚌 100m

Schwäbisch Gmünd ▲ Taubentalstr
46/1, 73525 Schwäbisch Gmünd. ✆
(7171) 2260 ⚲ 60 ● DM 20,00 ᴮᴮⁱⁿᶜ
ꛬ(L D) 🚊 Schwäbisch Gmünd 1km

Schwäbisch Hall ▲ Langenfelderweg
5, 74523 Schwäbisch Hall. ✆ (791)
41050 **FAX** (791) 47998 ⚲ 130 ●
DM 22,00 ꛬ(L D) ♦♦♦ 🔲 P 🚊
Schwäbisch Hall 2km, Schwäbisch
Hall- Hessental 7km 🚌 1 700m
ap Bausparkasse

Schwarzburg ▲ "Hans Breuer" Am
Buschbach 2, 07427 Schwarzburg. ✆
(36730) 22223 **FAX** (36730) 32937
Open: 07.00-22.00hrs, 1.1-22.12;
28-31.12 ⚲ 163 ● DM 18,00 ᴮᴮⁱⁿᶜ
ꛬ ♦♦♦ P 🚊 Schwarzburg 3km 🚌
400m Ⓡ

Schweinfurt ▲ Niederwerrnerstr 17
1/2, 97421 Schweinfurt (Bavaria). ✆
(9721) 21404 **FAX** (9721) 23581
Open: 9.1-21.12 ⚲ 110 ● DM 20,00
ᴮᴮⁱⁿᶜ ꛬ ♦♦♦ 🚊 1.3km 🚌 50m
ap Mozartstr.

Schwerin ▲ Waldschulweg 3, 19061
Schwerin. ✆ (385) 213005 **FAX** (385)
213005 **Open:** 08.00-09.00hrs,
15.00-24.00hrs, 4.2-18.12 ⚲ 91 ●
DM 20,00 ᴮᴮⁱⁿᶜ ꛬ(L D) ♦♦♦ P 🚊

Schwerin 5km 🚌 200m 🚂 1 100m ap Platz d Jugend-Zoo

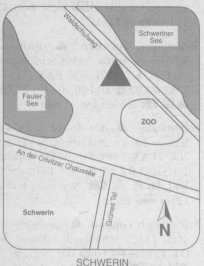

SCHWERIN

Seebrugg ☞ **Schluchsee**

Sigmaringen ▲ "Hohenzollern- JH", Hohenzollernstr 31, 72488 Sigmaringen. ☎ (7571) 13277 **FAX** (7571) 61159 🛏 129 ● DM 20,00 BB inc ⅋⅋(L D) 👫 **P** 🚲 🚈 Sigmaringen 5km 🚌 500m ap Krankenhaus

Silberborn ▲ Schiesshäuser Str, 37603 Holzminden. ☎ (5536) 568 **FAX** (5536) 1533 🛏 161 ● DM 20,00 BB inc ⅋⅋ 👫 🏠 **P** 🚈 Holzminden 10km 🚌 1km

Singen ▲ 1 NE Friedingerstr 28, 78224 Singen. ☎ (7731) 42590 **FAX** (7731) 48842 🛏 105 ● DM 20,00 BB inc ⅋⅋ 👫 **P** 🚈 Singen 12km 🚌 7364 500m ap Hallenbad -Waldeckstraße

Soest ▲ Kaiser-Friedrich-Platz 2, 59494 Soest. ☎ (2921) 16283 **FAX** (2921) 14623 **Open:** 21.1-22.12 🛏 70 ● DM 20,00 BB inc ⅋⅋ 🏠 **P** 🚈 Soest 1.5km 🚌 642 400m ap Brunowall

Sohlberg ☞ **Ottenhöfen**

Solingen-   Gräfrath   ▲ Flockertsholzerweg 10, 42653 Solingen. ☎ (212) 591198 **FAX** (212) 594179 🛏 138 ● DM 24,00 BB inc ⅋⅋ **P** 🚈 Wuppertal 25km 🚌 683,695

Sonnenbühl ☞ **Erpfingen**

Sorpesee ▲ Am Sorpesee 7, 59846 Sundern- Langscheid. ☎ (2935) 1776 **FAX** (2935) 7254 **Open:** 1.4-19.12 🛏 140 ● DM 21,50 BB inc ⅋⅋ 🏠 **P** ⚓ 🚈 Neheim Hüsten oder Arnsberg 15km 🚌 500m ap Am Sorpesee

Sosa ▲ "Skihütte", Am Fröhlichwald 9, 08326 Sosa. ☎ (37752) 8268 **Open:** 07.00-22.00hrs, 1.1-31.7; 1.9-31.12 🛏 28 ● DM 17,00 ⅋⅋(B L) **P** 🚲 🚈 Aue-Blauenthal Sosa 3km 🚌 T 355, T 366 500m ap "Wendeschleife"

Spalt-Wernfels ⚠ Burgweg 7-9, 91174 Spalt (Bavaria). ☎ (9873) 515 **FAX** (9873) 244 **Open:** 1.1-19.12; 28-31.12 🛏 150 ● DM 22,00 BB inc ⅋⅋ 🐦 👫 📖 🚈 Georgsgmünd 10km 🚌 3622 150m

Speyer ▲ Geibstr 5, 67346 Speyer. ☎ (6232) 75380 **FAX** (6232) 621883 **Open:** From 1.4 🛏 81 ● DM 26,30 BB inc ⅋⅋(L D)

Spiekeroog ▲ Bid' Utkiek 1, 26474 Spiekeroog, (North Sea). ☎ (4976) 329 **Open:** 15.3-30.10 🛏 54 ● (Full Board) 👫 ① ⚓ 🚢 Neuharlingersiel ®

Springe ▲ In der Worth 25, 31832 Springe. ☎ (5041) 1455 **FAX** (5041) 2963 🛏 85 ● DM 20,00 BB inc ⅋⅋ **P** 🚈 Springe 2km

St Blasien ☞ **Menzenschwand**

St Englmar-Maibrunn ▲ Haus Nr 5, 94379 St Englmar (Bavaria). ☎ (9965) 271 **FAX** (9965) 1342 **Open:** 1.1-31.10; 16-31.12 🛏 59 ● DM

20,00 BB|inc 🍴 � ⚓ 🚂 Straubing 30km 🚌 200m

St Goar ▲ Bismarckweg 17, 56329 St Goar. 📞 (6741) 388 **FAX** (6741) 2869 🛏 130 ⬤ DM 19,50 BB|inc 🍴(L D) ♟ ⚓

St Goarshausen ▲ Auf der Loreley, 56346 St Goarshausen. 📞 (6771) 2619 🛏 190 🍴 ♟

St Ingbert ▲ Neue Bahnhofstr 33, 66386 St Ingbert. 📞 (6894) 6102 **FAX** (6894) 870231 🛏 50 ⬤ DM 20,50 BB|inc 🍴(L D) ♟

St Michaelisdonn ▲ Am Sportplatz 1, 25693 St Michaelisdonn. 📞 (4853) 923 **FAX** (4853) 8576 🛏 70 ⬤ DM 20,00 BB|inc 🍴(L D) ♿ 🔲 🚲 🚂 St Michaelisdonn 1km

Stade ▲ Kehdinger Mühren 11, 21682 Stade. 📞 (4141) 46368 **FAX** (4141) 2817 **Open:** 1.2-22.12 🛏 105 ⬤ DM 18,00 BB|inc 🍴(L D) 🅿 🚂 Stade 1km

Steinbach/Donnersberg ▲ Südwestausgang, 67808 Steinbach. 📞 (6357) 360 **FAX** (6357) 1583 🛏 104 ⬤ DM 21,50 BB|inc 🍴(L D) ♟

Steinebach ☞ **Wörthsee**

Stralsund ▲ Am Kütertor 1, 18439 Stralsund. 📞 (3831) 292160 **FAX** (3831) 297676 **Open:** 08.00-09.00hrs, 15.00-24.00hrs, 14.1-18.12 🛏 180 ⬤ DM 20,00 BB|inc 🍴(D) ♟ 🏬 🚂 Stralsund 1.4km 🚌 4, 5 20m Ⓡ

Stralsund- Devin ▲ Strandstr 21, 18439 Stralsund- Devin. 📞 (3831) 490289 **FAX** (3831) 490291 **Open:** 08.00-09.00hrs, 15.00-21.00hrs, 4.2-30.10 🛏 204 ⬤ DM 20,00 BB|inc 🍴(L D) ♟ ♿ 🚲 🅿 ⚓ 🚂 Stralsund 6km 🚌 3 800m ap Devin Ⓡ

Straubing ▲ Friedhofstr 12, 94315 Straubing (Bavaria). 📞 (9421) 80436

FAX (9421) 12094 **Open:** 1.4-31.10 🛏 57 ⬤ DM 16,50 BB|inc 🚂 2km

Strehla ▲ Torgauer Str 33, 01616 Strehla. 📞 (35264) 90733 **Open:** 07.00-20.00hrs 🛏 72 ⬤ DM 20,00 BB|inc 🍴 ♟ 🏠 🅿 ⚓ 🚂 Riesa 10km 🚌 R 434 Riesa- Torgau 20m ap "Kleine Baste"

Streitberg ☞ **Wiesenttal**

Strub- Berchtesgaden ▲ Gebirgsjägerstr 52, 83489 Strub (Bavaria). 📞 (8652) 2190 **FAX** (8652) 66328 **Open:** 1.1-31.10; 27-31.12 🛏 360 ⬤ DM 20,00 BB|inc 🍴(D) ♂ ♟ 🔲 🚂 5km 🚌 200m

Stuttgart (*see town plan on next page*) ⚠ 1 SE Haußmannstr 27, 70188 Stuttgart (enter via Werastr, Kernerstr). 📞 (711) 241583 **FAX** (711) 2361041 🛏 261 ⬤ DM 22,00 BB|inc 🍴(L D) ♟ ✈ Stuttgart 🚂 Stuttgart 500m 🚌 42 Gablenberg 300m ap Eugensplatz 🚃 15 Heumaden 300m ap Eugensplatz

Sudelfeld ☞ **Bayrischzell**

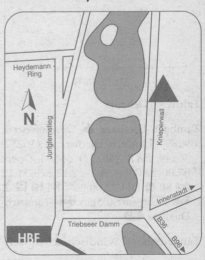

STRALSUND

Syke ▲ 3 W "Oskar- Heidrich- JH", Nordwohlder Str 59, 28857 Syke. 📞

(4242) 50314 **FAX** (4242) 66346 🛏
128 ● DM 22,00 ⵀⵀⵀ(L D) ⵀⵀⵀ ♿ 🏠 🅿
🚂 Syke 3km

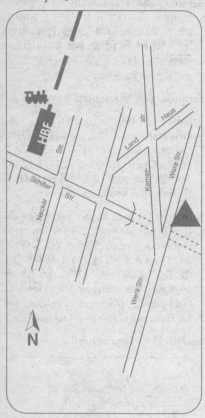

STUTTGART

Taltitz ☞ **Oelsnitz**

Tambach-Dietharz ▲ Oberhoferstr 3,
99897 Tambach-Dietharz. ☎ (36252)
36149 **FAX** (36252) 36564 **Open:**
07.00-22.00hrs, 1.1-22.12; 28-31.12
🛏 80 ● DM 22,00 ᴮᴮinc ⵀⵀⵀ ⵀⵀⵀ 🅿 ⵣ
🚂 Georgenthal 5km 🚌 Tambach-
Dietharz ®

Tannenlohe ☞ **Windischeschenbach**

Tauberbischofsheim ▲ 2NW
Schirrmannweg 2, 97941
Tauberbischofsheim. ☎ (9341) 3152
FAX (9341) 95052 🛏 103 ● DM

20,00 ᴮᴮinc ⵀⵀⵀ ⵀⵀⵀ 🅿 🚂
Tauberbischofsheim 2km

Tecklenburg ▲ "Ferdinand-
Eimermacher-JH", Am Herrengarten 5,
49545 Tecklenburg. ☎ (5482) 360
FAX (5482) 7937 🛏 116 ● DM 20,00
ᴮᴮinc ⵀⵀⵀ ⧊ 🅿 🚂 Lengerich 8km 🚌
145 800m ap Am Friedhof

Teterow ▲ Am Seebahnhof 7, 17166
Teterow. ☎ (3996) 172668 **FAX** (3996)
172668 **Open:** 08.00-09.00hrs,
15.00-22.00hrs, 1.2-18.12 🛏 100 ●
DM 19,00 ᴮᴮinc ⵀⵀⵀ(D) ⵀⵀⵀ 🅿 🚂
Teterow 900m 🚌 1km ®

Thale ⛺ Bodetal Waldkater 1, 06502
Thale. ☎ (3947) 2881 **FAX** (3947)
2881 **Open:** 06.00-22.00hrs,
1.1-23.12; 27-31.12 🛏 204 ● DM
22,00 ᴮᴮinc ⵀⵀⵀ ⵀⵀⵀ ⬜ ⧊ 🅿 ⵣ 🚂 Thale
1.5km 🚌 1.5km

Thallichtenberg ⛺ "Burg
Lichtenberg", Burgstr 12, 66871
Thallichtenberg. ☎ (6381) 2632 **FAX**
(6381) 80933 🛏 104 ● DM 25,10
ᴮᴮinc ⵀⵀⵀ(L D) ⵀⵀⵀ ♿

Tharandt ▲ Pienner Str 55, 01737
Tharandt. ☎ (35203) 37272 **Open:**
07.00-09.00hrs, 15.00-22.00hrs 🛏 69
● DM 20,00 ᴮᴮinc ⵀⵀⵀ ⵀⵀⵀ ⬜ 🅿 🚂
Tharandt "Edle Krone" 1km 🚌 R 400
Dresden-Freiburg 2.5km ap Tharandt
Post

Tholey ▲ Am Schaumberg 2, 66636
Tholey. ☎ (6853) 2271 **FAX** (6853)
5534 🛏 45 ● DM 20,50 ᴮᴮinc ⵀⵀⵀ(L D)
ⵀⵀⵀ

Thülsfelder Talsperre ▲ Am
Campingplatz 7, 49681 Garrel-
Petersfeld. ☎ (4495) 475 **FAX** (4495)
365 🛏 186 ● DM 20,00-24,00 ᴮᴮinc
ⵀⵀⵀ(L D) ⧊ ⚙ 🚂 Cloppenburg 13km

TITISEE-NEUSTADT (2 Hostels)

Titisee-Neustadt-**OT Neustadt** ▲ 2NE
"JH Rudenberg", Ortsteil Neustadt,

Haus Nr 6, 79822 Titisee-Neustadt. ✆
(7651) 7360 **FAX** (7651) 4299 ✉ 146
⬤ DM 22,00 ᴮᴮⁱⁿᶜ � ▥ P ⚲ ᚏ
Neustadt 3km

Titisee-Neustadt - **OT Titisee** ▲ 2NW
"JH Veltishof", Ortsteil Titisee,
Bruderhalde 27, 79822 Titisee-
Neustadt. ✆ (7652) 238 **FAX** (7652)
756 ✉ 128 ⬤ DM 22,00 ᴮᴮⁱⁿᶜ ▥ aff
P ⚲ ᚏ Titisee ᚏᚏ 7300
ap Feuerwehrheim - JH

Todtnauberg ▲ 1N "Fleinerhaus", OT
Todtnauberg, Radschertstr 12, 79674
Todtnau. ✆ (7671) 275 **FAX** (7671)
721 ✉ 146 ⬤ DM 22,00 ᴮᴮⁱⁿᶜ ▥ aff
P ⚲ ᚏ Freiburg 30km ᚏᚏ 7215
2km ap Rathaus

Tönning ▲ Badallee 28, 25832
Tönning. ✆ (4861) 1280 **FAX** (4861)
5956 **Open:** 23.1-14.12 ✉ 133 ⬤ DM
22,00 ᴮᴮⁱⁿᶜ ▥(L D) ⚲ ▥ P ⚲ ᚏ
Tönning 1km

Torfhaus ▲ Nr 3, 38667 Torfhaus. ✆
(5320) 242 **FAX** (5320) 254 ✉ 174
⬤ DM 22,00 ᴮᴮⁱⁿᶜ ▥ aff ⚲ ⚲ P ⚲
ᚏ Bad Harzburg 10km ᚏᚏ 200m

Tossens ▲ Meidgrodenweg 1, 26969
Butjadingen. ✆ (4736) 716 **FAX**
(4736) 817 **Open:** 1.5-30.9 ✉ 121 ⬤
DM 18,00 ᴮᴮⁱⁿᶜ ▥(L D) ⚲ P ⚲ ▲
ᚏ Nordenham 30km ᚏᚏ Tossens
R

Traben-Trarbach ⛺ **CC** Hirtenpfad,
56841 Traben-Trarbach. ✆ (6541) 9278
FAX (6541) 3759 ✉ 176 ⬤ DM 25,10
ᴮᴮⁱⁿᶜ ▥(L D) ⚲ aff ⚲

Traunstein ▲ Traunerstr 22, 83278
Traunstein (Bavaria). ✆ (861) 4742
FAX (861) 12382 **Open:** 16.1-30.11
✉ 57 ⬤ DM 18,00 ᴮᴮⁱⁿᶜ ▥(D) ᚏ
2km

Travemünde ▲ "Jugendfreizeitstätte
Priwall", Mecklenburger Landstr 69,

23570 Travemünde. ✆ (4502) 2576
FAX (4502) 4620 **Open:** 1.4-15.10 ✉
96 ⬤ DM 18,00 ᴮᴮⁱⁿᶜ ▥(L D) P ▲
ᚏ Travemünde 2.5km

Triberg/Schw ▲ 2SE Rohrbacher Str
35, 78098 Triberg. ✆ (7722) 4110
FAX (7722) 6662 ✉ 125 ⬤ DM 22,00
ᴮᴮⁱⁿᶜ ▥ aff ▥ P ⚲ ᚏ Triberg 3km

Trier ⛺ 3SW **CC** YGH, An der
Jugendherberge 4, 54292 Trier. ✆ (651)
146620 **FAX** (651) 1466230 ✉ 270
⬤ DM 26,30 ᴮᴮⁱⁿᶜ ▥(L D) aff ⚲

Tübingen ▲ Gartenstr 22/2, 72074
Tübingen. ✆ (7071) 23002 **FAX**
(7071) 25061 ✉ 204 ⬤ DM 22,00
ᴮᴮⁱⁿᶜ ▥(L D) aff ▥ P ᚏ Tübingen
1km ᚏᚏ 11 100m ap YH **R**

Überlingen ⛺ 2SE "Martin- Buber-
Jugendbegegnungsstätte", Alte
Nussdorfer Str 26, 88662 Überlingen.
✆ (7551) 4204 **FAX** (7551) 1277 ✉
251 ⬤ DM 22,00 ᴮᴮⁱⁿᶜ ▥ aff ▥ P ▲
ᚏ Überlingen Bhf West ᚏᚏ RAB
500m ap Kramerwerke

Ueckermünde- Bellin ▲ 7W
Jugendherberge Oderhaff, 17375
Ueckermünde. ✆ (39771) 22411 **FAX**
(39771) 22411 **Open:** 08.00-09.00hrs,
11.30-21.00hrs, 1.2-30.11 ✉ 105 ⬤
DM 20,00 ᴮᴮⁱⁿᶜ aff P ▲ ᚏ
Ueckermünde 4km ᚏᚏ to Alt-Warp
50m ap Bungalowsiedling **R**

Uelsen ▲ 2S Linnenbachweg 12,
49843 Uelsen. ✆ (5942) 718 **FAX**
(5942) 2606 **Open:** 15.3-20.10 ✉ 88
⬤ DM 20,00 ᴮᴮⁱⁿᶜ ▥ ⚲ ᚏ Bad
Bentheim 32km ᚏᚏ Uelsen 3km

Uelzen ▲ Fischerhof 1, 29525 Uelzen.
✆ (581) 5312 **FAX** (581) 14210 ✉
166 ⬤ DM 20,00 ᴮᴮⁱⁿᶜ ▥ aff ▥ ⚲ P
ᚏ Uelzen 5km ᚏᚏ 200m
ap Fischerhof

Ulm ▲ "Geschwister- Scholl- JH", Grimmelfinger Weg 45, 89077 Ulm. ☎ (731) 384455 **FAX** (731) 384511 ✉ 153 ● DM 22,00 BBinc ❍(L D) 🗇 🅿 🚃 Ulm 4km 🚌 Linie 4 200m ap Schulzentrum 🚃 Linie 1 Söflingen ap "Ehinger Tor"

Urach ☞ **Bad Urach**

Urfeld ☞ **Walchensee**

Uslar ▲ Kupferhammer 13, 37170 Uslar. ☎ (5571) 2298 **FAX** (5571) 1288 ✉ 104 ● DM 22,00 BBinc ❍ ♦♦♦ ♿ 🚗 🅿 🚃 Uslar 2km

Velbert ▲ Am Buschberg 17, 42549 Velbert (YH + YGH). ☎ (2051) 84317 ✉ 80 ● DM 37,00 BBinc ❍ ♦♦♦ ♿ 🅿 🚃 Essen 15km 🚌 149, 169

Verden ▲ Saumurplatz 1, 27283 Verden. ☎ (4231) 61163 **FAX** (4231) 68121 ✉ 124 ● DM 22,00 BBinc ❍(L D) ♦♦♦ ♿ 🚗 🅿 🚃 Verden 4km 🚌 4km

Villingen ▲ 2NW OT Villingen, St-Georgener- Str 36, 78048 Villingen-Schwenningen. ☎ (7721) 54149 **FAX** (7721) 52616 ✉ 133 ● DM 20,00 BBinc ❍ ♦♦♦ 🗇 🅿 🚃 Villingen 2km 🚌 3 300m ap Triberger Str.

Vlotho ▲ Auf dem Amtshausberg, Oeynhauser Str 15, 32602 Vlotho. ☎ (5733) 4063 **FAX** (5733) 18139 ● 108 ● DM 20,00 BBinc ❍ 🚗 🅿 🚃 Vlotho 800m 🚌 800m ap Am alten Amtsgericht

Vöhl ☞ **Hessenstein**

Wabern ☞ **Mosenberg**

Walchensee- Urfeld ▲ Mittenwalder Str 17, 82432 Walchensee (Bavaria). ☎ (8851) 230 **FAX** (8851) 1022 **Open:** 1.1-31.10; 27-31.12 ✉ 97 ● DM 22,00 BBinc ❍(D) ♦♦♦ ⚓ Alt 830m 🚃 Kochel 9km 🚌 9608, 50m

Waldeck ▲ 2.5NW Klippenberg 3, 34513 Waldeck. ☎ (5623) 5313 **FAX** (5623) 6254 **Open:** 1.1-23.12; 27-31.12 ✉ 165 ● DM 23,00 BBinc ❍ ♦♦♦ 🅿 ⚓ 🚃 Waldeck 4km

Waldhäuser ☞ **Neuschönau**

Waldmünchen ▲ Schlosshof 1, 93449 Waldmünchen (Bavaria). ☎ (9972) 94140 **FAX** (9972) 941433 ✉ 130 ● DM 22,00 BBinc ❍ ♦♦♦ ♿ 🚗 🗇 🌂 Alt 520m 🚃 1km 🚌 500m

Walldürn ▲ 3N Auf der Heide 37, 74731 Walldürn. ☎ (6282) 283 **FAX** (6282) 40194 ✉ 108 ● DM 20,00 BBinc ❍ ♦♦♦ 🅿 🚃 Walldürn 3km

Waltersdorf ▲ Am Jägerwäldchen 2, 02799 Waltersdorf. ☎ (35841) 2650 **FAX** (35841) 2650 **Open:** 07.00-22.00hrs ✉ 166 ● DM 20,00 - 22,00 BBinc ❍ ♦♦♦ 🌂 🚲 🚃 Großschönau 5km 🚌 Zittau-Oybin R6, Jägerwaldchen 50m

Wandlitz ▲ Prenzlauer Chausee 146, 16348 Wandlitz. ☎ (33397) 22109 **FAX** (33397) 22109 **Open:** 07.00-22.00hrs ✉ 176 ● DM 22,00 ❍ ♦♦♦ ⚓ 🚃 Wandlitzsee 500m

Wangerooge ▲ 4W "Westturm", 26486 Wangerooge, (North Sea) ☎ (4469) 439 **FAX** (4469) 8578 **Open:** 1.5-30.9 ✉ 136 ● (Full Board) ❍(L D) 🗗 🚗 🚲 ⚓ 🚢 Harlesiel 🅁

Waren ▲ Auf dem Nesselberg 2, 17192 Waren. ☎ (3991) 667606 **FAX** (3991) 667606 **Open:** 08.00-09.00hrs, 15.00-22.00hrs, 16.3-31.10 ✉ 60 ● DM 20,00 BBinc 🗗 ♦♦♦ 🅿 ⚓ 🚃 Waren Müritz 2.5km 🚌 1,3,5 500m ap Wasserwerk 🅁

Warmbad ☞ **Gehringswalde**

Weikersheim ▲ YGH "Haus der Musik", Im Heiligen Wöhr, 97990 Weikersheim. ☎ (7934) 7025, 7026

FAX (7934) 7709 ⇋ 143 BBinc ▮O▮(L D)
▮▮▮ ⚄ ▣ ▣ ⛆ Weikersheim 1km ⛍
300m ap Marktplatz

Weilburg ▲ 2E Am Steinbühl, 35781
Weilburg-Odersbach. ☎ (6471) 7116
FAX (6471) 1542 **Open:** 1.1-23.12;
27-31.12 ⇋ 135 ● DM 23,50 BBinc
▮O▮ ▮▮▮ ▣ ⚓ ⛆ Weilburg 4km

WEIMAR (4 Hostels)

Weimar - Maxim Gorki ⚠ YGH, Zum
Wilden Graben 12, 99425 Weimar. ☎
(3643) 3471 **FAX** (3643) 3471 **Open:**
06.00-01.00hrs, 4.1-22.12; 28.12-4.1.98
⇋ 60 ● DM 24,00 BBinc ▮O▮ ▮▮▮ ⚎ ▣
⛆ Weimar 4km ⛍ 100m Ⓡ

Weimar - "Germania" ⚠ Carl-August
Allee 13, 99423 Weimar. ☎ (3643)
850490 **FAX** (3643) 850491 **Open:**
07.00-22.00hrs, 7.1-22.12 ⇋ 121 ●
DM 22,00 BBinc ▮O▮ ▮▮▮ ⛆ Weimar
200m ⛍ 200m Ⓡ

Weimar - "Am Poseckschen Garten"
▲ Humboldtstr 17, 99423 Weimar.
☎ (3643) 64021 **FAX** (3643) 64021
Open: 06.30-10.00, 14.30-00.30hrs,
1.5-21.12; 28-31.12 ⇋ 112 ● DM
22,00 BBinc ▮O▮ ▮▮▮ ⛆ Weimar 4km
⛍ 1, 6 100m

Weimar - "Am Ettersberg" JGH ⚠
Ettersberg-Siedlung, 99427 Weimar ☎
(3643) 3471 **FAX** (3643) 3471 **Open:**
06.00-01.00hrs, 1.1-23.12, 28-31.12
⇋ 60 ● DM 24,00 BBinc ▮O▮ ▮▮▮ ▣ ▣
⚓ ⛆ Weimar 4km ⛍ Ettersberg-
Siedlung 500m Ⓡ (JGH "Maxim
Gorki", Weimar)

Weinheim/Bgstr ⚠ 2W Breslauer Str
46, 69469 Weinheim. ☎ (6201) 68484
FAX (6201) 182730 ⇋ 143 ● DM
22,00 BBinc ▮O▮ ▮▮▮ ▣ ▣ ⛆ Weinheim
4km ⛉ OEG 200m ap Stahlbad

Weiskirchen ▲ Jugendherbergsstr 12,
66709 Weiskirchen. ☎ (6876) 231

FAX (6876) 1444 ⇋ 124 ● DM 21,50
BBinc ▮O▮(L D) ▮▮▮ ⚄

Weißenbrunn ☞ **Leinburg**

Werdau ▲ Jugendheimweg 1, 08412
Werdau. ☎ (3761) 3514 **Open:**
07.00-22.00hrs ⇋ 40 ● DM 17,00
▮O▮ ▮▮▮ ⚎ ▣ ▣ ⚓ ⛆ 2.5km ⛍
Zwickau-Werdau T 129, T 130, T 131
2.5km ap Hbf

Wernfels ☞ **Spalt**

Wertheim ▲ 2W "Frankenland", Alte-
Steige 16, 97877 Wertheim. ☎ (9342)
6451 **FAX** (9342) 7354 ⇋ 105 ● DM
20,00 BBinc ▮O▮ ▮▮▮ ▣ ⛆ Wertheim
2km

Westensee ▲ Am See 24, 24259
Westensee. ☎ (4305) 542 **FAX** (4305)
1360 ⇋ 139 ● DM 20,00 BBinc
▮O▮(L D) ⚄ ▣ ⚲ ⛆ Kiel 20km ⛍
500m

Westerstede ⚠ 2SW
"Hössensportanlage", Jahnallee 2,
26655 Westerstede. ☎ (4488) 84690
FAX (4488) 78317 **Open:** 3.1-21.12
Shut: Sun 1.11-15.3 ⇋ 68 ● DM
24,00 BBinc ▮O▮(L D) ▮▮▮ ▣ ⚲ ⛆
Oldenburg 28km ⛍ 28km

Wetzlar ⚠ 2SW "Jugendgästehaus",
Richard-Schirrmann-Str 3, 35578
Wetzlar. ☎ (6441) 71068 **FAX** (6441)
75826 **Open:** 1.1-23.12; 27-31.12 ⇋
190 ● DM 26,50 BBinc ▮O▮ ▮▮▮ ⚄ ▣
⛆ Wetzlar 5km ⛍ 12 600m
ap Sturzkopf

Wewelsburg ▲ "Jugendburg",
Burgwall 17, 33142 Büren-
Wewelsburg. ☎ (2955) 6155 **FAX**
(2955) 6946 **Open:** 1-9.1; 11.2-31.12
⇋ 210 ● DM 21,50 BBinc ▮O▮ ⚎ ⚎ ▣
⚲ ⛆ Paderborn 15km ⛍ 500m
ap Dierkes

Wieden ▲ 2W "JH Belchen",
Oberwieden 16, 79695 Wieden. ☎
(7673) 538 **FAX** (7673) 504 ⇋ 155

⊜ DM 20,00 [BB]inc ᵀ⊙⅂ ⅲⅰ P ⅄ ⊞ Münstertal ☲ 300m ap Wiedener Eck

Wiehl ▲ An der Krähenhardt 6, 51674 Wiehl. ☎ (2262) 93410 **FAX** (2262) 91598 🚲 175 ⊜ DM 24,00 [BB]inc ᵀ⊙⅂ ⅲⅰ P ⊞ Köln-Dieringhausen 30km ☲ 302

Wiesbaden ▲ [2W] Blücherstr 66, 65195 Wiesbaden. ☎ (611) 48657, 449081 **FAX** (611) 441119 **Open:** 1.1-23.12; 27-31.12 🚲 161 ⊜ DM 24,00 [BB]inc ᵀ⊙⅂ ⅲⅰ P ⊜ ⊞ Wiesbaden 3km ☲ 14 300m ap Gneisenaustraße

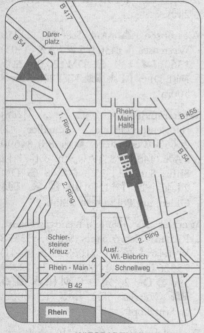

WIESBADEN

Wiesenttal-Streitberg ▲ Am Gailing 6, 91346 Wiesenttal (Bavaria). ☎ (9196) 288 **FAX** (9196) 1543 **Open:** 16.1-14.11 🚲 122 ⊜ DM 20,00 [BB]inc ᵀ⊙⅂ ⅲⅰ ⊡ ⊞ Ebermannstadt 4km ☲ 200m

Wildenstein, Burg ▲ 88637 Leibertingen. ☎ (7466) 411 **FAX**

(7466) 417 🚲 165 ⊜ DM 22,00 [BB]inc ᵀ⊙⅂(L D) ⅲⅰ 🎮 ⊡ P ⊞ Beuron 5km ⓡ

Wildeshausen ▲ Am Fillerberg 9, 27793 Wildeshausen. ☎ (4431) 2223 **Open:** 1.4-31.10 🚲 46 ⊜ DM 20,00 [BB]inc ᵀ⊙⅂(L D) ☋ ⊞ Wildeshausen 2km

Wilhelmshaven ▲ [3E] Freiligrathstr 131, 26386 Wilhelmshaven. ☎ (4421) 60048 **FAX** (4421) 64716 **Open:** 1.1-31.10; 1-31.12 🚲 126 ⊜ DM 22,00 [BB]inc ᵀ⊙⅂(L D) 🏛 P ☋ ⊜ ⊞ Wilhelmshaven 3km ☲ 1km

Willingen ▲ [4NE] Am Lukasheim 9-12, 34508 Willingen. ☎ (5632) 6347 **FAX** (5632) 4343 **Open:** 1.1-23.12; 27-31.12 🚲 124 ⊜ DM 23,50 [BB]inc ᵀ⊙⅂ ⅲⅰ P ⅄ Alt 650m ⊜ ⊞ Willingen 6km

Windischeschenbach-Tannenlohe ▲ Tannenlohe 45, 92670 Windischeschenbach (Bavaria). ☎ (9637) 267, 1067 **FAX** (9637) 276 **Open:** 16.1-14.12 🚲 162 ⊜ DM 22,00 [BB]inc ᵀ⊙⅂ ⅲⅰ ♿ ⊡ ⊞ Wiesau/Reuth 11km

Windischleuba ▲ JH 'Schloss Windischleuba', Pestalozziplatz 1, 04603 Windischleuba. ☎ (3447) 834471 **FAX** (3447) 832702 **Open:** 06.00-22.00hrs, 31.1-15.12 🚲 146 ᵀ⊙⅂ ⅲⅰ 🎮 P ⊞ Altenburg 7km ☲ Altenburg-W or Frohburg, or Geithain 200m

Wingst ▲ Molkereistr 11, 21789 Wingst. ☎ (4778) 262 **FAX** (4778) 7594 **Open:** 1.3-31.1.98 🚲 202 ⊜ DM 20,00 [BB]inc ᵀ⊙⅂(L D) ♿ P ⊞ Wingst 1km

Winterberg ▲ Astenberg 1, 59955 Winterberg. ☎ (2981) 2289 **FAX** (2981) 569 **Open:** 1.1-31.10; 1-31.12 🚲 170 ⊜ DM 21,50 [BB]inc ᵀ⊙⅂ 🏛 P ⅄ ☋ ⊞ Winterberg 6km ☲ 960, 50m

Wipperfürth ▲ Ostlandstr, 51688 Wipperfürth. ✆ (2267) 1228 **FAX** (2267) 80977 ⌑ 144 ⊖ DM 24,00 BBinc ⦿ ☞ ⚲ 🅿 ⛟ Bergisch-Gladbach 20km 🚌

Wittdün ▲ Mittelstr 1, 25940 Wittdün auf Amrum. ✆ (4682) 2010 **FAX** (4682) 1747 **Open:** 6.1-30.11 ⌑ 212 ⊖ DM 22,00 BBinc ⦿(L D) ⚲ ① ⛴ WDR Line 500m Ⓡ (1.1-15.3, 15-30.11)

Wittenberg-Lutherstadt ▲ JH Schloss Wittenberg, 06886 Lutherstadt-Wittenberg. ✆ (3491) 403255 **FAX** (3491) 403255 **Open:** 06.30-22.00hrs (weekends 17.00-22.00hrs) ⌑ 104 ⊖ DM 20,00 BBinc ⦿ 🎠 ☐ 🅿 ⛟ Lutherstadt Wittenberg 2km 🚌 Bahnhof Elbtor 500m

Wolfsburg ⚠ Lessingstr 60, 38440 Wolfsburg ✆ (5361) 13337 **FAX** (5361) 16630 ⌑ 68 ⊖ DM 22,00 BBinc ⦿ ⚲ 🎠 🅿 ⛟ Wolfsburg 3km

Wolfstein ▲ Rötherweg 24, 67752 Wolfstein. ✆ (6304) 1408 **FAX** (6304) 683 ⌑ 160 ⊖ DM 20,50 BBinc ⦿(L D) ⦿ ⚲ ☐

Worms ⚠ ⦿ Dechaneigasse 1, 67547 Worms. ✆ (6241) 25780 **FAX** (6241) 27394 ⌑ 114 ⊖ DM 26,30 BBinc ⦿(L D) ⦿

Worpswede ▲ Hammeweg 2, 27726 Worpswede. ✆ (4792) 1360 **FAX** (4792) 4381 ⌑ 178 ⊖ DM 22,00 BBinc ⦿(L D) ⦿ ⚲ 🎠 🅿 ⚲ ⛴ ⛴ Bremen 25km 🚌 140 25km

Wörthsee-Steinebach ▲ Herbergsstr 10, 82237 Wörthsee (Bavaria). ✆ (8153) 7206 **FAX** (8153) 89214 **Open:** 1.2-30.11 ⌑ 45 ⊖ DM 16,50 BBinc ⦿(D)

Wunsiedel ⚠ Am Katharinenberg 4, 95632 Wunsiedel (Bavaria). ✆ (9232) 1851 **FAX** (9232) 70629 **Open:** 1.1-31.10 ⌑ 112 ⊖ DM 22,00 BBinc

⦿(L D) ⦿ ⦿ ⚲ ☐ ⛟ Hohenbrunn 2km 🚌 1km

Wuppertal- Barmen ▲ Obere Lichtenplatzerstr 70, 42287 Wuppertal. ✆ (202) 552372 **FAX** (202) 557354 ⌑ 140 ⊖ DM 25,00 BBinc ⦿ ☞ ⛟ Wuppertal-Barmen 5km 🚌 610, 640

Würzburg ⚠ ⦙IBN⦙ "JGH", Burkarderstr 44, 97082 Würzburg (Bavaria). ✆ (931) 42590 **FAX** (931) 416862 ⌑ 292 ⊖ DM 25,00-29,00 BBinc ⦿(D) ⦿ ⚲ ⛟ 3km 🚌 3, 5 500m

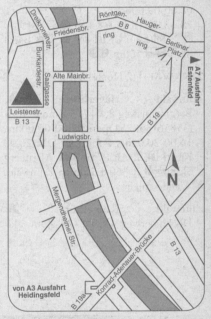

WÜZBURG

Wüstewohlde ▲ Wüstewohlde Nr 20, 27624 Ringstedt. ✆ (4708) 234 **FAX** (4708) 234 **Open:** 1.4-30.11 ⌑ 72 ⊖ DM 20,00 BBinc ⦿(L D) 🅿

Wyk auf Föhr ▲ Fehrstieg 41, 25938 Wyk. ✆ (4681) 2355 **FAX** (4681) 5527 **Open:** 1.2-22.12 ⌑ 162 ⊖ DM 22,00 BBinc ⦿(L D) ① ⛴ WDR Line 200m 🚌 500m

Zeven-Bademühlen ▲ 4W Haus Nr 1, 27404 Zeven. ☎ (4281) 2550 **FAX** (4281) 80293 ✉ 130 ● DM 22,00 BB^{inc} ⵌ(L D) ⑂ ⌂ P ⛴ Bremen 42km 🚌 Bremen 42km ap Bademühlen

Zielow ▲ 17207 Zielow. ☎ (39923) 2547 **FAX** (39923) 2547 **Open:** 08.00-09.00hrs, 15.00-22.00hrs ✉ 94 ● DM 17,50 BB^{inc} ⵌ(L D) ⑂ ⌂ P ⚲ ⚓ 🚂 Waren 30km 🚌 3km ap Vipperow **R**

Zingst ▲ Glebbe 14, 18374 Zingst. ☎ (38232) 465 **FAX** (38232) 465 **Open:** 08.00-09.00hrs, 15.00-22.00hrs, 28.12.96-18.12 ✉ 160 ● DM 19,00 BB^{inc} ⵌ(L D) ⑂ P ⚲ ⚓ 🚂 Barth 8km 🚌 500m **R**

ZINNWALD (2 Hostels)

Zinnwald - "Jägerhütte" ▲ Bergmannsweg 8, 01773 Zinnwald. ☎ (35056) 35825 **Open:** 07.00-09.00hrs, 16.00-20.00hrs ✉ 60 ● DM 20,00 ⵌ ⑂ P ⚲ Alt 875m 🚂 Altenberg 5km 🚌 R 360 1.2km ap Zinnwald, Wendeschleife

Zinnwald - "Klügelhütte" ▲ Hochmoorweg 12, 01773 Zinnwald-

Georgenfeld. ☎ (35056) 35882 **Open:** 07.00-09.00hrs, 15.00-20.00hrs ✉ 60 ● DM 17,00 ⵌ ⚲ ⑂ ⌂ ⚲ Alt 850m 🚂 Altenberg 4km 🚌 R 360 800m ap Zinnwald, Grenzsteinhof

Zöblitz ▲ Freiberger Str 37, 09517 Zöblitz. ☎ (37363) 7920 **Open:** 07.00-22.00hrs ✉ 55 ● DM 20,00 ⵌ ⚲ P ⚲ Alt 600m ⛴ Chemnitz-Zöblitz 1.2km 🚌 Chemnitz-Zöblitz 1km **R**

Zuflucht ▲ Schwarzwaldhochstrasse, 72250 Zuflucht. ☎ (7804) 611 **FAX** (7804) 1323 ✉ 234 ● DM 22,00 BB^{inc} ⵌ(L D) ⑂ ⚲ P ⚲ Alt 968m 🚂 Freudenstadt 17km, Oppenau 9km 🚌 10m ap Zuflucht **R**

Zwiesel ▲ Hindenburgstr 26, 94227 Zwiesel (Bavaria). ☎ (9922) 1061 **FAX** (9922) 60191 **Open:** 1.1-31.10; 27-31.12 ✉ 53 ● DM 20,00 BB^{inc} ⵌ(D) ⑂ ⚲ Alt 550m 🚂 4km

Zwingenberg ▲ 1NE "Carl-Ulrich-JH" Auf dem Berg 41, 64673 Zwingenberg. ☎ (6251) 75938 **FAX** (6251) 788113 **Open:** 1.1-23.12; 27-31.12 ✉ 125 ● DM 20,50 BB^{inc} ⵌ 🚂 Zwingenberg 1km

GREECE (HELLAS)

GRECE

GRIECHENLAND

GRECIA

IYHF Athens International Hostel,
16 Victor Hugo Street,
Athens, Greece.

☎ (3) (1) 5234170
FAX (3) (1) 5234015

Capital:	Athens
Language:	Greek (Hellenic)
Currency:	GDR (drachma)
Population:	10,257,000
Size:	131,044 sq km

GREECE

GREEK HOSTELS

Due to the change of circumstances in Greece, there is no YHA recognised by the IYHF. For the time being we are including only limited hostel information, but we hope to add futher hostels in the future. For further information please contact the Athens International Youth Hostel.

PASSPORTS AND VISAS

EC citizens can enter Greece with their identity card. Other Europeans need a valid passport. All non-Europeans should contact their local Greek Consulate for visa requirements.

HEALTH

No vaccinations are required. Some medical services are provided to EC citizens, but in general medical insurance is advisable.

BANKING HOURS

All major tourist centres have at least one bank open 08.00-18.00hrs. Otherwise hours are 08.00-14.00hrs Monday to Thursday and 08.00-13.30hrs on Friday.

POST OFFICES

Monday to Friday 08.00-14.00hrs. Post offices in Athens and major tourist centres operate extended hours of 08.00-19.00hrs.

SHOPPING HOURS

In general, Monday, Wednesday and Saturday 08.00-14.00hrs; Tuesday, Thursday and Friday 08.00-13.30hrs and 17.00-20.00hrs.

TRAVEL

Air
There is a good airline network to Europe and all major Greek cities and islands.

Rail
The main lines run from north to south, with limited branch lines at Central and Northern Greece and Peloponese. Eurail and Inter-Rail cards are accepted.

Bus
An extensive bus network runs between all cities and villages, with frequent departures from Athens.

Ferry
There is an extensive ferry and boat network to all the Greek islands and Italy, Cyprus and Israel. Eurail and Inter-Rail card holders can have free ferry transportation between Brindisi and Patras.

Driving
Driving is on the right. An emergency triangle, fire extinguisher, first aid kit and use of safety belts are mandatory. For EC citizens, their national (pink) driving licence is valid. Other motorists should obtain an international driving licence. International motor insurance (green card) is compulsory.

PUBLIC HOLIDAYS

New Year's Day, 1 January; Epiphany, 6 January; Shrove Monday; Day of Independence, 25 March; Good Friday, 28 March; Easter, 30/31 March; May Day, 1 May; Ascension of the Virgin, 15 August; National Holiday, 28 October; Christmas, 25/26 December.

TELEPHONE INFORMATION

International Code	Country Code	Main City Area Codes
00	30	Athens 1

FRANÇAIS

AUBERGES DE JEUNESSE GRECQUES

Du fait de changements survenus dans la situation des auberges grecques, il n'y a pas d'Association d'Auberges de Jeunesse reconnue par l'IYHF en Grèce. Pour le moment, nous n'avons introduit que les coordonnées d'un nombre limité d'auberges mais nous espérons pouvoir être en mesure d'en ajouter davantage à l'avenir. Pour obtenir un complément d'informations, veuillez contacter l'Auberge Internationale d'Athènes.

PASSEPORTS ET VISAS

Les citoyens de la CE peuvent entrer en Grèce avec leur carte d'identité. Les autres Européens doivent être munis d'un passeport valide. Tous les non-Européens doivent s'adresser à leur consulat grec local en ce qui concerne un visa.

SOINS MEDICAUX

Aucune vaccination n'est requise. Les citoyens de la CE ont droit à certains soins médicaux, mais en général, il est préférable de souscrire à une police d'assurance maladie.

HEURES D'OUVERTURE DES BANQUES

Tous les grands centres touristiques ont au moins une banque ouverte de 8h à 18h. Sinon, les banques sont ouvertes de 8h à 14h du lundi au jeudi et de 8h à 13h30 le vendredi.

BUREAUX DE POSTE

Les bureaux de poste sont ouverts du lundi au vendredi de 8h à 14h. Les bureaux d'Athènes et ceux des grands centres touristiques ouvrent plus longtemps, de 8h à 19h.

HEURES D'OUVERTURE DES MAGASINS

Les magasins sont en général ouverts le lundi, le mercredi et le samedi, de 8h à 14h et le mardi, le jeudi et le vendredi, de 8h à 13h30 et de 17h à 20h.

DEPLACEMENTS

Avions

Il y a un bon réseau aérien à destination de l'Europe et de toutes les grandes villes et îles grecques.

Trains

Les grandes lignes vont du nord au sud, avec un nombre limité de lignes secondaires au centre et au nord du pays et dans le Péloponnèse. Les cartes Eurail et Inter-Rail sont acceptées.

Autobus

Toutes les grandes villes et tous les villages sont reliés par un vaste réseau d'autobus; les départs depuis Athènes sont fréquents.

Ferry-boats

Tout un service de ferry-boats et de bateaux dessert la totalité des îles grecques, ainsi que l'Italie, Chypre et Israël. Les voyageurs munis de cartes Eurail et Inter-Rail peuvent bénéficier de transport gratuit par ferry entre Brindisi et Patras.

Automobiles

La conduite est à droite. Les conducteurs doivent transporter un triangle de présignalisation, un extincteur et une trousse de premiers secours, et le port des ceintures de sécurité est obligatoire. Pour les citoyens de la CE, leur permis de conduire national (rose) suffira. Les autres automobilistes devront obtenir un permis de conduire international. Il est obligatoire d'avoir une assurance automobile internationale (carte verte).

JOURS FERIES

Nouvel an, 1er janvier; Epiphanie, 6 janvier; Lundi gras; Fête de l'Indépendance, 25 mars; Vendredi saint, 28 mars; Pâques, 30/31 mars; Fête du travail, 1er mai; Ascension de la Vierge, 15 août; Fête nationale, 28 octobre; Noël, 25/26 décembre.

TELEPHONE

Indicatif International	Indicatif du Pays	Indicatifs régionaux des Villes principales
00	30	Athènes 1

DEUTSCH

GRIECHISCHE JUGENDHERBERGEN

Aufgrund einer veränderten Situationen in Griechenland wird von der Internationalen Förderation für Jugendherbergen kein griechischer Jugendherbergsverband anerkannt. Momentan nur wenig Informationen über die griechischen Jugendherbergen. Für Einzelheiten wenden Sie sich bitte an der 'Athens International' Hostel.

PÄSSE UND VISA

Staatsbürger eines EG-Landes können mit ihrem Personalaüsweis nach Griechenland einreisen. Andere Europäer brauchen einen gültigen Reisepaß. Alle Nichteuropäer sollten sich beim nächsten griechischen Konsulat nach den Visumsvorschriften erkundigen.

GESUNDHEIT

Impfungen sind nicht erforderlich. Gewisse ärztliche Leistungen werden auch Staatsbürgern eines EG-Landes geboten, aber im allgemeinen empfiehlt sich der Abschluß einer Krankenversicherung.

GESCHÄFTSSTUNDEN DER BANKEN

Alle bekannten Fremdenverkehrsorte haben mindestens eine Bank, die von 8.00-18.00 Uhr geöffnet ist. Sonst sind Banken montags bis donnerstags von 8.00-14.00 Uhr und freitags von 8.00-13.30 Uhr geöffnel.

POSTÄMTER

Montags bis freitags von 8.00-14.00 Uhr. In Athen und größeren Fremdenverkehrsorten sind Postämter jedoch von 8.00-19.00 Uhr geöffnet.

LADENÖFFNUNGSZEITEN

Im allgemeinen montags, mittwochs und samstags von 8.00-14.00 Uhr und dienstags, donnerstags und freitags von 8.00-13.30 Uhr und von 17.00-20.00 Uhr.

REISEN

Flugverkehr

In andere Länder Europas und in alle größeren Städte in Griechenland sowie auf die bekannteren Inseln gibt es gute Flugverbindungen.

Eisenbahn

Die Haupteisenbahnlinien verlaufen von Norden nach Süden. Der Mitte und im Norden Griechenlands sowie auf dem Peloponnes gibt es ein beschränktes Netz von Nebenstrecken. Es werden auch Eurail- und Inter-Rail-Karten akzeptiert.

Busse

Zwischen allen Städten und Dörfern gibt es einen umfangreichen Busverkehr. Besonders von Athen aus verkehren die Busse sehr häufig.

Fähren

Auf alle griechischen Inseln und nach Italien, Zypern und Israel verkehren zahlreiche Fähren und Schiffe. Wer im Besitz einer Eurail- oder Inter-Rail-Karte ist, kann die Fähre zwischen Brindisi und Patras kostenlos benutzen.

Autofahren

In Griechenland herrscht Rechtsverkehr. Man muß ein Warndreieck, ein Feuerlöschgerät und einen Erste-Hilfe-Kasten mit sich führen, und das Tragen von Sicherheitsgurten ist Pflicht. Der von einem EG-Land ausgestellte (rosarote) Führerschein gilt auch in Griechenland. Andere Autofahrer sollten sich einen internationalen Führerschein beschaffen. Eine internationale Kraftfahrzeugversicherung (grüne Karte) ist Pflicht.

FEIERTAGE

Neujahr, 1. Januar; Erscheinungsfest, 6. Januar; Rosenmontag; Unabhängigkeitstag, 25. März; Karfreitag, 28. März; Ostern, 30./31. März; Maitag, 1. Mai; Mariä Himmelfahrt, 15. August; Nationalfeiertag, 28. Oktober; Weihnachten, 25./26. Dezember.

FERNSPRECHINFORMATIONEN

Internationale Kennzahl	Landes- Kennzahl	größere Städte - Ortsnetzkennzahlen
00	30	Athen 1

$$\boxed{\text{ESPAÑOL}}$$

ALBERGUES DE JUVENTUD GRIEGOS

En Grecia no existe una Asociación de Albergues Juveniles reconocida por la IYHF por haber cambiado la situación. Por el momento, sólo incluimos información limitada sobre albergues, pero esperamos poder añadir más albergues en el futuro. Rogamos contactar con el Albergue de Juventud Internacional de Atenas para más información.

PASAPORTES Y VISADOS

Los ciudadanos de la CE pueden entrar en Grecia con el carnet de identidad. Los demás ciudadanos europeos necesitan un pasaporte en regla. Todos los ciudadanos no europeos deben ponerse en contacto con el Consulado de Grecia de su país para los requisitos del visado.

SANIDAD

No hacen falta vacunas. Se facilitan algunos servicios médicos a ciudadanos de la CE, pero en general se recomienda hacerse un seguro médico.

HORARIO DE LOS BANCOS

Todos los grandes centros turísticos tienen al menos un banco abierto desde las 08.00 hasta las 18.00 horas. Si no, las horas de apertura al público son de 08.00 a 14.00 de lunes a jueves y de 08.00 a 13.30 los viernes.

OFICINAS DE CORREOS

De lunes a viernes, de 08.00 a 14.00 horas. Las oficinas de correos de los principales centros turísticos y de Atenas amplían el horario de 08.00 a 19.00 horas.

HORARIO COMERCIAL

En general los lunes, miércoles y sábados de 08.00 a 14.00 horas. Los martes, jueves y viernes de 08.00 a 13.30 horas y de 17.00 a 20.00 horas.

DESPLAZAMIENTOS

Avión
Hay una buena red de líneas aéreas que vuelan a Europa y a las principales ciudades e islas griegas.

Tren
Las líneas principales van de norte a sur, con líneas secundarias limitadas en el centro y norte de Grecia y en el Peloponeso. Se aceptan billetes Euraíl e Inter-Raíl.

Autobús
Una extensa red de autocares comunica a todas las ciudades y pueblos, con salidas frecuentes desde Atenas.

Ferry
Hay una extensa red de ferrys y barcos a todas las islas griegas y a Italia, Chipre e Israel. Los titulares de las tarjetas Euraíl e Inter-Raíl pueden viajar gratis en ferry desde Brindisi hasta Patras.

Coche
Se conduce por la derecha. Es obligatorio llevar el triángulo de emergencia, un extintor de incendios, un botiquín de primeros auxilios y el cinturón de seguridad. Para los ciudadanos de la CE el permiso de conducir nacional (rosa) es suficiente. Los conductores de otros países deben tener un permiso internacional. Es obligatorio el seguro internacional de vehículos (carta verde).

DIAS FESTIVOS

Año Nuevo, 1 enero; Día de Reyes (Epifanía), 6 enero; Lunes de Carnaval; Día de la Independencia, 25 marzo; Viernes Santo, 28 marzo; Pascua, 30/31 marzo; Primero de Mayo, 1 mayo; Ascensión de la Virgen, 15 agosto; Fiesta Nacional, 28 octubre; Navidad, 25/26 diciembre.

INFORMACION TELEFONICA

Código Internacional	Código Nacional	Indicativo de área de las Ciudades principales
00	30	Atenas 1

Athens International `1.2NW` `IBN`
IYHF Athens International Hostel, 16 Victor Hugo St, 10438 Athens. (1) 5234170 **FAX** (1) 5234015 140
`BB`inc Omonia Sq. 500m

Pireas 8km Larisis 800m, Peloponisou 600m 051 300m ap Menandrou Str. 1 150m ap Peroke `U` Omonia Sq. 500m `R` (direct to YH Jun - Sep)

HUNGARY
HONGRIE
UNGARN
HUNGRIA

Magyarországi Ifjusági Szállások Szövetsége,
H-1065 Budapest, Bajcsy-Zsilinszky ut 31. II/3.

Postal address: H-1396 Budapest, PF. 483

☎ (36) (1) 1319705 / 1113297
FAX (36) (1) 1319705 / 1113297

Travel Section:
Express Travel Centre,
Szabadság tér 16, 1054 Budapest.
☎ (36) (1) 1317777, 1324108
FAX (36) (1) 1533172

IBN Booking Centre for outward bookings
■ Budapest-Express Travel, Express Office No. 204,
    1052 Budapest V, Semmelweis u.4.
    ☎ (36) (1) 1178600, **FAX** (36) (1) 1176823

Capital:	Budapest
Language:	Hungarian
Currency:	Ft (forints)
Population:	10,890,000
Size:	93, 030, sq km

HUNGARY

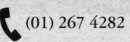
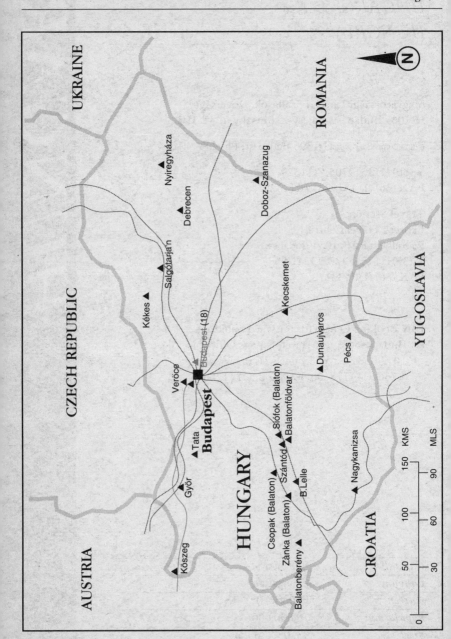

ENGLISH

HUNGARIAN HOSTELS

Hostels are open 24hrs. Expect to pay US$3.00-29.00 per night including sheets. All hostels serve meals or use restaurants near by, a few have self-catering facilities.

Express as Travel Section offers central booking for groups and concessions for youth and student travel.

All hostels can accept families - advance booking recommended!

Advance booking for individuals to hostels or hostel booking centres if seasonal hostel closed:
MTW Hostels: 1134 Budapest XIII, Dózsa Gy ut 152. ☎ (1) 1298644, 1408585 **FAX** (1) 1208425
Universum Hostels: 1029 Budapest II, Báthory L u 18. **FAX** (1) 2757046

General Services: On-the-spot booking on arrival for individuals in Budapest in Express offices during working hours: Express Main Office, 1052 Budapest V, Semmelweis u 4 ☎ (1) 1178600 **FAX** (1) 1176823

PASSPORTS AND VISAS

Hungary is visa-free for citizens of most European countries, Canada and the USA.

HEALTH

There are no vaccination requirements for visitors entering Hungary.

BANKING HOURS

Banks are open weekdays between 09.00 and 13.00hrs.

POST OFFICES

Generally open 08.00-16.00hrs or 08.00-19.00hrs. In Budapest Keleti and Nyugati Railway Stations the post offices are open 0700-21.00hrs.

SHOPPING HOURS

Shops are normally open between 10.00 and 18.00hrs, however they are open later on Thursday until 19.00hrs but on Saturday close early at 14.00hrs.

TRAVEL

Travel in Hungary is very centralized, when entering or leaving it is easiest to go via Budapest.

Air
EXPRESS flight offices can arrange flights and youth discount air tickets.

Rail
There is a reliable train service. Train tickets and youth discount tickets are available from EXPRESS ticket offices. In Budapest there is a good underground/subway system.

Bus
There is a reliable bus service. Central information in Central Bus Station, Erzsébet ter. In Budapest and main cities there are good bus, tram and trolley bus services.

Ferry
There is a good ferry service on the Balaton and Danube from May to October.

Driving
Drinking alcohol and driving is strictly forbidden in Hungary.

PUBLIC HOLIDAYS

New Year, 1 January; 15 March; Easter Monday, 31 March; 1 May; Whitsun Monday, 19 May; 20 August; 23 October; Christmas, 25/26 December.

TELEPHONE INFORMATION

International Code	Country Code	Main City Area Codes
00	36	Budapest 1

FRANÇAIS

AUBERGES DE JEUNESSE HONGROISES

Les auberges sont ouvertes jour et nuit. Une nuit, draps compris, vous coûtera aux environs de 3 à 29 \$US. Toutes les auberges servent des repas ou utilisent les restaurants locaux. Quelques-unes ont une cuisine à la disposition des touristes.

Express, la section voyage, offre un service de réservation central aux groupes, ainsi que des tarifs voyage spéciaux aux jeunes et aux étudiants.

Toutes les auberges peuvent recevoir des familles - il est conseillé de réserver à l'avance!

Réservations à l'avance pour les individus vers les auberges ou aux centres de réservation si l'auberge saisonnière est fermée:

MTW Auberges: 1134 Budapest XIII, Dózsa Gy ut 152, ✆ (1) 129 8644 ou (1) 140 8585 **FAX** (1) 120 8425
Auberges Universum: 1029 Budapest II, Báthory L. u. 18, **FAX** (1) 275 70 46

Services Généraux: Réservation sur place à l'arrivée à Budapest pour les individus dans les bureaux Express, pendant les heures de travail: Bureau Principal d'Express, 1052 Budapest V, Semmelweis u 4, ✆ (1) 1178 600 **FAX** (1) 1176 823

PASSEPORTS ET VISAS

Les visas ne sont pas requis pour les citoyens de la plupart des pays européens, du Canada et des Etats-Unis.

SOINS MEDICAUX

Aucune vaccination n'est requise pour les étrangers se rendant en Hongrie.

HEURES D'OUVERTURE DES BANQUES

Les banques sont ouvertes en semaine de 9h à 13h.

BUREAUX DE POSTE

En général, ils sont ouverts de 8h à 16h ou de 8h à 19h. Dans les gares Keleti et Nyugati de Budapest, les bureaux de poste sont ouverts de 7h à 21h.

HEURES D'OUVERTURE DES MAGASINS

Les magasins sont normalement ouverts entre 10h et 18h; ils sont ouverts plus longtemps le jeudi, jusqu'à 19h, mais ferment tôt le samedi, à 14h.

DEPLACEMENTS

Les transports en Hongrie sont très centralisés. Il est plus facile de passer par Budapest pour entrer ou sortir du pays.

Avions

Les bureaux EXPRESS peuvent organiser des vols et des billets à prix réduit pour les jeunes.

Trains

Les trains sont fiables. Les billets normaux et les billets à tarif spécial pour les jeunes sont vendus aux guichets EXPRESS. Budapest possède un bon réseau de métro.

Autobus

Les autobus sont fiables. Pour des renseignements centralisés, s'adresser à la station d'autobus centrale d'Erzsébet ter. A Budapest et dans les grandes villes, les services d'autobus, de trams et de trolleybus sont bons.

Ferry-boats

Il y a un bon service de ferry-boats sur le lac Balaton et le Danube de mai à octobre.

Automobiles

Il est formellement interdit en Hongrie de conduire après avoir consommé de l'alcool.

JOURS FERIES

Nouvel an, 1er janvier; 15 mars; Lundi de Pâques, 31 mars; 1er mai; Lundi de Pentecôte, 19 mai; 20 août; 23 octobre; Noël, du 25 au 26 décembre.

TELEPHONE

Indicatif International	Indicatif du Pays	Indicatifs régionaux des Villes principales
00	36	Budapest 1

DEUTSCH

UNGARISCHE JUGENDHERBERGEN

Die Herbergen sind 24 Stunden geöffnet. Es ist mit einem Preis von US$3,00-29,00 pro Nacht, einschließlich Bettlaken, zu rechnen. Alle Herbergen bieten Mahlzeiten, manchmal in einem nahegelegenen Restaurant, einige haben Einrichtungen für Selbstversorger.

Express Travel als Reisedienst ist eine Buchungszentrale für Gruppen. Für junge Leute und Studenten werden Ermäßigungen geboten.

Alle Herbergen können auch Familien aufnehmen - Vorausbuchung ist ratsam!

Vorausbuchungen für Einzelreisende können in den Jugendherbergen oder Reservierungszentralen vorgenommen werden wenn sommerhostel geschlossen. **MTW Herbergen:** 1134 Budapest XIII, Dózsa Gy ut 152 ☎ 1 129 8644, 1 140 8585 **FAX** 1 120 8425

Universum-Herbergen: 1029 Budapest II, Báthory L. ut 18 **FAX** 1 275 7046

Allgemeine Dienst: Bei Ankunft in Budapest können Einzelreisende während der Öffnungszeiten in den Express-Geschäftsstellen buchen: Hauptbüro Express, 1052 Budapest V, Semmelweis u 4 ☎1 1178 600 **FAX** 1 1176-823

PÄSSE UND VISA

Staatsangehörige der meisten europäischen Länder, Kanadas und der USA brauchen für Ungarn kein Visum.

GESUNDHEIT

Es gibt keine Impfvorschriften für nach Ungarn reisende Besucher.

GESCHÄFTSSTUNDEN DER BANKEN

Die Banken sind werktags zwischen 9.00 und 13.00 Uhr geöffnet.

POSTÄMTER

Im allgemeinen von 8.00-16.00 Uhr oder von 8.00-19.00 Uhr geöffnet. Auf den Bahnhöfen Budapest Keleti und Nyugati ist die Post zwischen 7.00 und 21.00 Uhr geöffnet.

LADENÖFFNUNGSZEITEN

Die Geschäfte sind im allgemeinen zwischen 10.00 und 18.00 Uhr geöffnet. Donnerstags wird jedoch erst um 19.00 Uhr und samstags schon um 14.00 Uhr geschlossen.

REISEN

Das Reisen ist in Ungarn sehr zentralisiert. Bei der Ein- und Ausreise fährt man am besten über Budapest.

Flugverkehr
EXPRESS-Flugbüros können Flüge buchen und für junge Leute ermäßigte Flugtickets beschaffen.

Eisenbahn
Es gibt einen zuverlässigen Zugverkehr. Fahrkarten-mit Ermäßigung für junge Leute-sind in den EXPRESS-Fahrkartenverkaufsstellen erhältlich. In Budapest gibt es ein gutes U-Bahn-Netz.

Busse
Es gibt einen zuverlässigen Busverkehr. Auskunftszentrale in der Zentralen Bus-Station, Erzsébet ter. In Budapest und anderen größeren Städten gibt es einen guten Bus-, Straßenbahn- und Obusverkehr.

Fähren
Auf dem Plattensee und der Donau gibt es von Mai bis Oktober einen guten Fährverkehr.

Autofahren
Autofahren nach Alkoholgenuß ist in Ungarn streng verboten.

FEIERTAGE

Neujahr, 1. Januar; 15. März; Ostermontag, 31. März; 1. Mai; Pfingstmontag, 19. Mai; 20. August; 23. Oktober; Weihnachten, 25./26. Dezember.

FERNSPRECHINFORMATIONEN

Internationale Kennzahl	Landes-Kennzahl	größere Städte - Ortsnetzkennzahlen
00	36	Budapest 1

ESPAÑOL

ALBERGUES DE JUVENTUD HUNGAROS

Los albergues están abiertos 24 horas al día. Cuestan entre 3,00 y 29,00 $US por noche, incluyendo la ropa de cama. Todos los albergues sirven comidas o utilizan restaurantes próximos. Algunos tienen cocina para huéspedes.

Express, la Sección de Viajes, ofrece un servicio centralizado de reservas para grupos y precios especiales para jóvenes y estudiantes.

Todos los albergues pueden alojar a familias - ¡se recomienda reservar con antelación!

Para hacer reservas individuales con antelación, ponerse en contacto con los albergues o con los centros de reservas de albergues si está cerrado el albergue estacional:

Albergues MTW: 1134 Budapest XIII, Dózsa Gy ut 152, ☎ (1) 129 8644, 1408585 **FAX** (1) 1208425

Albergues Universum: 1029 Budapest II, Báthory L u 18, **FAX** (1) 2757046

Servicios Generales: Al llegar a Budapest, las reservas se pueden hacer en el acto en las oficinas de Express en horas de trabajo: Oficina Principal de Express, 1052 Budapest V, Semmelweis u 4, ☎ (1) 1178600 **FAX** (1) 1176823

PASAPORTES Y VISADOS

En Hungría no necesitan visado los ciudadanos de la mayoría de los países europeos, Canadá y Estados Unidos.

SANIDAD

No hay requisitos de vacunación para los visitantes que entren en Hungría.

HORARIO DE BANCOS

Los bancos abren los días laborables entre 09.00 y 13.00 horas.

CASAS DE CORREO

Por lo general, abren de 08.00 a 16.00 horas o de 08.00 a 19.00 horas. En las estaciones de tren de Keleti y Nyugati en Budapest, las casas de correo están abiertas de 07.00 a 21.00 horas.

HORARIO COMERCIAL

Las tiendas suelen abrir entre 10.00 y 18.00 horas, aunque están abiertas hasta más tarde los jueves (19.00 horas) y el sábado cierran más temprano, a las 14.00 horas.

DESPLAZAMIENTOS

Las comunicaciones en Hungría están muy centralizadas, es mejor entrar y salir del país a través de Budapest.

Avión
Se pueden conseguir billetes y descuentos para jóvenes en las oficinas de EXPRESS.

Tren
El servicio ferroviario es fiable. Se pueden conseguir billetes de tren y descuentos para jóvenes en las oficinas de venta de billetes de EXPRESS. Budapest cuenta con un buen sistema de metro.

Autobús
El servicio de autobús es fiable. La oficina de información central se encuentra en la Estación Central de Autobuses, Erzsébet ter. En Budapest y en las ciudades principales, hay buenos servicios de autobús, tranvía y trolebús.

Ferry
Existe un buen servicio de ferry en el Balaton y el Danubio de mayo a octubre.

Coche
Está estrictamente prohibido en Hungría conducir habiendo bebido alcohol.

DIAS FESTIVOS

Año Nuevo, 1 enero; 15 marzo; Lunes de Pascua de Resurrección, 31 marzo; 1 mayo; Lunes de Pentecostés, 19 mayo; 20 agosto; 23 octubre; Navidad, 25/26 diciembre.

INFORMACION TELEFONICA

Código Internacional	Código Nacional	Indicativo de área de las Ciudades principales
00	36	Budapest 1

DISCOUNTS AND CONCESSIONS

Eurolines: 10% discount on coach fares

Hostels in this country may also display this symbol.

Les auberges de ce pays pourront également afficher ce symbole.

Jugendherbergen in diesem Land können auch dieses Symbol zeigen.

Es posible que los albergues de este país exhiban además este símbolo.

BALATON (7 Hostels)

Balaton - **Balatonföldvár** Express International Youth Centre, Hotel Juventus, József Attila u 9, 8623 Balatonföldvár. ✆ (84) 340313 **FAX** (84) 340303 **Open:** 1.5-30.9 ⬚ 200 ⬤ US$7.00-14.00 🍴 �203

Balaton - **Csopak** Ifjúsági Üdülő, Sport u 9, 8229 Csopak/Balaton. ✆ (87) 446505 **FAX** (87) 446515 **Open:** 1.5-30.9 ⬚ 292 ⬤ US$4.00-10.00 ♦ 🚆 500m 🚌 500m

Balaton - **Zánka** Gyermeküdülő Centrum, 8250 Zánka/Balaton Nord. ✆ (87) 468440 **FAX** (87) 468269 ⬚ 2500 ⬤ US$8.00-18.00 🍴 ♦ ⚓ 🚆 Zánka

Balaton - **Siófok** Hotel Ezüstpart, Liszt F sétány 3, H 8609 Siófok/Balaton. ✆ (84) 350622 **FAX** (84) 350358 ⬚ 1660 (Wi 700) ⬤ US$16.00-29.00 BB|inc 🍴 ♦ ⬚ 🚿 🅿 ⚓ 🚆 Balatonszéplak Felső 400m Ⓡ

Balaton - **Napfény - Beach Hostel** 0.1 SW 8649 Balatonberény, Balaton u. 2. ✆ (85) 377608, 377682 **FAX** (85) 377682 **Open:** 1.5-15.10 ⬚ 400 ⬤ USD 9-18 BB|inc 🍴 ♦ ⚓ ⬚ 🚿 🅿 ⚓ 🚆 100m

Balaton - **Hungest Sellő II. Üdülő** 0.3 W 8638 Balatonlelle, Szent I. u. 44. ✆ (85) 350313 **FAX** (85) 350313 **Open:** 1.6-30.9 ⬚ 24 ⬤ USD 12.00 🍴 ♦ 🅿 🚆 300m 🚌 300m

Balaton - **Aranyhid Üdülő Hunguest** 8622 Szántód, Móricz Zs. u. 2. ✆ (84) 348708 **Open:** 1.6-15.9 ⬚ 84 ⬤ USD 5.00 🍴 ♦ ⬚ ⚓ ⚓ 2km 🚌 500m Ⓡ Wi: Hunguest, 113 Budapest, Dózsa Gy. 1113

BUDAPEST (18 Hostels)
(see town plan on following page)

Budapest - **Csillebérci Szabadidő** - és Ifjúsági Központ, Konkoly Thege Miklós u 21, 1535 Budapest XII. ✆ (1) 1565772 **FAX** (1) 1759327 ⬚ 200 ⬤ US$6.00-22.00 🚌 90

Budapest - Hotel Express IBN Beethoven u 9, 1126 Budapest XII. ✆ (1) 1752528 **FAX** (1) 1753082 ⬚ 120 ⬤ US$14.00-34.00 BB|inc ♦ 🚆 Déli pu 1km 🚌 59, 100m Ⓤ No 2, 1km

Budapest - **Hostel Vásárhelyi** Kruspér u 2, 1111 Budapest XI. ☎ (1) 4634326, (1) 4634356 **FAX** (1) 2757046 **Open:** 1.7-3.9 ⊠ 600 ● US$10.00-13.00 ♂ ♦♦♦ ▣ ♨ ⌂ 1, 7, 86 ⓡ (Universum)

Budapest - **Hostel Rózsa** Bercsényi u 28, 1117 Budapest XI. ☎ (1) 4634250, (1) 1666677 **FAX** (1) 2757046 **Open:** 1.7-31.8 ⊠ 200 ● US$10.00 ♂ ♦♦♦ ▣ ♨ Ⓟ ⌂ 1,7,86, 200m 🚋 4,6,47, 200m ⓡ (Universum)

Budapest - **Hostel Landler** Bartók B 17, 1114 Budapest XI. ☎ (1) 4633621, 4633622 **FAX** (1) 2457046 **Open:** 1.7-31.8 ⊠ 250 ● US$8.00-10.00 ♂ ♦♦♦ ▣ ♨ Ⓟ ⌂ 1,7,86, 50m 🚋 47,49,18,19, 50m ⓡ (Universum)

Budapest - **Hostel Bakfark** Bakfark Bálint u 1, 1022 Budapest II. ☎ (1) 2015419 **Open:** 10.6-30.8 ⊠ 80 ● US$8.00 ♂ ♦♦♦ Ⓤ 2 Moszkva tér 200m ⓡ MTW centre

Budapest - **Hostel Diáksportszálló** More than Ways, Dózsa György 152, 1134 Budapest. ☎ (1) 1298644, 1408585 **FAX** (1) 1208425 ⊠ 140 ● US$6.50-10.00 ♂ ▣ ♨ Ⓤ 3 300m ⓡ MTW centre

Budapest - **Apáczai** Papnövelde u 4-6, 1053 Budapest V. ☎ (1) 2670311 **FAX** (1) 2757046 **Open:** 23.6-25.8 ⊠ 160 ● US$8.00-10.00 ▣(B) ♂ ♦♦♦ ▣ Ⓤ 3, 300m ⓡ Universum

Budapest - **Hotel Nova** Tejut u 1, Csepel Island, 1214 Budapest XXI. ☎ (1) 2775374 **FAX** (1) 2768371 ⊠ 250 ● US$4.00-5.50 ▣ ♂ ♨ 🚌 Csepel HÉV ⌂ 38 ⓡ

Budapest - **Hotel Flandria** Szegedi ut 27, 1135 Budapest XIII. ☎ (1) 2703181 **FAX** (1) 1208853 ⊠ 116 ● US$7.50-12.00 ▣ ♦♦♦ ♨ ⌂ 30, 4

Budapest - **Hotel Touring** Pünkösdfürdő u 38, 1039 Budapest III. ☎ (1) 2503184 **FAX** (1) 1801595 ⊠ 227 ● US$9.00-34.00 ▣inc ▣ ♂ ♦♦♦ ♿ Ⓟ 🚢 Pünkösdfürdő/Danube 500m 🚌 HÉV Békásmegyer 500m ⌂ 145, 146

Budapest - **Hotel Griff** Bartók B ut 152, 1113 Budapest XI. ☎ (1) 2042666 **FAX** (1) 2042062 ⊠ 340 ● US$4.50-13.00 ▣ ♂ ♦♦♦ ♿ ▣ ⌂ 1 50m 🚋 19, 49 50m

Budapest - **Sirály** Margitsziget, 1138 Budapest XIII. ☎ (1) 1530501 **FAX** (1) 3222205, (1) 3222801 **Open:** 15.4-30.10 ⊠ 36 ● US$6.00 ▣(B) Ⓘ ⚓ 🚢 Margitsziget ⌂ 26 ⓡ (MTK, Erzsébet krt 24, 1073 Budapest ☎/**FAX** (1) 3222205)

Budapest - **Ananda** XIV Kőszeg u 21, 1141 Budapest. ☎ (1) 1319896, (1) 2202413 **FAX** (1) 2202413 ⊠ 64 ● US$6.50-8.00 ▣inc ▣ ▣ Ⓤ 2 Örs vezér tér 400m

Budapest - **Central Park Hostel** [2NE] Budapest, XIV., Aztósi Dürer, 23. (ELTE Kollégium) ☎ (1) 3431416, 3415118 **FAX** (1) 3415118 **Open:** 8.7-2.9 ⊠ 180 ● USD 10.00 ▣(B) ♂ ♦♦♦ ▣ ⌂ No.7 100m ⓡ Granterra, 1026 Budapest, Trombitas u. 29/A, **FAX** (1) 1566263

Budapest - **Hotel Góliat** [5NE] Budapest 1135, XIII., Kerekes u. 12-20. ☎ (1) 2701465, 1494985 **FAX** (1) 1494985 ⊠ 492 ● USD 4.00-5.00 ▣ ♦♦♦ ▣ ♨ Ⓟ 🚋 No.1 300m

Budapest - **Hostel Schönherz** [2SW] Budapest XI., Irinyi J. u. 42. **Open:** 1.7-31.8 ⊠ 600 ● USD 10.00-12.00 ♦♦♦ ▣ Ⓟ 🚋 No.4 100m ⓡ MTW Center, 1134 Budapest, Dózsa Gy. 152., **FAX** (1) 1208425

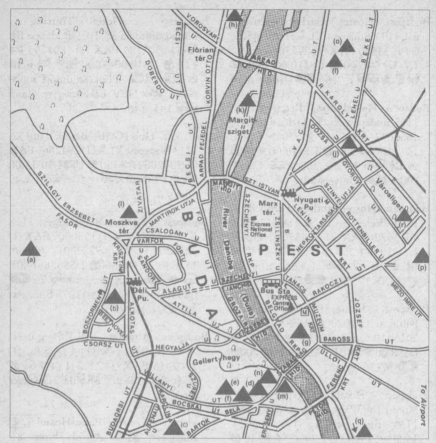

BUDAPEST - (a) Csillebérc Gyermek, (b) Express, (c) Griff, (d) Universitas, (e) Rózsa, (f) Landler, (g) Apáczai, (h) Touring, (i) Flandria, (j) Diáksport, (k) Sirály, (l) Bakfark, (m) Vásárhelyi, (n) Schönherz, (o) Góliát, (p) Ananda, (q) Nova, (r) Centrál

Budapest - Hostel Universitas 2SW Budapest XI., Irinyi J. u. 9. **Open:** 30.6-31.8 ⚌ 450 ⊜ USD 8.50-10.00 ¶◯(B) ††† ⚏ 6, 4 300m ℝ (MTW Center, 1134 Budapest, Dózsa Gy. 152., **FAX** (1) 1208425)

Debrecen West Tourist Turistaszálló, Wesselényi u 4, 4024 Debrecen. ✆ (52) 420891 **FAX** (52) 413266 ⚌ 80 ⊜ US$7.50 ¶◯(B) ♂ ††† ▣ ⚏ ℙ ⛨ Debrecen 500m ℝ (Baumann Reisen, MÁV állomás, 4024 Debrecen **FAX** (52) 413266)

Doboz Békés Megyei Gyermek és Ifjúsági Alapitvány, Szanazugi Tábora,

Doboz-Szanazug 5624. ✆ (66) 362348, 441141 **FAX** (66) 362348, 441593 **Open:** 1.5-30.9 ⚌ 140 ⊜ US$3.50-6.00 ℝ (Shut:GYIK, 5601 Bekescsaba, Pf.118 ✆ (66) 441593, **FAX** (66) 441141)

Dunaujváros Kerpely Antal Kollégium, Dózsa Gy u 33-37, 2400 Dunaujváros. ✆ (25) 310434 **FAX** (25) 310434 ⚌ 110 ⊜ US$3.50-6.00 ¶◯ ♂ ††† ▣ ℙ ⛨ Dunaujváros 1.5km ⚏ 1km

Györ - Rèvèsz Panzió 9026 Györ, Hèdervári u. 22. ✆ (96) 320667 ⚌ 20 ¶◯ ††† ▣ ℙ ⚏ No.16, 11 200m

KECSKEMÉT (2 Hostels)

Kecskemét - GAMF Ságvári Kollégium Hostel Izsáki u 10, 6000 Kecskemét. ☎ (76) 321916 **FAX** (76) 481304 ✉ 230 (1.7-30.8); 30 (31.8-30.6) ● US$ 4.00 ⁙ ⚓ ♔ 🚌 1

Kecskemét - Juniperus Panzió 2E 6000 Kecskemét, Kisfài 285. ☎ (76) 481536, 480273 **FAX** (76) 414772 ✉ 43 ● USD 8.00-12.00 ⁙ ⚓ ♔ ◻ ℗ 🚌 No.3, 25 500m

Kékes - Kékes Panzió 3221 Kékestetö, Pf. 7. ☎ (37) 367060 **FAX** (37) 367086 ✉ 22 ● USD 5.00-8.00 ⁙ ♔ ℗ ⚲ Alt 1000m 🚌 300m

Köszeg - Hunguest Gyermeküdülö 1.5NE 9730 Köszeg, Ürhajósok Útja 2. ☎ (94) 360169 **FAX** (94) 360169 ✉ 147 ● USD 5.00-14.00 ⁙ ♔ ⛩ ℗ ⚲ 🚲 Köszeg 2.5km 🚌 Köszeg 1.5km local bus 800m

Nagykanizsa Marika Panzió, 8800 Nagykanizsa, Cserfa u. 9./Sugár u. 26. ☎ (93) 318800 **FAX** (93) 318800 ✉ 24 ● US$11.50-20.00 ⁙ ♔ 🛏 Nagykanizsa

Nyiregyháza Paradise Hostel and Youth Center, Esély Alapitvány, Sóstófürdö, Sóstói u 76, 4431 Nyiregyháza. ☎ (42) 402011, 402038 **FAX** (42) 402011,

402038 **Open:** 15.4-15.10 ✉ 200 ● US$3.00-7.00 ⁙ ♔ ℗ 🚌 8

PÉCS (2 Hostels)

Pécs - Hotel Laterum 4NE 7633 Pécs, Hajnòczy 37-39. ☎ (72) 254963, 255829 **FAX** (72) 252131 ✉ 100 ● USD 5.00-15.00 ⁙ ♔ ℗ 🚌 No.2, 2/A

Pécs - Mandulàs Camping 3NW Pécs, Angyàn J. u. 2. ☎ (72) 315981 **Open:** 15.4-15.10 ✉ 130 ● USD 8.00-15.00 ⁙ ⚓ ♔ ℗ 🚌 No.34 200m Ⓡ (Mecsek Tours, 7621 Pécs, Seichenyi t. 9., ☎ / **FAX** (72) 214866)

Salgótarjàn - Strand Hotel 3N 3100 Salgótarjàn, Tóstrand 1. Pf. 83. ☎ (32) 430277, 430085 **FAX** (32) 430837 ✉ 72 ● USD 4.50-8.00 ⁙ ♔ ⚓ 🚌 600m

Tata - Fènyes Fürdö Camping 2890 Tata, Fènyes Fasor. ☎ (34) 381591 **FAX** (34) 381591 **Open:** 1.5-30.9 ● USD 4.00-7.00 ⁙ ⚓ ♔ 🛏 1.5km + local 🚌 100m

Verőce- Danube Bend Express International Youth Centre, Motel and Touring Hotel, 2623 Kismaros. ☎ (27) 350166 **Open:** 15.4-15.10 ✉ 200 ● US$7.00-10.00 ⁙ ♔ ♿ ℗ 🛏 Kismaros 500m

ICELAND
ISLANDE
ISLAND
ISLANDIA

Bandalag Íslenskra Farfugla,
Sundlaugavegur 34,
105 Reykjavík, Iceland.

☎ (354) 553 8110
FAX (354) 588 9201

Office Hours: Monday-Friday, 09.00-17.00hrs

Travel Section: c/o Bandalag Íslenskra Farfugla,
Sundlaugavegur 34,
105 Reykjavík, Iceland.

☎ (354) 553 8110
FAX (354) 588 9201

Capital:	Reykjavík
Language:	Icelandic
Currency:	Kr (kronúr)
Population:	265,000
Size:	103,000 sq km

ICELAND

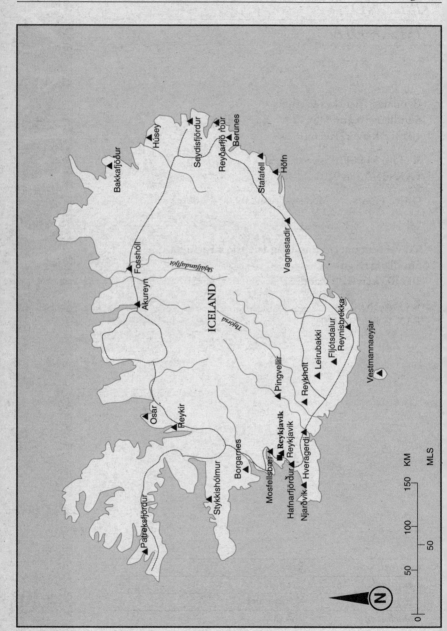

ENGLISH

ICELAND HOSTELS

Get beyond Reykjavík and sample the wild and remote side of Iceland. 31 hostels encircle the country, all have family rooms except Fljótsdalur.

Hostels are normally open between 08.00 and 01.00hrs, Reykjavík, Akureyri and Höfn are open until 24.00hrs but have limited access between 11.00 and 16.00hrs. Expect to pay in the region of Kr 1,000-1,250 plus linen hire if needed. Self-catering is available. Some hostels provide meals, but they must be booked on arrival.

Late arrivals are accepted in all hostels, but they must be booked in advance.

PASSPORTS AND VISA

A valid passport is always needed to enter Iceland, except for nationals of Norway, Sweden, Finland, Denmark, the Faroe Islands and Greenland.

BANKING HOURS

Banks are open Monday to Friday between 09.15 and 16.00hrs.

POST OFFICES

Post Offices are open Monday to Friday between 09.00 and 16.30hrs.

SHOPPING HOURS

Shops are open Monday to Friday 09.00-18.00hrs and Saturday 10.00-14.00hrs. Shops are usually closed on Sunday.

TRAVEL

Rail
There is no rail network in Iceland.

Bus
In summer buses run daily to most places in Iceland and in July and August into the highland. It is possible to buy a circlebus or omnibus pass from June to August and this is one of the best ways to travel in Iceland. These passes are available at our Travel Section office.

Ferry
During June, July and August there is a ferry, once a week, from Denmark and Norway.

Driving
In summer it is possible to drive all around Iceland and in bigger vehicles into the highland. In winter you must get information about the road conditions before you start to travel, due to weather and snow conditions.

PUBLIC HOLIDAYS

New Year, 1 January; Easter, 30/31 March; 1 May; Ascension Day, 16 May; Whit Sun/Monday, 26/27 May; National Day, 17 June; 5 August; Christmas, 24/25/26 December.

TELEPHONE INFORMATION

International Code	Country Code	Main City Area Codes
00	354	No Area Codes

FRANÇAIS

AUBERGES DE JEUNESSE ISLANDAISES

Au-delà de Reykjavík, vous ferez l'expérience du côté sauvage et reculé de l'Islande. 31 auberges font le tour du pays et toutes ont des chambres familiales sauf celle de Fljötsdalur.

Les auberges sont normalement ouvertes de 8h à 1h; celles de Reykjavík, Akureyri et Höfn sont ouvertes jusqu'à minuit mais sont d'accès limité entre 11h et 16h. Une nuit vous coûtera entre 1 000 et 1 250 KIS, plus location de draps le cas échéant. Il est possible de faire sa propre cuisine. Certaines auberges servent des repas mais ils doivent être réservés à l'arrivée.

Les arrivées tardives sont acceptées, mais doivent avoir été réservées à l'avance.

PASSEPORTS ET VISAS

Un passeport valide est toujours requis pour entrer en Islande, sauf pour les citoyens de Norvège, de Suède, de Finlande, du Danemark, des Iles Féroé et du Groenland.

HEURES D'OUVERTURE DES BANQUES

Les banques sont ouvertes du lundi au vendredi, de 9h15 à 16h.

BUREAUX DE POSTE

Les bureaux de poste sont ouverts du lundi au vendredi, de 9h à 16h30.

HEURES D'OUVERTURE DES MAGASINS

Les magasins sont ouverts du lundi au vendredi de 9h à 18h, et le samedi de 10h à 14h. Ils sont en général fermés le dimanche.

DEPLACEMENTS

Trains
Il n'y a pas de réseau ferroviaire en Islande.

Autobus
En été, les autobus assurent un service journalier vers la plupart des régions d'Islande, et en juillet et août vers les hautes terres. Il est possible de se procurer une carte circlebus ou omnibus de juin à août et cela représente la meilleure façon de se déplacer dans le pays. Ces cartes sont en vente au bureau de notre Service voyages.

Ferry-boats
En juin, juillet et août, il y a un ferry, une fois par semaine, en provenance du Danemark et de la Norvège.

Automobiles
En été, il est possible de conduire dans tout le pays et, avec des véhicules plus lourds, dans les hautes terres. En hiver, il est essentiel d'obtenir des renseignements sur l'état des routes avant d'entreprendre un voyage, en vue du temps et de la neige.

JOURS FERIES

Nouvel an, 1er janvier; Pâques, 30-31 mars; 1er mai; Ascension, 16 mai; Pentecôte 26/27 mai; Fête Nationale, 17 juin; 5 août; Noël, 24, 25 et 26 décembre.

TELEPHONE

Indicatif International	Indicatif du Pays	Indicatif rÚgionaux des Villes principales
00	354	Pas d'indicatifs régionaux

DEUTSCH

ISLÄNDISCHE JUGENDHERBERGEN

Sie sollten versuchen, Reykjavík hinter sich zu lassen und die abgelegene Seite Islands, die von wilder Schönheit geprägt ist, näher kennenzulernen. Über das ganze Land verstreut gibt es 31 Herbergen, alle mit Familienzimmer, außer der Herberge in Fljötsdalur.

Die Herbergen sind normalerweise von 8.00 bis 1.00 Uhr geöffnet. Die in Reykjavík, Akureyri und Höfn sind bis 24.00 Uhr geöffnet, aber zwischen 11.00 und 16.00 Uhr nur beschränkt zugänglich. Es ist mit einem Preis von ca Kr 1.000-1.250 plus, bei Bedarf, einer Gebühr für die Miete von Bettwäsche zu rechnen. Es gibt auch Einrichtungen für Selbstversorger. In einigen Herbergen gibt es Mahlzeiten, die bei der Ankunft bestellt werden müssen.

In allen Herbergen werden auch Spätankömmlinge aufgenommen, sofern sie sich im voraus angemeldet haben.

PÄSSE UND VISA

Wer nicht aus Norwegen, Schweden, Finnland, Dänemark, von den Faröer Inseln oder aus Grönland stammt, braucht für die Einreise nach Island immer einen gültigen Reisepaß.

GESCHÄFTSSTUNDEN DER BANKEN

Banken sind montags bis freitags zwischen 9.15 und 16.00 Uhr geöffnet.

POSTÄMTER

Postämter sind montags bis freitags zwischen 9.00 und 16.30 Uhr geöffnet.

LADENÖFFNUNGSZEITEN

Die Geschäfte sind montags bis freitags von 9.00-18.00 Uhr und samstags von 10.00-14.00 Uhr geöffnet. Sonntags sind sie normalerweise geschlossen.

REISEN

Eisenbahn
In Island gibt es keine Eisenbahn.

Busse
Im Sommer gibt es einen täglichen Busverkehr an die meisten Orte in Island und im Juli und August auch ins Hochland. Von Juni bis August kann man einen Rindreisebus- oder Omnibus-Paß kaufen. Damit läßt sich Island besonders gut bereisen. Diese Pässe gibt es in der Geschäftsstelle der Reiseabteilung des isländischen JH-Verbandes.

Fähren
Im Juni, Juli und August kommt einmal in der Woche eine Fähre aus Dänemark und Norwegen.

Autofahren
Im Sommer kann man quer durch Island und mit größeren Fahrzeugen auch ins Hochland fahren. Im Winter muß man sich wegen des Wetters und der Schneefälle nach den Straßenverhältnissen erkundigen.

FEIERTAGE

Neujahr, 1. Januar; Ostern 30-31 März; 1. Mai; Himmelfahrt 16. Mai; Pfingsten, 26./27. Mai; Nationalfest, 17. Juni; 5. August; Weihnachten, 24./25. und 26. Dezember.

FERNSPRECHINFORMATIONEN

Internationale Kennzahl	Landes-Kennzahl	größere Städte - Ortsnetzkennzahlen
00	354	Keine Ortsnetzkennzahlen

ESPAÑOL

ALBERGUES DE JUVENTUD ISLANDESES

Vaya más allá de Reykjavik y descubra el lado remoto y salvaje de Islandia. Un total de 31 albergues rodea el país, todos con habitaciones familiares salvo el de Fljötsdalur.

Los albergues suelen abrir de 08.00 a 01.00 horas. Reykjavik, Akureyri y Höfn están abiertos hasta las 24.00 horas, pero tienen acceso limitado entre las 11.00 y las 16.00 horas. Se paga alrededor de Kr 1.000-1.250 más alquiler de ropa de cama, de ser necesario. Disponen de cocinas para huéspedes. Algunos albergues sirven comidas, pero hay que encargarlas al llegar.

Todos los albergues aceptan que se llegue tarde, pero hay que informarles de ello con antelación.

PASAPORTES Y VISADOS

Siempre se requiere un pasaporte válido para entrar en Islandia, excepto los ciudadanos de Noruega, Suecia, Finlandia, Dinamarca, Islas Faroe y Groenlandia.

HORARIO DE BANCOS

Los bancos abren de lunes a viernes de 09.15 a 16.00 horas.

CASAS DE CORREO

Las casas de correo abren de lunes a viernes de 09.00 a 16.30 horas.

HORARIO COMERCIAL

El horario de las tiendas es de lunes a viernes de 09.00 a 18.00 horas y los sábados de 10.00 a 14.00 horas. Las tiendas normalmente cierran los domingos.

DESPLAZAMIENTOS

Tren
No existe red ferroviaria en Islandia.

Autobús
En verano los autobuses funcionan a diario y recorren casi toda Islandia. En julio y agosto, llegan hasta las tierras altas. Se puede comprar un pase de autobús circular u omnibús desde junio a agosto, lo que representa una de las mejores maneras de viajar en Islandia. Estos pases pueden conseguirse en la Sección de Viajes de nuestra oficina.

Ferry
En junio, julio y agosto sale un ferry semanal desde Dinamarca y Noruega.

Coche
En verano se puede conducir por toda Islandia y, en vehículos más grandes, hasta las tierras altas. En invierno hay que informarse previamente sobre el estado de las carreteras debido al tiempo y la nieve.

DIAS FESTIVOS

Año Nuevo, 1 enero; Pascua, 30/31 marzo; 1 mayo; Día de la Ascensión, 16 mayo; Domingo y Lunes de Pentecostés, 26 y 27 mayo; Día Nacional, 17 junio; 5 agosto; Navidad, 24, 25 y 26 diciembre.

INFORMACION TELEFONICA

Código Internacional	Código Nacional	Indicativo de área de las Ciudades principales
00	354	Sin indicativo de área

Hostels in this country may also display this symbol.

Les auberges de ce pays pourront également afficher ce symbole.

Jugendherbergen in diesem Land können auch dieses Symbol zeigen.

Es posible que los albergues de este país exhiban además este símbolo.

Akureyri - **Stórholt** CC Stórholt 1, 600 Akureyri. ☎ 4623657 **FAX** 4625037 ⊠ 49 ♂ ♦♦♦ 🅿 ✈ 4km 🚌 10m

Bakkafjörður Skólagata 5, 685 Bakkafjörður. ☎ 4731686 **FAX** 4731668 Open: 1.6-31.8 ⊠ 17 (+ 50 mattresses) ▯◎▮ ♂ ♦♦♦ ▣ 🅿 🚌 from Akureyri Mon,Wed; from Vopnafjöður Tue,Thu

Berunes Berufjörd, 765 Djúpivogur. ☎ 4788988 **FAX** 4788988 Open: 15.5-15.9 ⊠ 20 ▯◎▮ ♂ ♦♦♦ 🎟 🅿 🚌 100m

Fljótsdalur Fljótshlið, 861 Hvolsvollur. ☎ 4878498, 4878497 Open: 15.4-15.10 ⊠ 15 ♂ 🎟 🅿 🚌 27km

Fosshóll CC Barðárdal, 645 Fosshóll. ☎ 4643108 **FAX** 4643318 Open: 15.4-15.10 ⊠ 50 ▯◎▮ ♂ ♦♦♦ 🅿 🚌 (daily Su) 100m

HAFNARFJÖRðUR (2 Hostels)

Hafnarfjörður - **Arahús** Strandgata 21, 220 Hafnarfjörður. ☎ 5550795, 5550612 **FAX** 5553330 ⊠ 23 ♂ ♦♦♦

Hafnarfjörður - **Hraunbyrgi** CC Hraunbrún 57, 220 Hafnarfjörður. ☎ 5650900, 8534205 **FAX** 5551211 Open: 1.6-31.8 ⊠ 23 ♂ ♦♦♦

Hamar Golfskálinn Hamri, 310 Borgarnes. ☎ 4371663 **FAX** 4371041 **Open:** 1.6-15.9 ⊠ 14 ▯◎▮ ♂ ♦♦♦ 🅿 🚌 from Borgarnes 3km

Höfn Nýibær, Hafnarbraut 8, 780 Höfn. ☎ 4781736 **FAX** 4781736 **Open:** 15.5-30.9 ⊠ 27 ▯◎▮(B) ♂ ♦♦♦ 🅿 ✈ Höfn 8km A🚌 To YH 200m

Húsey Hróarstungu, 701 Egilsstadir. ☎ 4713010 **FAX** 4713009 **Open:** 1.6-25.9 ⊠ 20 ♂ ♦♦♦ 🅿

Hveragerði Ból, Hveramörk 14, 810 Hveragerði. ☎ 4834198, 4834588 **FAX** 4834088 Open: 1.5-31.8 ⊠ 33 ▯◎▮ ♂ ♦♦♦ 🅿 🚌 100m

Leirubakki CC Landssveit, Rang 851 Hella. ☎ 4876591 **FAX** 4876591 ⊠ 50 ▯◎▮ (order in advance) ♂ ♦♦♦ 🅿 🚌 daily 100m

Mosfellsbær CC Reykjahvoll, 270 Mosfellsbær ☎ 5667237 **FAX** 5667235 **Open:** 1.5-31.10 ⊠ 20 ▯◎▮(B) ♦♦♦ ♿ ▣ 🚌 170

Njarðvík Pórustig 1, 260 Njarðvík. ☎ 4215662, 4214372 **FAX** 4215316 **Open:** 1.6-25.8 ⊠ 60 ● inc transport to Keflavik ✈ ▯◎▮(B) ♂ ♦♦♦ ♿ ▣ 🅿 ☙ ✈ Keflavík 6km

Njarðvík- Strönd Njarðvíkurbraut 48-50, 260 Innri Njarðvík. ☎ 4216211 FAX 4216211 ✉ 28 ☂ ♦♦♦ ✈ Keflavík 10km

Ósar Pverárhreppi, V- Hún, 531 Hvammstangi. ☎ 4512678, 8539828 FAX 4512678 ✉ 18 ⦅B⦆ ☂ ♦♦♦ ▣ 🚐 30km

Patreksfjörður Afahús, Aðalstræti 65, 450 Patreksfjörður. ☎ 4561280, 4561275 ✉ 8 ☂ ♦♦♦ ▣

Þingvellir ⟨CC⟩ Hótel Valhöll, Þingvellir, 801 Selfoss. ☎ 4822622 FAX 4834775 Open: 1.6-31.8 ✉ 27 ⦅ ☂ ▣ 🚐 ap YH

Reydarfjördur Búdargata 4, 730 Reydarfjördur. ☎ 4741447 FAX 4741447 ✉ 25 ⦅B⦆ ☂ ♦♦♦ ⊞ ▣

Reykholt Biskupstungum, 801 Selfoss. ☎ 4868830, 4868811 FAX 4868709 Open: 1.6-31.8 ✉ 70 ⦅B⦆ ☂ ♦♦♦ ▣ 🚐 400m

Reykjavík ⟦3W⟧ ⟨CC⟩ Sundlaugavegur 34, PO Box 1045, 121 Reykjavík. ☎ 5538110 FAX 5889201 Open: 5.1-20.12 ✉ 104 ⦅B⦆ ☂ ♦♦♦ ▣ ✈ 5km A🚐 City bus 1 change to bus 5 in the centre 5km 🚐 5, 10m (🚐 to national airport leaves from YH every morning Jun-Aug)

Reynisbrekka Mýrdalur, 870 Vík. ☎ 4871106, 4871243 FAX 4871303 Open: 1.6-15.9 ✉ 25 ⦅ ☂ ♦♦♦ ▣ ▣ 🚐 4km

Seyðisfjörður Hafaldan, Ránargata 9, 710 Seyðisfjörður. ☎ 4721410 FAX 4721486 ✉ 28 ☂ ♦♦♦ ▣ 🚐 100m

Sæberg Reykir, Hrútafjörður, 500 Brú. ☎ 4510015 FAX 4510034 ✉ 30 ⦅B⦆ ☂ ♦♦♦ ▣ 🚐 1km

Stafafell Lóni, 781 Höfn. ☎ 4781717 FAX 4781785 ✉ 50 ☂ ♦♦♦ ⊞ ▣ 🚐 100m

Stykkishólmur Höfðagata 1, 340 Stykkishólmur. ☎ 4381095 FAX 4381579 Open: 1.4-30.9 ✉ 50 ☂ ♦♦♦ ▣ ⛴ 500m 🚐 500m

Vagnsstadir ⟨CC⟩ Sudursveit, A- Skaftafellssysla, 781 Höfn. ☎ 4781048, 4781567 FAX 4782167 Open: 10.6-10.9 ✉ 26 ☂ ♦♦♦ 🚐 350m

Vestmannaeyjar Faxastigur 38, 900 Vestmannaeyjar. ☎ 4812915 FAX 4811497 Open: 1.6-15.9 ✉ 35 ☂ ♦♦♦ ① ▣ ✈ 2km ⛴ Vestmannaeyjar 500m

REYKJAVÍK

IRELAND (NORTHERN)
IRLANDE DU NORD
NORDIRLAND
IRLANDA DEL NORTE

ASSURED STANDARD

Youth Hostel Association of Northern Ireland,
22 Donegall Road, Belfast,
BT12 5JN, Northern Ireland.

☎ (44) (1232) 324733
FAX (44) (1232) 439699

Office Hours: Monday-Friday, 09.00-17.00hrs

Travel Section: c/o Youth Hostel Association
of Northern Ireland,
22 Donegall Road, Belfast,
BT12 5JN, Northern Ireland.

IBN Booking Centre for outward bookings:
■ **Belfast,** *via National Office above.*

Capital:	Belfast
Language:	English
Currency:	£ (Sterling)
Population:	1,578,100
Size:	14,120 sq km

IRELAND (Northern)

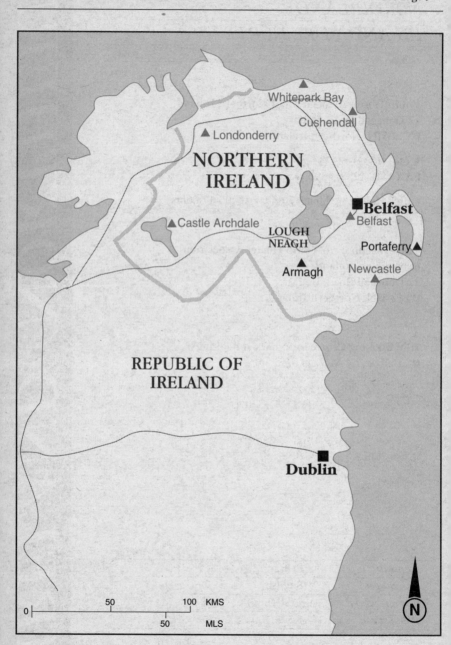

ENGLISH

NORTHERN IRELAND HOSTELS

Less travelled than the neighbouring Republic, Northern Ireland, with its 8 Youth Hostels, has many attractions of its own. Dramatic lakeland scenery in the west contrasts with the wild and rugged Antrim coast and the unique Giant's Causeway.

Hostels are normally open 07.30-11.00hrs and 17.00-23.30hrs, with longer hours at some hostels. Expect to pay in the region of £6.00-£13.00 per night including bedlinen. All hostels have self catering facilities, except Belfast.

Most hostels are closed 22.12-2.1, and many close for other periods between November and February. Check with the hostel or YHANI. All hostels take advance bookings made with a credit card except Barholm.

PASSPORTS AND VISAS

You will need a valid passport. Not many visitors now require visas but do check in advance.

HEALTH

An international Certificate of Vaccination is not required to enter the UK, but you should check if one is needed on your re-entry into your own country.

Medical Insurance is essential because visitors are only eligible for free **emergency** treatment at National Health Service Accident and Emergency departments of hospitals. If you are admitted to hospital as an in-patient, even from an accident and emergency department, or referred to an out-patient clinic, you will be asked to pay unless you are a national of an EC country, resident in any member country, or a national or resident of a country which has a reciprocal health care agreement with the UK. You are strongly advised to take out adequate insurance cover before travelling.

BANKING HOURS

Generally open weekdays 09.30-15.30hrs, but many stay open for an extra hour. All are closed on Sundays and Public Holidays.

POST OFFICES

Open weekdays 09.00-17.30hrs and Saturdays 09.00-12.30hrs. They are closed on Sundays and Public Holidays.

SHOPPING HOURS

Generally Monday-Saturday 09.00-17.30hrs, although this may vary in larger towns. Some shops do stay open late on Wednesday/Thursday/Friday until 20.00/21.00hrs.

TRAVEL

Rail

Main routes are served by rail. An Emerald Card is available which gives unlimited travel throughout the whole of Ireland using bus and rail networks.

Bus

There is an excellent network of regular bus services and in particular good bus links between those towns which are not served by train. Freedom of Northern Ireland Tickets provide 7 days' unlimited travel throughout Northern Ireland and are available from bus stations. The Emerald Card gives unlimited travel throughout the whole of Ireland using bus and rail networks.

Driving

If you want to drive a motor vehicle you must be over the age of 17. Driving is on the left-hand side of the road. Seat belts are required to be worn in both the front and back of cars, if seat belts are fitted. The drink driving laws are very strict so don't do it! The AA and RAC are just two of the motoring organizations offering, amongst other things, breakdown and recovery services.

PUBLIC HOLIDAYS

New Years Day, 1 January; Good Friday, 28 March; Easter Monday, 31 March; May Day, 5 May; Bank Holiday, 26 May; Bank Holiday, 14 July; Bank Holiday, 25 August; Christmas 25/26 December.

TELEPHONE INFORMATION

International Code	Country Code	Main City Area Codes
00	44	Belfast 1232

FRANÇAIS

AUBERGES DE JEUNESSE NORD-IRLANDAISES

Moins visitée que sa voisine, la République d'Irlande, l'Irlande du Nord, avec ses 8 auberges de jeunesse, ne manque cependant pas d'attractions touristiques. Les régions de lacs spectaculaires à l'ouest contrastent avec la côte sauvage et déchiquetée d'Antrim et avec l'unique Giant's Causeway (Chaussée des Géants).

Les auberges sont en principe ouvertes de 7h30 à 11h et de 17h à 23h30, et certaines ouvrent plus longtemps. Une nuit vous coûtera entre 6,00 et 13,00 livres, draps compris. Toutes les auberges offrent la possibilité de cuisiner, sauf celle de Belfast.

La plupart des auberges sont fermées du 22 décembre au 2 janvier, et beaucoup ferment pendant certaines périodes entre novembre et février. Vérifiez avec l'auberge ou YHANI. Toutes les auberges, sauf celle de Barholm, acceptent les réservations d'avance faites par carte de crédit.

PASSEPORTS ET VISAS

Les voyageurs doivent être munis d'un passeport valide. De nos jours, peu de visiteurs doivent avoir un visa mais vérifiez à l'avance.

SOINS MEDICAUX

Il n'est pas nécessaire d'être muni d'un certificat international de vaccination mais il vous est conseillé de vérifier qu'il ne vous en faudra pas un pour rentrer dans votre pays.

Il est essentiel d'être couvert par une assurance maladie car les visiteurs ne peuvent bénéficier que d'un traitement **d'urgence** gratuit dans les services d'accidents et d'urgence des hôpitaux de la Sécurité sociale. Si vous êtes hospitalisé, même à la demande d'un service d'accidents et d'urgence, ou si vous êtes envoyé dans un service de consultations externes, il vous faudra payer, à moins d'être un citoyen d'un pays du Marché commun, de résider dans un pays membre ou d'être un citoyen ou de résider dans un pays ayant passé un accord médical réciproque avec le Royaume-Uni. Il vous est fortement conseillé de souscrire à une police d'assurance avant votre départ.

HEURES D'OUVERTURE DES BANQUES

En général, les banques sont ouvertes en semaine de 9h30 à 15h30, mais beaucoup restent ouvertes une heure de plus. Elles sont toutes fermées le dimanche et les jours fériés.

BUREAUX DE POSTE

Les bureaux de poste sont ouverts en semaine de 9h à 17h30, et le samedi de 9h à 12h30. Ils sont fermés le dimanche et les jours fériés.

HEURES D'OUVERTURE DES MAGASINS

En général, les magasins sont ouverts du lundi au samedi de 9h à 17h30, bien que cela puisse varier dans les grandes villes. Certains magasins restent ouverts tard le mercredi/jeudi/vendredi jusqu'à 20h/21h.

DEPLACEMENTS

Trains

Les itinéraires principaux sont desservis par le train. La carte Emeraude donne droit à des déplacements illimités dans toute l'Irlande, sur les réseaux d'autobus et ferroviaires.

Autobus

Un excellent réseau d'autobus assure des services réguliers et les villes qui ne sont pas sur les lignes de chemin de fer sont particulièrement bien desservies par les autobus. Les billets 'Freedom of Northern Ireland' donnent droit à des déplacements illimités pendant 7 jours à travers l'Irlande du Nord et sont en vente dans les gares d'autobus. La carte Emeraude donne droit à des déplacements illimités dans toute l'Irlande, sur les réseaux d'autobus et ferroviaires.

Automobiles

Vous devez avoir plus de 17 ans si vous voulez conduire une voiture. La conduite est à gauche. Le port des ceintures de sécurité est obligatoire à l'avant et à l'arrière des véhicules, s'ils en sont équipés. Les lois sur l'alcool au volant sont très strictes; ne prenez pas de risques! Les organisations automobiles, dont AA et RAC, offrent, entre autres, des services de dépannage et de recouvrement de véhicule.

JOURS FERIES

Nouvel an, 1er janvier; Vendredi saint, 28 mars; Lundi de Pâques, 31 mars; Fête du travail, 5 mai; Jours fériés, 26 mai, 14 juillet, 25 août; Noël, 25 et 26 décembre.

TELEPHONE

Indicatif International	Indicatif du Pays	Indicatifs régionaux des Villes principales
00	44	Belfast 1232

DEUTSCH

JUGENDHERBERGEN IN NORDIRLAND

Nordirland wird nicht so viel bereist wie die benachbarte Republik, bietet aber ebenfalls viele Sehenswürdigkeiten und 8 Jugendherbergen. Von der wild zerklüfteten Küste von Antrim und dem einmaligen Giant's Causeway hebt sich im Westen eine phantastische Seenlandschaft ab.

Die Herbergen sind gewöhnlich von 07.30-11.00 Uhr und von 17.00-23.30 Uhr, einige auch etwas länger, geöffnet. Es ist mit einem Preis von ca £6,00-13,00 pro Nacht, einschließlich Bettwäsche, zu rechnen. Alle Herbergen haben Einrichtungen für Selbstversorger, außer Belfast.

Die meisten Herbergen sind vom 22.12.-2.1. geschlossen, und viele schließen zwischen November und Februar auch zu anderen Zeiten. Erkundigen Sie sich in der jeweiligen Herberge oder bei der YHANI. Alle Herbergen, außer der in Barholm, nehmen bei Bezahlung mit einer Kreditkarte Voranmeldungen entgegen.

PÄSSE UND VISA

Sie brauchen einen gültigen Reisepaß. Ein Visum wird nur noch von wenigen Reisenden benötigt. Sie sollten sich aber im voraus erkundigen.

GESUNDHEIT

Wer ins Vereinigte Königreich einreist, braucht kein internationales Impfzeugnis, sollte sich aber erkundigen, ob bei der Rückkehr in sein Heimatland eines verlangt wird.

Eine Krankenversicherung ist erforderlich, da Besucher nur in Notfällen Anspruch auf kostenlose Behandlung durch die Unfall- oder Notfallabteilung eines Krankenhauses des National Health Service haben. Wenn Sie (ob von der Unfall- oder Notfallabteilung eines Krankenhauses oder von einem anderen Arzt) zur stationären Behandlung in ein Krankenhaus eingewiesen oder an die ambulante Abteilung überwiesen werden, müssen Sie selbst bezahlen, es sei denn, Sie besitzen die Staatsangehörigkeit eines EU-Landes oder Sie sind in einem Mitgliedsstaat wohnhaft oder Sie besitzen die Staatsangehörigkeit eines Landes, mit dem das Vereinigte Königreich einen gegenseitigen Vertrag über die Gesundheitspflege abgeschlossen hat, bzw Sie sind in einem solchen Land wohnhaft. Wir raten Ihnen dringend zum Abschluß einer ausreichenden Versicherung vor Antritt Ihrer Reise.

GESCHÄFTSSTUNDEN DER BANKEN

Im allgemeinen werktags von 09.30-15.30 Uhr geöffnet, aber viele schließen erst eine Stunde später. An Sonn- und Feiertagen sind alle Banken geschlossen.

POSTÄMTER

Öffnungszeiten: werktags von 09.00-17.30 Uhr und samstags von 09.00-12.30 Uhr. An Sonn- und Feiertagen sind alle Postämter geschlossen.

LADENÖFFNUNGSZEITEN

Im allgemeinen montags bis samstags von 09.00-17.30 Uhr, in größeren Städten oft anders. Einige Geschäfte sind mittwochs/donnerstags/freitags bis 20.00/21.00 Uhr geöffnet.

REISEN

Eisenbahn
Die wichtigsten Orte sind an das Eisenbahnnetz angeschlossen. Es gibt eine 'Emerald Card', die in ganz Irland zu unbeschränkter Benutzung des Bus- und Schienennetzes berechtigt.

Busse
Es gibt ein ausgezeichnetes Linienbusnetz, und zwischen Städten, die nicht mit der Bahn erreicht werden können, gibt es besonders gute Busverbindungen. 'Freedom of Northern Ireland Tickets', die auf Busbahnhöfen erhältlich sind, berechtigen zu siebentägigem unbegrenztem Reisen in ganz Nordirland. Die 'Emerald Card' berechtigt in ganz Irland zu unbeschränkter Benutzung des Bus- und Schienennetzes.

Autofahren
Wer ein Kraftfahrzeug führen will, muß über 17 Jahre alt sein. Es herrscht Linksverkehr. Sowohl auf den Vorder- als auch auf den Rücksitzen müssen im Auto, sofern vorhanden, Sicherheitsgurte angelegt werden. Die Gesetze über das Autofahren nach dem Genuß von Alkohol sind sehr streng - unterlassen Sie es daher! Die AA und der RAC sind nur zwei Kraftfahrzeugorganisationen, die u.a. einen Pannen- und Rückführdienst bieten.

FEIERTAGE

Neujahr, 1. Januar; Karfreitag, 28. März; Ostermontag, 31. März; Maitag, 5. Mai; Bankfeiertag, 26. Mai; Bankfeiertag, 14. Juli; Bankfeiertag, 25. August; Weihnachten, 25/26. Dezember

FERNSPRECHINFORMATIONEN

Internationale Kennzahl	Landes-Kennzahl	größere Städte - Ortsnetzkennzahlen
00	44	Belfast 1232

ESPAÑOL

ALBERGUES DE JUVENTUD DE IRLANDA DEL NORTE

Menos concurrida por los turistas que la vecina República de Irlanda, Irlanda del Norte con sus 8 albergues juveniles tiene un gran atractivo propio. Los espectaculares paisajes de lagos del oeste del país contrastan con la agreste y rocosa costa de Antrim y el singular Arrecife de los Gigantes.

Los albergues suelen abrir de 07.30 a 11.00 horas y de 17.00 a 23.30 horas, ofreciendo algunos un horario más amplio. Se paga alrededor de £6,00-13,00 por noche incluyendo ropa de cama. Todos los albergues tienen cocina para huéspedes, salvo el de Belfast.

La mayor parte de los albergues cierra entre el 22 de diciembre y el 2 de enero y algunos cierran en determinados períodos de noviembre y febrero. Confírmelo con el albergue deseado o con YHANI. Todos los albergues aceptan reservas anticipadas con tarjeta de crédito, salvo el de Barholm.

PASAPORTES Y VISADOS

Se necesita un pasaporte válido. En la actualidad muy pocos visitantes requieren visado, pero se recomienda confirmarlo con antelación.

SANIDAD

Para entrar en el Reino Unido no se precisa un Certificado Internacional de Vacunación, pero se aconseja verificar la necesidad de presentar uno al regresar a su país de origen.

Un seguro médico es fundamental porque los visitantes sólo tienen derecho a tratamiento gratuito de **urgencia** en el departamento de Accidentes y Urgencias de los hospitales del Servicio Nacional de Sanidad. Si se le ingresa en un hospital como paciente interno, aunque venga del departamento de urgencias, o se le manda a una consulta para pacientes externos, se le pedirá que pague el coste del servicio a menos que sea ciudadano de un país de la CE, residente en cualquier país miembro, o ciudadano o residente en un país que tenga un acuerdo de asistencia sanitaria mutua con el Reino Unido. Se recomienda encarecidamente suscribir un seguro adecuado antes de viajar al Reino Unido.

HORARIO DE BANCOS

Por lo general abren los días laborables de 09.30 a 15.30 horas, aunque muchos están abiertos una hora más. Todos los bancos cierran los domingos y festivos.

CASAS DE CORREO

Abren los días laborables de 09.00 a 17.30 horas y los sábados de 09.00 a 12.30 horas. Todas cierran los domingos y festivos.

HORARIO COMERCIAL

Por lo general las tiendas abren de lunes a sábado de 09.00 a 17.30 horas, aunque el horario puede variar en las poblaciones más importantes. Algunas tiendas abren hasta más tarde los miércoles/jueves/viernes hasta las 20.00/21.00 horas.

DESPLAZAMIENTOS

Tren
Las principales rutas están cubiertas por servicios de tren. Se puede comprar un pase Emerald Card que permite viajar de forma ilimitada por toda Irlanda en tren y en autobús.

Autobús
Existe una excelente red de servicios regulares de autobús que es especialmente buena entre las poblaciones a las que no se llega en tren. Los billetes Freedom of Northern Ireland permiten viajar de forma ilimitada durante 7 días por toda Irlanda del Norte y se pueden comprar en las estaciones de autobús. El pase Emerald Card permite viajar de forma ilimitada por toda Irlanda en tren y en autobús.

Coche
Para conducir un automóvil hay que ser mayor de 17 años. La conducción es por la izquierda de la carretera. Es obligatorio llevar cinturones de seguridad en los asientos delanteros y en los traseros de haberlos. La legislación sobre conducción bajo efectos del alcohol es muy estricta ¡No se arriesgue! La AA y la RAC son dos de las organizaciones de automovilismo que ofrecen, entre otros, servicios de asistencia en carretera y de grúa.

DIAS FESTIVOS

Año Nuevo, 1 enero; Viernes Santo, 28 marzo; Lunes de Pascua, 31 marzo; Fiesta de Mayo, 5 mayo; Día Festivo, 26 mayo; Día Festivo, 14 julio; Día Festivo, 25 agosto; Navidad 25 y 26 diciembre.

INFORMACION TELEFONICA

Código Internacional	Código Nacional	Indicativo de área de las Ciudades principales
00	44	Belfast 1232

DISCOUNTS AND CONCESSIONS

Stena Line: 10% reduction on passenger fares; Belfast - Stranraer. Contact YHANI office for details.
Car+Van Hire:
McCausland Car Hire, Grosvenor Rd, Belfast; **Carriageway Cars**, 92 Bloomfield Road, Belfast, BTS 5LU. 10% off
Other local discounts are available on outdoor equipment and attractions.

Hostels in this country may also display this symbol.

Les auberges de ce pays pourront également afficher ce symbole.

Jugendherbergen in diesem Land können auch dieses Symbol zeigen.

Es posible que los albergues de este país exhiban además este símbolo.

Armagh City ⛺ CC 39 Abbey Street, Armagh, BT61 1EB ☎ (1232) 324733 **FAX** (1232) 439699 **Open:** Su 97 ⇌ 64 ● £7.00-13 .00 ⑩ ☞ ♂♀ ♿ ▣ ♨ 🅿 ⮷ ✈ Belfast International 5km

Belfast International ⛺ 2SE IBN CC 22 Donegall Rd, Belfast BT12 5JN. ☎ (1232) 324733 **FAX** (1232) 439699 **Open:** 24hrs ⇌ 128 ● £12.00-13.00 ⑩ ☞ ♂♀ ♿ ▣ ♨ 🅿 ⮷ ✈ Belfast International 30km 🚢 Larne Harbour 35.7km, Donegall Quay 3.2km 🚌 Central 5km 🚆 89, 90 from City centre ap YH R

BELFAST - International

Castle Archdale ⛺ IBN CC Irvinestown, Co Fermanagh BT94 1PP. ☎ (13656) 28118 ⇌ 55 ● £6.00-7.00 ⑩ (Advance booking YH) ☞ ♂♀ ⚒ ▣ ♨ 🅿 ⮷ ⚓ 🚌 Kesh 3.2km R

Cushendall ⛺ IBN CC Layde Rd, Cushendall, Co Antrim BT44 0NQ. ☎ (12667) 71344 **FAX** (12667) 72042 ⇌ 56 ● £6.00-7.00 ⑩ ☞ ♂♀ ♨ 🅿 ⚓ 🚌 1.6km ap Cushendall R

Londonderry ⛺ IBN CC The Oakgrove Manor, Derry YH, 4-6 Magazine St, Londonderry BT48 6HJ. ☎ (1504) 372273 **FAX** (1504) 372409 **Open:** 1.1-23.12; 27-31.12 ⇌ 120 ⑩(B) ☞ ♂♀ ♿ ▣ ⮷ ⚓ 🚌 1.5km R

Newcastle ⛺ IBN CC 30 Downs Rd, Newcastle, Co Down BT33 0AG. ☎ (13967) 22133 **FAX** (13967) 22133 ⇌ 40 ● £6.00-7.00 ⑩ ☞ ♂♀ ▣ ♨ 🅿 ⚓ 🚌 1.5km 🚆 150m

Portaferry ⛺ Barholm, 11 The Strand, Portaferry, Co Down BT22 1PS. ☎ (12477) 29598 **FAX** (12477) 29598 ⇌ 42 ⑩(B) ♂♀ ♿ ▣ ♨ 🅿 ✈ Belfast 550m 🚢 Belfast 320m 🚌 Belfast Central 320m 🚆 10, Belfast Oxford St 320m R

Whitepark Bay ⛺ IBN CC 157 Whitepark Bay Rd, Ballintoy, Ballycastle, Co Antrim BT54 6NH. ☎ (12657) 31745 **FAX** (12657) 32034 ⇌ 62 ● £7.00-13.00 ⑩(B D) ☞ ♂♀ ♿ ▣ 🅿 ⮷ ✈ Belfast International 80km R

IRELAND (REPUBLIC OF)
IRLANDE (REPUBLIQUE D')
IRLAND
IRLANDA (REPUBLICA DE)

An Óige, Irish Youth Hostel Association,
61 Mountjoy Street, Dublin 7, Republic of Ireland.

☎ (353) (1) 8304555
FAX (353) (1) 8305808

Office Hours: Monday-Friday, 09.30-17.30hrs.
Also Saturday (1.4-30.9) 10.00-12.30hrs.

Travel Section: c/o An Óige,
Irish Youth Hostel Association,
61 Mountjoy Street, Dublin 7, Republic of Ireland.

☎ (353) (1) 8304555
FAX (353) (1) 8305808

Capital:	Dublin
Language:	English/Irish
Currency:	IR£ (Irish punt)
Population:	3,356,000
Size:	70,283 sq km

IRELAND (Republic of)

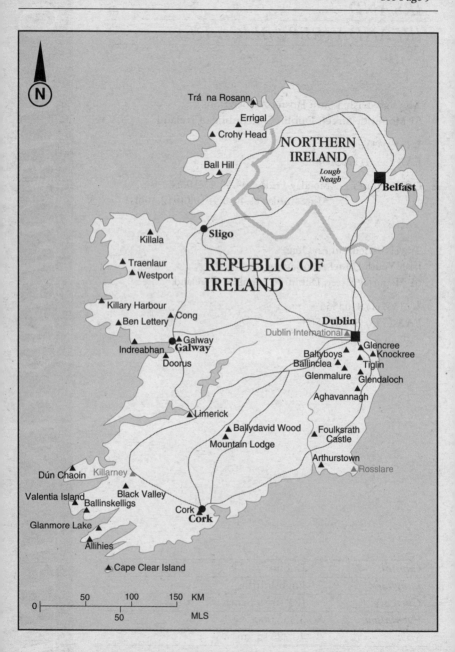

N

Trá na Rosann
▲ Errigal
▲ Crohy Head

NORTHERN
IRELAND
Lough Neagh
■ **Belfast**

▲ Ball Hill

▲ Killala
● **Sligo**

REPUBLIC OF
IRELAND

▲ Traenlaur
▲ Westport

▲ Killary Harbour
▲ Cong
▲ Ben Lettery

● **Dublin**
Dublin International ▲

Indreabhan ▲ ● Galway
Galway
▲ Glencree
▲ Knockree
Baltyboys ▲
Ballinclea ▲ ▲ Tiglin
Glenmalure ▲
▲ Glendaloch
▲ Doorus
▲ Aghavannagh

▲ Limerick

▲ Ballydavid Wood
Mountain Lodge

▲ Foulksrath
Castle

Arthurstown
▲   ▲ Rosslare

Dún Chaoin   Killarney

Valentia Island ▲
▲ Black Valley
▲ Ballinskelligs
Cork ▲
Cork

Glanmore Lake ▲

▲ Allihies

▲ Cape Clear Island

0 ├─── 50 ──── 100 ──── 150 ┤ KM
       ├──── 50 ────┤   MLS

ENGLISH

REPUBLIC OF IRELAND HOSTELS

The hospitality of the Irish is world renowned, and hostels are no exception. There are Youth Hostels in all major tourist areas.

There is access to hostels all day. Hostels with "*" next to their opening dates are also open weekends throughout the year. Dublin International Hostel is open 24 hours and Rosslare operates special opening times to coincide with ferry schedules. All hostels have self-catering facilities and most provide meals if advance notice is given. On average expect to pay in the region of IR£4.00-7.00, however the overnight fee including breakfast is IR£9.50 in Dublin and IR£8.00 in Galway.

PASSPORTS AND VISAS

With the exception of nationals of the United Kingdom a valid passport or National Identity card is required.

EC nationals and those from the following countries do not require a visa: Andorra, Austria, Cyprus, Czech & Slovak Republics, Finland, Hungary, Iceland, Liechtenstein, Malta, Norway, San Marino, Sweden, Switzerland and Vatican City.

HEALTH

Visitors from the United Kingdom are entitled to urgent medical treatment without charge, when it is obtained at a public hospital or from a doctor participating in the General Medical Service Scheme. Evidence of residence in the UK is required - for example, Social Security documentation, driving licence.

Visitors from other EC member states are entitled to urgent medical treatment without charge, provided that they present the EC form E111 which should be obtained from the health authorities of their own country before travelling.

Visitors from countries outside the EC may be charged for any treatment.

BANKING HOURS

Monday, Tuesday, Wednesday and Friday 10.00-16.00hrs. Thursday only, 10.00-17.00hrs.

POST OFFICES

Post offices are open Monday to Friday, 09.00-17.30hrs, however some are closed between 13.00 and 14.15hrs for lunch.

SHOPPING HOURS

Normally 09.00/09.30-17.30/18.00hrs. There is late night shopping on Thursday until 20.00hrs. Some provincial towns may have an early closing day but this will vary.

TRAVEL

Air
Good internal network operated by AER Lingus.

Rail
Irish Rail operates services to all main cities and towns.

Bus
Good bus services: Irish Bus (Bus Éireann) provides a nationwide network service. Irish Bus and/or Rambler tickets, Dublin Explorer tickets are available, as well as the Overlander ticket for travel to Northern Ireland.

Ferry
There are ferry services from various ports in Great Britain and France to Dublin, Dun
Laoghaire, Rosslare and Cork.

Driving
Driving is on the left. Seat belts must be worn in the front and back.

PUBLIC HOLIDAYS

New Year's Day, 1 January; St Patrick's Day, 17 March; Good Friday, 28 March; Easter
Monday, 31 March; May Bank Holiday, 5 May; June Bank Holiday, 2 June; August Bank
Holiday, 4 August; October Bank Holiday, 27 October; Christmas, 25/26 December.

TELEPHONE INFORMATION

International Code	Country Code	Main City Area Codes	
00	353	Dublin	1
		Cork	21
		Limerick	61
		Galway	91

FRANÇAIS

AUBERGES DE JEUNESSE EN REPUBLIQUE IRLANDAISE

Les Irlandais sont connus dans le monde entier pour leur hospitalité, et les auberges ne font pas
exception à la règle. Il y a des auberges dans toutes les principales régions touristiques.

L'entrée dans les auberges est possible toute la journée. Les auberges dont les dates d'ouverture
sont accompagnées de "*" sont aussi ouvertes pendant le weekend toute l'année. L'auberge
internationale de Dublin est ouverte 24 heures sur 24 et celle de Rosslare a des heures
d'ouverture spéciales pour coïncider avec les horaires des bateaux. Toutes les auberges ont des
cuisines pour les voyageurs et la plupart servent des repas s'ils sont commandés à l'avance. En
principe, une nuit vous coûtera entre 4,00 et 7,00 £IR. En revanche, la nuitée, petit déjeuner
compris, est de 9.50 £IR à l'auberge de Dublin et de 8 £IR à l'auberge de Galway.

PASSEPORTS ET VISAS

A l'exception des citoyens du Royaume-Uni, les voyageurs doivent être munis d'un passeport
ou d'une carte d'identité nationale valide.

Les citoyens de la CE et ceux des pays suivants n'ont pas besoin de visa: Andorre, Autriche,
Chypre, les Républiques tchèque et slovaque, Finlande, Hongrie, Islande, Liechtenstein, Malte,
Norvège, Saint-Marin, Suède, Suisse et Cité du Vatican.

SOINS MEDICAUX

Les visiteurs du Royaume-Uni ont droit à un traitement médical d'urgence gratuit quand
celui-ci a été administré dans un hôpital public ou par un médecin participant au Plan Général
de Service Médical (General Medical Service Scheme). Il vous faudra fournir la preuve que vous
résidez au Royaume-Uni en présentant, par exemple, des papiers de Sécurité Sociale ou un
permis de conduire britannique.

Les visiteurs provenant d'autres pays de la CE. ont droit au traitement médical d'urgence
gratuit, à condition de présenter le formulaire E111 de la CE qui doit être obtenu auprès des
autorités médicales de leurs pays respectifs avant leur départ.

Les visiteurs provenant de pays en dehors de la CE. devront peut-être payer pour tout
traitement médical reçu.

HEURES D'OUVERTURE DES BANQUES

Les banques sont ouvertes les lundi, mardi, mercredi et vendredi de 10h à 16h. Le jeudi, elles ouvrent de 10h à 17h.

BUREAUX DE POSTE

Les bureaux de poste sont ouverts du lundi au vendredi, de 9h à 17h30, mais ferment entre 13h et 14h15.

HEURES D'OUVERTURE DES MAGASINS

Les magasins sont normalement ouverts de 9h/9h30 à 17h30/18h. Ils sont ouverts plus tard le jeudi, jusqu'à 20h. Dans certaines villes de province, il se peut que les magasins ferment tôt un jour par semaine, mais cela varie.

DEPLACEMENTS

Avions
Bonnes liaisons intérieures assurées par AER Lingus.

Trains
Irish Rail assure des services à destination de toutes les grandes villes.

Autobus
Les services d'autobus sont bons: Irish Bus (Bus Éireann) assure un service sur l'ensemble du territoire national. Vous pourrez vous procurer des billets Irish Bus et/ou Rambler, des billets Dublin Explorer de même que des billets Overlander pour vous rendre en Irlande du Nord.

Ferry-boats
Des lignes maritimes, en partance de plusieurs ports britanniques et français, assurent des services à destination de Dublin, Dun Laoghaire, Rosslare et Cork.

Automobiles
Les véhicules roulent à gauche. Le port des ceintures de sécurité est obligatoire à l'avant et à l'arrière.

JOURS FERIES

Nouvel an, 1er janvier; Fête de Saint Patrick, 17 mars; Vendredi Saint, 28 mars; Lundi de Pâques, 31 mars; Fête du Travail, 5 mai; Jour férié, 2 juin; Jour férié, 4 août; Jour férié, 27 octobre; Noël, 25/26 décembre.

TELEPHONE

Indicatif International	Indicatif du Pays	Indicatifs régionaux des Villes principales	
00	353	Dublin	1
		Cork	21
		Limerick	61
		Galway	91

DEUTSCH

JUGENDHERBERGEN IN DER REPUBLIK IRLAND

Die Gastfreundschaft der Iren ist weltbekannt, und sie erstreckt sich auch auf Jugendherbergen. In allen bekannten Fremdenverkehrsgebieten gibt es Herbergen.

Die Herbergen sind den ganzen Tag über zugänglich. Wenn neben den Öffnungszeiten ein "*" steht, ist die betreffende Herberge ganzjährig auch am Wochenende geöffnet. Dublin International Hostel ist 24 Stunden geöffnet, und die Herberge in Rosslare hat besondere Öffnungszeiten, die den Fahrplänen der Fähren angepaßt sind. Alle Herbergen haben Einrichtungen für Selbstversorger, und in den meisten sind bei Vorbestellung auch Mahlzeiten erhältlich. Durchschnittlich ist mit einem Preis von ca IR£4,00-7,00 zu rechnen. In Dublin beträgt der Übernachtungspreis, einschließlich Frühstück, IR£9,50 und in Galway IR£8,00.

PÄSSE UND VISA

Mit Ausnahme von Staatsbürgern des Vereinigten Königreichs, brauchen alle Reisenden einen gültigen Reisepaß oder einen Personalausweis.

Staatsangehörige eines EG-Landes oder folgender Länder brauchen kein Visum: Andorra, Finnland, Island, Liechtenstein, Malta, Norwegen, Österreich, San Marino, Schweden, Schweiz, Tschechische und Slowakische Republik, Ungarn, Vatikanstadt und Zypern.

GESUNDHEIT

Besucher vom Vereinigten Königreich haben in Notfällen Anspruch auf kostenlose Behandlung, wenn sie in einem öffentlichen Krankenhaus oder von einem Arzt, der am "General Medical Service Scheme" beteiligt ist, behandelt werden. Sie müssen beweisen, daß sie im Vereinigten Königreich wohnhaft sind, zum Beispiel durch Sozialhilfepapier, Führerschein.

Besucher aus anderen EG-Länder haben Anspruch in Notfällen auf kostenlose Behandlung, wenn sie das EG-Formular E111, das sie im eigenen Land vor der Reise erwerben sollten, vorlegen.

Besucher aus Länder außerhalb der EG müssen die Behandlung selbst bezahlen.

GESCHÄFTSSTUNDEN DER BANKEN

Montags, dienstags, mittwochs und freitags von 10.00-16.00 Uhr, nur. donnerstags von 10.00-17.00 Uhr.

POSTÄMTER

Postämter sind montags bis freitags von 09.00-17.30 Uhr geöffnet, zwischen 13.00 und 14.15 Uhr findet aber eine Mittagspause statt.

LADENÖFFNUNGSZEITEN

Gewöhnlich von 09.00/09.30-17.30/18.00 Uhr. Donnerstags sind die Geschäfte bis 20.00 Uhr geöffnet. In einigen Provinzstädten sind die Geschäfte an einem Tag der Woche (nicht überall am gleichen Tag) nachmittags geschlossen.

REISEN

Flugverkehr
AER Lingus bietet gute Flugverbindungen.

Eisenbahn
Irish Rail bietet Eisenbahnverbindungen in allen größeren Städte.

Busse
Gute Busverbindungen: Irish Bus (Bus Eireann) bietet einen landesweiten Busverkehr. Es gibt Irish Bus und/oder Rambler Tickets, Dublin Explorer Tickets und für Reisen nach Nordirland Overlander Tickets.

Fähren
Es gibt einen Fährenverkehr zwischen verschiedenen Häfen in Großbritannien und Frankreich und Dublin, Dun Laoghaire, Rosslare und Cork.

Autofahren

Es herrscht Linksverkehr. Sowohl auf den Vorder- als auch auf den Rücksitzen müssen Sicherheitsgurte angelegt werden.

FEIERTAGE

Neujahr, 1. Januar; St Patrick's Day, 17. März; Karfreitag, 28. März; Ostermontag, 31. März; Mai Bankfeiertag, 5 Mai; Juni-Bankfeiertag, 2. Juni; August-Bankfeiertag, 4. August; Oktober-Bankfeiertag, 27. Oktober; Weihnachten, 25./26. Dezember.

FERNSPRECHINFORMATIONEN

Internationale Kennzahl	Landes- Kennzahl	größere Städte - Ortsnetzkennzahlen	
00	353	Dublin	1
		Cork	21
		Limerick	61
		Galway	91

ESPAÑOL

ALBERGUES DE JUVENTUD DE LA REPUBLICA DE IRLANDA

La hospitalidad de los irlandeses es conocida en todo el mundo y los albergues no son excepción. Hay albergues de juventud en todos los principales puntos turísticos del país.

Se puede acceder a los albergues durante todo el día. Los albergues que tengan "*" junto a sus fechas de apertura también están abiertos todos los fines de semana del año. El Albergue Internacional de Dublín está abierto 24 horas al día y el de Rosslare tiene un horario especial de apertura que coincide con el de los ferrys. Todos los albergues disponen de cocina para huéspedes y la mayoría sirven comidas si se avisa con suficiente antelación. Se paga alrededor de IR£4,00-7,00, si bien la tarifa de noche incluyendo desayuno es de IR£9,50 en Dublín y IR£8,00 en Galway.

PASAPORTES Y VISADOS

A excepción de los ciudadanos del Reino Unido, se requiere un pasaporte o documento nacional de identidad válido.

Los ciudadanos de países de la CE y de los siguientes países no requieren visado: Andorra, Austria, Chipre, Repúblicas Checa y Eslovaca, Finlandia, Hungría, Islandia, Liechtenstein, Malta, Noruega, San Marino, Suecia, Suiza y Ciudad del Vaticano.

SANIDAD

Los visitantes del Reino Unido tienen derecho a tratamiento médico de urgencia sin coste alguno cuando este se reciba en un hospital público o por un médico del Proyecto de Servicio Médico General (General Medical Service Scheme). Se requiere evidencia que demuestre su residencia en el Reino Unido, por ejemplo, documentos expedidos por la seguridad social, permiso de conducir.

Los visitantes de otros estados miembros de la CE. tienen derecho a tratamiento médico de urgencia sin coste, a condición de presentar el formulario E111 de la CE, el cual se debe solicitar a las autoridades sanitarias de sus respectivos países antes de viajar.

A los visitantes de países fuera de la CE. se les puede cobrar el tratamiento médico.

HORARIO DE BANCOS

Lunes, martes, miércoles y viernes de 10.00 a 16.00 horas. Jueves de 10.00 a 17.00 horas.

CASAS DE CORREO

Las casas de correo abren de lunes a viernes de 09.00 a 17.30 horas, estando cerradas entre 13.00 y 14.15 horas para el almuerzo.

HORARIO COMERCIAL

El horario normal es de 09.00/09.30 a 17.30/18.00 horas. Las tiendas abren hasta más tarde los jueves, 20.00 horas. Algunas poblaciones provinciales tienen un día que cierran antes, pero varía de una a otra.

DESPLAZAMIENTOS

Avión

Existe una buena red aérea nacional operada por AER Lingus.

Tren

La compañía ferroviaria Irish Rail ofrece servicios a todas las ciudades y poblaciones importantes.

Autobús

Buenos servicios de autobús: la compañía Irish Bus (Bus Éireann) presta servicios a través de una red nacional. Se pueden comprar billetes Irish Bus/Rambler, Dublin Explorer, así como el billete Overlander para viajar a Irlanda del Norte.

Ferry

Hay servicios de ferry desde varios puertos de Gran Bretaña y de Francia a Dublín, Dun Laoghaire, Rosslare y Cork.

Coche

La conducción es por la izquierda. Hay que llevar cinturones de seguridad en los asientos delanteros y traseros.

DIAS FESTIVOS

Año Nuevo, 1 enero; Día de San Patricio, 17 marzo; Viernes Santo, 28 marzo; Lunes de Pascua, 31 marzo; Fiesta de Mayo, 5 mayo; Fiesta de Junio, 2 junio; Fiesta de Agosto, 4 agosto; Fiesta de Octubre, 27 octubre; Navidad, 25/26 diciembre.

INFORMACION TELEFONICA

Código Internacional	Código Nacional	Indicativo de área de las Ciudades principales	
00	353	Dublín	1
		Cork	21
		Limerick	61
		Galway	91

DISCOUNTS AND CONCESSIONS

Use your membership card to save on admission charges, equipment and activities near hostels, as well as the following national discounts:

Island Ferries TEO: 10% off round trip to Aran Islands.
Island Ferry Service: 14% off return Baltimore to Cape Clear.
Irish Ferries: 20% discount to adult foot passengers.
Stena Sealink: 20% discount to adult foot passengers.

Discount on various visitor centres thoughout Ireland.
Discount off ticket prices at Abbey and Peacock Theatres in Dublin.

Hostels in this country may also display
this symbol.

*Les auberges de ce pays pourront également
afficher ce symbole.*

Jugendherbergen in diesem Land
können auch dieses Symbol zeigen.

*Es posible que los albergues de este país exhiban
además este símbolo.*

Aghavannagh Aghavannagh House,
Aughrim, Co Wicklow. ☎ (402) 36102,
Members: (402) 36366 (WDN) **Open:**
07.00-10.30hrs, 17.00-24.00hrs,
1.3-30.11 (weekends all year) ⬦ 60 ⬤
IR£4.50-6.50 ♂ 👫 ⌂ 🅿 🚻
Rathdrum 26km 🚌 Laragh 13km,
Hacketstown 12km **Ⓡ** (An Óige
office)

Allihies Cahermeelabo Allihies, Beara,
Co Cork. ☎ (27) 73014 **Open:**
07.00-10.30hrs, 17.00-24.00hrs,
1.6-30.9 ⬦ 34 ⬤ IR£4.00-6.00 ♂ 👫
🔲 ⌂ 🅿 ♿ ⚓ ✈ Cork 96km 🚢 Cork
96km 🚻 Killarney 90km 🚌 Private
bus Co. ☎ (27) 70007 18km

Arthurstown Coastguard Station,
Arthurstown, Co Wexford. ☎ (51)
389411 **Open:** 07.00-10.30hrs,
17.00-24.00hrs, 1.6-30.9 ⬦ 38 ⬤
IR£4.50-6.50 ♂ 👫 ⌂ 🅿 ⚓ 🚢
Passage East to Bally Hack 1.5km to
YH 🚻 Campile 8km 🚌 from
Waterford to Passage East

Ball Hill Donegal Town, Donegal. ☎
(73) 21174 **FAX** (73) 21174 **Open:**
07.00-24.00hrs, 1.4-30.9 ⬦ 66 ⬤
IR£4.50-6.50 ♂ 👫 ⌂ 🅿 ⚓ 🚻 Sligo
70km 🚌 Sligo to Donegal to
Killybegs 1km to YH

Ballinclea Donard, Co Wicklow. ☎ (45)
404657 **Open:** 07.00-10.30hrs,
17.00-24.00hrs, 1.3-30.11 (weekends
all year) ⬦ 40 ⬤ IR£4.00-6.00 ♂ 🅿
🚻 Newbridge 32km 🚌 65 from
City Centre to Donard 5km to YH **Ⓡ**
(An Óige office)

Ballinskelligs Prior House,
Ballinskelligs, Co Kerry. ☎ (66) 79229
Open: 07.00-10.30hrs, 17.00-24.00hrs,
1.4-30.9 ⬦ 24 ⬤ IR£4.00-6.00 ♂ ⌂
🅿 ⚓ 🚻 Killarney 77km 🚌
Killarney to Caherciveen 18km to YH

Ballydavid Wood House Glen of
Aherlow, Bansha, Co Tipperary. ☎ (62)
54148 **Open:** 07.00-10.30hrs,
17.00-24.00hrs, 1.3-30.11 (weekends
all year) ⬦ 40 ⬤ IR£4.50-6.50 🍴 ♂
⌂ 🅿 🚢 Rosslare Harbour 148km
🚻 Cahir 10km, Limerick Junction
16km 🚌 Limerick to Cahir
ap Tankerstown Cross

Baltyboys Blessington, Co Wicklow. ☎
(45) 867266 **Open:** 07.00-10.30hrs,
17.00-24.00hrs, 1.3-30.11 (weekends
all year) ⬦ 36 ⬤ IR£4.00-6.00 ♂ 🅿
⚓ 🚌 65 to Ballymore Eustace
ap Burgage Cross 3km to YH **Ⓡ** (An
Óige office)

Ben Lettery Clifden, Co Galway. ☎ (95)
51136 **FAX** (95) 51136 **Open:**
07.00-10.30hrs, 17.00-24.00hrs,
Easter-30.9 ⬦ 50 ⬤ IR£4.50-6.50 ♂
🅿 🚻 Galway 64km 🚌 Galway to
Clifden ap YH

Black Valley Beaufort, Killarney, Co
Kerry. 📞 (64) 34712 **Open:**
07.00-10.30hrs, 17.00-24.00hrs 📨 50
⬤ IR£4.50-6.50 🍴 👕 👫 🚿 🅿 🚌
Killarney 19km 🚌 Killarney 19km

Cape Clear Island South Harbour, Cape
Clear Island, Skibbereen, Co Cork. 📞
(28) 39144 **Open:** 07.00-10.30hrs,
17.00-24.00hrs, Easter-31.10 📨 48 ⬤
IR£4.50-6.50 🍴 🚇 ⛴ Baltimore 🚌
Cork 100km 🚌 Skibbereen to
Baltimore

Cong Lisloughrey, Quay Rd, Cong, Co
Mayo. 📞 (92) 46089 **FAX** (92) 46448
Open: 07.00-24.00hrs 📨 118 ⬤
IR£5.00-7.00 🍴(B) 👕 👫 🚇 🅿 🚲 ⚓
🚌 Galway 39km 🚌 Clifden or
Galway to Cong 2km

Cork 2W CC 1-2 Redclyffe, Western
Rd, Cork. 📞 (21) 543396 Members
FAX (21) 343715 **Open:**
07.00-23.45hrs 📨 110 ⬤
IR£5.00-7.00 🍴(B) 👕 🅿 🚲 ✈ Cork
8km A🚌 to Cork City Centre ⛴
Cork 16km 🚌 Cork 5km 🚌 No 8
from Patrick St ap YH

07.00-10.30hrs,   17.00-24.00hrs,
Easter-30.9 📨 36 ⬤ IR£4.00-6.00 👕
👫 🅿 🚌 Derry 98km 🚌 Derry or
Dublin to Dungloe YH 10km from
Dungloe

Doorus House Kinvara, Co Galway. 📞
(91) 37512 Warden, (91) 37173
Members **FAX** (91) 37512 **Open:**
07.00-24.00hrs   📨   56   ⬤
IR£4.50-6.50 🍴(B) 👕 🏠 🅿 🚌
Galway 30km 🚌 Galway to
Ballyvaughan ap Nogra Cross 3km to YH

Dublin - Dublin International (*see town
plan on next page*) 2NW IBN CC 61
Mountjoy St., Dublin 7. 📞 (1) 8301766
FAX (1) 8301600 📨 400 ⬤
IR£7.50-9.50 BB inc 🍴(B D) 👕 👫 ♿ 🅿
🚲 ✈ Dublin 10km A🚌 to City
Centre 🚌 10 N-bound ap YH

Dún Chaoin Ballyferriter, Tralee, Co
Kerry. 📞 (66) 56121 Warden, (66)
56145 Members **FAX** (66) 56355
Open: 07.00-10.30hrs, 17.00-24.00hrs
📨 60 ⬤ IR£5.00-7.00 🍴(B) 👕 👫 🅿
🚌 Tralee 64km 🚌 Tralee to Dingle
with connecting bus to YH

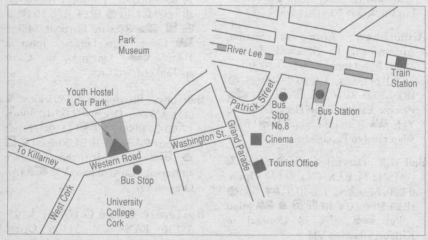

CORK

Crohy Head Dungloe, Lifford, Co
Donegal. 📞 (75) 21950 **Open:**

Errigal Dunlewy, Gweedore,
Letterkenny, Co Donegal. 📞 (75) 31180

Open: 07.00-10.30hrs, 17.00-24.00hrs 🚲 46 ⊝ IR£4.50-6.50 ⚑ 👬 🅿 🚌 Derry 177km 🚌 Derry to Letterkenny to Bunbeg ap Dunlewy Cross YH 3km

Foulksrath Castle Jenkinstown, Co Kilkenny. 📞 (56) 67144 Warden, (56) 67674 Members **FAX** (56) 67144 **Open:** 07.00-10.30hrs, 17.00-24.00hrs, 1.3-31.10 (weekends all year) 🚲 50 ⊝ IR£4.00-6.00 ⚑ ⛺ 🅿 🚲 🚌 Kilkenny 12km 🚌 Kilkenny to Ballyragget ap Conahy Cross 1km to YH

Galway CC⊃ St Mary's College, St Mary's Rd, Galway. 📞 (91) 527411 **FAX** (91) 528710 **Open:** 24.6-24.8 🚲 178 ⊝ IR£8.00 BB inc ⚑ 🅿 ✈ Shannon 20km 🚌 Galway 🅡 (Shut: An Óige office)

Glanmore Lake Lauragh, Killarney, Co Kerry. 📞 (64) 83181 **Open:** 07.00-10.30hrs, 17.00-23.00hrs, 30.3-30.9 🚲 36 ⊝ IR£4.00-6.00 ⚑ 🅿 🚌 Killarney 56km 🚌 Kenmare to Castletownbere ap Lauragh 6km to YH

Glencree Stone House, Glencree, Enniskerry, Co Wicklow. 📞 (1) 2864037 **Open:** 07.00-10.30hrs, 17.00-23.00hrs 🚲 40 ⊝ IR£4.00-6.00 ⚑ 🚌 Bray 16km 🚌 44 to Enniskerry 12km, 185 from Bray Station to Shop River 10km to YH 🅡 (An Óige office)

Glendaloch The Lodge, Glendalough, Co Wicklow. 📞 (404) 45342 Warden, (404) 45143 Members **FAX** (404) 45342 **Open:** 07.00-10.30hrs, 17.00-24.00hrs 🚲 46 ⊝ IR£4.50-6.50 ⚑ 🅿 🚌 Rathdrum 13km or Bray 29km 🚌 St Kevins to Glendalough from Dublin or Bray 🅡 (An Óige office)

Glenmalure Greenane, Co Wicklow. **Open:** 07.00-10.30hrs, 17.00-23.00hrs, 1.7-31.8 (weekends all year) 🚲 16 ⊝ IR£4.00-6.00 ⚑ 🅿 🚌 Rathdrum 16km 🚌 St Kevins from Bray or St Stephens Green (Dublin) 14km 🅡 (An Óige office)

Indreabhán Inverin, Co Galway. 📞 (91) 593154 **FAX** (91) 553638 **Open:** 07.00-10.30hrs, 17.00-24.00hrs 🚲 44 ⊝ IR£5.00-7.00 ⚑ 👬 🅿 🚌 Galway 31km 🚌 Galway to Carraroe ap YH

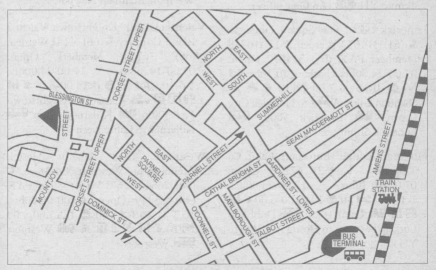

DUBLIN - International YH

Killala Killala House, Killala, Co Mayo.
 (96) 32172 **Open:** 07.00-10.30hrs,
17.00-24.00hrs   50
IR£4.50-6.50   P Ballina
13km Ballina to Killala to YH

Killarney IBN CC Aghadoe House,
Killarney, Co Kerry. (64) 31240
Warden, (64) 33355 Members **FAX**
(64) 34300 **Open:** 07.00-24.00hrs,
checkout 10.30hrs   220
IR£5.00-7.00 (B)   P
 Killarney 5km Courtesy
service to YH from

Killary Harbour Rosroe, Renvyle, Co
Galway. (95) 43417 **Open:**
07.00-10.30hrs,   17.00-24.00hrs,
1.3-30.9 (weekends all year) 44
IR£4.50-6.50   P Galway
82km Galway to Renvyle
ap Salruck YH 5km

Knockree Lacken House, Knockree,
Enniskerry, Co Wicklow. (1)
2864036 **Open:** 07.00-10.30hrs,
17.00-24.00hrs   56
IR£4.00-5.50 P Bray 13km
 44 Dublin to Enniskerry 6.5km,
185 from Bray Station to Shop River
4km to YH **R** (An Óige office)

Limerick CC 1 Pery Square, Limerick.
 (61) 314672 Warden, (61) 410718
Members **FAX** (61) 314672 **Open:**
07.00-24.00hrs, checkout 10.30hrs
66 IR£5.00-7.00 (B)
Shannon 24km A to Limerick City
Centre Limerick 500m
Limerick 500m

Mountain Lodge Burncourt, Cahir, Co
Tipperary. (52) 67277 **Open:**
07.00-10.30hrs,   17.00-24.00hrs,
1.3-30.9 30 IR£4.00-6.00
 P Cahir 16km Dublin to
Cork ap entrance to Hostel Ave 3km to
YH

Rosslare Harbour IBN CC Goulding
St, Rosslare Harbour, Co Wexford.
(53) 33399 **FAX** (53) 33624 **Open:**
07.00-24.00hrs (open at other times for
the ferry) 85 IR£5.00-7.00
 P   Rosslare 1km Rosslare
Harbour 1km Dublin to Rosslare
Harbour YH 1km

Tiglin Ashford, Co Wicklow. (404)
40259   **Open:**   07.00-10.30hrs,
17.00-24.00hrs   50
IR£4.00-6.00   P Wicklow
11km Dublin to Wicklow
ap Ashford 6km to YH **R** (An Óige
office)

Trá na Rosann Downings, Co Donegal.
 (74) 55374 **Open:** 07.00-10.30hrs,
17.00-24.00hrs, Easter-30.9 40
IR£4.00-6.00   P Derry
71km Derry to Letterkenny to
Downings YH 6km

Traenlaur Lodge Lough Feeagh,
Newport, Co Mayo. (98) 41358
Open: 07.00-10.30hrs, 17.00-23.00hrs,
Easter-30.9 32 IR£4.50-6.50
   P   Westport 19km
Westport Achill ap Newport

Valentia Island Knightstown, Valentia
Island, Co Kerry. (66) 76141 Warden,
(66)   76154   Members   **Open:**
07.00-10.30hrs,   17.00-24.00hrs,
1.6-30.9 40 IR£4.00-6.00
  P Reenard to Knightstown
Pier 500m Killarney 69km
Killarney to Cahirciveen

Westport Club Atlantic Hostel,
Altamont St, Westport, Co Mayo.
(98) 26644, 26717 **TX** 53974 **FAX**
(98) 25229 **Open:** 07.00-02.00hrs,
10.3-31.10 140 IR£5.00-9.00
(B)   P Westport
 Westport

ISRAEL
ISRAEL
ISRAEL
ISRAEL

ASSURED STANDARD

ISRAEL

Israel Youth Hostels Association,
International Convention Center, PO Box 6001
Jerusalem 91060, Israel

☎ (972) (2) 655 8400
FAX (972) (2) 655 8430

Office hours: Sunday-Thursday, 09.00-16.00hrs

Travel Section: c/o Israel Youth Hostels
Association,
International Convention Center, PO Box 6001
Jerusalem 91060, Israel

☎ (972) (2) 655 8400
FAX (972) (2) 655 8430

Capital:	Jerusalem
Language:	Hebrew/Arabic
Currency:	New shequel
Population:	5,000,000
Size:	20,770 sq km

ISRAEL

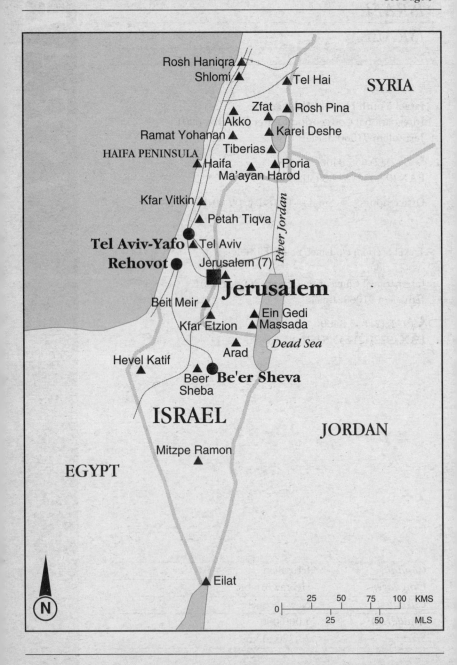

Rosh Haniqra
Shlomi
Tel Hai
SYRIA
Zfat
Rosh Pina
Akko
Karei Deshe
Ramat Yohanan
Tiberias
HAIFA PENINSULA
Haifa
Poria
Ma'ayan Harod
Kfar Vitkin
Petah Tiqva
Tel Aviv-Yafo Tel Aviv
Rehovot
Jerusalem (7)
River Jordan
Jerusalem
Beit Meir
Ein Gedi
Kfar Etzion
Massada
Dead Sea
Arad
Hevel Katif
Beer Sheba
Be'er Sheva
ISRAEL
JORDAN
Mitzpe Ramon
EGYPT

(N)

Eilat

25   50   75   100   KMS
0
25   50   MLS

ENGLISH

ISRAEL HOSTELS

Choose a hostel within the walled city of Jerusalem, or soak up the sun in Eilat. Israel has 32 Youth Hostels throughout the country.

Hostel reception desks are open 08.00-12.00hrs and 17.00-21.00hrs, some are also open during the day. Expect to pay about US$16.50-$20.00 for one night's bed and breakfast including sheets. Groups should order lunch and supper in advance.

PASSPORTS AND VISAS

Every visitor to Israel must hold a valid passport. Visitors may remain in Israel for up to three months from date of arrival, subject to the terms of the visa issued. Whilst nationals of many countries can obtain a visitor's visa, free of charge, at the point of entry, some should apply before their departure at any Israel diplomatic or consular mission - so check before you travel.

HEALTH

Dial 101 in most major urban areas for emergency or first aid assistance, provided by Magen David Adom (the Red Star of David - Israel's equivalent of the Red Cross). Medical assistance of a high professional standard is obtainable at all times; most doctors speak English and other foreign languages. The daily press carries listings of duty rotas for emergency hospitals, dental clinics and pharmacies open at night and on weekends and holidays.

BANKING HOURS

Most banks are open 08.30-12.30hrs Sunday to Thursday, 16.00-18.00hrs on Sundays, Tuesdays and Thursdays and 08.30-12.00hrs on Fridays and eves of major Jewish holidays. Bank branches in major hotels usually offer convenient banking hours.

Tourists may open local currency accounts or special non-resident foreign currency accounts at any bank, or use their international credit cards to withdraw cash in foreign or local currency at banks honouring the respective cards.

POST OFFICES

Post offices are generally open 08.00-13.00hrs, 16.00-18.30hrs Sunday to Thursday; Fridays 08.00-12.00hrs. Post offices are closed on the Sabbath and major holidays.

SHOPPING HOURS

Most shops are open Sunday to Thursday, 09.00-19.00hrs, although some close for a mid-day break between 13.00 and 16.00hrs. On Fridays and the eves of major Jewish Holidays, shops are open in the morning and close early in the afternoon. Moslem-owned establishments are closed on Fridays and Christian shops on Sundays.

TRAVEL

Air
Several airlines offer charter flights (3-10 passengers).

Rail
Israel Railways provides regular services between Tel Aviv and Herzliya, Netanya, Hadera, Haifa, Acre and Nahariya, as well as a daily train between Tel Aviv and Jerusalem, which follows a particularly beautiful scenic route. Seats may be reserved in advance. There is no train service on Sabbaths and major holidays.

Bus

Buses are the most popular means of transport throughout Israel for both urban and inter-city travel. The Egged Bus Cooperative operates nearly all inter-city bus lines, providing urban service in most cities and towns as well. Fares are reasonably priced and service is regular. Egged "Roundabout Bus" ticket is available. Reservations for long distance trips are advisable. Most bus lines do not operate on the Sabbath and on major Jewish Holidays.

Driving

Most major international car rental companies and several local ones have offices in Israel's major cities and at Ben-Gurion Airport. Advance reservations are recommended (vehicles may be reserved abroad). To rent a car you must be over 21 years of age and in possession of a valid national or international driving licence and an international credit card.

MAJOR JEWISH HOLIDAYS

1st Day of Pessah, 22 April; 7th Day of Pessah, 28 April; Pentecost, 11 June; Rosh Hashana, 2/3 October; Yom Kippur, 11 October; 1st Day of Sukkot, 16 October; Simhat Torah, 23 October.

TELEPHONE INFORMATION

International Code	Country Code	Main City Area Codes
00	972	Jerusalem 2
		Tel Aviv 3

FRANÇAIS

AUBERGES DE JEUNESSE ISRAELIENNES

Choisissez une auberge à l'intérieur de la ville fortifiée de Jérusalem, ou prenez le soleil à Eilat; Israël a 32 auberges de jeunesse disséminées dans le pays.

Les bureaux de réception des auberges sont ouverts de 8h à 12h et de 17h à 21h et certains sont aussi ouverts pendant la journée. Une nuit, petit déjeuner et draps compris, vous coûtera environ 16,50-20 $US. Il est conseillé aux groupes de commander leurs repas (déjeuner et dîner) à l'avance.

PASSEPORTS ET VISAS

Tous les visiteurs doivent être en possession d'un passeport valide. Ils peuvent rester en Israël pendant un maximum de 3 mois suivant la date de leur arrivée, conformément aux termes du visa émis. Les citoyens de nombreux pays peuvent obtenir un visa de visiteur gratuitement à l'entrée dans le pays, mais certains devront en faire la demande avant leur départ auprès d'une mission israélienne diplomatique ou consulaire - il est donc recommandé de s'informer avant le départ.

SOINS MEDICAUX

En cas d'urgence ou de besoin de premiers soins, appelez le 101 et Magen David Adom (l'Etoile rouge de David - l'équivalent israélien de la Croix rouge) viendra à votre aide. Il est possible d'obtenir une aide médicale professionnelle de très haute qualité en tous temps; la plupart des médecins parlent anglais ainsi que d'autres langues étrangères. La presse journalière imprime les listes des hôpitaux pour urgences, des cabinets dentaires et des pharmacies de garde ouverts la nuit et pendant le weekend et les vacances.

HEURES D'OUVERTURE DES BANQUES

La plupart des banques ouvrent de 8h30 à 12h30 du dimanche au jeudi, de 16h à 18h les dimanche, mardi et jeudi et de 8h30 à 12h le vendredi et la veille des fêtes israéliennes les plus importantes. Des guichets établis dans les hôtels principaux offrent des heures d'ouverture pratiques.

Les touristes peuvent ouvrir des comptes pour transactions en devises locales ou des comptes spéciaux pour non-résidents pour transactions en devises étrangères dans n'importe quelle banque. Ils peuvent également utiliser leurs cartes de crédit internationales pour retirer de l'argent en devises étrangères ou locales aux banques qui acceptent leurs cartes.

BUREAUX DE POSTE

Les bureaux de poste sont en général ouverts de 8h à 13h - 16h à 18h30 du dimanche au jeudi; ils sont ouverts de 8h à 12h le vendredi. Les bureaux de poste sont fermés le jour du Sabbat et pendant les jours fériés les plus importants.

HEURES D'OUVERTURE DES MAGASINS

La plupart des magasins sont ouverts du dimanche au jeudi de 9h à 19h, bien que certains ferment pendant une partie de la journée entre 13h et 16h. Le vendredi et la veille des fêtes juives les plus importantes, les magasins sont ouverts le matin et ferment tôt l'après-midi. Les établissements dont les propriétaires sont musulmans sont fermés le vendredi et les magasins chrétiens sont fermés le dimanche.

DEPLACEMENTS

Avions
Plusieurs lignes aériennes offrent des vols charter (3 à 10 passagers).

Trains
Israel Railways assurent des services réguliers entre Tel-Aviv et Herzliya, Netanya, Hadera, Haïfa, Acre et Nahariya, ainsi qu'un train journalier entre Tel-Aviv et Jérusalem, qui emprunte un itinéraire panoramique particulièrement beau. Il est possible de réserver des places à l'avance. Il n'y a pas de trains le jour du Sabbat et pendant les fêtes importantes.

Autobus
Les autobus sont le moyen de transport le plus utilisé dans tout le pays, que ce soit pour les déplacements urbains ou interurbains. La coopérative Egged Bus gère presque tous les services interurbains et assure également des services urbains dans la plupart des villes et grandes villes. Les tarifs sont raisonnables et les services sont réguliers. Il est possible de se procurer un billet Egged "Roundabout Bus". Les réservations pour les voyages sur grande distance sont conseillées. La plupart des services ne fonctionnent pas le jour du Sabbat et pendant les fêtes juives principales.

Automobiles
La plupart des grandes agences internationales de location de voitures ainsi que plusieurs agences locales ont des bureaux dans les grandes villes du pays et à l'aéroport Ben-Gurion. Il est conseillé de réserver à l'avance (les véhicules peuvent être réservés à l'étranger). Pour avoir le droit de louer une voiture, vous devez avoir plus de 21 ans et détenir un permis de conduire national valide ou un permis international ainsi qu'une carte de crédit internationale.

FETES JUIVES PRINCIPALES

1er jour de Pessah, 22 avril; 7ème jour de Pessah, 28 avril; Pentecôte, 11 juin; Rosh Hashana, 2/3 octobre; Yom Kippur, 11 october; 1er jour de Sukkot, 16 october; Simhat Torah, 23 octobre.

TELEPHONE

Indicatif International	Indicatif du Pays	Indicatifs régionaux des Villes principales
00	972	Jérusalem 2
		Tel-Aviv 3

DEUTSCH

ISRAELISCHE JUGENDHERBERGEN

Sie können eine Herberge innerhalb der Stadtmauern von Jerusalem wählen oder in Eilat die Sonne genießen. Über das ganze Land verstreut, gibt es in Israel 32 Jugendherbergen.

Der Empfang ist in den Herbergen von 08.00-12.00 Uhr und von 17.00-21.00 Uhr geöffnet. Einige Herbergen sind aber auch während des Tages geöffnet. Es ist mit einem Preis von etwa US$16,50-US$20,00 pro Übernachtung mit Frühstück, einschließlich Bettlaken, zu rechnen. Gruppen sollten ihr Mittag- und Abendessen im voraus bestellen.

PÄSSE UND VISA

Alle Israel-Reisenden müssen im Besitz eines gültigen Reisepasses sein. Vorbehaltlich der Bedingungen des ausgestellten Visums, können Besucher vom Tag der Ankunft an bis zu 3 Monate im Land bleiben. Staatsangehörige vieler Länder können bei der Einreise kostenlos ein Besuchervisum erhalten, aber gewisse Reisende müssen vor der Abreise bei einer israelischen diplomatischen Mission oder einem israelischen Konsulat ein Visum beantragen. Bitte erkundigen Sie sich vor der Abreise.

GESUNDHEIT

In den meisten größeren Städten ist die Nummer 101 zu wählen, wenn dringend ein Arzt oder Erste Hilfe benötigt wird. Dieser Service wird von Magen David Adom (dem Roten Stern Davids, der Organisation, die in Israel dem Roten Kreuz entspricht) zur Verfügung gestellt. Die ärztliche Versorgung ist immer erstklassig. Die meisten Ärzte sprechen Englisch und andere Fremdsprachen. Die Nacht-, Wochenend- und Feiertagsöffnungszeiten der Notdienste von Krankenhäusern, Zahnkliniken und Apotheken können der Tagespresse entnommen werden.

GESCHÄFTSSTUNDEN DER BANKEN

Die meisten Banken sind sonntags bis donnerstags von 08.30-12.30, sonntags, dienstags und donnerstags von 16.00-18.00 Uhr und freitags sowie am Vorabend hoher jüdischer Feiertage von 08.30-12.00 Uhr geöffnet. Bankfilialen in großen Hotels sind gewöhnlich zu sehr günstigen Zeiten geöffnet.

Touristen können bei jeder Bank Konten in einheimischer Währung oder spezielle Ausländer-Fremdwährungskonten eröffnen oder bei Banken, die internationale Kreditkarten akzeptieren, mit einer solchen Kreditkarte Geld in ausländischer oder einheimischer Währung abheben.

POSTÄMTER

Postämter sind im allgemeinen sonntags bis donnerstags von 08.00-13.00, 16.00-18.30 Uhr und freitags von 08.00-12.00 Uhr geöffnet. Am Sabbat und an hohen Feiertagen sind sie geschlossen.

LADENÖFFNUNGSZEITEN

Die meisten Geschäfte sind sonntags bis donnerstags von 09.00-19.00 Uhr geöffnet, aber einige machen zwischen 13.00 und 16.00 Uhr eine Mittagspause. Freitags und am Vorabend hoher jüdischer Feiertage sind die Geschäfte morgens geöffnet, aber sie schließen dann am frühen Nachmittag. Muslimen gehörende Geschäfte sind freitags, und Christen gehörende Geschäfte sonntags geschlossen.

REISEN

Flugverkehr
Mehrere Fluggesellschaften bieten Charterflüge (3-10 Passagiere) an.

Eisenbahn
Zwischen Tel Aviv und Herzliya, Netanya, Hadera, Haifa, Acre und Naharya gibt es einen regelmäßigen Eisenbahnverkehr, und auch zwischen Tel Aviv und Jerusalem verkehrt täglich ein Zug, der durch eine besonders schöne Landschaft führt. Plätze können im voraus reserviert werden. Am Sabbat und an hohen Feiertagen verkehren keine Züge.

Busse
Busse sind in ganz Israel sowohl im Stadt- als auch im Inter-City-Verkehr die beliebtesten Verkehrsmittel. Die Autobusgenossenschaft Egged betreibt fast alle Inter-City-Buslinien und bietet in den meisten Städten auch einen regelmäßigen städtischen Verkehr. Die Fahrpreise sind sehr angemessen. Es gibt ein Egged "Roundabout Bus"-Ticket. Für Fernreisen empfiehlt es sich, einen Platz zu reservieren. Am Sabbat und an hohen jüdischen Feiertagen liegt der Busverkehr größtenteils still.

Autofahren
Die meisten großen internationalen Mietwagen-Unternehmen und mehrere einheimische haben in größeren Städten in Israel und auf dem Flughafen Ben Gurion eine Niederlassung. Vorausbuchungen sind ratsam (Fahrzeuge können auch im Ausland vorbestellt werden). Wer einen Wagen mieten will, muß über 21 Jahre alt und im Besitz eines gültigen nationalen oder internationalen Führerscheines sowie einer internationalen Kreditkarte sein.

HOHE JÜDISCHE FEIERTAGE

1. Passahtag, 22. April; 7. Passahtag, 28. April; Pentekost, 11. Juni; Rosch Ha-Schana, 2/3. Oktober; Jom Kippur, 11. Oktober; 1. Sukkoth-Tag; 16. Oktober; Simhat Torah, 23. Oktober.

FERNSPRECHINFORMATIONEN

Internationale Kennzahl	Landes-Kennzahl	größere Städte - Ortsnetzkennzahlen
00	972	Jerusalem 2
		Tel Aviv 3

ESPAÑOL

ALBERGUES DE JUVENTUD ISRAELIES

Elija un albergue dentro de la ciudad amurallada de Jerusalén, o dése un baño de sol en Eilat. Israel tiene 32 albergues de juventud repartidos por todo el país.

La recepción de los albergues está abierta de 08.00 a 12.00 horas y de 17.00 a 21.00 horas. Algunas también abren durante el día. Se paga aproximadamente US$16,50-$20,00 por una noche incluyendo ropa de cama y desayuno. Los grupos deben encargar el almuerzo y la cena por adelantado.

PASAPORTES Y VISADOS

Todo visitante que entre en Israel deberá estar en posesión de un pasaporte válido. Los visitantes pueden permanecer en Israel durante un máximo de tres meses desde la fecha de llegada, según las condiciones del visado expedido. Si bien los ciudadanos de muchos países pueden obtener un visado de visitante, sin cargo, en el punto de entrada al país, algunos deben solicitarlo antes de salir en cualquier misión diplomática o consular israelí. Confírmelo antes de salir.

SANIDAD

Marque el 101 en las principales áreas urbanas para obtener asistencia de urgencia o de primeros auxilios, prestados por Magen David Adom (Estrella Roja de David, el equivalente de la Cruz Roja en Israel). En todo momento se puede conseguir asistencia médica de alto nivel. La mayoría de los médicos hablan inglés y otros idiomas. La prensa diaria lleva listas de los turnos de guardia de los hospitales de urgencias, clínicas dentales y farmacias abiertas por la noche, los fines de semana y días festivos.

HORARIO DE BANCOS

En su mayoría, los bancos abren de 08.00 a 13.00 horas de domingo a jueves, de 16.00 a 18.00 horas los domingos, martes y jueves, y de 08.30 a 12.00 horas los viernes y vísperas de las principales festividades judías. Las sucursales bancarias de los grandes hoteles suelen tener un cómodo horario de atención al público.

Los turistas pueden abrir cuentas en la moneda local o cuentas especiales de no residente de divisa extranjera en cualquier banco, o utilizar sus tarjetas de crédito internacionales para retirar efectivo en moneda local o extranjera en los bancos que acepten sus tarjetas.

CASAS DE CORREO

Por lo general las casas de correo abren de 08.00 a 13.00 - 16.00 a 18.30 horas de domingo a jueves; viernes de 08.00 a 12.00 horas. Las casas de correo están cerradas los sábados y los principales días festivos.

HORARIO COMERCIAL

La mayoría de las tiendas abren de domingo a jueves de 09.00 a 19.00 horas, si bien algunas cierran a la hora del almuerzo entre las 13.00 y las 16.00 horas. Los viernes y vísperas de las principales festividades judías, las tiendas están abiertas por la mañana y cierran a primera hora de la tarde. Los establecimientos propiedad de musulmanes cierran los viernes y los de cristianos los domingos.

DESPLAZAMIENTOS

Avión
Varias compañías ofrecen vuelos 'chárter' (3-10 pasajeros).

Tren
Israel Railways ofrece servicios regulares entre Tel Aviv y Herzliya, Netanya, Hadera, Haifa, Acre y Nahariya, así como un servicio diario entre Tel Aviv y Jerusalén que sigue una ruta panorámica de especial belleza. Se pueden reservar asientos con antelación. No hay servicio de trenes los sábados y los principales días festivos.

Autobús
El autobús es la forma más común de transporte en todo Israel tanto para desplazamientos urbanos como entre ciudades. La Cooperativa Egged Bus opera casi todas las líneas de autobús interurbanas, además de prestar un servicio urbano en la mayoría de las ciudades y poblaciones. Las tarifas son razonables y el servicio es regular. Se puede conseguir el billete "Roundabout Bus" (vuelta en autobús) de Egged. En el caso de desplazamientos de larga distancia se recomienda reservar. La mayoría de las líneas de autobús no operan los sábados ni durante las principales festividades judías.

Coche

La mayor parte de las compañías internacionales de alquiler de coches, así como varias nacionales, tienen oficinas en las principales ciudades de Israel y en el aeropuerto de Ben-Gurion. Se recomienda hacer la reserva con antelación (se pueden reservar vehículos desde el extranjero). Para alquilar un coche hay que tener más de 21 años y estar en posesión de un permiso nacional o internacional de conducir y de una tarjeta de crédito internacional.

PRINCIPALES FESTIVIDADES JUDIAS

Primer Día de Pessah, 22 abril; 7° Día de Pessah, 28 abril; Pentecostés, 11 junio; Rosh Hashana, 2/3 octubre; Yom Kippur, 11 octubre; Primer Día de Sukkot, 16 octubre; Simhat Torah, 23 octubre.

INFORMACION TELEFONICA

Código Internacional	Código Nacional	Indicativo de área de las Ciudades principales
00	972	Jerusalén 2
		Tel Aviv 3

DISCOUNTS AND CONCESSIONS

In addition to various local discounts, reduced air fares are available on some internal flights.

Hostels in this country may also display this symbol.

Les auberges de ce pays pourront également afficher ce symbole.

Jugendherbergen in diesem Land können auch dieses Symbol zeigen.

Es posible que los albergues de este país exhiban además este símbolo.

Akko (Acre) △ ⟨CC⟩ Old City, near lighthouse, PO Box 1090, Akko 24110. ☏ (4) 9911982 **FAX** (4) 9911982 ✉ 85 ⍾⎮ 🏠 🚌 from Akko 3, from Haifa 251

Arad ⚠ ⟨CC⟩ Blau-Weiss hostel, PO Box 34, Arad. ☏ (7) 9957150 **FAX** (7) 9955078 ✉ 180 ⍾⎮ ⍾⍾ 🅿 🚌 from Tel Aviv 389 🚃 from Beersheba 388

Beersheba/Beer Sheva ⚠ ⟨1N⟩ ⟨CC⟩ Bet Yatziv, PO Box 7, 79 Rehov Ha' Atzmaut, Beersheba. ☏ (7) 6277444,

6271490 **FAX** (7) 6275735 ✉ 250 ⍾⎮ ⍾⍾ ⟨⟩ 🅿 ⚓ 🚌 12, 13

Bet Meir ▲ ⟨CC⟩ Ramot Shapira, Bet Meir, PO Box 7216, Jerusalem. (20km W Jerusalem) ☏ (2) 5342691, 5343793 **FAX** (2) 5342098 ✉ 300 ⍾⎮ ⍾⍾ 🅿 🚌 85 20km

Eilat ⚠ ⟨CC⟩ Arava Rd, Eilat. ☏ (7) 6370088 **FAX** (7) 6375835 ✉ 502 ⍾⎮ ⍾⍾ ⟨⟩ 🅿 ⚓ 🚌 15 10m

Ein Gedi ▲ Beit Sarah, Ein Gedi, Mobile Post, Dead Sea 86980. ☏ (7) 6584165

FAX (7) 6584445 ✉ 200 ⏧ ⛹ 🅿
🚌 from Jerusalem, Tel Aviv,
Beersheba and Eilat

Haifa ▲ |8S| 'Carmel', Haifa, Mobile
Post, Hof Hacarmel. ☎ (4) 8531944
FAX (4) 8532516 ✉ 212 ⏧ ⛹ 🅿
🚌 43, 45

Hevel Katif ▲ Hadarom, Hevel Katif,
Hof Gaza, Mobile Post 79779. ☎ (7)
6847597 FAX (7) 6847680 ✉ 220 ⏧
⛹ ⛴ 🚌 from Ashkelon 36, from
Beersheba 38 Ⓡ

JERUSALEM (7 Hostels)

Jerusalem - Louise Waterman Wise ⛺
|3SW| ⊞ 8 Hapisga St, PO Box 16350,
Jerusalem, Bayit Vegan. ☎ (2) 6420990,
6423366 FAX (2) 6423362 ✉ 300 ⏧
⛹ ✈ 50km A🚌 Central Bus Station
🚌 5km 🚌 from Central Bus Station
18, 20, 39, 40 ap Mt Herzl

Jerusalem - Ein Karem △ |6SW| ⊞
PO Box 16091, Jerusalem. ☎ (2)
6416282 ✉ 90 ⏧ ✈ 50km A🚌
Central Bus Station 🚌 from Central
Bus Station 17

Jerusalem - Bet Bernstein △ |1W| Town
Centre, 1 Keren Hayessod St, Jerusalem.
☎ (2) 6258286 ✉ 80 ⏧ ⛹ ✈ 50km
🚌 2km 🚌 from Central Bus Station
7, 8, 9, 14, 31, 32

Jerusalem - Forest ⛺ |6SW| ⊞ PO Box
3353, Jerusalem 91032. ☎ (2) 6752911
FAX (2) 6413522 ✉ 140 ⏧ ⛹ 🅿 ⛴
✈ 50km A🚌 Central Bus Station 🚌
from Central Bus Station 33

Jerusalem - Old City ▲ |2E| PO Box
7880, 2 Rehov Ararat, Jewish Quarter,
Old City, Jerusalem. ☎ (2) 6288611 ✉
80 ⏧ ⛹ ⊞ ✈ 50km A🚌 Central
Bus Station 🚌 from Central Bus
Station 13, 20

Jerusalem - Beit Shmuel ⛺ |1E| 13 King
David St, Jerusalem. ☎ (2) 6203467

FAX (2) 6203466 ✉ 240 ⏧ ⛹ ✈
50km A🚌 Central Bus Station 🚌
from Central Bus Station 5, 6, 15, 18,
21, 30, 31

Jerusalem - "Hadavidka" ⛺ 67 Ha
Nevi'im St, Jerusalem. ☎ (2) 5384555
FAX (2) 5388790 ✉ 248 ⏧ ⛹ ⛴ 🅿
✈ Ben Gurion 50km A🚌 ap Central
Bus Station 2km ⛴ Haifa 150km 🚌
Jerusalem   4km   🚌
39,36,35,23,21,20,18,13

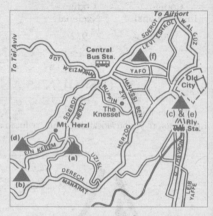

JERUSALEM -
(a) Louise Waterman Wise, (b) Ein Karem,
(c) Bet Bernstein, (d) Jerusalem Forest,
(e) Old City, (f) Hadavidka

Karei Deshe ⛺ Yoram, Karei Deshe,
Mobile Post, Korazim 12365. ☎ (6)
6720601 FAX (6) 6724818 ✉ 280 ⏧
👦 ⛹ ⛴ ⊞ 🅿 ⛴ 🚌 from Tiberias
Central Bus Station 459, 841

Kfar Etzion △ ⊞ Har Hebron. ☎ (2)
9935133, 9935233 ✉ 273 ⏧ 👦 ⛹
🚌 from Jerusalem Central Bus Station
160, 161

Kfar Vitkin ▲ ⊞ Emek Hefer, Pob
596, Kfar Vitkin 40200 ☎ (9) 8666032
FAX (9) 8666032 ✉ 200 ⏧ ⛹ 🅿
🚌 from Haifa 901, 921, from Tel Aviv
702, 852, 902

Maayan Harod ⛺ ⊞ Hankin, Maayan
Harod, Mobile Post, Gilboa. ☎ (6)

6531660 **FAX** (6) 6531660 ✉ 135 🍴
👫 🅿 ⚑ 🚌 from Afula to Beit-She'an

Metzada (Massada) ⚠ Isaac H Taylor
Hostel, Metzada, Mobile Post, Dead Sea
86935. 📞 (7) 6584349 **FAX** (7)
6584650 ✉ 150 🍴 👫 🚌 from
Jerusalem, Tel Aviv, Beersheba and
Eilat

Mitzpe Ramon ⚠ CC Bet Noam, PO
Box 2, Mitzpe Ramon 80600. 📞 (7)
6588443 **FAX** (7) 6588074 ✉ 160 🍴
👫 🏛 🅿 🚌 from Tel Aviv, Beersheba,
Eilat

Petah Tiqva ▲ CC Yad Labanim,
Petah Tiqva 49404, Yahalom St. 📞 (3)
9226666 **FAX** (3) 9226666 ✉ 204 🍴
👫 🚌 from Tel Aviv 11km 50, 51,
from Petah Tiqva 62, 75

Poria ⚠ Taiber, Poria, PO Box 232,
Tiberias 14104. 📞 (6) 6750050 **FAX**
(6) 6751628 ✉ 155 🍴 👫 🅿 🚌 4km

Ramat Yohanan △ CC Young Judea,
Ramat Yohanan Post, Kfar Makkabi
30030. (Haifa 18km) 📞 (4) 8442976
FAX (4) 8442976 ✉ 180 🍴 ☕ 👫 🅿
🚌 from Haifa Central Bus Station 66
18km

Rosh Haniqra ⚠ CC PO Box 3067,
Naharia. 📞 (4) 9825169 **FAX** (4)
9821330 ✉ 220 🍴 👫 🅿 ⚑ 🚌 from
Naharia 20 Ⓡ

Rosh Pina ▲ CC Nature Friends,
Rehov HaHalutzim, Rosh Pina 1200 📞
(6) 6937086 ✉ 100 🍴 👫 🚌 from
Haifa Central Bus Station 500, 501

Shlomi ⚠ PO Box 2120, Shlomi. (5km
E of Rosh Haniqra) 📞 (4) 9808975 **FAX**
(4) 9809163 ✉ 400 🍴 👫 ♿ 🏛 🅿
🚌 from Nahariya 22, 23

Tel Aviv ⚠ 3N CC 36 Bnei Dan St,
Tel Aviv 62260 📞 (3) 5441748,
5460719 **FAX** (3) 5441030 ✉ 305 🍴
♿ 🏛 ✈ 20 A 🚌 Terminal 🚌 Dan
5, 27 ap Pinkass St

TEL AVIV

Tel Hai △ CC Mobile Post, Upper
Galilee 12210. 📞 (6) 6940043 **FAX** (6)
6941743 ✉ 75 🍴 ☕ 👫 🚌 from
Kiryat Shmona Central Bus Station 20,
23

Tiberias ⚠ CC Yosef Meyouhas
Hostel, PO Box 81, Tiberias 14100. 📞
(6) 6721775, 6790350 **FAX** (6)
6720372 ✉ 248 🍴 👫 🏛

Zfat ⚠ CC Bet Benyamin, PO Box
1139, Zfat 13401. 📞 (6) 6921086 **FAX**
(6) 6973514 ✉ 120 🍴 👫 🚌 from
Zfat Central Bus Station 6, 7

25 or younger ?

The GO 25 Card is your key to thousands of special discounts on Travel, Accommodation, Museums and Tours.

Available at Youth and Student Travel Offices around the world and recognised at hundreds of establishments in sixty countries.

ITALY
ITALIE
ITALIEN
ITALIA

ASSURED STANDARD

Associazione Italiana Alberghi per la Gioventù,
Via Cavour 44, 00184 Roma, Italy.

📞 (39) (6) 4871152
FAX (39) (6) 4880492
E-Mail: aig@uni.net
Internet Address: HTTP://www.TRAVEL.IT/HOSTELS

Office Hours:　　Monday-Thursday, 07.30-17.30hrs,
　　　　　　　　　Friday 07.30-15.30hrs

Central Booking: c/o Associazione Italiana Alberghi per la
Gioventù, Via Cavour 44, 00184 Roma, Italy.

📞 (39) (6) 4871152
FAX (39) (6) 4880492

IBN Booking Centres for outward bookings:
- Rome, *via National Office above.*
- Florence - AIG Regional Office,
  Viale Augusto Righi 2/4, Florence.
  📞 (39) (55) 600315 FAX (39) (55) 610300
- Genoa - AIG Regional Office,
  Salita Salvatore Viale n 1, Genoa.
- Naples - AIG Regional Office,
  Salita d Grotta a Piedigrotta 23, Naples.
- Venice - AIG Regional Office,
  Calle Castelforte S Rocco, 3101 San Polo, Venice.
  📞 (39) (41) 5204414 FAX (39) (41) 5204034

Capital:	Rome
Language:	Italian
Currency:	L (lire)
Population:	57,000,000
Size:	301,225 sq km

ITALY

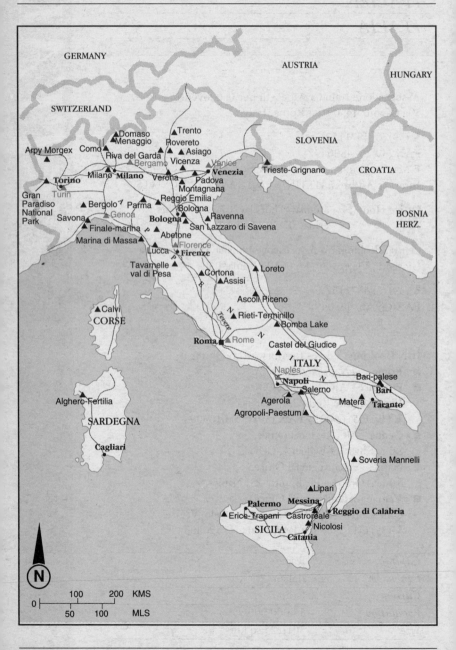

ENGLISH

ITALIAN HOSTELS

Italy has about 50 hostels in cities and in the countryside.

Expect to pay in the region of 18,000 - 30,000 lire including sheets and in most cases breakfast otherwise where available 2500 lire. Other meals when available upto 14,000 lire and packed lunches 10,000 lire.

A free fax booking service exists, connecting the "art" cities of Florence, Naples, Rome and Venice.

PASSPORTS AND VISAS

A valid passport or visitors card is required.

HEALTH

Health Service is available to nationals of EC countries. Other nationals should obtain private health insurance before travelling.

BANKING HOURS

Banks are open 08.30-13.20hrs and for one hour in the afternoon, generally 15.00-16.00hrs but check locally as times of opening in the afternoon vary from bank to bank.

Banks are not open on Saturdays, Sundays or National Holidays. Tourists can change money at main railway stations and airports.

POST OFFICES

Post Offices are open Monday to Friday 08.30-13.30hrs, Saturday 08.30-12.30hrs. In the main cities the main post offices are open 08.30-18.30hrs.

SHOPPING HOURS

Shops are generally open 08.30/09.00-13.00hrs and 15.30/16.00-19.30/20.00hrs.

TRAVEL

Rail
Rail is the cheapest way to travel in Italy. 'Ferrovie dello Stato' (FS) offers an extensive network of railways. High speed trains operate between the main cities. A supplement is payable. FS offer discounts to members - see Concessions.

Bus
Every city has its own bus system. A bus service operates between smaller cities that cannot be reached by train.

Ferry
There are several ferry companies which link the mainland to the islands.

Driving
Visitors must carry their Vehicle Registration Book which must either be in their name or include the owner's written permission to drive the vehicle. The highway network is one of the largest in Europe.

PUBLIC HOLIDAYS

New Year, 1 January; Epiphany, 6 January; Easter Monday, 31 March; Liberation Day, 25 April; Labour Day, 1 May; Virgin Mary Day, 15 August; Religious Holiday, 1 November; Religious Holiday, 8 December; Christmas, 25 December; St Stephens Day, 26 December.

TELEPHONE INFORMATION

International Code	Country Code	Main City Area Codes	
00	39	Florence	55
		Milan	2
		Naples	81
		Rome	6
		Venice	41

FRANÇAIS

AUBERGES DE JEUNESSE ITALIENNES

Environ 50 auberges sont disséminées dans les villes et la campagne italiennes.

Une nuit vous coûtera environ de 18 000 à 30 000 lires, draps et, dans la plupart des cas, petit déjeuner compris. Lorsqu'il n'est pas compris dans le prix de la nuitée et dans les établissements où il est servi, un petit déjeûner vous coûtera 2 500 lires. Les autres repas, quand ils sont proposés, coûtent jusqu'à 14 000 lires et les paniers-repas, 10 000 lires.

Un service gratuit de réservation par téléfax est offert et relie les villes d'art de Florence, Naples, Rome et Venise.

PASSEPORTS ET VISAS

Un passeport valide ou une carte de visiteur est nécessaire.

SOINS MEDICAUX

Les citoyens des pays du Marché commun bénéficient des soins procurés selon le système de la Sécurité sociale. Il est conseillé aux citoyens d'autres pays de souscrire à une assurance maladie privée avant leur départ.

HEURES D'OUVERTURE DES BANQUES

Les banques sont ouvertes de 8h30 à 13h20 et pendant une heure au cours de l'après-midi, en général de 15h à 16h, mais il est prudent de vérifier les horaires locaux car les heures d'ouverture l'après-midi varient selon les banques.

Les banques n'ouvrent pas le samedi, le dimanche et les jours fériés. Les touristes peuvent changer de l'argent dans les gares principales et dans les aéroports.

BUREAUX DE POSTE

Les bureaux de poste sont ouverts du lundi au vendredi de 8h30 à 13h30 et le samedi de 8h30 à 12h30. Dans les grandes villes, les bureaux principaux sont ouverts de 8h30 à 18h30.

HEURES D'OUVERTURE DES MAGASINS

Les magasins sont généralement ouverts de 8h30/9h à 13h et de 15h30/16h à 19h30/20h.

DEPLACEMENTS

Trains

Le train est le moyen le moins cher de voyager en Italie. Les "Ferrovie dello Stato" (FS) gèrent un vaste réseau ferroviaire. Des trains à grande vitesse relient les grandes villes. Il faut payer un supplément. FS offre des réductions aux adhérents - voir la section 'Concessions'

Autobus

Chaque grande ville gère son propre système d'autobus. Les villes moins importantes auxquelles on ne peut pas se rendre par le train sont desservies par un service d'autobus.

Ferry-boats

Plusieurs compagnies maritimes relient le pays aux îles.

Automobiles

Les visiteurs doivent être munis des papiers de leur voiture, qui doivent être à leur nom. Si le véhicule ne leur appartient pas, les papiers devront être accompagnés de l'autorisation écrite du propriétaire du véhicule. Le réseau autoroutier est l'un des plus développés d'Europe.

JOURS FERIES

Nouvel an, 1er janvier; Epiphanie, 6 janvier; Lundi de Pâques, 31 mars; Fête de la Libération, 25 avril; Fête du travail, 1er mai; Fête de la Vierge, 15 août; Fête religieuse, 1er novembre; Fête religieuse, 8 décembre; Noël, 25 décembre; St Stéphane, 26 décembre.

TELEPHONE

Indicatif International	Indicatif du Pays	Indicatifs régionaux des Villes principales	
00	39	Florence	55
		Milan	2
		Naples	81
		Rome	6
		Venise	41

DEUTSCH

ITALIENISCHE JUGENDHERBERGEN

Italien hat in Städten und auf dem Land ungefähr 50 Jugendherbergen.

Es ist mit einem Preis von etwa 18.000 - 30.000 Lire, einschließlich Bettlaken, und in den meisten Fällen Frühstück, zu rechnen. Wenn nicht im Preis enthalten, kostet das Frühstück 2500 lire. Weitere Mahlzeiten (wenn verfügbar) kosten bis zu max. 14.000 lire. Abgepacktes Mittagessen kostet 10.000 lire.

Unter den Kunststädten Florenz, Neapel, Rom und Venedig gibt es einen kostenlosen Telefax-Buchungsservice.

PÄSSE UND VISA

Es wird ein gültiger Reisepaß oder gültiger Personalausweis verlangt.

GESUNDHEIT

Der Gesundheitsdienst steht Staatsangehörigen der EU-Länder zur Verfügung. Staatsangehörige anderer Länder sollten vor Antritt ihrer Reise eine private Krankenversicherung abschließen.

GESCHÄFTSSTUNDEN DER BANKEN

Die Banken sind von 08.30-13.20 Uhr und eine Stunde am Nachmittag, gewöhnlich zwischen 15.00 und 16.00 Uhr, geöffnet. Erkundigen Sie sich am Ort, da sich die Öffnungszeiten am Nachmittag von Bank zu Bank unterscheiden.

Samstags, sonn- und feiertags sind die Banken nicht geöffnet. Touristen können auf großen Bahnhöfen und Flugplätzen Geld wechseln.

POSTÄMTER

Postämter sind montags bis freitags von 08.30-13.30 Uhr und samstags von 08.30-12.30 Uhr geöffnet. In größeren Städten sind die Hauptpostämter von 08.30-18.30 Uhr geöffnet.

LADENÖFFNUNGSZEITEN

Geschäfte sind in der Regel von 08.30/09.00 Uhr bis 13.00 Uhr sowie zwischen 15.30/16.00 Uhr und 19,30/20.00 Uhr geöffnet.

REISEN

Eisenbahn

Die Eisenbahn ist das billigste Verkehrsmittel in Italien. 'Ferrovie dello Stato' (FS) verfügt über ein umfangreiches Schienennetz. Zwischen größeren Städten sind Hochgeschwindigkeitszüge eingesetzt, für die ein Zuschlag erhoben wird. FS bietet Mitgliedern Rabatte an. (siehe 'Concessions').

Busse

Jede Stadt hat ihr eigenes Bussystem. Zwischen kleineren Städten, die nicht mit der Bahn erreicht werden können, verkehren Busse.

Fähren

Es gibt mehrere Fähren, die das Festland mit den Inseln verbinden.

Autofahren

Besucher müssen ihren Kraftfahrzeugbrief mit sich führen, der entweder auf ihren eigenen Namen ausgestellt oder von einer schriftlichen Fahrerlaubnis des Fahrzeughalters begleitet sein muß. Italien verfügt über eines der umfangreichsten Straßennetze Europas.

FEIERTAGE

Neujahr, 1. Januar; Erscheinungsfest, 6. Januar; Ostermontag, 31. März; Tag der Befreiung, 25. April; Tag der Arbeit, 1. Mai; Mariä Himmelfahrt, 15. August; Allerheiligen, 1. November; Tag der unbefleckten Empfängnis, 8. Dezember; Weihnachten, 25. Dezember; zweiter Weihnachtstag, 26. Dezember.

FERNSPRECHINFORMATIONEN

Internationale Kennzahl	Landes-Kennzahl	größere Städte - Ortsnetzkennzahlen	
00	39	Florenz	55
		Mailand	2
		Neapel	81
		Rom	6
		Venedig	41

ESPAÑOL

ALBERGUES DE JUVENTUD ITALIANOS

Italia tiene unos 50 albergues en las ciudades y en el campo.

Se pagan unas 18.000 - 30.000 liras incluyendo ropa de cama y, en la mayoría de los casos, desayuno. Donde no esté incluido en el precio y se pueda obtener, el desayuno cuesta 2.500 liras. Las demás comidas, donde se puedan obtener, cuestan 14.000 liras o menos y las meriendas 10.000 liras.

Existe un servicio gratuito de reservas por fax que conecta las ciudades 'artísticas' de Florencia, Nápoles, Roma y Venecia.

PASAPORTES Y VISADOS

Se requiere un pasaporte válido o tarjeta de visitante.

SANIDAD

Los ciudadanos de países de la CE disponen de asistencia sanitaria. Los ciudadanos de otros países deberían suscribir un seguro privado de salud antes de viajar.

HORARIO DE BANCOS

Los bancos abren de 08.30 a 13.20 horas y durante una hora por la tarde, por lo general, de 15.00 a 16.00 horas, pero es conveniente confirmarlo a nivel local puesto que el horario de la tarde varía de un banco a otro.

Los bancos están cerrados los sábados, domingos y días festivos. Los turistas pueden cambiar moneda en las principales estaciones ferroviarias y aeropuertos.

CASAS DE CORREO

Las casas de correo abren de lunes a viernes de 08.30 a 13.30 horas, sábado de 08.30 a 12.30 horas. En las grandes ciudades, las principales oficinas de correos abren de 08.30 a 18.30 horas.

HORARIO COMERCIAL

Por lo general las tiendas abren de 08.30/09.00 a 13.00 horas y de 15.30/16.00 a 19.30/20.00 horas.

DESPLAZAMIENTOS

Tren
El tren es el medio de transporte más barato en Italia. 'Ferrovie dello Stato' (FS) ofrece una completa red ferroviaria. Existen servicios de alta velocidad entre las principales ciudades, para los que hay que pagar un suplemento. FS ofrece descuentos a los socios - ver concesiones.

Autobús
Cada ciudad tiene su propio sistema de autobús. Un servicio de autobús opera entre las poblaciones más pequeñas a las que no se puede acceder por tren.

Ferry
Hay varias compañías de ferry que enlazan la Italia peninsular con las islas.

Coche
Los visitantes deben llevar la documentación de su automóvil que debe estar a su nombre o incluir una autorización escrita del propietario para conducir el vehículo. La red de autopistas es de las mayores de Europa.

DIAS FESTIVOS

Año Nuevo, 1 enero; Epifanía, 6 enero; Lunes de Pascua, 31 marzo; Día de la Liberación, 25 abril; Día del Trabajo, 1 mayo; Día de la Virgen María, 15 agosto; Festividad religiosa, 1 noviembre; Festividad religiosa, 8 diciembre; Navidad, 25 diciembre; Día de San Esteban, 26 diciembre.

INFORMACION TELEFONICA

Código Internacional	Código Nacional	Indicativo de área de las Ciudades principales	
00	39	Florencia	55
		Milán	2
		Nápoles	81
		Roma	6
		Venecia	41

DISCOUNTS AND CONCESSIONS

Your membership card entitles you to discounts off local attractions and facilities at many hostels. In addition the following national discounts are available:

Hertz - Car Hire: Various discounts, use code CDP 670513 (only available to people over 25)
Brek Restaurant Chains: 10% discount.
Italian Railways & Ferries: By purchasing a FS card at 10,000 lire, 20% discount (2nd Class), 30% discount (1st Class) travelling by train Tues, Wed, Sat. 13% discount travelling by ferry to Sardinia on the price of seats, berths and car passage. Discounts on ferries every day. Further information, when applicable, can be obtained from Italian Railway Stations.
Lebole and Visa Department Stores: Free entrance.
Mondadori Book Shops: 10% discount.
International Student Identity Card (ISIC): obtainable from many AIG offices. 20% discount on production of IYHF membership card.

Hostels in this country may also display this symbol.

Les auberges de ce pays pourront également afficher ce symbole.

Jugendherbergen in diesem Land können auch dieses Symbol zeigen.

Es posible que los albergues de este país exhiban además este símbolo.

Abetone ▲ 'Renzo Bizzarri', Strada Statale dell'Abetone, 51021 Abetone PT. 📞 (573) 60117 **Open:** 07.00-10.00hrs, 15.30-24.00hrs, 1.12-30.4; 15.6-30.9 (Grps 1.1-31.12) ⛴ 64 ⊖ 18,000 lire ᴮᴮⁱⁿᶜ 🍽 ⁂ 🔒 🅿 ⛏ Alt 1380m 🚲 🚍 Pistoia 40km 🚌 50m Ⓡ

Agerola- San Lazzaro △ 'Beata Solitudo', Piazza Generale Avitabile, 80051 Agerola-San Lazzaro NA. 📞 (81) 8025048 **FAX** (81) 8025048 **Open:** 07.00-09.00hrs, 15.30-23.30hrs ⛴ 16 ⊖ 14,000 lire ⛅ 🅿 ⚓ ⛴ Salerno 40km 🚍 Gragnano 16km 🚌 50m

Agropoli-Paestum ▲ La Lanterna YH, Via Lanterna 8, Loc.tà San Marco, 84043

Agropoli SA. 📞 (974) 838364 **FAX** (974) 838364 **Open:** 07.00-10.00hrs, 15.30-23.30hrs, 15.3-30.10 ⛴ 56 ⊖ 15,000 lire (⁂ 16,000 lire) 🍽 🔒 🅿 ⚓ 🚍 Agropoli 1km 🚌 100m

Alghero- Fertilia △ 'Ostello dei Giuliani', Via Zara 1, 07040 Alghero-Fertilia SS. 📞 (79) 930353 **FAX** (79) 930353 **Open:** 07.00-9.00hrs, 12.00-14.30hrs, 15.30-24.00hrs ⛴ 50 ⊖ 14,000 lire 🍽 🛗 🅿 ⚓ ✈ Alghero-Fertilia 2km A🚌 200m ⛴ Porto Torres 35km 🚍 Alghero 6km 🚌 200m

Arpy Morgex △ Centro Di Soggiorno, Loc.Arpy, 11017 Morgex AO. 📞 (165) 841684 **FAX** (165) 841684 (**Shut:** 📞

(10) 296680, **FAX** (10) 290734) **Open:**
1.1-4.5; 14.6-7.9; 22-31.12 (Grps
1.1-31.12) ✌ 130 Su; 70 Wi ● 28,000
- 30,000 lire BBinc ⍾ ⛄ ⛭ 📮 ☈ Alt
1700m ⚙ ✈ Torino Caselle 99km 🚌
Morgex 7km 🚐 Private on request

Ascoli Piceno ▲ 'Ostello de
Longobardi', Via Soderini 26,
Palazzetto Longobardo, 63100 Ascoli
Piceno AP. ☏ (736) 259007 **Open:**
07.30-24.00hrs (key on request) ✌ 30
● 16,000 lire ⍾(L D) ⛇ 🏠 📮 🚌
Ascoli Piceno 1km 🚐 50m

Asiago ▲ Ekar YH, Costalunga Ekar 1,
36012 Asiago VI. ☏ /**FAX**: (424)
455138 (Shut: (424) 463195) **Open:**
07.00-24.00hrs; 1.12-31.3, 20.6-10.9
(1.1-31.12 on request) ✌ 130 ●
20,000 lire (⍾ 25,000 lire) BBinc ⍾ ⛭
📮 ☈ Alt 1000m 🚌 Bassano del
Grappa 25km 🚐 100m (R)
(1.1-31.12)

Assisi ▲ 'Ostello Della Pace', Via
Valecchie 177, 06081 Assisi PG. ☏ (75)
816767 **FAX** (75) 816767 **Open:**
07.00-10.00hrs, 15.30-23.30hrs,
1-9.1; 1.3-31.12 ✌ 60 ● 20,000 lire
(⍾ 25,000 lire) BBinc ⍾ ⛭ 🏠 🖥 📮 ⚙
🚌 Assisi-Santa Maria Degli Angeli
1.5km 🚐 500m (R)

Bari- Palese ▲ 6NW 'Ostello del
Levante', Via Nicola Massaro 33, 70057
Bari- Palese (Lungomare) BA. ☏ (80)
5300282 **FAX** (80) 5300282 **Open:**
07.00-10.00hrs, 15.30-23.30hrs,
15.1-20.12 ✌ 70 ● 16,000 lire BBinc
⍾ 📮 ♨ ✈ Bari Palese 4km 🚌 Bari
8km 🚐 1 500m

Bergamo ⚠ IBN Via Galileo Ferraris
1, 24123 Bergamo BG ☏ /**FAX**: (35)
361724   **Open:**   07.30-10.00hrs,
15.30-24.00hrs ✌ 68 ● 25,000 -
30,000 lire BBinc ⍾ ⛭ ⛇ 🖥 ⛭ 📮 ⚙
✈ Orio al Serio (Bergamo) 7km A🚐
🚌 Bergamo 2km 🚐 14 100m

Bergolo △ Le Langhe YH, Via Roma
22, 12070 Bergolo CN ☏ (173) 87016,
87161 **FAX** (173) 87069 **Open:**
08.00-10.00hrs, 15.30-22.30hrs ✌ 46
● 12,000 lire (⍾ 14,000 lire) ⛇ ⍾ ✈
Torino Caselle 120km 🚌 Acqui
Terme 38km 🚐 Line "Geloso"
Savona- Cortemilia and/or line
"Francone" Acquiterme- Cortemilia-
Bergolo (Info ☏ (173) 833106)

BOLOGNA (2 Hostels)

Bologna - San Sisto 1 YH ▲ 6NE Via
Viadagola 14, 40127 Bologna BO. ☏
(51) 519202 **FAX** (51) 519202 **Open:**
07.00-10.00hrs, 15.30-23.30hrs,
20.1-19.12 ✌ 50 ● 18,000 lire BBinc
📮 ✈ Bologna Borgo Panigale 15km
🚌 Bologna Centrale 6km 🚐
93-301-20B-14C 500m

Bologna - San Sisto 2 YH ⚠ 6NE Due
Torri- San Sisto 2, Via Viadagola 5,
40127 Bologna BO. ☏ (51) 501810
FAX (51) 501810 **Open:**
07.00-10.00hrs, 15.30-23.30hrs,
20.1-19.12 ✌ 75 ● 20,000 lire BBinc
⍾ ⛭ ⛇ 📮 ✈ Bologna Borgo Panigale
15km A🚐 6km 🚌 Bologna Centrale
6km 🚐 93-301-20B-14C 500m

Bomba Lake ▲ CC Isola Verde YH,
Via Lago, 66042 Bomba CH. ☏ (872)
860475 **FAX** (872) 860450 **Open:**
08.00-24.00hrs ✌ 44 ● 18,000 lire
⍾ ⛭ 🖥 ⛭ 📮 ⚙ ⚓ 🚌 Lago di Bomba
150m 🚐 1.5km

Castel del Giudice ▲ "La Castellana"
YH, Via Fontana Vecchia 1, 86080
Castel del Giudice IS ☏ (865) 946222
FAX (865) 946222 **Open:**
07.00-24.00hrs ✌ 60 ● 14,000 lire
BBinc ⍾ ⛭ ⛭ 📮 ☈ Alt 800m ⛴
Pescara 95km 🚌 Castel Di Sangro
15km 🚐 Line "La Sangritana" 200m
ap "Castel Del Giudice" 200m

Castroreale △ 'Ostello Delle Aquile',
Salita Federico II d'Aragona, 98053

Castroreale Centro ME. ☎ (90) 9746398, 9746078 **FAX** (90) 9746446 **Open:** 07.00-09.00hrs, 15.30-23.30hrs, 1.4-31.10 ⚲ 24 ⊜ 13,000 lire ☞ 🏠 ① ⛴ Milazzo 20km ♨ Barcellona 11km 🚍 100m Ⓡ (Antonino Bellinvia, Via Malasá 22, 98053 Castroreale ME)

Como ▲ ⊂⊂ 'Villa Olmo YH', Via Bellinzona 2, 22100 Como CO. ☎ (31) 573800 **FAX** (31) 573800 **Open:** 07.00-10.00hrs, 15.30-23.30hrs, 1.3-30.11 ⚲ 76 ⊜ 15,000 lire (♀♀ 16,000 lire) ᴮᴮⁱⁿᶜ ⏀ ♀♀ 🏠 ▣ ℗ ⮺ ▲ ♨ Como 1km 🚍 1, 6, 11, 14 20m Ⓡ (♀♀)

Cortona ▲ 'San Marco YH', Via Maffei 57, 52044 Cortona AR. ☎ (575) 601392 (Shut: (575) 601765) **FAX** (575) 601392 **Open:** 07.00-10.00hrs, 15.30-24.00hrs, 15.3-15.10 (Grps 1.1-31.12) ⚲ 68 ⊜ 18,000 lire ᴮᴮⁱⁿᶜ ⏀ ♀♀ 🏠 ⮺ ♨ Cortona-Camucia 3km 🚍 70m Ⓡ (Shut: Sergio Cherubini, Case Sparse 79, 52044 Cortona AR)

Domaso YH △ Via Case Sparse 12, 22013 Domaso CO. ☎ (344) 96094 **Open:** 07.00-23.30hrs, 1.3-31.10 ⚲ 30 ⊜ 14,000 lire ᴮᴮⁱⁿᶜ ⏀ ☞ ℗ ▲ ♨ Colico 16km 🚍 50m

Erice-Trapani △ ⊂⊂ G.Amodeo YH, Strada Provinciale Trapani- Erice, Km 2⁰, 91100 Raganzili Erice TP. ☎ (923) 552964 **FAX** (923) 539398 **Open:** 07.00-10.00hrs, 15.30-24.00hrs ⚲ 52 ⊜ 19,000 lire ᴮᴮⁱⁿᶜ ⏀ ♀♀ ① ℗ ⮺ ✈ 100km A🚍 2km ⛴ 4km ♨ Trapani, East Area Erice 3km 🚍 20m

Finale- Marina ▲ 'Wuillermin Castle YH', Via Generale Caviglia 46, 17024 Finale-Marina SV. ☎ (19) 690515 **FAX** (19) 690515 **Open:** 07.00-10.00hrs, 15.30-23.30hrs, 15.3-15.10 ⚲ 71 ⊜ 18,000 lire ᴮᴮⁱⁿᶜ ⏀ (B D) 🏠 ⮺ ▲ ♨ Finale 1km 🚍 50m

Florence △ 3NE ℐBN 'Villa Camerata', Viale Augusto Righi 2-4, 50137 FI. ☎ (55) 601451 **FAX** (55) 610300 **Open:** 07.00-10.00hrs, 13.00-23.30hrs ⚲ 322 ⊜ 23,000 - 32,000 lire ᴮᴮⁱⁿᶜ ⏀ ♀♀ ♿ 🏠 ▣ ℗ ✈ Firenze Peretola 10km ♨ Santa Maria Novella 5km 🚍 17/B 400m

FLORENCE

Genoa △ ℐBN Via Costanzi 120N-16136, Genova GE. ☎ (10) 2422457 **FAX** (10) 2422457 **Open:** 07.00-10.00hrs, 15.30-23.30hrs, 22.1-21.12 ⚲ 213 ⊜ 22,000 - 30,000 lire ᴮᴮⁱⁿᶜ ⏀ ♀♀ ♿ ▣ ℗ ✈ Genova C Colombo 8km A🚍 2.5km ⛴ 3km ♨ Principe 2km 🚍 35, 40 50m

GENOA

Gran Paradiso National Park-Noasca
⛰ Centro di Soggiorno "Parco Nazionale" YH, frazione Gere Sopra, 10080 Noasca TO. 📞 (124) 901107 FAX (124) 901107 Open: 07.00-24.00hrs 🛏 70 ⬤ 25,000 lire (Jun-Sep), 27,000 lire (Oct-May) 🅱🅱inc 🍽 🚻 ♿ 🅿 ⚐ Alt 1100m 🚴 ✈ Torino - Caselle 40km 🚆 Pont Canavese (+bus) 10km 🚌 Line Torino - Ceresole Reale 100m

Lipari △ Via Castello 17, 98055 Lipari ME. 📞 (90) 9811540 (Shut: (90) 9812527) FAX (90) 9811715 Open: 07.00-09.00hrs, 12.00-14.00hrs, 15.30-24.00hrs 🛏 120 ⬤ 14,000 lire 🍽 ☞ ① 🗄 ⛴ Lipari 400m 🚆 Milazzo 40km ⓡ (Shut: Antonino Giardina, Via Torrente Aurora 16, 98052 Lipari-Canneto ME).

Loreto ⛰ Via Aldo Moro, 60025 Loreto AN 📞 (71) 7501026 FAX (71) 7501026 Open: 07.00-10.00hrs, 15.30-23.30hrs 🛏 138 ⬤ 23,000 - 35,000 lire 🍽 🚻 ♿ 🗄 🏭 🅿 ✈ Falconara 30km 🚆 Loreto 2km 🚌 100m

Lucca ▲ 'Il Serchio YH', Via del Brennero, 55100 Lucca LU. 📞 (583) 341811 (Shut: (586) 862517) FAX (583) 341811 Open: 07.00-10.00hrs, 15.30-23.30hrs, 10.3-10.10 (Grps 1.1-31.12) 🛏 90 ⬤ 16,000 lire 🅱🅱inc 🍽 🚻 ♿ 🅿 🚆 Lucca 1.5km 🚌 11, 1 100m ⓡ (Shut: Renato Stasi, Via del Fagiano 7, 57100 Livorno Li)

Marina di Massa e Carrara ▲ Ostello Apuano, Viale delle Pinete 237, 54037 Marina di Massa e Carrara (Partaccia) MS. 📞 (585) 780034 (Shut: (585) 786670) FAX (585) 74858 Open: 07.00-23.30hrs, 16.3-30.9 🛏 200 ⬤ 14,000 lire 🍽 ☞ 🚻 🅿 🚴 ✈ Pisa G Galilei 50km 🚆 Carrara 3km 🚌 Line Via Avenza Mare 300m

Matera ▲ Sassi YH, Via San Giovanni Vecchio 89, 75100 Matera, MT. 📞 (835)

331009 FAX (835) 333733 Open: 08.00-11.00hrs, 15.30-24.00hrs 🛏 50 ⬤ 18,000 lire 🅱🅱inc 🚻 🏭 🚴 ✈ Bari Palese 60km 🚆 Matera 300m 🚌 ap YH

Menaggio ▲ 'La Primula YH', Via Quattro Novembre 86 (Casate), 22017 Menaggio CO. 📞 (344) 32356 FAX (344) 32356 Open: 07.00-10.00hrs, 15.30-23.30hrs, 15.3-5.11 🛏 50 ⬤ 15,000 lire (🚻 16,000 lire) 🅱🅱inc 🍽 ☞ 🚻 🗄 🅿 🚴 ⚑ 🚆 Varenna 4km 🚌 100m

Milano ▲ 3NW 'Piero Rotta YH', Via Martino Bassi 2 (QT8-San Siro), 20148 Milano MI. 📞 (2) 39267095 FAX (2) 39267095 Open: 07.00-10.00hrs, 17.00-00.30hrs, 13.1-23.12 🛏 350 ⬤ 23,000 lire (🚻 25,000 lire) 🅱🅱inc 🚻 🗄 🅿 ✈ Milano Malpensa 40km 🚆 Centrale 3km 🚌 90, 91 300m Ⓤ QT8 MM1 500m

MILANO

Montagnana ▲ 'Rocca degli Alberi YH', Castello degli Alberi (Porta Legnago), 35044 Montagnana PD. 📞 (429) 81076 (Shut: (49) 650124) FAX (429) 81076 (Shut: (49) 650794 Open: 07.00-10.00hrs, 15.00-23.00hrs, 1.4-15.10 🛏 48 ⬤ 16,000 lire (🚻 18,000 lire) 🚻 🏭 🅿 🚆 Montagnana 500m 🚌 200m ⓡ (🚻)

Naples [1N] [IBN] 'Mergellina YH', Salita della Grotta a Piedigrotta 23, 80122 Naples NA. ☎ (81) 7612346 **FAX** (81) 7612391 **Open:** 06.30-11.00hrs, 14.00-00.30hrs ✉ 200 ● 22,000 lire (♦♦♦ and 2 bedded rooms 25,000 lire) BB inc ⦿ ♦♦♦ ⛪ ℗ ✈ Napoli Capodichino 5km ⛴ 2km ➤ Mergellina 200m 🚌 200m U 200m

NAPLES

Nicolosi △ Etna YH, Via della Quercia 7, 95030 Nicolosi CT. ☎ (95) 7914686 **FAX** (95) 7914575 **Open:** 24hrs ✉ 50 ● 19,000 lire ⦿ ♂ ♦♦♦ ♿ ① ⦿ ♨ Alt 700m ☞ ✈ Fontanarossa-Catania 20km A🚌 AST- AMT 300m ⛴ Catania 13km ➤ Catania Centrale 13km 🚌 AST Catania-Nicolosi 300m

Padova ▲ Città di Padova YH, Via A. Aleardi 30, 35122 Padova PD. ☎ (49) 8752219 **FAX** (49) 654210 **Open:** Mon-Fri 07.00-10.00hrs, 14.30-23.00hrs, Sat- Sun 07.00-09.30hrs, 17.00-23.00hrs, 1.2-14.12 ✉ 112 ● 20,000 lire BB inc ♦♦♦ ⛪ ℗ ✈ Venezia Marco Polo 40km ➤ Padova 2km 🚌 3, 8, 12, 18, 22 250m

Parma ▲ 'Cittadella', Parco Cittadella 5, 43100 Parma PR. ☎ (521) 961434 **Open:** 06.30-10.00hrs, 15.30-23.30hrs,

1.4-31.10 ✉ 50 ● 15,000 lire ➤ Parma 1.5km 🚌 400m

Ravenna 'Dante YH', Via Aurelio Nicolodi 12 (quartiere Trieste), 48100 Ravenna RA. ☎ (544) 421164 **FAX** (544) 421164 **Open:** 07.00-10.00hrs, 15.30-23.30hrs, 1.4-31.10 ✉ 140 ● 20,000 lire (♦♦♦ 22,000 lire) BB inc ⦿ ♦♦♦ ℗ ➤ Ravenna 1km 🚌 1, 11 200m

Reggio Emilia YH ▲ Via dell 'Abbadessa 8, 42100 Reggio Emilia RE. ☎ (522) 454795 **Open:** 07.00-10.00hrs, 15.30-24.00hrs ✉ 36 ● 16,000 lire ⦿(L D) (B: Grps) ♂ ℗ ☞ ✈ 50km ➤ Reggio Emilia 500m 🚌 100m R

Rieti- Terminillo 'Ostello della Neve', Anello Panoramico (Campoforogna), 02017 Rieti- Terminillo RI. ☎ (746) 261169 **FAX** (746) 261169 **Open:** 07.00-23.30hrs, 1.12-15.5; 15.6-31.8 ✉ 120 ● 18,000 lire (♦♦♦ 20,000 lire) BB inc ⦿ ♦♦♦ ℗ ☨ Alt 1680m ➤ Rieti 25km 🚌 250m R

Riva del Garda ▲ 'Benacus YH', Piazza Cavour 10, 38066 Riva del Garda TN. ☎ (464) 554911 **FAX** (464) 556554 **Open:** 07.00-12.00hrs, 15.30-24.00hrs, 1.3-31.10 (Grps 20.12-10.1) ✉ 100 ● 16,000 lire BB inc ⦿ ⦿ ℗ ➤ Rovereto 21km 🚌 100m R

Rome (*see town plan on next page*) ▲ [5NW] [IBN] 'Foro Italico - A F Pessina YH', Viale delle Olimpiadi 61, 00194 Roma RM. ☎ (6) 3236267 **FAX** (6) 3242613 **Open:** 07.00-10.00hrs, 12.00-24.00hrs ✉ 334 ● 23,000 lire - 24,000 lire BB inc ⦿ ♿ ⛪ ℗ ✈ Fiumicino 28km ➤ Termini 6km 🚌 32 50m U A Ottaviano 2km

Rovereto Città di Rovereto YH, Via delle Scuole 16/18, 38068 Rovereto TN. ☎ (464) 433707 **FAX** (464) 424137 **Open:** 07.00-10.00hrs,

15.30-23.30hrs ⚲ 90 ⊖ 20,000 lire
[BB]inc ⍾⍾⍾ ⎚ [P] 🚌 Rovereto 400m
🚐 200m

ROME

Salerno ▲ Irno YH, Via Luigi Guercio
112, 84100 Salerno SA. ☎ (89) 790251
FAX (89) 252649 **Open:**
05.00-11.00hrs, 15.30-24.00hrs ⚲
100 ⊖ 12,000 lire ⍾⍾⍾ ⛉ 🚲 🚢 700m
🚐 Salerno 700m 🚐 50m

San Lazzaro di Savena ▲ Village
Centro Europa Uno YH, Localita'
Cicogna, Via Emilia 297, 40068 San
Lazzaro di Savena - BO. ☎ (51) 6258352
FAX (51) 6258352 **Open:** 24hrs ⚲
54 ⊖ 22,000 lire ⛉ ⍾⍾⍾ ⚲ ⎚ 🚲 ✈
Bologna Borgo Panigale 14km 🚐
Bologna Centrale 9km 🚐
94-98-101-916 Extraurbani, 19
(evening)

SAVONA (2 Hostels)

Savona - 'Villa De Franceschini YH' ▲
Via alla Stra 29 (Conca Verde), 17100
Savona SV. ☎ (19) 263222 **FAX** (19)
263222 **Open:** 07.00-10.00hrs,
15.30-23.30hrs, 15.3-15.10 (Grps
1.1-31.12) ⚲ 244 ⊖ 15,000 lire (⍾⍾⍾
17,000 lire) [BB]inc ⍾⍾⍾ ⍾⍾⍾ ⚲ [P] ⚓ 🚐
Savona 3km

Savona - "Priamar Fortress" YH ⚐
Corso Giuseppe Mazzini, Fortezza

Priamar, 17100 Savona SV. ☎ (19)
812653 **FAX** (19) 812653 **Open:**
07.00-10.00hrs, 15.30-23.30hrs ⚲ 60
⊖ 19,000 lire [BB]inc ⍾⍾⍾ ⍾⍾⍾ 🏠 ⚓ 🚐
Savona 1km 🚐 2, 7, 8 100m

Soveria Mannelli ▲ ⎣CC⎤ 'La Pineta
YH', Localita' Bivio Bonacci, 88049
Soveria Mannelli-CZ. ☎ (968) 666079,
662115 **FAX** (968) 666145 **Open:**
07.00-10.00hrs, 15.30-23.30hrs,
1.4-31.10 (Grps 1.1-31.12) ⚲ 25 ⊖
17,000 lire ⍾⍾⍾ [P] ⚓ Alt 850m ✈
Lamezia Terme 25km A🚐 4km 🚐
4km 🚐 Line Catanzaro- Cosenza
100m ⓡ (Grps)

Tavarnelle Val di Pesa ▲ 'Ostello del
Chianti', Via Cassia, 50028 Tavarnelle
Val di Pesa FI. ☎ (55) 8077009 **FAX**
(55) 8050104 **Open:** 07.00-10.00hrs,
15.30-23.30hrs (key on request),
1.3-31.10 ⚲ 54 ⊖ 16,000 lire [BB]inc
⍾⍾⍾ [P] ✈ Firenze Peretola 35km 🚐
Poggibonsi 8km 🚐 Firenze- Siena
200m ⓡ

Trento ⚐ Giovane Europa YH, Via
Manzoni 17, 38100 Trento TN. ☎ (461)
234567 **FAX** (461) 234567 **Open:**
07.00-10.00hrs, 15.30-23.30hrs ⚲
120 ⊖ 20,000 lire [BB]inc ⍾⍾⍾ ⍾⍾⍾ 🏠 🚐
Trento 500m 🚐 50m

Trieste- Grignano ▲ ⎣8NE⎤ Tergeste
YH, Viale Miramare 331, 34136
Trieste, TS ☎ (40) 224102 **FAX** (40)
224102 **Open:** 07.00-10.00hrs,
12.00-24.00hrs ⚲ 74 ⊖ 18,000 lire
[BB]inc ⍾⍾⍾ [P] ⚓ ✈ Ronchi dei Legionari
35km 🚢 8km 🚐 Trieste 5km 🚐
200m ⓡ

Turin (*see town plan on next page*) ▲ ⎣2E⎤
⎣IBN⎤ 'Torino YH', Via Alby 1, 10131
Torino TO. ☎ (11) 6602939 FAX (11)
6604445 Open: 07.00-10.00hrs,
15.30-23.30hrs, 1.2-21.12 ⚲ 76 ⊖
19,000 - 23,000 lire [BB]inc ⍾⍾⍾ ⍾⍾⍾ ⎚ [P]
🚲 🚐 Portanuova 2km 🚐 52 300m

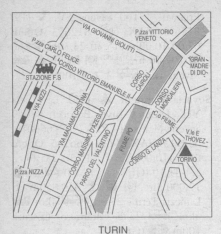

TURIN

37129 Verona VR. ☎ (45) 590360 **FAX**
(45) 8009127 **Open:** 07.00-23.00hrs
🛏 120 ⊖ 20,000 lire (👪 24,000 lire)
BB inc � ☂ 👪 🏠 ▣ ✈ Catullo 15km
🚂 Porta Nuova 3km 🚌 200m

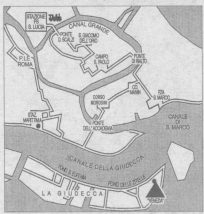

VENICE

Venice ⬛ 1S IBN 'Venezia YH',
Fondamenta Zitelle 86, Isola della
Giudecca, 30123 Venezia VE. ☎ (41)
5238211 **FAX** (41) 5235689 **Open:**
07.00-10.00hrs,   13.00-23.30hrs,
1-15.1; 1.2-31.12 🛏 260 ⊖ 24,000
lire BB inc ❢ 👪 ① ✈ Marco Polo 10km
🚢 Venezia Zattere 🚂 Santa Lucia
2km 🚌 Bus- boat 5, 84 150m
ap Zitelle Ⓡ (1.3-31.10)

Verona ▲ 3NW 'Villa Francescatti YH',
Salita Fontana del Ferro 15 (Veronetta),

Vicenza Piazza Matteotti **Open:** During
'97 🏠 🅿

LUXEMBOURG
LUXEMBOURG
LUXEMBURG
LUXEMBURGO

Centrale des Auberges de Jeunesse Luxembourgeoises, 2 rue du Fort Olisy, BP 374, L-2261 Luxembourg.

📞 (352) 225588 (Office only)
FAX (352) 463987

Office Hours: Monday-Friday, 08.15-12.00hrs and
                     14.00-18.00hrs

Travel Section: Centrale des Auberges de
Jeunesse Luxembourgeoises, 2 rue du Fort Olisy,
BP 374, L-2261 Luxembourg.

Capital:	Luxembourg
Language:	Lëtzebuergesch
Currency:	LUF (franc) and BEF
Population:	400,000
Size:	2,586 sq km

LUXEMBOURG

LUXEMBOURG YOUTH HOSTELS

With 13 hostels, this tiny country is well served by excellent facilities. Most hostels are open 07.30-10.00hrs and 17.00-23.00hrs. It is recommended that you check in between 17.00 and 21.00hrs (Luxembourg City hostel 14.00-23.00hrs). Between 14.00 and 17.00hrs there is only access to the common room.

Expect to pay in the region of 345-650 LUF for one night's bed and breakfast, plus linen hire if needed (125 LUF per stay). Most hostels have self-catering facilities only for individuals, for which there is no charge. Meals are also available. During peak periods your stay may be limited to three days and priority given to younger travellers. We recommend that you book in advance.

From December to February, all hostels except Luxembourg City, Larochette and Wiltz are open exclusively to groups of 10 or more, and reservations must be made at least 24 hours in advance.

PASSPORTS AND VISAS

Visitors from most East European, African, Asian and South American countries require a visa for entry to Luxembourg. For nationals of Australia, Canada and the USA, a valid passport is sufficient.

HEALTH

There are no special entry requirements, but you are advised to take out medical insurance.

BANKING HOURS

Hours of business are 08.30-12.00hrs and 13.00-16.30hrs Monday-Friday. There are also banking facilities in Luxembourg Station which operate 09.00-21.00hrs 7 days a week.

POST OFFICES

08.00-12.00hrs and 14.00-17.00hrs Monday-Friday.

SHOPPING HOURS

Shops are open 09.00-12.00hrs and 13.00-18.00hrs Monday-Saturday, but are closed on Monday morning.

TRAVEL

Rail
Rail travel is good.

Bus
Bus travel is good on weekdays, but there are many restrictions on Sundays.

Driving
Driving is on the right-hand side. A valid driving licence and motor insurance are needed. Safety belts must be worn in the front and back, and cars must carry a first aid kit and warning triangle.

PUBLIC HOLIDAYS

New Year, 1 January; Carnival, 10/11 February; Easter, 30/31 March; Labour Day, 1 May; Ascenscion Day, 8 May; Whitsun, 18/19 May; National Holiday, 23 June; Assumption, 15 August; 1 November; Christmas, 25/26 December.

TELEPHONE INFORMATION

International Code	Country Code	Main City Area Codes
00	352	Luxembourg - no area code

FRANÇAIS

AUBERGES DE JEUNESSE LUXEMBOURGEOISES

Ce tout petit pays, avec 13 auberges, offre d'excellents services. La plupart des auberges sont ouvertes de 7h30 à 10h00 et de 17h00 à 23h00. Il est recommandé d'arriver entre 17h00 et 21h00 (entre 14h00 et 23h00 pour l'auberge située à Luxembourg). Entre 14h00 et 17h00, seule la salle commune est ouverte.

Une nuit vous coûte entre 345 et 650 FLUX, petit déjeuner compris, plus éventuellement la location de draps (125 FLUX par séjour). La plupart des auberges ont une cuisine ajiste seulement pour membres individuels à titre gratuit. Les auberges servent aussi des repas. En haute saison, votre séjour peut être limité à trois nuits et priorité sera donnée aux jeunes voyageurs. Nous vous conseillons de réserver à l'avance.

De décembre à février, toutes les auberges, sauf celles de Luxembourg, Larochette et de Wiltz, ne sont ouvertes que pour les groupes de 10 personnes ou plus, et les réservations doivent être faites au moins 24 heures à l'avance.

PASSEPORTS ET VISAS

Les visiteurs venant de la plupart des pays d'Europe de l'est, d'Afrique, d'Asie et d'Amérique du Sud doivent être en possession d'un visa pour entrer au Luxembourg; un passeport valable suffit pour les citoyens australiens, canadiens et Nord-américains.

SOINS MEDICAUX

Il n'y a pas d'exigences spéciales pour entrer au Luxembourg mais il vous est conseillé de souscrire à une police d'assurance maladie.

HEURES D'OUVERTURE DES BANQUES

Les banques sont ouvertes du lundi au vendredi de 8h30 à 12h et de 13h à 16h30. Il y a aussi un guichet de banque à la gare de Luxembourg ouvert, de 9h à 21h, sept jours sur sept.

BUREAUX DE POSTES

Les bureaux de postes sont ouverts du lundi au vendredi de 8h à 12h et de 14h à 17h.

HEURES D'OUVERTURE DES MAGASINS

Les magasins sont ouverts du lundi au samedi de 9h à 12h et de 13h à 18h; fermés le lundi matin.

DEPLACEMENTS

Trains
Le réseau ferroviaire est bien développé.

Autobus
Les services d'autobus sont bons en semaine, mais sont soumis à de nombreuses restrictions le dimanche.

Automobiles
Conduite à droite. Il est nécessaire d'être en possession d'un permis de conduire valable et d'une assurance-voiture. Le port des ceintures de sécurité à l'avant et à l'arrière est obligatoire. Les voitures doivent être munies d'une trousse de premiers secours et d'un triangle de présignalisation.

JOURS FERIES

Nouvel an, 1er janvier; Carnaval, 10/11 février; Pâques, 30/31 mars; Fête du travail, 1er mai; Ascension, 8 mai; Pentecôte, 18/19 mai; Fête nationale, 23 juin; Assomption, 15 août; 1 novembre; Noël, 25/26 décembre.

TELEPHONE

Indicatif International	Indicatif du Pays	Indicatifs régionaux des Villes principales
00	352	Luxembourg - pas d'indicatif régional

DEUTSCH

LUXEMBURGISCHE JUGENDHERBERGEN

Mit 13 Herbergen verfügt dieses kleine Land über eine große Zahl ausgezeichneter Einrichtungen. Die meisten Herbergen sind von 07.30-10.00 Uhr und von 17.00-23.00 Uhr geöffnet. Wir empfehlen jedoch, zwischen 17.00 und 21.00 Uhr anzukommen (in der Jugendherberge der Stadt Luxemburg zwischen 14.00 und 23.00 Uhr). Zwischen 14.00 und 17.00 Uhr ist nur der Gemeinschaftsraum zugänglich.

Es ist mit einem Preis von ungefähr 345-650 LUF für eine Übernachtung mit Frühstück zu rechnen. Dazu kommt bei Bedarf noch die Gebühr für die Miete von Bettwäsche (125 LUF pro Aufenthalt). Die meisten Herbergen haben kostenlose Einrichtungen nur für individuelle Selbstversorger. Es sind aber auch Mahlzeiten erhältlich. In der Hauptsaison kann der Aufenthalt auf drei Tage beschränkt werden. Jüngere Reisende werden dann bevorzugt behandelt. Wir empfehlen Voranmeldung.

Von Dezember bis Februar sind alle Herbergen, außer in Luxemburg-Stadt, Larochette und Wiltz, nur für Gruppen von mindestens 10 Personen geöffnet, die sich mindestens 24 Stunden im voraus anmelden müssen.

PÄSSE UND VISA

Besucher aus den meisten osteuropäischen, afrikanischen, asiatischen und südamerikanischen Ländern brauchen für die Einreise nach Luxemburg ein Visum. Für Staatsbürger Australiens, Kanadas und der USA genügt ein gültiger Reisepaß.

GESUNDHEIT

Es gibt keine besonderen Vorschriften für die Einreise. Wir raten jedoch zum Abschluß einer Krankenversicherung.

GESCHÄFTSSTUNDEN DER BANKEN

Banken sind montags-freitags von 08.30-12.00 Uhr und von 13.00-16.30 Uhr geöffnet. Auf dem Bahnhof von Luxemburg gibt es ebenfalls eine Bank, die an 7 Tagen der Woche von 09.00-21.00 Uhr geöffnet ist.

POSTÄMTER

Montags-freitags von 08.00-12.00 Uhr und von 14.00-17.00 Uhr

LADENÖFFNUNGSZEITEN

Die Geschäfte sind montags von 13.00-18.00 Uhr und dienstags-samstags von 09.00-12.00 Uhr und von 13.00-18.00 Uhr geöffnet.

REISEN

Eisenbahn
Die Eisenbahnverbindungen sind gut.

Busse
Werktags sind die Busverbindungen gut, aber sonntags sind sie sehr beschränkt.

Autofahren
Es herrscht Rechtsverkehr. Man braucht einen gültigen Führerschein und eine Kraftfahrzeugversicherung. Sowohl auf den Vorder- als auch auf den Rücksitzen müssen Sicherheitsgurte getragen werden, und das Auto muß einen Verbandkasten sowie ein Warndreieck mitführen.

FEIERTAGE
Neujahr, 1. Januar; Karneval, 10/11. Februar; Ostern, 30/31. März; Tag der Arbeit, 1. Mai; Himmelfahrt, 8. Mai; Pfingsten, 18/19. Mai; Nationalfeiertag, 23. Juni; Mariä Himmelfahrt, 15. August; 1. November; Weihnachten, 25/26. Dezember

FERNSPRECHINFORMATIONEN

Internationale Kennzahl	Landes-Kennzahl	größere Städte - Ortsnetzkennzahlen
00	352	Luxemburg - keine Ortsnetzkennzahl

ESPAÑOL

ALBERGUES DE JUVENTUD DE LUXEMBURGO
Con 13 albergues, este pequeño país está bien servido en cuanto a instalaciones de calidad. La mayoría de albergues abren de 07.30 a 10.00 horas y de 17.00 a 23.00 horas. Se recomienda registrarse a la llegada entre las 17.00 y las 21.00 horas (albergue de la ciudad de Luxemburgo, entre 14.00 y 23.00 horas). Entre las 14.00 y las 17.00 horas sólo hay acceso a la sala común.

Se paga alrededor de 345-650 LUF por noche incluyendo desayuno, más alquiler de ropa de cama si es necesario (125 LUF por estancia). La mayoría de albergues tienen cocina para huéspedes individuales, por la que no se cobra. También sirven comidas. En los períodos de máxima actividad la estancia puede verse limitada a 3 noches y se da prioridad a los visitantes más jóvenes. Recomendamos hacer la reserva con antelación.

De diciembre a febrero, todos los albergues excepto el de la ciudad de Luxemburgo, Larochette, y el de Wiltz sólo abren para grupos de 10 personas o más, y se tienen que reservar por lo menos con 24 horas de antelación.

PASAPORTES Y VISADOS
Los ciudadanos de la mayoría de los países de Europa del Este, Africa, Asia y Sudamérica necesitan visado para entrar en Luxemburgo. Para los ciudadanos de Australia, Canadá y EE.UU. basta con un pasaporte válido.

SANIDAD
No hay requisitos especiales de entrada, pero se recomienda suscribir un seguro de asistencia sanitaria.

HORARIO DE BANCOS
El horario es de 08.30 a 12.00 horas y de 13.00 a 16.30 horas de lunes a viernes. En la estación de Luxemburgo hay servicios bancarios abiertos de 09.00 a 21.00 horas 7 días a la semana.

OFICINAS DE CORREOS
De 08.00 a 12.00 horas y de 14.00 a 17.00 horas de lunes a viernes.

HORARIO COMERCIAL
Las tiendas abren de 09.00 a 12.00 horas y de 13.00 a 18.00 horas de lunes a sábado, pero cierran los lunes por la mañana.

DESPLAZAMIENTOS

Tren
Los servicios ferroviarios son buenos.

Autobús
Los servicios de autobús son buenos los días laborables pero muy limitados los domingos.

Coche
La conducción es por la derecha de la carretera. Se necesita un permiso de conducir y seguro válidos. Es obligatorio llevar puestos los cinturones de seguridad en los asientos delanteros y traseros, y los coches deben llevar un botiquín de primeros auxilios y un triángulo de advertencia.

DIAS FESTIVOS

Año Nuevo, 1 enero; Carnaval, 10/11 febrero; Pascua, 30/31 marzo; Fiesta del Trabajo, 1 mayo; Día de la Ascensión, 8 mayo; Pentecostés, 18/19 mayo; Fiesta Nacional, 23 junio; Asunción, 15 agosto; 1 noviembre; Navidad, 25/26 diciembre.

INFORMACION TELEFONICA

Código Internacional	Código Nacional	Indicativo de área de las Ciudades principales
00	352	Luxemburgo - sin indicativo de área

DISCOUNTS AND CONCESSIONS

The Luxembourg City hostel offers discounts on city tours and other attractions.

Hostels in this country may also display this symbol.

Les auberges de ce pays pourront également afficher ce symbole.

Jugendherbergen in diesem Land können auch dieses Symbol zeigen.

Es posible que los albergues de este país exhiban además este símbolo.

Beaufort 6 rue de l'Auberge, L-6315 Beaufort. ☎ (352) 86075 **FAX** (352) 869467 **Shut:** 18-19.1; 22-23.2; 6-30.3; 6.10-2.11; 22-23.11; 24-31.12 🛏 88 ● 345-425 LUF ᴮᴮ|ⁱⁿᶜ ⊙|(L D) ☞ 🅿 🚌 200m **Ⓡ** (Grps)

Bourglinster 2 rue de Gonderange, L-6161 Bourglinster. ☎ (352) 780146 **FAX** (352) 789484 **Shut:** 8-16.2; 1-31.1; 1-9.11; 1-31.12 🛏 90 ● 345-425 LUF ᴮᴮ|ⁱⁿᶜ ⊙|(L D) ☞ 🏠 🅿 🚌 100m **Ⓡ** (Grps)

Echternach 9 rue A Duchscher, L-6434 Echternach. ☎ (352) 720158 **FAX** (352) 728735 **Shut:** 10.2-9.3; 22-23.3; 4-5.10; 22-23.11; 1-31.12 🛏 120 ● 345-425 LUF ᴮᴮ|ⁱⁿᶜ ⊙|(L D) ☞ 👫 ⚲ ⚓ 🚌 200m **Ⓡ** (Grps)

Eisenborn   Centre de Formation et de Rencontre, 5 rue de la Forêt, L-6196 Eisenborn. ☎ (352) 780355, 780544 **FAX** (352) 788459 **Open:** Grps only 🛏 52 ⊖ 650 LUF BB|inc ¶○¶(L D) ♿ P 🚌 500m ®

Ettelbrück   Rue G D Joséphine Charlotte, BP 17, L-9001 Ettelbrück. ☎ (352) 82269 **FAX** (352) 816935 **Shut:** 1-31.1; 22-23.2; 22-23.3; 18-19.10; 8-9.11; 1-31.12 🛏 70 ⊖ 345-600 LUF BB|inc ¶○¶(L D) ♂ ¶¶¶ P 🚕 Ettelbrück 1.5km 🚌 250m ® (Grps)

Grevenmacher   15 Gruewereck, L-6734 Grevenmacher. ☎ (352) 750222 **FAX** (352) 759146 **Open:** 15.3-30.11 🛏 54 ⊖ 345-425 LUF BB|inc ¶○¶(L D) ¶¶¶ P 🚲 🚌 500m

Hollenfels   2 rue du Château, L-7435 Hollenfels. ☎ (352) 307037 **FAX** (352) 305783 **Shut:** 4-12.1; 23.2-22.3; 17.11-15.12 🛏 109 ⊖ 345-425 LUF BB|inc ¶○¶(L D) ♂ ¶¶¶ P 🚌 100m ® (Grps)

Larochette   45 Osterbour, L-7622 Larochette. ☎ (352) 87081, 878324 **FAX** (352) 878326 🛏 74 ⊖ 550-780 LUF BB|inc ¶○¶(L D) ¶¶¶ 🔲 P 🚌 300m

Lultzhausen   rue du Village, L-9666 Lultzhausen. ☎ (352) 89424 **FAX** (352) 899245 **Shut:** 17.2-24.3; 18-19.10; 1-15.11; 15.12-1.1.98 🛏 90 ⊖ 345-425 LUF BB|inc ¶○¶(L D) ♂ ¶¶¶ P ⛑ 🚌 50m ® (Grps)

Luxembourg City-Mansfeld ⌈1 NE⌉ ⌊IBN⌋ ⌊CC⌋ 2 rue du Fort Olisy (Pfaffenthal),

L-2261 Luxembourg. ☎ (352) 226889, 221920 **FAX** (352) 223360 🛏 292 ⊖ ·415-730 LUF BB|inc ¶○¶(L D) ♂ ¶¶¶ 🔲 P 🚲 ✈ Findel 8km A🚌 9 🚆 Luxembourg 3km 🚌 9 from 🚆 150m ap YH

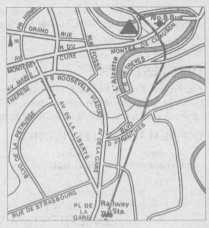

LUXEMBOURG - City

Troisvierges   24-26 rue de la Gare, L-9906 Troisvierges. ☎ (352) 98018 **FAX** (352) 979624 **Open:** 1-31.1; 1.3-14.11; 1-31.12 🛏 60 ⊖ 385-480 LUF BB|inc ¶○¶(L D) ♂ ¶¶¶ P 🚕 Troisvierges 50m

Vianden   3 Montée du Château, L-9408 Vianden. ☎ (352) 84177 **FAX** (352) 849427 **Shut:** 1.1-28.2; 15-16.3; 11-12.10; 15-16.11; 1-31.12 🛏 96 ⊖ 345-425 LUF BB|inc ¶○¶(L D) ♂ ¶¶¶ P 🚌 1.5km ® (Grps)

Wiltz   6 rue de la Montagne, L-9538 Wiltz. ☎ (352) 958039 **FAX** (352) 959440 🛏 72 ⊖ 385-480 LUF BB|inc ¶○¶(L D) ♂ ¶¶¶ 🔲 P 🚲 🚕 Wiltz 2km

NETHERLANDS

PAYS-BAS

NIEDERLANDE

PAISES BAJOS

ASSURED STANDARD

Stichting Nederlandse Jeugdherberg
Centrale NJHC,
Prof Tulpstraat 2, 1018 HA Amsterdam,
Netherlands.

☎ (31) (20) 5513155
FAX (31) (20) 6234986

Office Hours: Monday-Friday, 09.00-17.00hrs

Travel Section: Future Line Travel BV,
Prof Tulpplein 4, 1018 GX Amsterdam,
Netherlands.

☎ (31) (20) 6222859
FAX (31) (20) 6390199

IBN Booking Centre for outward bookings:
■ **Amsterdam**-Future Line Travel, *via Travel Section above.*
☎ (31) (20) 5513155 **FAX** (31) (20) 6390199.

Capital:	Amsterdam
Language:	Dutch
Currency:	Fl (guilders)
Population:	15,423,000
Size:	40,844 sq km

NETHERLANDS

NETHERLANDS

WESTERN UNION | MONEY TRANSFER®
The fastest way to send money worldwide.℠

☎ 06 0566

Money
from home
in minutes
See Page 9

ENGLISH

NETHERLANDS HOSTELS

From the bustle of Amsterdam to the tranquillity of the islands, there are 34 Youth Hostels in the Netherlands to choose from. All hostels are participating in Hostelling International's new Assured Standards Scheme see page six for details.

Where no opening dates are indicated, hostels are open all year, except for the days around Christmas and New Year. Both Amsterdam hostels, Rotterdam, Noordwijk, Texel-Panorama and Terschelling hostels remain open throughout this period. Arnhem is open at Christmas, and Bunnik at New Year. Many are open to groups all year round, and certain hostels will accept advance reservations for their closed periods. You are advised to check with the individual hostel.

The overnight fee varies according to grade and season. Expect to pay in the region of FL 20.75-30.25 including breakfast. Linen hire FL 6.25 although hostellers can bring their own to keep costs down. Family rooms do have different prices.

Category	1/11-1/3	1/3-1/7 1/9-1/11	1/7-1/9 and public holidays
	Fl	Fl	Fl
I	-	20.75	22.75
II	22.75	23.75	26.00
III	24.75	26.00	28.00
IV	27.25	28.25	30.25

PASSPORTS AND VISAS

Citizens of nearly all European countries do not need a visa for a stay of up to three months. All you need is a valid passport and in many cases even a national identity card. Canadians do not require a visa but nationals of other countries outside Europe should check before travelling.

HEALTH

For citizens of the EU the Netherlands provides free medical treatment and prescribed medicine. Presentation of an E111 form, obtainable from your own social security office is sufficient. For citizens outside the EU medical insurance is recommended.

BANKING HOURS

Normal banking hours are 09.00-17.00hrs, Monday to Friday.

POST OFFICES

Post offices are normally open Monday to Friday 09.00-17.00hrs. Some larger post offices are also open on Saturday morning.

SHOPPING HOURS

Most shops are open Monday to Friday 09.00-18.00hrs, and Saturday 09.00-17.00hrs. Late night shopping: Thursday or Friday until 21.00hrs.

TRAVEL

Air

By air, most travellers fly through Amsterdam's Schiphol airport which passenger surveys constantly rate as one of the world's favourite airports. It has around 100 direct connections within Europe, plus the same again worldwide. International flights also serve the airports at Rotterdam, Eindhoven and Maastricht.

Rail
A Netherlands Railways inter-city network links major cities, while smaller towns are served by what the Dutch refer to as 'stop' trains. There's a train every 30 minutes on most lines. Trains are clean, comfortable and run on time.

Bus and Trams
Buy a 'Strippenkaart', valid for buses, trams and metros nationwide. Available from newsagents, tobacconists, stations and VVV offices. The card is based on a zone system and you feed it into punch machines at the stations, on board or have the driver stamp it. You cancel one strip for the trip and one strip per zone you intend travelling through. In one zone the stamp is valid for an hour and you can change vehicles and routes within that time without having to stamp anew - much cheaper than buying a single ticket on a bus or tram. If you travel through more than one zone the stamp has a longer validity (details on the back of the 'Strippenkaart').

Ferry
The major ferry ports are Vlissingen, Rotterdam and Hoek van Holland. French and Belgian ports also provide connections. Ferries are extremely comfortable and well stabilized.

Once in the Netherlands there is a ferry service between Vlissingen and Breskens, at least once every hour but always 10 minutes before the hour.

Driving
The Netherlands has an excellent highway system which links smoothly to the major European autoroutes north, south and east.

Cycling
The Netherlands has an outstanding network of cycling paths, which often lead through beautiful countryside.

PUBLIC HOLIDAYS

New Year's Day, 1 January; Good Friday, 28 March; Easter Monday, 31 March; Ascension Day, 8 May; Whitsun, 18/19 May; Christmas, 25/26 December.

Queen's Day (30 April) and Liberation Day (5 May) are public holidays for the Civil Service. Shops, offices etc need not necessarily be closed.

TELEPHONE INFORMATION

International Code	Country Code	Main City Area Codes	
00	31	Amsterdam	20
		The Hague	70
		Rotterdam	10

When dialling within the Netherlands all area codes should be prefixed with an '0'.

FRANÇAIS

AUBERGES DE JEUNESSE NEERLANDAISES

De la ville affairée d'Amsterdam aux îles tranquilles, vous pouvez choisir parmi 34 auberges de jeunesse aux Pays-Bas. Toutes les auberges participent au nouveau Plan Hostelling International pour la Garantie des Normes en auberge (voir page 15 pour plus de détails).

Si aucune date d'ouverture n'est précisée, cela veut dire que les auberges sont ouvertes toute l'année, sauf aux environs de Noël et du nouvel an. Les deux auberges d'Amsterdam, celles de Rotterdam, Noordwijk, Texel-Panorama et Terschelling restent ouvertes pendant cette période. L'auberge d'Arnhem est ouverte à Noël et celle de Bunnik est ouverte au nouvel an. Beaucoup accueillent les groupes toute l'année et certaines acceptent les réservations à l'avance pour leurs périodes de fermeture. Nous vous conseillons de vérifier auprès de l'auberge en question.

Le prix de la nuitée varie selon la catégorie de l'auberge et la saison. Une nuit vous coûtera entre 20,75 et 30,25 FL, petit-déjeûner compris. La location de draps coûte 6,25 FL bien qu'il soit possible aux ajistes d'apporter les leurs dans un souci d'économie. Les prix sont différents pour les chambres familiales.

Catégorie	1/11 - 1/3	1/3 - 1/7 1/9 - 1/11	1/7 - 1/9 et jours fériés
	Fl	Fl	Fl
I	–	20,75	22,75
II	22,75	23,75	26,00
III	24,75	26,00	28,00
IV	27,25	28,25	30,25

PASSEPORTS ET VISAS

Les citoyens de presque tous les pays européens n'ont pas besoin de visa pour un séjour de trois mois maximum. Un passeport valide sera suffisant, et bien souvent, une carte d'identité nationale fera l'affaire. Les Canadiens n'ont pas besoin de visa mais il est conseillé aux citoyens d'autres pays en dehors de l'Europe de vérifier avant leur départ.

SOINS MEDICAUX

Les Pays-Bas offrent aux citoyens de la CE un traitement médical et des médicaments sur ordonnance gratuits. Le formulaire E111, disponible auprès du bureau de votre sécurité sociale, sera suffisant. Il est conseillé aux citoyens de pays n'appartenant pas à la CE de souscrire à une police d'assurance maladie.

HEURES D'OUVERTURE DES BANQUES

Les banques sont normalement ouvertes de 9h à 17h du lundi au vendredi.

BUREAUX DE POSTE

Les bureaux de poste sont normalement ouverts du lundi au vendredi de 9h à 17h. Certains des bureaux plus importants ouvrent aussi le samedi matin.

HEURES D'OUVERTURE DES MAGASINS

La plupart des magasins sont ouverts du lundi au vendredi de 9h à 18h, et le samedi de 9h à 17h. Ils sont ouverts jusqu'à 21h le jeudi ou le vendredi.

DEPLACEMENTS

Avions

La plupart des passagers aériens passent par l'aéroport Schiphol d'Amsterdam, qui, d'après les sondages, ressort toujours comme l'un des aéroports préférés dans le monde. Il offre environ 100 correspondances directes en Europe et autant dans le monde. Les vols internationaux desservent aussi les aéroports de Rotterdam, Eindhoven et Maastricht.

Trains

Un réseau interurbain, géré par Netherlands Railways, relie les grandes villes, et les villes plus petites sont desservies par ce que les Hollandais appellent des trains 'stop'. Il y a un train toutes les 30 minutes sur la plupart des lignes. Ils sont propres, confortables et à l'heure.

Autobus et Trams

Achetez une carte 'Strippenkaart', valide pour les autobus, les trams et réseaux de métro dans tout le pays. Vous la trouverez en vente dans les maisons de la presse, les bureaux de tabac, les gares et les bureaux VVV. La carte est basée sur un système de zones, et vous devez la faire poinçonner dans des machines prévues à cet effet, en gare ou à bord du véhicule ou bien encore la faire tamponner par le conducteur. Il vous coûtera un coupon de votre carte pour chaque trajet ou pour chaque zone que vous traversez. A l'intérieur d'une zone, le tampon est valable une heure et vous pouvez changer de véhicule et d'itinéraire pendant cette heure sans avoir à faire retamponner votre carte - ce qui revient bien moins cher que d'acheter un ticket simple dans un autobus ou un tram. Si vous voyagez sur plus d'une zone, le tampon est valable plus longtemps (voir le dos de la "strippenkaart" pour plus de détails).

Ferry-boats

Les ports principaux d'où partent les bateaux sont Flessingue, Rotterdam et Hoek van Holland. Les ports français et belges assurent aussi des liaisons. Les bateaux sont extrêmement confortables et bien stabilisés.

Une fois que vous êtes aux Pays-Bas, il y a un service maritime entre Flessingue et Breskens, au moins toutes les heures, mais toujours 10 minutes avant l'heure.

Automobiles

Les Pays-Bas ont un excellent réseau routier, bien relié aux principales autoroutes européennes au nord, au sud et à l'est.

Bicyclettes

Les Pays-Bas ont un excellent réseau de pistes cyclables, qui sillonnent souvent une très belle campagne.

JOURS FERIES

Nouvel an, 1er janvier; Vendredi saint, 28 mars; Lundi de Pâques, 31 mars; Ascension, 8 mai; Pentecôte, 18/19 mai; Noël, 25/26 décembre.

La Fête de la Reine (30 avril) et la Fête de la Libération (5 mai) sont des jours fériés pour les fonctionnaires. Commerces et bureaux privés ne sont pas nécessairement fermés.

TELEPHONE

Indicatif International	Indicatif du Pays	Indicatifs régionaux des Villes principales	
00	31	Amsterdam	20
		La Haye	70
		Rotterdam	10

Pour téléphoner à l'intérieur des Pays Bas, l'indicatif des zones principales devra toujours être précédé d'un 0.

DEUTSCH

NIEDERLÄNDISCHE JUGENDHERBERGEN

In den Niederlanden gibt es von der lebhaften Stadt Amsterdam bis zu den ruhigen Inseln 34 Jugendherbergen. Alle Jugendherbergen sind dem "Assured Standard"-Schema der Hostelling International angeschlossen. (siehe Seite 24).

Wenn keine Öffnungszeiten angegeben sind, ist die Herberge - außer um Weihnachten und Neujahr herum - ganzjährig geöffnet. Beide Amsterdamer Herbergen sowie die Herbergen in Rotterdam, Noordwijk, Texel-Panorama und Terschelling sind auch während dieser Zeit immer geöffnet. Die Herberge in Arnheim ist an Weihnachten und die in Bunnik an Neujahr geöffnet. Viele sind für Gruppen das ganze Jahr über geöffnet, und gewisse Herbergen nehmen für die Zeit, in der sie normalerweise geschlossen sind, Vorausbuchungen an. Wir raten Ihnen, sich bei der jeweiligen Herberge zu erkundigen.

Die Übernachtungen unterscheiden sich im Preis entsprechend der Saison sowie der Klasse. Es ist mit einem Preis von ungefähr hfl 20,75-30,25 (Frühstück einschließlich) zu rechnen. Die Gebühr für die Bettwäsche beträgt hfl 6,25. Es gibt besondere Preise für Familienzimmer. Man kann aber auch eigene Bettwäsche mitbringen.

Kategorie	1/11 - 1/3	1/3 - 1/7	1/7 - 1/9
		1/9 - 1/11	und Feiertage
	Fl	Fl	Fl
I	-	20,75	22,75
II	22,75	23,75	26,00
III	24,75	26,00	28,00
IV	27,25	28,25	30,25

PÄSSE UND VISA

Staatsangehörige fast aller europäischen Länder brauchen für einen Aufenthalt von bis zu drei Monaten kein Visum. Ein gültiger Reisepaß genügt, und in vielen Fällen genügt sogar ein Personalausweis. Kanadier brauchen kein Visum, aber Staatsbürger anderer nichteuropäischer Länder sollten sich vor Antritt ihrer Reise nach den Bestimmungen erkundigen.

GESUNDHEIT

Staatsbürger der EU werden in den Niederlanden kostenlos von einem Arzt behandelt und brauchen auch für verschriebene Arzneimittel nichts zu bezahlen. Es genügt die Vorlage eines Formulars E111, das von Ihrer eigenen Sozialversicherungsbehörde erhältlich ist. Staatsbürgern von Ländern außerhalb der EU wird empfohlen, eine Krankenversicherung abzuschließen.

GESCHÄFTSSTUNDEN DER BANKEN

Banken sind normalerweise montags bis freitags von 09.00-17.00 Uhr geöffnet.

POSTÄMTER

Postämter sind normalerweise montags bis freitags von 09.00-17.00 Uhr geöffnet. Einige größere Postämter sind auch am Samstagvormittag geöffnet.

LADENÖFFNUNGSZEITEN

Die meisten Geschäfte sind montags bis freitags von 09.00-18.00 Uhr und samstags von 09.00-17.00 Uhr geöffnet. Donnerstags oder freitags schließen sie erst um 21.00 Uhr.

REISEN

Flugverkehr

Die meisten Flugreisenden fliegen über den Amsterdamer Flughafen Schiphol, der von den Passagieren bei Umfragen immer wieder als einer der beliebtesten Flughäfen der Welt angegeben wird. Es gibt ungefähr 100 direkte Verbindungen innerhalb Europas und etwa die gleiche Zahl in andere Teile der Welt. Auch die Flughäfen Rotterdam, Eindhoven und Maastricht sind auf internationalen Flugverkehr eingestellt.

Eisenbahn

Das Inter-City-Netz der niederländischen Eisenbahn verbindet alle größeren Städte, während in die kleineren Städte die sogenannten 'Stopp'-Züge fahren. Auf den meisten Strecken verkehrt alle 30 Minuten ein Zug. Die Züge sind sauber, bequem und pünktlich.

Busse und Straßenbahnen

Eine 'Strippenkaart' gilt landesweit für alle Busse, Straßenbahnen und U-Bahnen. Sie kann bei Zeitungs- und Tabakwarenhändlern, auf Bahnhöfen und in VVV-Geschäftsstellen gekauft werden. Die Karte beruht auf einem Zonensystem. Man steckt sie entweder am Bahnhof in eine Entwertungsmaschine oder läßt sie vom Fahrer stempeln. Es wird jeweils ein Streifen für die Fahrt und ein Streifen für jede Zone, durch die man fahren will, entwertet. In einer Zone, gilt der Stempel eine Stunde lang, und innerhalb dieser Zeit kann man von einem Verkehrsmittel auf ein anderes umsteigen oder eine andere Strecke benutzen, ohne die Karte noch einmal stempeln lassen zu müssen. Das ist viel billiger als der Kauf einzelner Karten im Bus oder in der Straßenbahn. Wenn man durch mehrere Zonen fahren will, hat der Stempel eine längere Gültigkeit. (siehe Einzelheiten auf der Rückseite der 'Strippenkaart')

Fähren

Die wichtigsten Fährenhäfen sind Vlissingen, Rotterdam und Hoek van Holland. Französische und belgische Häfen bieten auch gute Verbindungen. Die Fähren sind sehr komfortabel und gut stabilisiert.

Innerhalb der Niederlande gibt es mindestens einmal pro Stunde und immer 10 Minuten vor der vollen Stunde einen Fährenverkehr zwischen Vlissingen und Breskens.

Autofahren

Die Niederlande haben ein ausgezeichnetes Straßennetz mit nahtloser Anbindung an die wichtigsten europäischen Autobahnen in nördlicher, südlicher und östlicher Richtung.

Radfahren

Die Niederlande haben ein hervorragendes Netz von Radwegen, die oft durch besonders schöne Landschaften führen.

FEIERTAGE

Neujahr, 1. Januar; Karfreitag, 28. März; Ostermontag, 31. März; Himmelfahrt, 8. Mai; Pfingsten, 18./19. Mai; Weihnachten, 25./26. Dezember.

Der Geburtstag der Königin, 30. April und der Tag der Befreiung, 5. Mai sind für den Staatsdienst Feiertage. Geschäfte und Buros sind nicht unbedingt geschlossen.

FERNSPRECHINFORMATIONEN

Internationale Kennzahl	Landes- Kennzahl	größere Städte - Ortsnetzkennzahlen	
00	31	Amsterdam	20
		Den Haag	70
		Rotterdam	10

Wann man innerhalb der Niederlande eine Nummer wählt, muß man die Ortsnetzkennzahlen mit der Vorwahl '0' voranstellen.

ESPAÑOL

ALBERGUES DE JUVENTUD NEERLANDESES

Desde el bullicio de Amsterdam a la tranquilidad de las islas, hay 34 albergues juveniles entre los que elegir en los Países Bajos. Todos los albergues participan en el nuevo Plan de Normas Garantizadas, véase la página 33 para más detalles.

Si no se indican las fechas de apertura, significa que el albergue abre todo el año, excepto algunos días en Navidad y Año Nuevo. Los dos albergues de Amsterdam y los de Rotterdam, Noordwijk, Texel-Panorama y Terschelling están abiertos durante esas fechas. El de Arnhem está abierto en Navidad y el de Bunnik en Año Nuevo. Muchos aceptan grupos durante todo el año y algunos aceptan reservas con antelación para sus períodos de cierre. Se recomienda confirmarlo con el albergue deseado.

El precio de una noche varía según la categoría del albergue y la temporada. Se paga alrededor de Fl 20,75-30,25 incluyendo el desayuno. Las habitaciones familiares tienen precios diferentes. El alquiler de la ropa de cama cuesta Fl 6,25, pero se recomienda a los huéspedes que se traigan la suya para más economía.

Categoría	1/11-1/3	1/3-1/7 1/9-1/11	1/7-1/9 y días feriados
	Fl	Fl	Fl
I	-	20,75	22,75
II	22,75	23,75	26,00
III	24,75	26,00	28,00
IV	27,25	28,25	30,25

PASAPORTES Y VISADOS

Los ciudadanos de casi todos los países europeos no necesitan visado para una estancia máxima de tres meses. Lo único que necesitan es un pasaporte válido y, en muchos casos, basta con un documento nacional de identidad. Los canadienses no necesitan visado, pero se recomienda a los ciudadanos de países que no sean europeos verificar antes de viajar si necesitan visado.

SANIDAD

Los Países Bajos ofrecen tratamiento médico y medicamentos con receta gratuitos a los ciudadanos de la CEE. Para ello, basta con presentar el formulario E111 que puede obtener en su propia oficina de la seguridad social. Se recomienda a los ciudadanos de países fuera de la CEE que se hagan un seguro de enfermedad.

HORARIO DE LOS BANCOS

El horario normal es de 09.00 a 17.00 horas de lunes a viernes.

CASAS DE CORREO

Las casas de correo abren normalmente de lunes a viernes de 09.00 a 17.00 horas. Algunas oficinas más grandes también abren los sábados por la mañana.

HORARIO COMERCIAL

La mayoría de las tiendas abre de lunes a viernes de 09.00 a 18.00 horas y los sábados de 09.00 a 17.00 horas. Los jueves y viernes algunas abren hasta las 21.00 horas.

DESPLAZAMIENTOS

Avión
Si viajan en avión, la mayoría de los turistas pasan por el aeropuerto de Schiphol en Amsterdam. Las encuestas realizadas entre los pasajeros siempre lo califican como uno de los mejores del mundo. Ofrece unas 100 conexiones directas dentro de Europa y otras tantas con el resto del mundo. Los vuelos internacionales también van a los aeropuertos de Rotterdam, Eindhoven y Maastricht.

Tren
La red de trenes rápidos interurbanos de la compañía ferroviaria neerlandesa enlaza las principales ciudades, mientras que las poblaciones más pequeñas se alcanzan con lo que los neerlandeses llaman trenes 'con paradas'. En la mayoría de las líneas pasa un tren cada 30 minutos. Los trenes están limpios, son cómodos y puntuales.

Autobús y tranvía
Compre una tarjeta 'Strippenkaart', válida para autobuses, tranvías y metros en todo el país. Se puede comprar en las papelerías, estancos, estaciones y oficinas de VVV. La tarjeta funciona según un sistema de zonas y hay que picarla en una máquina en las estaciones, a bordo del vehículo o pedirle al conductor que la selle. Se pica una tira por trayecto y una tira por zona que se vaya a pasar. Dentro de una zona, el sello vale para una hora y se puede cambiar de vehículo y de ruta dentro de dicho plazo sin tener que picar de nuevo. Es mucho más barato que comprar un billete sencillo en cada autobús o tranvía. Si se atraviesa más de una zona, el sello vale para más tiempo (véase la información al dorso de la 'Strippenkaart').

Ferry
Los principales puertos de ferry son Vlissingen, Rotterdam y Hoek van Holland. Algunos puertos franceses y belgas también ofrecen conexiones. Los ferrys son muy cómodos y bien estabilizados.

Dentro de los Países Bajos, hay un servicio de ferry entre Vlissingen y Breskens por lo menos una vez por hora, pero siempre 10 minutos antes de la hora en punto.

Coche
Los Países Bajos cuentan con una excelente red de autopistas por la que se accede fácilmente a las principales autopistas europeas hacia el norte, sur y este.

Bicicleta
Los Países Bajos tienen una red excepcional de pistas de ciclismo, las cuales, con frecuencia, atraviesan bellos paisajes campestres.

DIAS FESTIVOS

Año Nuevo, 1 enero; Viernes Santo, 28 marzo; Lunes de Pascua, 31 marzo; Día de la Ascensión, 8 mayo; Pentecostés, 18/19 mayo; Navidad, 25/26 diciembre.

El Día de la Reina (30 abril) y el Día de la Liberación (5 mayo) son días feriados para los funcionarios del Estado. Las tiendas y oficinas no siempre cierran estos días.

INFORMACION TELEFONICA

Código Internacional	Código Nacional	Indicativo de área de las Ciudades principales	
00	31	Amsterdam	20
		La Haya	70
		Rotterdam	10

Al marcar un número dentro de los Países Bajos, todos los indicativos de área deben ir precedidos por el número 0.

DISCOUNTS AND CONCESSIONS

Many hostels offer discounts off attractions, tours etc in their area. In addition there are a number of discounts available through Future Line Travel in Amsterdam, including up to 45% off ferry crossings to England.

There is no charge for cash currency exchange when you show your membership card at any GWK office, situated at main railway stations and border crossings.

Budget Rent-a-Car: 15% discount on international standard rates on presentation of a Hostelling International membership card. Tel: (31) (0) 23-5671222 (Reservation Department) for information.

Hostels in this country may also display this symbol.

Les auberges de ce pays pourront également afficher ce symbole.

Jugendherbergen in diesem Land können auch dieses Symbol zeigen.

Es posible que los albergues de este país exhiban además este símbolo.

Ameland ● In '96 the main building of the YH on Ameland was burnt down. There are plans to start a new hostel in combination with an environmental study centre in '97. For more information please ℅ (20) 5513155.

AMSTERDAM (2 Hostels)

Amsterdam - Vondelpark ⚠ IBN Zandpad 5, 1054 GA Amsterdam. ℅ (20) 6831744 **FAX** (20) 6166591 ✉ 476 ● Category III BBinc ⼦❘ ⼦⼦⼦ ⽥ ⼩⽊ ✈ Schiphol 10km 🚌 Amsterdam CS 3.5km 🚋 1, 2, 5 ap Leidseplein Ⓡ Accommodation reserved without a deposit held until 16.00hrs ● Renovations during '97

Amsterdam - Stadsdoelen ▲ 1S IBN Kloveniersburgwal 97, 1011 KB Amsterdam. ℅ (20) 6246832 **FAX** (20) 6391035 ✉ 184 ● Category II BBinc ⼦❘ ⽥ ⼩⽊ ✈ Schiphol 10km 🚌 Amsterdam CS 1.5km 🚋 4, 9, 16, 24, 25 ap Munt Ⓤ Nieuwmarkt Ⓡ Accommodation reserved without deposit held until 16.00hrs

Apeldoorn ⚠ Asselsestraat 330, 7312 TS Apeldoorn. ℅ (55) 3553118 **FAX** (55) 3553811 **Open:** 24.3-27.10 (Grps 1.1-31.12) ✉ 117 ● Category III BBinc ⼦❘ ⼦⼦⼦ ⽥ ⼩⽊ ✈ Schiphol 95km 🚌 Apeldoorn 3km 🚌 4, 7 ap Asselsestraat/Polhoutlaan

Arnhem ⚠ 4NW IBN Diepenbrocklaan 27, 6815 AH Arnhem. ℅ (26) 4420114 **FAX** (26) 3514892 ✉ 194 ● Category III BBinc ⼦❘ ⼦⼦⼦ ⽥ ⼩⽊ ✈ Schiphol 110km 🚌 Arnhem 4km 🚌 GVA 3 ap 'Gemeente Ziekenhuis'

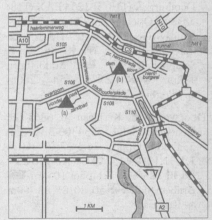

AMSTERDAM -
(a) Vondelpark, (b) Stadsdoelen

Bakkum ▲ Heereweg 84, 1901 ME Bakkum. ℅ (251) 652226 **FAX** (251) 670027 ✉ 152 ● Category II BBinc ⼦❘ ⼦⼦⼦ ⼩ ⽥ ⼩ ✈ Schiphol 40km 🚌 Castricum 3.5km 🚌 NZH 164 Ⓡ (1.11-1.4)

Bergen op Zoom ▲ Boslustweg 1, 4624 RB Bergen op Zoom. ℅ (164) 233261 **FAX** (164) 239133 **Open:**

24.3-27.10 (Grps 1.1-31.12) ✉ 176 ● Category II [BB]inc ⑩ ✿ ⑈ ⑤ P ⑯ ⚠ ✈ Schiphol 150km 🚍 Bergen op Zoom 3km 🚌 21, 22 800m ap Hospital

Bunnik ▲ Rhijnauwenselaan 14, 3981 HH Bunnik. ✆ (30) 6561277 FAX (30) 6571065 ✉ 140 ● Category II [BB]inc ⑩ ⑈ ⑃ P ⚠ ✈ Schiphol 55km 🚍 CS Utrecht 5km 🚌 40, 41 ap Rhijnauwen YH

Chaam ▲ Putvenweg 1, 4861 RB Chaam. ✆ (161) 491323 FAX (161) 491756 Open: 24.3-27.10 (Grps 1.1-31.12) ✉ 119 ● Category II [BB]inc ⑩ ⑈ ⑁ ⑤ P ✈ Schiphol 133km 🚍 Breda/Tilburg 15km 🚌 BBA 132 3km ap Chaam Dorpstraat

Domburg ⛺ Duinvlietweg 8, 4356 ND Domburg. ✆ (118) 581254 FAX (118) 583342 Open: 24.3-27.10 + Spring-holiday (Grps 1.1-31.12) ✉ 106 ● Category III [BB]inc ⑩ ⑈ ⑃ ⚠ ✈ Schiphol 190km 🚍 Middelburg 13km 🚌 ZWN 54 200m ap Westhove YH

Doorwerth ▲ Kerklaan 50, 6865 GZ Doorwerth. ✆ (26) 3334300 FAX (26) 3337060 Open: 24.3-27.10 (Grps 1.1-31.12) ✉ 132 ● Category III [BB]inc ⑩ ⑈ P ⑯ ✈ Schiphol 105km 🚍 Arnhem 8km 🚌 50, 80, 81, 88 700m ap Kerklaan

Dordrecht ⛺ Baanhoekweg 25, 3313 LP Dordrecht. ✆ (78) 6212167 FAX (78) 6212163 ✉ 121 ● Category III [BB]inc ⑩ ⑈ ⑁ ⑤ P ⑯ ⚠ ✈ Schiphol 90km 🚍 Dordrecht 7km 🚌 5 50m ap Holdiepweg

Egmond ▲ Herenweg 118, 1935 AJ Egmond. ✆ (72) 5062269 FAX (72) 5067034 Open: 24.3-27.10 (Grps 1.1-31.12) ✉ 130 ● Category II [BB]inc ⑩ ⑈ ⑤ P ⑯ ⚠ ✈ Schiphol 50km 🚍 Heiloo 4km, Castricum 6km 🚌

from Heiloo NZH 166, from Castricum NZH 164 ap Rinnegom

Elst {U} ▲ Veenendaalsestraatweg 65, 3921 EB Elst. ✆ (318) 471219 FAX (318) 472460 Open: 14.6-17.8 (Grps 1.1-31.12) ✉ 200 ● Category II [BB]inc ⑩ ⑈ ⑃ ⑤ P ⑯ ✈ Schiphol 80km 🚍 Veenendaal - Centrum 4.5km 🚌 CN 51 ap YH

Gorssel ▲ Dortherweg 34, 7216 PT, Gorssel. ✆ (573) 431615 FAX (573) 431832 Open: 24.3-27.10 (Grps 1.1-31.12) ✉ 92 ● Category II [BB]inc ⑩ ✿ ⑈ ⑤ ⑯ ✈ Schiphol 110km 🚍 Deventer 10km 🚌 GVM bus 36, 56 Deventer-Borculo ap Drie Kievitten

Grou ▲ Raadhuisstraat 18, 9001 AG Grou. ✆ (566) 621528 FAX (566) 621005 ✉ 210 ● Category III [BB]inc ⑩ ⑈ ⑃ ⑤ P ⑯ ⚠ ✈ Schiphol 140km 🚍 Grou-Irnsum 1km 🚌 FRAM 95

Den Haag ▲ [7SW] Monsterseweg 4, 2553 RL Den Haag. ✆ (70) 3970011 FAX (70) 3972251 ✉ 335 ● Category III (from 1.6 category IV) [BB]inc ⑩ ⑈ P ⚠ ✈ Schiphol 50km 🚍 Den Haag CS 10km 🚌 ZWN 122, 123 ap Ockenburgh YH ● From 1.6: at Scheepmakers-straat 27, 2515 VA Den Haag.

Haarlem ▲ Jan Gijzenpad 3, 2024 CL Haarlem. ✆ (23) 5373793 FAX (23) 5371176 Open: 24.3-27.10 ✉ 110 ● Category I [BB]inc ⑩ ✿ P ⚠ ✈ Schiphol 15km 🚍 Santpoort- Zuid 500m, Haarlem 3km 🚌 2 ap YH

The Hague ☞ Den Haag

Heeg ▲ 't Eilân 65, 8621 CT Heeg. ✆ (515) 442258 FAX (515) 442550 Open: 24.3-27.10 (Grps 1.1-31.12) ✉ 160 ● Category II [BB]inc ⑩ ⑈ ⑃ ⑤ P ⑯ ✈ Schiphol 125km 🚍 Ylst 5km 🚌 Fram 46

Heemskerk ▲ Tolweg 9, 1967 NG Heemskerk. ☏ (251) 232288 **FAX** (251) 251024 **Open:** 24.3-27.10 (Grps 1.1-31.12) ⇄ 176 ⊜ Category III ᴮᴮⁱⁿᶜ ⑪ ⑯ 🏠 🅿 ⚒ ✈ Schiphol 25km 🚌 Heemskerk 2km, Beverwijk 4km 🚐 NZH 176 from Beverwijk

Hoorn ▲ Schellinkhouterdijk 1a, 1621 MJ Hoorn. ☏ (229) 214256 **Open:** 1.7-1.9 ⇄ 50 ⊜ Category I ᴮᴮⁱⁿᶜ ⑪ 🅿 ⚓ ✈ Schiphol 50km 🚌 Hoorn 2km 🚐 NZH 133, 137, 147 ap Julianaplein

Maastricht ⚠ ⟦IBN⟧ Dousbergweg 4, 6216 GC Maastricht. ☏ (43) 3466777 **FAX** (43) 3466755 ⇄ 250 ⊜ Category III ᴮᴮⁱⁿᶜ ⑪ ⑯ 🅿 ✈ Schiphol 225km 🚌 Maastricht 4km 🚐 8

Meppel ▲ Leonard Springerlaan 14, 7941 GW Meppel. ☏ (522) 251706 **FAX** (522) 262287 **Open:** 24.3-15.9 (Grps 1.1-31.12) ⇄ 74 ⊜ Category II ᴮᴮⁱⁿᶜ ⑪ ⑯ 🅿 ✈ Schiphol 140km 🚌 Meppel 500m

Nijverdal ▲ Duivenbreeweg 43, 7441 EA Nijverdal. ☏ (548) 612252 **FAX** (548) 615372 **Open:** 1.5-1.9 (Grps 1.1-31.12) ⇄ 96 ⊜ Category II ᴮᴮⁱⁿᶜ ⑪ ⑯ 🅿 ⚒ ✈ Schiphol 145km 🚌 Nijverdal 2.5km, Almelo 16km 🚐 from Almelo TET 71, 74 or 75

Noordwijk ▲ Langevelderlaan 45, 2204 BC Noordwijk. ☏ (252) 372920 **FAX** (252) 377061 **Open:** 24.3-27.10 (Grps 1.1-31.12) ⇄ 130 ⊜ Category III ᴮᴮⁱⁿᶜ ⑪ ⑯ 🅿 ⚒ ✈ Schiphol 35km 🚌 Leiden 15km 🚐 60, 61 600m ap Langeveld ⓡ (1.11-1.4)

Roderesch ▲ Esweg 18, 9305 TB Roderesch. ☏ (50) 5019114 **FAX** (50) 5013932 **Open:** 2.6-29.8 ⇄ 96 ⊜ Category II ᴮᴮⁱⁿᶜ ⑪ ⑯ ⑯ ⚒ ✈ Schiphol 185km 🚌 Groningen 16km, Assen 20km 🚐 Groningen FRAM 82, Assen FRAM 83 1km

Rotterdam ▲ ⟦2 SW⟧ ⟦IBN⟧ Rochussenstraat 107-109, 3015 EH Rotterdam. ☏ (10) 4365763 **FAX** (10) 4365569 ⇄ 152 ⊜ Category III ᴮᴮⁱⁿᶜ ⑪ ⑯ ✈ Schiphol 95km 🚌 Rotterdam CS 3km 🚋 4 ap Saftlevenstraat ⟦U⟧ Dijkzigt

ROTTERDAM

Scheemda ▲ Esbörgstraat 16, PO Box 12, 9679 ZG Scheemda. ☏ (597) 591255 **FAX** (597) 591132 **Open:** 1.1-15.12 ⇄ 100 ⊜ Category I ᴮᴮⁱⁿᶜ ⑪ ⑯ 🅿 ✈ Schiphol 225km 🚌 Scheemda 1.5km 🚐 79 from Groningen or Winschoten ap YH

Sneek ▲ Oude Oppenhuizerweg 20, 8606 JC Sneek. ☏ (515) 412132 **FAX** (515) 412188 **Open:** 24.3-27.10 (Grps 1.1-31.12) ⇄ 112 ⊜ Category II ᴮᴮⁱⁿᶜ ⑪ ⑯ (partly) ⑯ 🅿 ⚓ ✈ Schiphol 135km 🚌 Sneek 2.5km 🚐 FRAM 99

Soest ▲ Bosstraat 16, 3766 AG Soest. ☏ (35) 6012296 **FAX** (35) 6028921 **Open:** 24.3-27.10 (Grps 1.1-31-12) ⇄ 138 ⊜ Category II ᴮᴮⁱⁿᶜ ⑪ ⑯ ⑯ 🅿 ✈ Schiphol 50km 🚌 Soest-Zuid 500m 🚐 70, 72

Terschelling ⚠ Burg Van Heusdenweg 39, 8881 EE West- Terschelling. ☏ (562) 442338 **FAX** (562) 443312 ⇄

144 ● Category III [BB]inc ⍟ 🚻 ♿ ①
⬛ P ⛴ ⬥ ✈ Schiphol 130km 🚢
Harlingen-Terschelling 🚌 Harlingen
- Haven 🚌 any from 🚢 ap YH Ⓡ
(28.10-23.3)

TEXEL (2 Hostels)

Texel - **Panorama** ⛰ Schansweg 7, 1791
LK Den Burg, Texel. 📞 (222) 315441
FAX (222) 313889 **Open:** 1.4-1.11
(Grps 1.1-31.12) ✉ 140 ● Category
III [BB]inc ⍟ 🚻 ① P ⛴ ⬥ ✈ Schiphol
95km 🚢 Den Helder-Texel 🚌 Den
Helder 10km 🚌 29 from 🚢 300m
ap Schilderend Ⓡ (1.11-1.4)

Texel - **De Eyercoogh** ⛰ For
information and reservation please
contact 'Panorama', Schansweg 7, 1791
LK Den Burg, Texel 📞 (222) 315441
FAX (222) 313889 **Open:** 1.7-31.8
(Grps 1.4-1.11) ✉ 102 ● Category I
[BB]inc ⍟ ① P ⛴ ⬥ ✈ Schiphol 95km
🚢 Den Helder-Texel 🚌 Den Helder
· 10km 🚌 28 from 🚢 200m
ap Gasthuisstraat

Valkenswaard ⛰ Past Heerkensdreef
20, 5552 BG Valkenswaard. 📞 (40)
2015334 **FAX** (40) 2047932 **Open:**
24.3-27.10 (Grps 1.1-31.12) ✉ 136
● Category II [BB]inc ⍟ 🚻 ⬛ P ⛴ ✈
Schiphol 145km 🚌 Eindhoven 9km
🚌 BBA 171, 172, 177 ap first stop
in Valkenswaard

NORWAY
NORVEGE
NORWEGEN
NORUEGA

ASSURED STANDARD

Norske Vandrerhjem,
Dronningensgate 26, N-0154 Oslo, Norway.

☎ (47) 22421410
FAX(47) 22424476

Office Hours: Monday-Friday, 08.30-16.00hrs

Travel Section: Terra Nova Travel, Dronningensgate 26,
N-0154 Oslo, Norway.

☎ (47) 22421410
FAX(47) 22424476

Terra Nova Travel, Nygaten 3,
N-5017 Bergen, Norway.

☎ (47) 55322377
FAX (47) 55323015

IBN Booking Centres for outward bookings.
■   Oslo - **Terra Nova Travel,** *via Travel Section above.*

Capital:	Oslo
Language:	Norwegian
Currency:	NOK (krone)
Population:	4,155,000
Size:	324,219 sq km

NORWAY

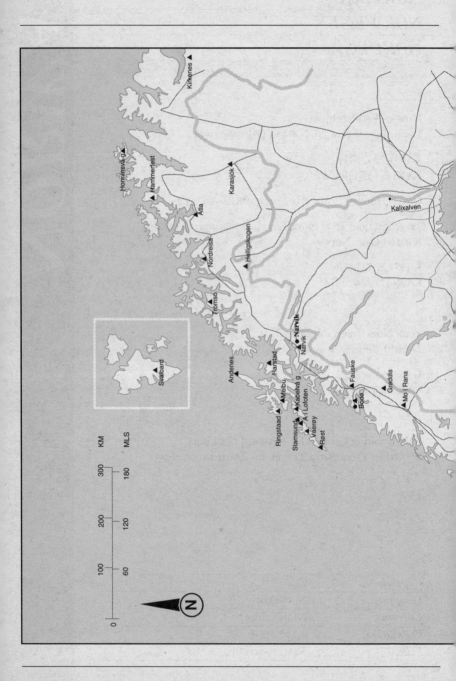

NORWEGIAN HOSTELS

All hostels in Norway have excellent family accommodation. Single and double rooms are available on request.

Hostels are open 07.00-23.00hrs, although most hostels are closed in the middle of the day. Expect to pay in the region of 70-165 NOK per night plus linen hire if required. Breakfast is often included in the overnight price. Self-catering facilities do not usually provide pots and pans, crockery or cutlery.

Advance booking is essential between 1 October and 30 April. Bookings for individuals are accepted without prepayment.

HEALTH

Nationals of countries which have a reciprocal agreement with the Norwegian Ministry of Health and Social Affairs have the same rights as Norwegians to medical care on production of their passport. Ambulance travel and hospital in-patient treatment is free. Doctors, however, are paid in cash. You also have to pay for prescribed medicines.

If you need attention outside surgery hours, there will be a casualty ward you can go to.

It is always advisable to take out medical insurance before you travel, even more so if your own country does not have a reciprocal agreement with Norway.

BANKING HOURS

Every large village and town in Norway has a bank, although rural branches may have restricted opening hours. Standard opening times are Monday to Friday 08.15-15.00hrs (15.30hrs in winter) and Thursday 08.15-17.00hrs. In the Oslo area several branches of NOR Bank are open until 16.00hrs, Monday to Thursday, between 6 July and 14 August.

POST OFFICES

Opening hours vary somewhat from place to place but are generally from 08.00 or 08.30hrs to 16.00 or 17.00hrs, Monday to Friday, and from 08.00 to 13.00hrs on Saturdays.

SHOPPING HOURS

Generally 09.00-17.00hrs, but many shops in the larger towns are open until 18.00-20.00hrs or even later.

TRAVEL

Air

Due to the expanse of the country Norway is exceptionally well served by domestic airlines. There are about fifty airports and airfields making even the far north seem like a quick jaunt away. Fares are very reasonable, young people up to 25 years of age can get a half-price standby ticket. Very low off peak offers, called 'mini pris' and 'lavpris', are available.

Rail

Norwegian State Railways has a well developed network running right from the southern tip, all the way up to Bodø on the north west coast. The trains are modern and efficient and most have compartments specially adapted for the disabled on medium and long distance routes. Fares are reasonable and there are a wide range of special reductions available. For instance, the ScanRail Pass is a flexible rail pass for Scandinavia.

Bus
Where the rail network stops, the bus goes further. You will find that you can get to practically any little village you want to by bus. Usually it is not necessary to book in advance, but pay the driver on boarding. NOR-WAY Bussekspress guarantees a seat for all passengers.

Ferry
Norway's geography means that taking a boat is often the quickest and cheapest way of getting around. In the fjord area, it is unavoidable to all intents and purposes. These ferries operate from very early in the morning until late at night, providing a continuous service and you never have to wait long.

Driving
A full driving licence is required along with your registration documents and a minimum of third party insurance, a green card is highly recommended. You must carry a red warning triangle to leave in front of your car in case of a breakdown.

It is obligatory to drive with dipped headlights on, even during the day, and all passengers must wear a seat-belt. Right-hand drive cars must have black adhesive triangles, often supplied by the ferry company you travel with, or clip on beam deflectors, so as not to dazzle oncoming drivers.

TELEPHONE INFORMATION

International Code	Country Code	Main City Area Codes
095	47	No area codes

FRANÇAIS

AUBERGES DE JEUNESSE NORVEGIENNES

Toutes les auberges norvégiennes ont d'excellentes chambres familiales. Des chambres à un ou deux lits sont disponibles sur demande.

Les auberges sont ouvertes de 7h à 23h, bien que la plupart d'entre elles soient fermées au milieu de la journée. Une nuit vous coûtera entre 70 et 165 KRN, plus location de draps le cas échéant. Le petit déjeûner est souvent inclus dans le prix de la nuitée. Les cuisines à la disposition des voyageurs ne sont en principe pas équipées de casseroles, d'assiettes ni de couverts.

Il est essentiel de réserver à l'avance entre le 1er octobre et le 30 avril. Les réservations faites par des individus sont acceptées sans paiement d'avance.

SOINS MEDICAUX

Les citoyens de pays ayant passé un accord réciproque avec le Ministère norvégien de la Santé et des Affaires sociales ont les mêmes droits que les Norvégiens quand il s'agit d'obtenir des soins médicaux, au vu de leur passeport. Les ambulances et les hospitalisations sont gratuites. Toutefois, les médecins sont payés en espèces. Vous devrez aussi payer les médicaments prescrits par le médecin.

Si vous devez voir un médecin en dehors des heures de consultation, il faudra vous rendre à une salle des urgences.

Il est toujours conseillé de souscrire à une police d'assurance maladie avant le départ, surtout si votre pays n'a pas passé d'accord réciproque avec la Norvège.

HEURES D'OUVERTURE DES BANQUES

Tous les grands villages et toutes les villes de Norvège ont une banque, bien que les succursales rurales puissent avoir des horaires réduits. Les heures d'ouverture normales vont du lundi au vendredi, de 8h15 à 15h (15h30 en hiver). Le jeudi, les banques sont ouvertes de 8h15 à 17h. Aux alentours d'Oslo, plusieurs succursales de la banque NOR sont ouvertes jusqu'à 16h, du lundi au jeudi, entre le 6 juillet et le 14 août.

BUREAUX DE POSTE

Les heures d'ouverture varient quelque peu selon les endroits, mais en général, les bureaux de poste ouvrent de 8h ou 8h30 à 16h ou 17h, du lundi au vendredi, et de 8h à 13h le samedi.

HEURES D'OUVERTURE DES MAGASINS

En général, les magasins sont ouverts de 9h à 17h, mais de nombreux magasins dans les plus grandes villes ouvrent jusqu'à 18h00-20h00 et même plus tard.

DEPLACEMENTS

Avions

Vu l'étendue du pays, la Norvège est exceptionnellement bien desservie par des lignes intérieures. Il y a environ 50 aéroports et terrains d'aviation grâce auxquels même l'extrême nord ne paraît être qu'à une courte distance. Les tarifs sont très raisonnables et les jeunes jusqu'à 25 ans peuvent bénéficier de billets demi-tarif stand-by (sans garantie). Il est possible d'obtenir, pendant la basse saison, des tarifs appelés 'mini pris' et 'lavpris'.

Trains

Les chemins de fer norvégiens ont un réseau très développé, partant de l'extrémité sud jusqu'à Bodø sur la côte nord-ouest. Les trains sont modernes, ils fonctionnent bien et offrent pour la plupart des compartiments spécialement équipés pour les personnes handicapées, sur les moyennes et longues distances. Les tarifs sont raisonnables et de nombreuses réductions spéciales sont disponibles. Par exemple, la carte ScanRail est une carte flexible pour la Scandinavie.

Autobus

Là où le train s'arrête, le bus continue. Vous trouverez que vous pouvez vous rendre dans pratiquement n'importe quel petit village en autobus. En principe, il n'est pas nécessaire de réserver à l'avance, mais vous devez payer le conducteur en montant à bord. La compagnie NOR-WAY Bussekspress garantit un siège pour tous les passagers.

Ferry-boats

La situation géographique de la Norvège fait que souvent, la façon la plus rapide et la moins chère de se déplacer est par bateau. Dans la région des fjords, cela est tout à fait inévitable. Ces bateaux sont en service très tôt le matin jusque tard le soir, assurant ainsi un service continu, sans jamais obliger les voyageurs à attendre longtemps.

Automobiles

Les conducteurs doivent être munis d'un permis de conduire et des papiers de leur véhicule, ainsi qu'une assurance au tiers au minimum; la carte verte est fortement conseillée. Il est obligatoire de transporter un triangle de présignalisation, qui doit être placé à l'avant du véhicule en panne.

Il est obligatoire de conduire en codes, même pendant la journée, et tous les passagers doivent porter une ceinture de sécurité. Les phares des véhicules ayant le volant à droite doivent être munis de triangles noirs adhésifs, souvent fournis par les compagnies maritimes, ou de déflecteurs amovibles, de façon à ne pas éblouir les conducteurs venant en face.

TELEPHONE

Indicatif International	Indicatif du Pays	Indicatifs régionaux Villes principales
095	47	Pas d'indicatifs régionaux

DEUTSCH

NORWEGISCHE JUGENDHERBERGEN

Alle Herbergen in Norwegen verfügen über ausgezeichnete Familienunterkünfte. Auf Anfrage gibt es auch Einzel- und Doppelzimmer.

Die Herbergen sind von 07.00-23.00 Uhr geöffnet, die meisten schließen zur Mittagszeit. Es ist mit einem Preis von 70-165 nkr pro Nacht plus, bei Bedarf, einer Gebühr für die Miete von Bettwäsche zu rechnen. Oft ist das Frühstück in dem Preis der Übernachtung enthalten. Für Selbstversorger werden normalerweise keine Töpfe oder Pfannen und weder Geschirr noch Besteck zur Verfügung gestellt.

Zwischen dem 1. Oktober und dem 30. April ist Vorausbuchung erforderlich. Bei Einzelbuchungen wird keine Vorauszahlung verlangt.

GESUNDHEIT

Staatsbürger von Ländern, die mit dem norwegischen Ministerium für Gesundheit und soziale Angelegenheiten einen gegenseitigen Vertrag geschlossen haben, haben bei Vorlage ihres Passes den gleichen Anspruch auf ärztliche Behandlung wie Norweger. Die Beförderung mit einem Krankenwagen und stationäre Behandlung in einem Krankenhaus sind kostenlos. Ärzte müssen jedoch in bar bezahlt werden. Man muß auch selbst für verschriebene Arzneimittel aufkommen.

Für Patienten, die außerhalb der Sprechstundenzeit einen Arzt brauchen, gibt es einen Notdienst.

Es empfiehlt sich immer, vor Antritt der Reise eine Krankenversicherung abzuschließen, besonders, wenn das eigene Land keinen gegenseitigen Vertrag mit Norwegen hat.

GESCHÄFTSSTUNDEN DER BANKEN

In jedem größeren Dorf und jeder Stadt in Norwegen gibt es eine Bank. Die ländlichen Filialen haben aber oft beschränkte Öffnungszeiten. Die normalen Öffnungszeiten sind montags bis freitags von 08.15-15.00 Uhr (15.30 Uhr im Winter) und donnerstags von 08.15-17.00 Uhr geöffnet. In der Gegend von Oslo sind verschiedene Filialen der NOR Bank vom 6. Juli bis 14. August montags bis donnerstags bis 16.00 Uhr geöffnet.

POSTÄMTER

Die Öffnungszeiten sind von Ort zu Ort etwas unterschiedlich, aber im allgemeinen sind Postämter montags bis freitags von 08.00 oder 08.30 Uhr bis 16.00 oder 17.00 Uhr und samstags von 08.00 bis 13.00 Uhr geöffnet.

LADENÖFFNUNGSZEITEN

Normalerweise von 09.00-17.00 Uhr, aber viele Geschäfte in den größen Städten sind bis 20.00 Uhr oder später geöffnet.

REISEN

Flugverkehr

Wegen der weiten Ausdehnung des Landes ist der inländische Flugverkehr in Norwegen besonders gut ausgebaut. Es gibt etwa 50 Flughäfen und Flugfelder, so daß selbst der ferne Norden nur einen Katzensprung entfernt ist. Das Fliegen ist sehr preiswert. Junge Leute bis zu 25 Jahren können zum halben Preis ein Standby-Ticket bekommen. Außerhalb der Saison gibt es besonders preisgünstige Flüge zum sogenannten 'mini pris' und 'lavpris'.

Eisenbahn

Die norwegische Staatsbahn verfügt über ein gut ausgebautes Schienennetz, das sich von der Südspitze des Landes bis hinauf nach Bodø an der Nordwestküste erstreckt. Die Züge sind modern und leistungsfähig, und die meisten haben auf mittleren und langen Strecken behindertenfreundliche Abteile. Die Fahrpreise sind angemessen, und es gibt vielerlei Sonderermäßigungen. So ist zum Beispiel der ScanRail Pass ein flexibler Eisenbahnpaß für Skandinavien.

Busse

Wo das Schienennetz aufhört, geht es mit dem Bus weiter. Sie werden feststellen, daß Sie praktisch jedes kleine Dorf mit dem Bus erreichen können. Im allgemeinen braucht man nicht zu reservieren. Man bezahlt einfach den Fahrer beim Einstieg in den Bus. NOR-WAY Bussekspress garantiert allen Passagieren einen Sitzplatz.

Fähren

Aufgrund der geographischen Lage Norwegens kommt man in diesem Land oft mit dem Schiff am schnellsten und billigsten von Ort zu Ort. Im Fjord-Gebiet geht das eigentlich gar nicht anders. Diese Fähren verkehren ununterbrochen vom frühen Morgen bis spät in die Nacht, so daß man nie lange zu warten braucht.

Autofahren

Man braucht einen Führerschein sowie Autopapiere und mindestens eine Haftpflichtversicherung. Eine grüne Karte ist sehr empfehlenswert. Man muß ein rotes Warndreieck mit sich führen, das im Falle einer Panne vor dem Wagen aufgestellt werden kann.

Man muß auch bei Tag immer mit Abblendlicht fahren, und alle Passagiere müssen einen Sicherheitsgurt tragen. Fahrzeuge mit Rechtslenkung müssen auf ihre Scheinwerfer schwarze Dreiecke kleben, die oft von den Fährunternehmen verteilt werden, oder Strahlablenker aufklemmen, damit entgegenkommende Fahrer nicht geblendet werden.

FERNSPRECHINFORMATIONEN

Internationale Kennzahl	Landes- Kennzahl	größere Städte - Ortsnetzkennzahlen
095	47	Keine Ortsnetzkennzahlen

ESPAÑOL

ALBERGUES DE JUVENTUD NORUEGOS

Todos los albergues de Noruega ofrecen excelente alojamiento familiar. También se pueden solicitar habitaciones individuales y dobles.

Los albergues abren de 07.00 a 23.00 horas, aunque la mayoría de los albergues cierra unas horas durante el día. Se paga alrededor de 70-165 NOK por noche más alquiler de ropa de cama, de ser necesario. El desayuno está incluido en el precio de la estancia de noche. Las cocinas para huéspedes no acostumbran a tener cazos, sartenes, vajilla ni cubertería.

Entre el 1 de octubre y el 30 de abril es imprescindible hacer la reserva con antelación. Las reservas individuales se aceptan sin necesidad de anticipado.

SANIDAD

Los ciudadanos de países que tengan un acuerdo mutuo con el Ministerio Noruego de Sanidad y Asuntos Sociales tienen los mismos derechos que los noruegos a recibir atención médica previa presentación de su pasaporte. El servicio de ambulancia y el tratamiento hospitalario para ingresados es gratuito. No obstante, hay que pagar a los médicos en efectivo. También se paga por las medicinas recetadas.

Si precisa atención médica fuera de las horas de consulta, puede dirigirse al departamento de urgencias.

Se recomienda suscribir un seguro médico antes de viajar, sobre todo si su país de origen no tiene acuerdo mutuo con Noruega.

HORARIO DE BANCOS

Todos los pueblos grandes de Noruega tienen un banco, aunque las sucursales rurales en algunos casos tienen un horario limitado de atención al público. El horario normal es de lunes a viernes de 08.15 a 15.00 horas (15.30 horas en invierno) y los jueves de 08.15 a 17.00 horas. En la zona de Oslo varias sucursales del Banco NOR abren hasta las 16.00 horas de lunes a jueves entre el 6 de julio y el 14 de agosto.

CASAS DE CORREOS

El horario varía un poco de una población a otra, pero por lo general es de 08.00 o 08.30 horas a 16.00 o 17.00 horas, de lunes a viernes, y de 08.00 a 13.00 horas los sábados.

HORARIO COMERCIAL

Por lo general, las tiendas abren de 09.00 a 17.00 horas, pero muchas tiendas en las ciudades más grandes abren hasta las 18.00-20.00 horas e incluso más tarde.

DESPLAZAMIENTOS

Avión

Dada la extensión del país, Noruega está excepcionalmente bien servida por aerolíneas nacionales. Hay unos cincuenta aeropuertos y aeródromos que hacen que hasta el extremo norte del país parezca que esté a un paso. Las tarifas son muy razonables, los jóvenes de hasta 25 años pueden conseguir billetes en lista de espera a mitad de precio. También pueden obtenerse ofertas muy interesantes para vuelos en temporada baja, denominadas 'mini pris' y 'lavpris'.

Tren

Los ferrocarriles estatales noruegos tienen una red muy amplia que va desde el extremo sur del país hasta Bodø en la costa noroeste. Los trenes son modernos y efectivos y la mayoría tiene compartimientos especialmente adaptados para personas discapacitadas en trayectos de distancia media/larga. Las tarifas son razonables y hay una amplia oferta de descuentos especiales. Por ejemplo, el pase ScanRail es un abono flexible para viajar en tren por toda Escandinavia.

Autobús

Donde acaba la red ferroviaria, los autobuses continúan. Se puede llegar a prácticamente cualquier pueblo pequeño en autobús. Normalmente no es necesario reservar con antelación, sólo hay que pagar al conductor en el momento de subir al vehículo. NOR-WAY Bussekspress garantiza un asiento a todos los pasajeros.

Ferry

La geografía de Noruega hace que subirse a un barco sea, con frecuencia, la manera más rápida y más barata de desplazarse. En la zona de los fiordos, es inevitable a todos los efectos. Estos ferrys operan desde muy temprano por la mañana hasta última hora de la tarde, ofreciendo un servicio continuo por el que nunca hay que esperar mucho tiempo.

Coche

Se requiere un permiso de conducir, además de la documentación del vehículo y, como mínimo, un seguro a terceros. Se recomienda encarecidamente sacarse una tarjeta verde. Hay que llevar un triángulo rojo de advertencia para colocar frente al coche en caso de avería.

Es obligatorio conducir con las luces cortas encendidas, incluso durante el día, y todos los pasajeros deben llevar el cinturón de seguridad puesto. Los coches con volante a la derecha deben llevar un adhesivo con un triángulo negro, con frecuencia suministrados por la compañía de ferry que los transporte, o acoplar deflectores para los faros de modo que no deslumbren a los coches que vengan de cara.

INFORMACION TELEFONICA

Código Internacional	Código Nacional	Indicativo de área dé las Ciudades principales
095	47	Sin indicativo de área

DISCOUNTS AND CONCESSIONS

Many hostels offer discounts off attractions, tours etc in their area. In addition there are a number of travel discounts available from Terra Nova Travel. The following ferry companies give discounts on production of a membership card.

Båtservice, Oslo: 50% off
Flaggruten (Partrederiet) 25% off
Hardanger Snnhordlandske Dampskipsselskap: 25% off
Rutelaget Askøy-Bergen A/S: Student discount rate applies
Stena Line: 10% off

NORSKE VANDRERHJEM

Hostels in this country may also display this symbol.

Les auberges de ce pays pourront également afficher ce symbole.

Jugendherbergen in diesem Land können auch dieses Symbol zeigen.

Es posible que los albergues de este país exhiban además este símbolo.

Å ▲ Lofoten YH, 8392 Sørvågen, Nordland. ☎ 76091121, 76091162 **FAX** 76091282 ⌂ 70 ⍾ ✿ ⍾⍾⍾ ⊞ ☐ ☐ ☐ ⚲ ⚓ ✈ 45km A⛟ ⛴ 5km ⛟

Ålesund YH ▲ ⟨CC⟩ Parkgaten 14, 6003 Ålesund ☎ 70120425 **FAX** 70120442 **Open:** 1.5-30.9 ⌂ 52 ✿ ⍾⍾⍾ ☐ ✈ 7km ⛴ 800m ⛟ 100m

Alvdal YH ▲ Sandli, 2560 Alvdal ☎ 62487074 **FAX** 62487074 **Open:** 15.6-31.8 ⌂ 28 ⍾⍾⍾(B) ✿ ⍾⍾⍾ ☐ ⚲ ✈ 77km ⛟ 200m

Åndalsnes ▲ Setnes YH, 6300 Åndalsnes, Møre og Romsdal. ☎ 71221382 **FAX** 71226835 **Open:**

15.5-15.9 ⌂ 89 ⍾ ✿ ⍾⍾⍾ ⚲ ☐ ☐ ⚲ ⚓ ⛴ 2km ⍾⍾⍾ 2km ⛟ 500m ⓡ (16.9-14.5)

Alta YH ▲ Midtbakkvn 52, 9500 Alta, Finnmark. ☎ 78434409 **FAX** 78434409 **Open:** 20.6-20.8 **Shut:** 12.00-17.00hrs ⌂ 59 ✿ ⚲ ✈ 3km ⛟ 50m

Andenes ▲ Lankanholmen Sjøhus, 8480 Andenes ☎ 76142850 **FAX** 76142855 **Open:** 15.5-15.9 ⌂ 14 ⍾ ✿ ⍾⍾⍾ ☐ ⚓ A⛟ 500m ⛴ 500m ⛟ 10m

Balestrand YH ▲ ⟨CC⟩ 5850 Balestrand , Sogn og Fjordane. ☎ 57691303 **FAX** 57691670 **Open:**

14.6-17.8 🏊 58 ⭐(D) ♂ 👪 🔟 🅿 🚲
⚓ 🚢 150m 🚌 150m

Bergen Montana YH 🔺 6SE IBN
CC Johan Blyttsvei 30, 5030 Landås,
Bergen, Hordaland. 📞 55292900 FAX
55290475 Open: 5.1-22.12 🏊 230
BBinc ⭐ (1.5-30.9) ♂ 👪 🔟 🅿 🚲 ✈
20km A🚌 5km 🚢 6km 🚆 6km
🚌 200m Ⓡ (Grps 23.12-4.1)

BERGEN

Bodø YH Lokomotivet 🔺 Sjøgt 55,
Box 536, 8001 Bodø 📞 75521122 FAX
75521122 🏊 40 ♂ 👪 🔟 ✈ Bodø 10km
🚢 Bodø 50m 🚆 next to YH

Borlaug YH 🔺 CC 5897 Steinklepp,
Sogn og Fjordane. 📞 57668750,
57668780 Open: 10.1-20.12 🏊 44 ⭐
♂ 👪 🅿 🚊 ✈ 60km 🚢 43km 🚆
78km 🚌 30m

Bømlo YH 🔺 Olavskolen, 5437 Finnås,
Hordaland. 📞 53425300 FAX
53425388 Open: 24.5-18.8 🏊 72
⭐(B) ♂ 👪 🔟 🔟 🛏 🅿 ⚓ ✈ Stord
20km 🚢 20km 🚌 500m

Bøverdalen YH 🔺 2687 Bøverdalen,
Oppland. 📞 61212064 FAX 61212064
Open: 25.5-30.9 🏊 34 ⭐ ♂ 👪 🏠 🔟
🅿 🚌 100m

Byrkjelo YH 🔺 6867 Byrkjelo, Sogn
og Fjordane. 📞 57867321 Open:

15.5-15.9 🏊 11 ⭐ 👪 🅿 🚲 ✈ 30km
🚢 20km 🚌 50m

Dombås YH 🔺 2660 Dombås,
Oppland. 📞 61241045 FAX 61241145
🏊 94 ⭐ ♂ 👪 ♿ 🏠 🔟 🛏 🅿 🚊 Alt
700m 🚲 ⚓ 🚆 1km

Evje YH in Setesdal 🔺 4670 Hornes,
Aust-Agder. 📞 38153313, 37930422
FAX 38153313, 37930422 Open:
27.6-2.8 🏊 70 ⭐(B) ♂ 👪 🔟 🅿 ⚓ ✈
59km A🚌 56km 🚢 Kristiansand
56km 🚆 Kristiansand 56km 🚌
250m Ⓡ (Att. B.ness, Tveite 1, 4653
Hægeland)

Fauske YH 🔺 Nyvn 6, 8200 Fauske,
Nordland. 📞 75646706 FAX
75645995 Open: 1.6-15.8 🏊 94
⭐(B D) (Grps only, must book in
advance) ♂ 👪 ♿ 🔟 🅿 ⚓ 🚆 1.2km
🚌 250m

Flåm YH 🔺 5743 Flåm. 📞 57632121
FAX 57632380 Open: 1.5-1.10 🏊 20
♂ 👪 🔟 🅿 🚲 ⚓ 🚢 300m 🚆 300m
🚌 300m

Florø YH Åsgården 🔺 CC
Havrenesveien 32 B, 6900 Florø 📞
57740689 FAX 57743820 Open:
1.5-1.9 🏊 50 ⭐(B) ♂ 👪 ♿ 🔟 🚲 ⚓
✈ 1km 🚢 1km 🚌 50m

Folldal YH 🔺 2584 Dalholen,
Hedmark. 📞 62493108 FAX
62493108 Open: 15.6-15.9 🏊 47
⭐(B D) ♂ 👪 🔟 🅿 🚲 ⚓ 🚆 15km
🚌 200m

Førde YH 🔺 CC Box 557, Kronborg,
Førde Camping, 6801 Førde, Sogn &
Fjordane. 📞 57826500 FAX 57826555
Open: 15.4-15.10 (Grps 1.1-31.12) 🏊
30 ♂ 👪 ♿ 🔟 🛏 🅿 🚲 ⚓ ✈ Førde
20km A🚌 1.5km 🚢 2km Ⓡ

Geilo YH 🔺 CC Gjeilegutv 1, PB 130,
3581 Geilo, Buskerud. 📞 32090300
FAX 32091896 Open: 1.1-30.4;

1.6-30.9; 1.11-23.12 🛏 140 🍽 ☞ 👫
🗗 🅿 ⚓ Alt 780m 🚲 ⛵ ✈ 50km 🚌
200m 🚌 100m

Gjøvik YH ▲ 🆑 Hovdetun Parkvn,
2800 Gjøvik, Oppland. 📞 61171011
FAX 61172602 **Open:** 1.1-23.12 🛏
152 🍽(L D) (book in advance) ☞ 👫 🗗
🅿 ⚓ ⛵ 🚌 1km 🚌 300m

Graddis YH ▲ Postadresse: 8255
Røkland, Nordland 📞 75694341 **FAX**
75694388 **Open:** 15.6-31.8 🛏 26
🍽(L D) ☞ 👫 🗗 🅿 ⛵ ✈ 160km 🚢
60km 🚌 30km 🚌 6km

Grungebru YH ▲ 3893 Vinjesvingen,
Telemark. 📞 35072765 **FAX**
35072816 **Open:** 15.6-15.8 🛏 22
🍽(B D) ☞ 👫 🗗 🅿 🚲 ⛵ 🚌 120km
🚌 50m ⓡ

Halden YH ▲ Flintvn, Tosterødberget
skole, Gimle, 1750 Halden, Østfold. 📞
69180077 **FAX** 69175097 **Open:**
21.6-12.8 🛏 21 ☞ 👫 🗗 🅿 ⛵ 🚢
3km 🚌 3km 🚌 300m

Hamar YH ▲ 🆑 Vikingskipet
Vandrerhjem Og Motell, Åkersvikvn
10, 2300 Hamar, Hedmark. 📞
62526060 FAX 62532460 🛏 138 🍽
👫 ♿ 🗗 🅿 ⚓ ⛵ ✈ 2km 🚌 Hamar
2km 🚌 50m

Hammerfest YH ▲ 🆑 Idrettsvn. 52,
9600 Hammerfest 📞 78413667,
94782074 **Open:** 23.6-23.8 🛏 36 ☞
👫 🆔 🗗 🏛 ⛵ ✈ 5km 🚢 1km

Harstad YH ▲ 🆑 Trondarnes
Folkehøgskole, Boks A Trondenes,
9401 Harstad, Troms. 📞 77064154
FAX 77065633 **Open:** 1.6-25.8 🛏
101 🍽(B) (D Grps) ☞ 👫 🆔 🗗 🅿 ✈
50km A🚌 3km 🚢 3km 🚌 50m

Hellesylt YH ▲ 6218 Hellesylt, Møre
og Romsdal. 📞 70265128, 70263657
FAX 70265728 **Open:** 1.6-1.9 🛏 54

🍽(B D) (book in advance) ☞ 👫 🗗 🅿
⛵ ✈ 100km 🚢 300m 🚌 100m

Helligskogen YH ▲ Uranusvn. 36,
9024 Tomasjord, Troms. 📞 76942598
FAX 77715460 **Open:** 20.6-20.8 🛏
40 🍽(B) ☞ 👫 🏛 🅿 ⓡ 21.8-19.6

Hemsedal YH ▲ 3560 Hemsedal,
Buskerud. 📞 32060315 **FAX**
32060745 **Open:** 15.5-15.9 🛏 90
🍽(B D) ☞ 👫 🅿 🚲 ⛵ 🚌 290km
🚌 50m

Hitra YH ▲ 🆑 Dolmsundet Hotell
Og Feriesenter, 7250 Melandsjø, Sør-
Trøndelag. 📞 72445979 **FAX**
72445050 🛏 35 🍽 ☞ 👫 ♿ 🆔 🗗 🅿
⛵ 🚢 10km 🚌 50m

Hønefoss YH ▲ Box 347, Ringeriksgt
20, 3501 Hønefoss, Buskerud. 📞
32122903 **FAX** 32123614 **Open:**
1.9-25.8 (Grps only 1.1-31.12) 🛏 60
🍽(B D) ☞ 👫 🗗 🅿 ⛵ ✈ 35km A🚌
3km 🚌 3km 🚌 1km

Honningsvåg △ Nordkapp YH, Boks
361, 9751 Honningsvåg, Finnmark. 📞
78473377 **FAX** 78471177 **Open:**
20.5-20.9 🛏 18 ☞ 🏛 🅿 ⛵ ✈ 5km
🚢 5km 🚌 50m

Horten ▲ Borre YH, Langgrunn, 3190
Horton, Vestfold. 📞 33073026,
33042590 **Open:** 15.6-15.8 (Grps
16.8-15.6) 🛏 73 🍽(B) ☞ 👫 🅿 ⛵ 🚌
600m ⓡ (16.8-15.8)

Hovden YH ▲ 🆑 'Hovdehytta', Boks
8, 4695 Hovden. 📞 37939522 **FAX**
37939522 **Open:** 20.6-20.8 🛏 60
🍽(B D) 👫 🅿 🚲 ⛵ 🚌 200m ⓡ
(1.7-15.8)

Husnes YH ▲ c/o Hybelhuset, 5460
Husnes 📞 53472200 **FAX** 53472200
Open: 20.6-20.8 🛏 60 👫 🗗 🚲 ⛵
🚢 4km 🚌 100m

Jørpeland YH ▲ Preikestolhytta, 4100
Jørpeland. 📞 51840200 (from 1.6-31.8

\(94531111) **Open:** 1.6-30.8 **\(pa\)** 56
🍴 ⅲ 🏠 🅿 ⚓ 🚢 20km 🚌 200m

Kabelvåg ▲ Vandrerhjem, Vågan Folkehøgskole, 8310 Kabelvåg. **\(**
76078103 **FAX** 76078117 **Open:**
10.6-10.8 **\(pa\)** 100 🍴(B) 🛌 ⅲ 🛈 📷 🅿
⚓ ✈ Svolvær 12km 🚢 Svolvær 5km
🚌 500m

Karasjok YH ▲ Kautokeinovn, 9730
Karasjok, Finnmark **\(** 78466135 **FAX**
78466623 **\(pa\)** 66 🛌 ⅲ 📷 🅿 ⚓ ✈ Banak
75km A🚌 1km 🚌 1km

Kirkenes YH Hesseng ▲ Hessengvn 4, Box 30, 9912, Hesseng **\(** 78996009
Open: 20.6-20.8 **\(pa\)** 40 ⅲ ♿ 📷 🅿 ⚲
✈ Kirkenes 8km 🚢 5km

Kjeldal ▲ **CC** YH Kanalheimen, 3740
Lunde, Telemark **\(** 35947405,
94284512, 94464610 **Shut:** 33441643
FAX 33441697 **Open:** 1.6-30.8 **\(pa\)** 60
🍴(B) 🛌 ⅲ ♿ 🏠 📷 🅿 ⚲ ⚓ 🍺 3.5km
🚌 3.5km

Kongsberg YH ⚠ Vinjesgt 1, 3600
Kongsberg, Buskerud. **\(** 32732024
FAX 32720534 **Open:** 1.1-23.12;
26-31.12 **\(pa\)** 98 Wi 📶ⁱⁿᶜ 🍴 🛌 ⅲ ♿
🅿 ⚓ Alt 179m ⚲ ⚓ ✈ Oslo 83km
🍺 1km 🚌 200m

KONGSBERG

Kongsvinger ▲ **CC** Vandrerhjem,
Vinger Hotel, Østre Solør veg 6, 2200

Kongsvinger. **\(** 62817222 **FAX**
62817035 **Open:** 20.6-31.8 **\(pa\)** 37
🍴(B D) ⅲ 🅿 🍺 500m 🚌 300m

Kragerø YH ▲ Lovisenbergvn 20, 3770
Kragerø, Telemark. **\(** 35983333 **FAX**
35982152 **Open:** 14.6-16.8 **\(pa\)** 100
🍴(D) 🛌 ⅲ ♿ 📷 🅿 ⚲ ⚓ ✈ 70km
🚢 2km 🍺 25km 🚌 250m

Kristiansand YH (*see town plan on next page*)
▲ **CC** "Tangen", Skansen 8, 4610
Kristiansand, Vest-Agder. **\(** 38028310
FAX 38027505 **Open:** 15.1-15.12 **\(pa\)**
191 ⊝ **NOK** 150/175 📶ⁱⁿᶜ 🛌 ⅲ ♿ 📷
🅿 ⚲ ⚓ ✈ Kjevik 20km A🚌 400m
🚢 1.2km 🍺 Kristiansand 1.4km
🚌 400m

Kristiansund N 'Atlanten' YH ▲ **CC**
Dalav 22, 6500 Kristiansund N, Møre
og Romsdal. **\(** 71671104 **FAX**
71671158 **Open:** 1.6-30.9 **\(pa\)** 62 🍴
🛌 ⅲ ♿ 📷 🅿 ⚓ ✈ 5km A🚌 500m
🚢 1km 🚌 500m

Kviteseid YH ▲ Bræk's, 3850
Kviteseid, Telemark. **\(** 35053261
Open: 1.5-31.8 **\(pa\)** 34 🍴(B) 🛌 ⅲ 📷
🅿 ⚓ 🚢 30km 🍺 50km 🚌 10m

Leira YH ▲ Valdres Folkehøgskule,
2920 Leira. **\(** 61362025 **FAX**
61362305 **Open:** 25.5-10.8 **\(pa\)** 78
🍴(B) 🛌 ⅲ 📷 🅿 ⚓ ✈ 8km 🚌 100m

Levanger YH ▲ 7600 Levanger, Nord-Trøndelag. **\(** 74081638 **FAX**
74081638 **Open:** 1.5-31.8 **\(pa\)** 48
🍴(B D) 🛌 ⅲ ♿ 🅿 🚢 800m 🍺
800m 🚌 100m

Lillehammer YH ▲ Skyss- stasjonen,
Jernbanetorget 2, 2600 Lillehammer,
Oppland. **\(** 61262566 **FAX** 61262577
\(pa\) 128 📶ⁱⁿᶜ 🍴 ⅲ ♿ 📷 🅿 ⚓ ⚲ ⚓
🚢 1km 🍺 10m 🚌 10m

Lillesand YH ▲ Møglestv V G S, 4790
Lillesand, Aust- Agder. **\(** 37270744
FAX 37272327 **Open:** 15.6-15.8 **\(pa\)**
60 🍴(B) 🛌 ⅲ 🏠 📷 🅿 ⚓ ✈ 20km
A🚌 800m 🍺 30km 🚌 100m

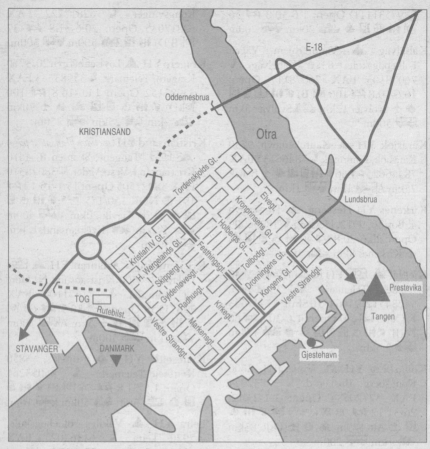

KRISTIANSAND

Mandal Kjøbmandsgaarden YH ▲
ᴇᴄᴄ Store Elvegate 57, 4500 Mandal.
📞 38261276 **FAX** 38263302 **Open:**
1.6-31.8 🛏 48 ⑩(B) 👕 👪 ♿ 🎪 🅿
🚲 ⛵ ✈ 60km A🚌 100m ⛴
Kristansand 200m 🚌 100m

Melbu YH ▲ ᴇᴄᴄ P A Kvaalsgt 5, Box
121, 8401 Melbu, Nordland. 📞
76157106, 76159130 **FAX** 76158382
🛏 100 ⑩ (book in advance) 👕 👪 🎪
① 🖸 🅿 🚲 ⛵ ✈ 23km A🚌 ⛴
400m 🚌 50m

Meråker YH ▲ Brenna Camping, 7530
Meråker. 📞 74810234 **FAX** 74810300
Open: 15.6-15.8 🛏 59 ⑩(B) 👕 👪 🖸

🅿 🚲 ✈ 45km 👪 2km 🚌 300m
Ⓡ

Mjølfjell YH ▲ 5728 Reimegrend,
Hordaland. 📞 56518111 **FAX**
56514000 **Open:** 20.2-30.4 🛏 68
⑩(B) 👕 👪 ♿ 🎪 🖸 🅿 ⚓ Alt 670m 🚲
⛵ 👪 Mjølfjell 6km; Ørneberget
(local) 300m Ⓡ (1.5-19.2)

Mo i Rana ▲ ᴇᴄᴄ Mo YH, 8600 Mo,
Nordland. 📞 75150963 **FAX**
75151530 **Open:** 2.5-15.9 🛏 60 ⑩(B)
👕 👪 🖸 🅿 ⛵ ✈ 16km ⛴ 2km 👪
2km 🚌 2km

Moi YH Lundheim ▲ 1 NE 4460 Moi,
Norway 📞 51401105 **FAX** 51401862

Open: 07.00-10.00hrs, 17.00-23.00hrs, 9.6-10.8 ⊠ 40 ⌑(B) ♂ ♦♦♦ ♿ 🅿 ☀ ♨ ⚓ ✈ Stavanger 100km ⛴ Kristiansand 150km ⚒ Moi 1km

Moss YH ▲ Vansjøheimen, Nesparken, 1530 Moss, Østfold. ☎ 69255334 **FAX** 69250166 **Open:** 1.6-1.9 (Grps only 2.9-30.5) ⊠ 67 ⌑ (book in advance) ♂ ♦♦♦ 🔲 🅿 ♨ ⚓ ⛴ 2km ⚒ 2km ⛁ 500m

Narvik YH ▲ ㏄ Nordkalotten, Box 3084, Havnegt 3, 8500 Narvik, Nordland. ☎ 76942598 **FAX** 76942999 **Open:** 1.4-31.10 ⊠ 123 ㏌ ⌑ ♂ ♦♦♦ ⊞ 🅿 ⚑ ✈ 3km A⛁ 2km ⛴ 100m ⚒ 2km ⛁ 2km

Nesbyen YH ▲ ㏄ Sutøya Feriepark, 3540 Nesbyen. ☎ 32071397 **FAX** 32070111 **Open:** 1.5-1.10 ⊠ 40 ⌑ ♂ ♦♦♦ 🔲 🅿 ⚓ ⚒ Nesbyen 4km ⛁ 100m

Notodden YH ▲ Sauheradsvn 3, 3670 Notodden. ☎ 35010460 **Open:** 1.6-31.8 **Shut:** 11.00-16.00hrs ⊠ 56 ㏌ ♂ ♦♦♦ ♿ 🔲 🅿 ⚓ ⛴ 500m ⚒ 200m ⛁ 100m

Odda YH ▲ ㏄ 'Sørfjordheimen' Bustetungaten 2, 5750 Odda, Hordaland. ☎ 53641411 **FAX** 53642990 **Open:** 2.1-15.12 ⊠ 48 ⌑(B D) ♂ ♦♦♦ 🔲 🅿 ⛴ 500m ⛁ 500m

Oppdal YH ▲ ㏄ Oppdalstunet, Sletvold Park Apartments, Gamle Kongevei, 7340 Oppdal ☎ 72422311 **FAX** 72422313 ⊠ 64 ⌑(B D) ♂ ♦♦♦ 🔲 ♨ 🅿 ⚑ Alt 600m ♨ ⚓ ✈ Trondheim 160km ⚒ Oppdal 1.5km ⛁ 800m

Ørje YH ▲ Vågelsbye, 1870 Ørje. ☎ 69811750 **FAX** 69811511 **Open:** 1.6-1.9 ⊠ 16 ♂ ♦♦♦ ⊞ ♨ 🅿 ⚓ ⚒ Mysen 25km ⛁ 100m

Osen YH ▲ ㏄ Berget Turisttun, 2460 Osen, Hedmark. ☎ 62444934 **Open:** 15.6-15.8 ⊠ 35 ⌑(B D) ♂ ♦♦♦ 🔲 ♨ 🅿 ♨ ⚓ ⚒ 30km ⛁ 5km

OSLO (3 Hostels)

Oslo - Oslo YH, LBM Ekeberg ▲ Kongsvn.82, N- 1109 Oslo, PB.23 Bekkelagshogda. ☎ 22745090 **FAX** 22747505 **Open:** 1.6-14.8 ⊠ 51 ㏌ ♂ ♦♦♦ ♿ 🔲 ♨ 🅿 ✈ Fornebu 14km A⛁ 4km ⛴ Oslo 5km ⚒ Oslo S, 4km ⛁ ND.18 & 19 100m ⓡ (15.8-31.5 ☎ 22152185, **FAX** 22713497)

Oslo - Haraldsheim ▲ ⑤NE ㏌ ㏄ Oslo YH, Haraldsheim, Haraldsheimvn 4, 0409 Oslo. ☎ 22222965, 22155043 **FAX** 22221025 **Open:** 2.1-22.12 ⊠ 270 ⌑ ♂ ♦♦♦ 🔲 🅿 ⚑ ⛴ 5km ⚒ Oslo S 5km, Grefsen 1km ⛁ 500m ⛁ 10, 11 Kjelsås

OSLO - Haraldsheim

Oslo - Holtekilen (*see town plan on next page*) ▲ ⑨W (Su YH) Oslo YH, Holtekilen, Michelets vei 55, N-1320 Stabekk. ☎ 67533853 **FAX** 67591230 **Open:** 28.5-18.8 ⊠ 184 ㏌ ⌑ ♦♦♦ ♿ 🔲 🅿 ✈ Fornebo 5km ⚒ Oslo S 10km, 1km ⛁ 100m ⓡ (Oslo YH Holtekilen, Norske Vandrerhjem Reg Øst, Pb 41 Grefsen, N-0409 Oslo ☎ 22152185 **FAX** 22713497)

OSLO - Holtekilen

Ringstad YH ▲ 8475 Straumsjøen - Vesterålen ✆ 76137480 **Open:** 20.6-20.8

Rjukan YH ▲ Birkelandsgt 2, 3660 Rjukan, Telemark. ✆ 35090527 **FAX** 35090527 ⇄ 78 ⵏⵏ ⵏ ⵏⵏ ⵏ 🅿 ⵏ 🚌 100m

Røros YH ▲ Idrettsparken, Øravn 25, 7460 Røros, Sør- Trøndelag. ✆ 72411089 **FAX** 72412377 ⇄ 162 ⵏⵏ(L D) ⵏ ⵏⵏ ⵏ ⵏ 🅿 ⵏ Alt 628m ᨠ ⵏ ✈ 2km 🚋 500m 🚌 500m

Røst YH ▲ Fiskarheimen, Box 100, 8064 Røst, Nordland. ✆ 76096109 **FAX** 76096109 **Open:** 1.5-30.8 ⇄ 38 ⓑⓑ inc ⵏⵏ ⵏ ⵏⵏ ⵏ ① ⵏ 🅿 ᨠ ⵏ ✈ 4km 🚢 1km

Røvær YH ▲ 5517 Røvær, Rogaland. ✆ 52718035, 52718034 **FAX** 52718054 **Open:** 15.6-15.8 (Grps 1.1-31.12) ⇄ 32 ⵏⵏ ⵏ ⵏⵏ ⵏ ⵏ ① ⵏ ⵏ ✈ 20km 🚢 45 min from Haugesund, 20m from YH; ferry 20m Ⓡ (Grps)

Runde YH ▲ 6096 Runde ✆ 70085916 **FAX** 70085870 ⇄ 36 ⵏ ① ⵏ ⵏ 🚢 45km 🚌 ap YH

Sarpsborg ⛺ Tuneheimen YH, Tuneon 44, 1710 Sarpsborg, Østfold. ✆

69145001 **FAX** 69145001 ⇄ 83 ⵏⵏ ⵏ ⵏⵏ ⵏ 🅿 ᨠ ⵏ 🚋 2km 🚌 100m

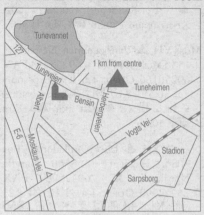

SARPSBORG

Sjoa YH ▲ 2670 Sjoa, Oppland. ✆ 61236200 **FAX** 61236014 **Open:** 2.1-23.12 ⇄ 83 ⵏⵏ ⵏ ⵏⵏ ⵏ ⵏ ⵏ 🅿 ⵏ ᨠ ⵏ 🚋 1km 🚌 100m

Sjusjøen YH ▲ ⒸⒸ Fjellheimen Fjellstue, 2612 Sjusjøen. ✆ 62363409 **FAX** 62363404 **Open:** 18.6-20.8 (Grps 1.1-31.12) ⇄ 60 ⓑⓑ inc ⵏⵏ ⵏ Alt 830m ᨠ ⵏ 🚋 Lillehammer 23km 🚌 100m

Skien YH ▲ ⒸⒸ Moflatvn 65, 3733 Skien, Telemark. ✆ 35599551 **FAX** 35546240 ⇄ 88 ⵏⵏ ⵏ ⵏⵏ ⵏ ⵏ 🅿 ⵏ Alt 50m ᨠ ⵏ ✈ 1km 🚢 3km 🚋 4km 🚌 200m

Skjolden YH ▲ ⒸⒸ 5833 Skjolden, Sogn og Fjordane. ✆ 57686615 **Shut:** 57686676 **FAX** 57686676 **Open:** 20.5-15.9 ⇄ 35 ⵏⵏ(L D) ⵏ ⵏⵏ ⵏ 🅿 ⵏ ✈ 70km 🚢 75km 🚌 100m

Skjåk YH ▲ 2692 Bismo, Oppland. ✆ 61214026 **Open:** 1.6-1.9 ⇄ 53 ⵏⵏ ⵏ ⵏⵏ ⵏ 🅿 ⵏ 🚌 100m

Snåsa YH ▲ ⒸⒸ 7760 Snåsa, Nord-Trøndelag. ✆ 74151057 **FAX** 74151615 **Open:** 1.6-30.8 ⇄ 56 ⵏⵏ

🛌 👬👬 ⚡ 🏠 🔲 🅿 🚲 ⛵ ✈ 70km 🚢
1km 👬👬👬 2.5km 🚌 3km

Sogndal YH ▲ P.b. 174 5801 Sogndal, Sogn og Fjordane. 📞 57672033 **FAX** 57673145 **Open**: 19.6-20.8 🚋 90 🍴 🛌 👬👬 🔲 🅿 A🚌 50m 🚢 500m 🚌 50m

Stamsund YH ▲ Justad Rorbuer, 8340 Stamsund, Nordland. 📞 76089334, 76089166 **FAX** 76089739 🚋 60 🛌 👬👬⚡ 🏠 🔲 🅿 🚲 ⛵ 🚢 1.5km 🚌 200m

Stavanger YH ▲ Mosvangen, Tjensvoll 1B, 4021 Stavanger, Rogaland 📞 51872900 **FAX** 51870630 **Open**: 1.6-1.9 🚋 44 🛌 👬👬 🅿 🚢 4km 👬👬👬 3km 🚌 1km

Stryn YH ▲ 🆑 6880 Stryn, Sogn og Fjordane. 📞. 57871106, 57871336 **FAX** 57871106 **Open**: 20.5-10.9 🚋 60 [BB]ⁱⁿᶜ 🛌 👬👬👬 🔲 🅿 🚲 ⛵ 🚢 🚌

Sunndalsøra YH ▲ 🆑 Trædal, 6600 Sunndalsøra, Møre og Romsdal. 📞 71691301 **FAX** 71690555 **Open**: 1.1-20.12 🚋 55 🍴(B D) 🛌 👬👬⚡ 🏠 🔲 🅿 ⛵ 🚌 2.5km

Svalbard YH ▲ 🆑 Nybyen Gjestehus, Spitsbergen Travel Box 500, 9170 Longyearbyen. 📞 79022450 **FAX** 79021005 **Open**: 1.4-30.9 (Reception 1.1-31.12) 🚋 24 [BB]ⁱⁿᶜ 🛌 👬👬 🏠 🔲 🔲 🏊 🚲 ✈ 6km A🚌 1km 🚢 (24.6-30.8) 1.5km Ⓡ

Svolvær ☞ **Kabelvåg**

Tønsberg YH ▲ Dr Blancas gt 22, 3111 Tønsberg, Vestfold. 📞 33312848, 33310401 **FAX** 33312848 **Open**: 2.1-22.12 🚋 59 Wi, 32 Su 🍴 🛌 👬👬 🔲 🅿 🚲 ⛵ ✈ 27km A🚌 500m 🚢 500m 👬👬👬 200m 🚌 500m

Tromsø YH ▲ Elverhøy, Gitta Jønsonsv 4, 9012 Tromsø, Troms. 📞 77685319 **FAX** 76942999 **Open**:

20.6-19.8 **Shut**: 11.00-17.00hrs 🚋 77 🛌 🔲 ① 🅿 ✈ Tromsø 3.5km 🚢 Tromsø 1km Ⓡ 20.8-19.6 📞 76942598 **FAX** 76942999

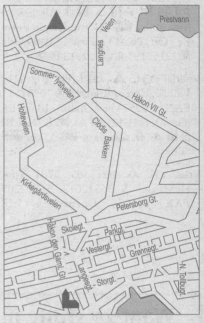

TROMSØ

Trondheim YH (*see town plan on next page*) ▲ 🆑 Rosenborg, Weidemannsvei 41, 7043 Trondheim, Sør-Trøndelag. 📞 73530490 **FAX** 73535288 **Open**: 5.1-18.12 🚋 200 [BB]ⁱⁿᶜ 🍴 🛌 👬👬 🔲 🅿 🚲 ⛵ ✈ 35km A🚌 1.5km 🚢 2km 👬👬👬 2km 🚌 300m 🚃 100m

Uvdal YH ▲ 3632 Uvdal, Buskerud. 📞 32743020 **FAX** 32743020 **Open**: 1.6-1.9 + Easter 🚋 48 🍴 🛌 👬👬 🏠 🔲 🅿 🏊 ⛵ 🚌 30m Ⓡ (2.9-31.5)

Værøy YH ▲ Langodden Rorbu Camping, 8063 Værøy, Nordland. 📞 76095375, 76095352 **FAX** 76095701 **Open**: 15.5-15.9 🚋 60 🛌 👬👬 🏠 ① 🔲 🅿 🚲 ⛵ 🚢 4km

Val YH ▲ 7953 Strand i Namdalen. 📞 74394190 **FAX** 74394251 **Open**:

25.6-15.8 ⊠ 28 ⦿ ✆ ⅲ ♿ ▣ ℗ ⚓
✈ 30km ⛴ 20km 🚌 500m

Valdresflya YH ▲ 2953 Beitostoelen, Oppland. ✆ 94107021 **Open:** 1.6-15.9 ⊠ 46 ⦿ ✆ ⅲ ♿ ℗ ⚓ Alt 1389m 🚌 100m Ⓡ (Norske Vandrerhjem Reg Øst, Pb 41 Grefsen, N-0409 Oslo ✆ 22152195 **FAX** 22713497)

Valldal YH ▲ 🆑 Pb 20, 6210 Valldal, Møre og Romsdal. ✆ 70257511 **FAX** 70257511 **Open:** 10.6-31.8 (Grps 1.1-31.12) ⊠ 44 ⦿(B D) ✆ ⅲ ▣ ℗ ⚶ ⚓ ⛴ 4km 🚊 55km 🚌 50m

Voss YH ⚠ Box 305, 5701 Voss, Hordaland. ✆ 56512017, 56512205 **FAX** 56510837 **Open:** 13.1-15.10

(Grps 16.10-12.1) ⊠ 180 ⦿ ✆ ⅲ ♿ ▣ ℗ ⚶ ⚶ ⚓ 🚊 700m 🚌 700m Ⓡ (Grps)

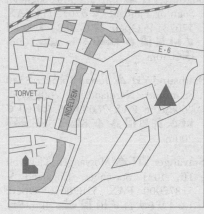

TRONDHEIM

POLAND
POLOGNE
POLEN
POLONIA

Polskie Towarzystwo Schronisk Młodzieżowych,
00-791 Warszawa, ul Chocimska 28,
Poland.

☎ (48) (22) 498354, 498128
FAX (48) (22) 498354, 498128

Office Hours: Monday-Friday, 08.00-17.00hrs

Travel Section: Travel Agency 'Junior',
00-791 Warszawa, ul Chocimska 28,
Poland.

☎ (48) (22) 498354, 498128
FAX (48) (22) 498354, 498128

Capital:	Warsaw
Language:	Polish
Currency:	Zł (złoty)
Population:	38,581,000
Size:	312,677 sq km

POLAND

POLAND

ENGLISH

POLISH HOSTELS

Priority is given to children and students under 26 years.

Hostels are open 06.00-22.00hrs, although dormitories are closed 10.00-17.00hrs. You should book in by 21.00hrs. Expect to pay in the region of US$5-12 per night unless otherwise stated, plus linen if needed. A fuel charge is made for use of self-catering facilities.

PASSPORTS AND VISAS

Citizens of Andorra, Argentina, Austria, Belgium, Bolivia, Bulgaria, Chile, Costa Rica, Croatia, Cuba, Cyprus, Czech Republic, Denmark, Estonia, Finland, France, Germany, Great Britain, Greece, Honduras, Hong Kong, Hungary, Iceland, Ireland, Italy, Korea, Latvia, Liechtenstein, Lithuania, Luxembourg, Macedonia, Malta, Monaco, Netherlands, Norway, Portugal, Romania, Russia, Slovak Republic, Slovenia, Spain, Sweden, Switzerland, Uruguay and USA do not require visas for short stays of 1 to 3 months. As the situation is changing, it is recommended that you check with your nearest Polish Embassy or Consulate for the latest situation.

BANKING HOURS

Banks are open Monday to Friday 08.00-16.00hrs.

POST OFFICES

Post offices are normally open Monday to Friday 08.00-20.00hrs. Some central post offices, in Warsaw at Świętokrzyska Street, are open 24 hours, 7 days a week.

SHOPPING HOURS

Shops are usually open Monday to Friday 11.00-19.00hrs, however there are some which are open 09.00-21.00hrs or on occasion 24hrs, even on Saturday and Sunday.

TRAVEL

Air

"LOT" airline offers domestic flights daily between Warsaw, Gdańsk, Wrocław, Rzeszów, Poznań, Szczecin. Tickets are sold by various travel agencies.

Rail

There is good network of railways. Rail is the cheapest means of travel. A supplementary charge is payable for express trains, inter-city trains and seat or bed reservation. Eurotrain, Inter-Rail and Wasteels tickets are available from main railway stations.

Bus

There are local bus services in all parts of the country. Bus fares are higher than train fares. Many travel agents offer long distance buses to other European cities. There are many city buses with frequent connections.

Ferry

There are regular connections between Świnoujście and Ystad, Copenhagen or Röne and between Gdańsk and Helsinki, Oxelösund or Ystad.

Driving

In order to drive in Poland you need the following documents: passport, insurance certificate, valid home drivers licence or international permit. There is a good network of roads with petrol stations, on average, every 30-40 km, which are normally open 06.00-22.00hrs although some are open 24hrs.

PUBLIC HOLIDAYS

New Year, 1 January; Easter, 30/31 March; Labour Day, 1 May; Constitution Day, 3 May; Corpus Christi, 29 May; National Holiday, 15 August; All Saints Day, 1 November; Independence Day, 11 November; Christmas, 25/26 December.

TELEPHONE INFORMATION

International Code	Country Code	Main City Area Codes	
00	48	Warsaw	22
		Kraków	12
		Poznań	61

FRANÇAIS

AUBERGES DE JEUNESSE POLONAISES

Priorité est donnée aux enfants et étudiants de moins de 26 ans.

Les auberges sont ouvertes de 6h à 22h, bien que les dortoirs soient fermés entre 10h et 17h. Vous êtes censé prendre possession de votre lit à 21h au plus tard. Une nuit vous coûtera entre 5-12 US\$, sauf indication contraire, plus location de draps le cas échéant. Il vous sera demandé une contribution aux frais d'utilisation d'énergie si vous utilisez la cuisine.

PASSEPORTS ET VISAS

Les citoyens d'Andorre, d'Argentine, d'Autriche, de Belgique, de Bolivie, de Bulgarie, du Chili, de Costa Rica, de Croatie, de Cuba, de Chypre, de la République Tchèque, du Danemark, d'Estonie, de Finlande, de France, d'Allemagne, de Grande-Bretagne, de Grèce, du Honduras, de Hong Kong, de Hongrie, d'Islande, d'Irlande, d'Italie, de Corée, de Lettonie, du Liechtenstein, de Lithuanie, du Luxembourg, de Macédonie, de Malte, de Monaco, des Pays-Bas, de Norvège, du Portugal, de Roumanie, de Russie, de la République Slovaque, de la Slovénie, d'Espagne, de Suède, de Suisse, d'Uruguay et États-Unis n'ont pas besoin de visa pour des brefs séjours de 1 à 3 mois. La situation étant en train de changer, nous vous conseillons de contacter votre ambassade ou consulat de Pologne la/le plus proche pour les dernières nouvelles à ce sujet.

HEURES D'OUVERTURE DES BANQUES

Les banques sont ouvertes du lundi au vendredi de 8h à 16h.

BUREAUX DE POSTE

Les bureaux de poste sont normalement ouverts du lundi au vendredi de 8h à 20h. Certains bureaux principaux, comme celui de Varsovie, situé dans la rue Świętokrzyska, sont ouverts 24 heures sur 24, 7 jours sur 7.

HEURES D'OUVERTURE DES MAGASINS

Les magasins sont en général ouverts du lundi au vendredi de 11h à 19h; toutefois, certains sont ouverts de 9h à 21h ou parfois 24 heures sur 24, même le samedi et le dimanche.

DEPLACEMENTS

Avions

La ligne aérienne "LOT" assure des vols intérieurs journaliers entre Varsovie, Dantzig, Wrocław, Rzeszów, Poznań et Szczecin. Les billets sont en vente dans diverses agences de voyages.

Trains
Le réseau ferroviaire est bon. Le train représente la façon la moins chère de voyager. Un supplément est à payer pour les trains express et les trains rapides interurbains, les réservations de places ou de lits. Les billets Eurotrain, Inter-Rail et Wasteels sont disponibles dans les gares principales.

Autobus
Des services d'autobus locaux desservent toutes les régions du pays. Voyager en autobus est plus cher que voyager par le train. De nombreuses agences de voyages offrent des voyages sur grande distance par autobus à destination d'autres grandes villes d'Europe. Il y a de nombreux autobus urbains avec des correspondances fréquentes.

Ferry-boats
Il y a des correspondances régulières entre Świnoujście et Ystad, Copenhague ou Röne et entre Dantzig et Helsinki, Oxelösund ou Ystad.

Automobiles
Pour avoir le droit de conduire en Pologne, il vous faut les documents suivants: passeport, certificat d'assurance, permis de conduire valide ou permis international. Il y a un bon réseau de routes, avec des stations-service, en moyenne, tous les 30 - 40 kilomètres, qui sont normalement ouvertes de 6h à 22h, certaines restant ouvertes jour et nuit.

JOURS FERIES
Nouvel an, 1er janvier; Pâques, 30/31 mars; Fête du Travail, 1er mai; Fête de la Constitution, 3 mai; Corpus Christi, 29 mai; Fête Nationale, 15 août; Toussaint, 1 novembre; Fête de l'Indépendance, 11 novembre; Noël, 25/26 décembre.

TELEPHONE

Indicatif International	Indicatif du Pays	Indicatifs régionaux des Villes principales	
00	48	Varsovie	22
		Cracovie	12
		Poznań	61

DEUTSCH

POLNISCHE JUGENDHERBERGEN
Kinder und Studenten unter 26 Jahren werden bevorzugt aufgenommen.

Die Herbergen sind von 06.00-22.00 Uhr geöffnet, aber die Schlafsäle sind zwischen 10.00 und 17.00 Uhr geschlossen. Man sollte bis 21.00 Uhr eintreffen. Es ist mit einem Preis von ca. US $5-12 pro Nacht, sofern nicht anders angegeben, plus, bei Bedarf, einer Gebühr für die Miete von Bettwäsche zu rechnen. Für die Verwendung der Einrichtungen für Selbstversorger wird eine Brennstoffgebühr erhoben.

PÄSSE UND VISA
Staatsbürger von Andorra, Argentinien, Belgien, Bolivien, Bulgarien, Chile, Costa Rica, Dänemark, Deutschland, Estland, Finnland, Frankreich, Griechenland, Großbritannien, Honduras, Hongkong, Irland, Island, Italien, Korea, Kroatien, Kuba, Lettland, Liechtenstein, Litauen, Luxemburg, Malta, Mazedonien, Monako, den Niederlanden, Norwegen, Österreich, Portugal, Rumänien, Rußland, Schweden, der Schweiz, der Slowakischen Republik, Slowenien, Spanien, der Tschechischen Republik, Ungarn, Uruguay, der Vereinigten Staaten, Zypern, brauchen für einen kurzen Aufenthalt von 1 bis 3 Monaten kein Visum. Da sich die Situation immer wieder ändert, empfehlen wir Ihnen, sich bei der nächsten Polnischen Botschaft oder dem nächsten Konsulat nach den neuesten Vorschriften zu erkundigen.

GESCHÄFTSSTUNDEN DER BANKEN

Banken sind montags bis freitags von 08.00-16.00 Uhr geöffnet.

POSTÄMTER

Postämter sind gewöhnlich montags bis freitags von 08.00-20.00 Uhr geöffnet. Einige zentrale Postämter in der Świętokrzyska-Straße in Warschau sind 24 Stunden geöffnet.

LADENÖFFNUNGSZEITEN

Die Geschäfte sind gewöhnlich montags bis freitags von 11.00-19.00 Uhr, einige aber auch von 09.00-21.00 Uhr und manche sogar 24 Stunden geöffnet, selbst samstags und sonntags.

REISEN

Flugverkehr
Die Fluggesellschaft "LOT" bietet täglich Inlandsflüge zwischen Warschau, Danzig, Breslau, Rzeszów, Posen und Stettin. Flugtickets werden von verschiedenen Reisebüros verkauft.

Eisenbahn
Es gibt ein gutes Schienennetz. Die Eisenbahn ist das billigste Verkehrsmittel. Für Expreßzüge, Intercityzüge und Platz- oder Bettenreservierungen ist ein Zuschlag zu bezahlen. Eurotrain, Inter-Rail und Wasteels Tickets werden auf Hauptbahnhöfen verkauft.

Busse
In allen Landesteilen gibt es einen örtlichen Busverkehr. Die Fahrpreise für Busse sind höher als die für die Eisenbahn. Viele Reisebüros verkaufen Fahrkarten für Fernverkehrsbusse in andere europäische Städte. Es gibt viele städtische Busse mit häufigem Verkehr.

Fähren
Zwischen Swinemünde und Ystad, Kopenhagen oder Rönne und zwischen Danzig und Helsinki, Oxelösund oder Ystad gibt es einen Linienverkehr.

Autofahren
Wer in Polen autofahren will, braucht folgende Dokumente: einen Reisepaß, ein Versicherungszertifikat, einen gültigen Führerschein des eigenen Landes oder einen internationalen Führerschein. Es gibt ein gutes Straßennetz, und die Entfernung zwischen den Tankstellen beträgt im allgemeinen 30-40 km. Tankstellen sind gewöhnlich von 06.00-22.00 Uhr, manche sogar 24 Stunden, geöffnet.

FEIERTAGE

Neujahr, 1. Januar; Ostern, 30./31. März; Tag der Arbeit, 1. Mai; Tag der Verfassung, 3. Mai; Fronleichnam, 29. Mai; Nationalfeiertag, 15. August; Allerheiligen, 1. November; Tag der Unabhängigkeit, 11. November; Weihnachten, 25./26. Dezember.

FERNSPRECHINFORMATIONEN

Internationale Kennzahl	Landes-Kennzahl	größere Städte - Ortsnetzkennzahlen	
00	48	Warschau	22
		Krakau	12
		Posen	61

ESPAÑOL

ALBERGUES DE JUVENTUD POLACOS

Se da prioridad a los niños y a los estudiantes menores de 26 años.

Los albergues abren de 06.00 a 22.00 horas, aunque los dormitorios están cerrados entre 10.00 y 17.00 horas. Hay que registrarse antes de las 21.00 horas. Se paga entre US$5,00 y 12,00 por noche, a menos que se indique lo contrario, más ropa de cama de ser necesaria. Para utilizar la cocina para huéspedes hay que pagar una tarifa de combustible.

PASAPORTES Y VISADOS

Los ciudadanos de Andorra, Argentina, Austria, Bélgica, Bolivia, Bulgaria, Chile, Costa Rica, Croacia, Cuba, Chipre, República Checa, Dinamarca, Estonia, Finlandia, Francia, Alemania, Gran Bretaña, Grecia, Honduras, Hong Kong, Hungría, Islandia, Irlanda, Italia, Corea, Letonia, Liechtenstein, Lituania, Luxemburgo, Macedonia, Malta, Mónaco, Países Bajos, Noruega, Portugal, Rumanía, Rusia, República Eslovaca, Eslovenia, España, Suecia, Suiza, Uruguay y EE.UU. no necesitan visado para estancias cortas de 1 a 3 meses. Dados los cambios que se están produciendo, se recomienda consultar con la embajada o consulado polaco más cercano en relación a los requisitos vigentes.

HORARIO DE BANCOS

Los bancos abren de lunes a viernes de 08.00 a 16.00 horas.

CASAS DE CORREO

Las casas de correo suelen abrir de lunes a viernes de 08.00 a 20.00 horas. Algunas oficinas centrales, en Varsovia en la calle Swietokrzyska, están abiertas 24 horas al día, 7 días a la semana.

HORARIO COMERCIAL

Las tiendas abren normalmente de lunes a viernes de 11.00 a 19.00 horas, si bien algunas abren de 09.00 a 21.00 horas y en algunos casos incluso están abiertas 24 horas al día, incluyendo sábados y domingos.

DESPLAZAMIENTOS

Avión
La aerolínea LOT ofrece vuelos nacionales diarios entre Varsovia, Gdansk, Wroclaw, Rzeszów, Poznan, Szczecin. Los billetes pueden comprarse en agencias de viajes.

Tren
Existe una buena red ferroviaria. El tren es el medio de transporte más barato. En el caso de los trenes expresos, de los trenes rápidos interurbanos y si se desea reservar un asiento o una cama, hay que pagar un suplemento. En las principales estaciones ferroviarias se pueden comprar los pases Eurotrain, Inter-Rail y Wasteels.

Autobús
Hay servicios locales de autobús en todo el país. Las tarifas de autobús son más altas que las de tren. Muchas agencias de viajes ofrecen servicios de autobús de larga distancia a otras ciudades europeas. Hay muchos autobuses urbanos con conexiones frecuentes.

Ferry
Hay servicios regulares entre Świnoujście e Ystad, Copenhague o Röne y entre Gdańsk y Helsinki, Oxelösund o Ystad.

Coche
Para conducir en Polonia se necesitan los siguientes documentos: pasaporte, póliza de seguro, permiso de conducir nacional o internacional válido. Existe una buena red de carreteras con gasolineras, más o menos cada 30-40 kilómetros, que suelen estar abiertas de 06.00 a 22.00 horas, abriendo algunas 24 horas al día.

DIAS FESTIVOS

Año Nuevo, 1 enero; Pascua, 30 y 31 marzo; Día del Trabajo, 1 mayo; Día de la Constitución, 3 mayo; Corpus Christi, 29 mayo; Fiesta Nacional, 15 agosto; Día de Todos los Santos, 1 noviembre; Día de la Independencia, 11 noviembre; Navidad, 25 y 26 diciembre.

INFORMACION TELEFONICA

Código Internacional	Código Nacional	Indicativo de área de las Ciudades principales
00	48	Varsovia 22
		Cracovia 12
		Poznań 61

Hostels in this country may also display this symbol.

Les auberges de ce pays pourront également afficher ce symbole.

Jugendherbergen in diesem Land können auch dieses Symbol zeigen.

Es posible que los albergues de este país exhiban además este símbolo.

Białowieża ul Gen Waszkiewicza 4, 17-230 Białowieża. ☎ (835) 12560 ✉ 60 ☎ ⅲ P

Białystok ul. Piłsudskiego 7b, 15-443 Białystok. ☎ (85) 524250 ✉ 50 ☎ ⛪ ♨ 700m

Biecz ul Parkowa 1, 38-250 Biecz. ☎ (18) 512411 ext.14 ✉ 75 ☎ ⅲ

Bielsko- Biała ul Komorowicka 25, 43-300 Bielsko-Biała. ☎ (33) 27466 ✉ 92 ☎ ⅲ

Bóbrka k/Krosna Bóbrka k/Krosna, 38-458 Chorkówka. ☎ (138) 13097 ✉ 30 ☎ ⅲ

Bóbrka k/Soliny Bóbrka k/Soliny, 38-612 Solina ☎ (1376) 1861 Open: 5.7-25.8 ✉ 45 ☎

Brzeg ul Wolności 14, 49-300 Brzeg. ☎ (77) 163620 Open: 5.7-25.8 ✉ 30 ☎ ⅲ

Bydgoszcz ul Sowińskiego 5, 85-083 Bydgoszcz. ☎ (52) 227570 ✉ 100 ☎ P ♨ 200m 🚋 8

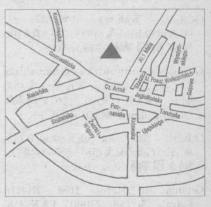

BYDGOSZCZ

Chełm ul. Czarnieckiego 8, 22-100 Chełm. ☎ (82) 640022 ✉ 67 ☎ P ♨ 2km

Chmielno ul.Gryfa Pomorskiego 33, 83-333 Chmielno. ☎ (58) 842205 ✉ 22 (1.7-31.8; 52) ☎ ♨ Garcz 2.5km

Ciechanów   ul 17 Stycznia 32, 06-400
   Ciechanów. ✆ (23) 722404, 724832 ✉
   32 ☝ 🅿

Cieszyn   ul. Kraszewskiego 13a, 43-400
   Cieszyn ✆ (33) 520801 ✉ 60 🍴 ☝ 🚿

Ciężkowice   ul. Św. Andrzeja 106,
   33-190 Ciężkowice ✆ (14) 525119 ✉
   40 ☝ 🚿

Częstochowa   ul. Jasnogórska 84/90,
   42-200 Częstochowa. ✆ (34) 243121
   Open: 1.7-31.8 ✉ 60 🚻

Dęblin   ul 15 Pułku Piechoty "Wilków"
   5, 08-522 Dęblin. ✆ (81) 830354
   Open: 1.7-25.8 ✉ 52 ☝ 🅿 🚿 100m

Elbląg   ul Browarna 1, 82-300 Elbląg. ✆
   (55) 325670 Open: 5.7-25.8 ✉ 70

Ełk   ul Sikorskiego 7a, 19-300 Ełk. ✆ (87)
   102514 ✉ 25 (1.7-31.8; 50) ☝ 🚿
   1.5km

Frombork   ul Elbląska 11, 14-530
   Frombork. ✆ (55) 67453 ✉ 120 ☝ 🅿

GDAŃSK (3 Hostels)

Gdańsk - **Wałowa**   ul. Wałowa 21,
   80-858 Gdańsk ✆ (58) 312313 ✉ 100
   🍴 ☝ 🚻 🅿 🚿 Główny 500m

Gdańsk - **Grunwaldzka**   Grunwaldzka
   244, 80-226 Gdańsk-Wrzeszcz. ✆ (58)
   411660 ✉ 30 (1.7-31.8; 96) ☝ 🚻 🚿
   Główny 9km 🚌 101 🚎 6, 15

Gdańsk - **Kartuska**   ul Kartuska 245,
   80-125 Gdańsk. ✆ (58) 326044 ✉ 122
   🍴 ☝ 🅿 🚿 Główny 3km

Gdynia   ul Morska 108C, 81-216
   Gdynia. ✆ (58) 270005 **FAX** (58)
   270005 ✉ 100 🍴 ☝ 🚻 🚢 Gdynia
   Skwer Kościuszki 5km 🚿 Dworzec
   Główny 3km 🚎 25, 22, 30

Gliwice - "**Ślązaczek**"   ul Gen. W.
   Andersa 60, 44-100 Gliwice ✆ (32)
   318575 **FAX** (32) 313799 ✉ 90 🍴
   ☝ 🚻 🅿

Głuchołazy   ul Skłodowskiej 1, 48-340
   Głuchołazy. ✆ (77) 391340 **Open:**
   5.7-25.8 ✉ 80 ☝ 🚿 200m

Gniezno   ul Pocztowa 11, 62-200
   Gniezno. ✆ (66) 262780 **FAX** (66)
   262780 ✉ 55 ☝ 🚻 🅿

Góra Św Anny   ul Szkolna 1, 47-154
   Góra Św Anny. ✆ (77) 617976 ✉ 50
   ☝ 🚻 🚿 Leśnica 4km, Zdzieszowice
   5km

Gorzów   Wielkopolski
   ul. St. Wyszyńskiego 8, 66-400 Gorzów
   Wlkp. ✆ (95) 27470 ✉ 70 ☝ 🚻 🅿

Gołaczów   ul. Górska 1, Gołaczów
   k/Kudowy, 57-343 Lewin Kłodzki. ✆
   (72) 661629 ✉ 44 ☝ ⚓

Grudziądz   ul Gen. Hallera 37, 86-300
   Grudziądz. ✆ (51) 20204 **FAX** (51)
   25808 ✉ 62 ☝ 🚿 Główny 2km
   🚌 1, 2

Iława   ul Mierosławskiego 6, 14-200
   Iława ✆ (88) 486464 ✉ 60 ⊖ US$4-5
   🍴 🅿 ⛵ 🚿 Iława 2km

Inowrocław   ul. Poznańska 345a,
   88-100 Inowrocław. ✆ (536) 77222
   Open: 1.7-25.8 ✉ 66 ☝ 🚿 5km
   🚌 3

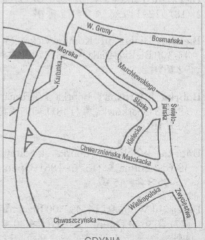

GDYNIA

Inowłódz Spalska 5, 97-215 Inowłódz. 📞 (44) 101122 **Open:** 1.7-31.8 🚲 25 📷 🚂 Tomaszów Mazowiecki 15km

Istebna Zaolzie - "**Zaolzianka**" 43-470 Istebna Zaolzie. 📞 (33) 556049 🚲 88 📷 👪 🏬 🅿 🏊

Jabłonki 38-606 Baligród 📞 26 🚲 40 📷

Jasło ul Czackiego 4, 38-200 Jasło. 📞 (136) 63464 **Open:** 5.7-25.8 🚲 25 📷

Jelenia Góra - "**Bartek**" ul Bartka Zwycięzcy 10, 58-500 Jelenia Góra. 📞 (75) 25746 🚲 56 📷 👪 🅿

Kalisz ul Wał Piastowski 3, 62-800 Kalisz. 📞 (62) 572402 🚲 36 (1.7-31.8; 51) 📷 🚂 500m

Kamień "**Halny**" Kamień k Świeradowa, 59-630 Mirsk. 📞 (75) 134336 🚲 60 📷 🅿 🏊

Kamień ul.Kłodzka 81, Kamień k/Jedliny Zdroju, 58-330 Jedlina Zdrój. 📞 (74) 15235 🚲 50 📷

Karpacz - "**Liczyrzepa**" ul Gimnazjalna 9, 58-540 Karpacz. 📞 (75) 619290 🚲 70 📷 👪 🏬 🏊

Kazimierz Dolny - "**Pod Wianuszkami**" ul Puławska 64, 24-120 Kazimierz Dolny. 📞 (81) 810327 🚲 90 BB inc 🍴 📷 👪 🏬 🅿 🏊

Kielce ul Szymanowskiego 5, 25-361 Kielce. 📞 (41) 23735 🚲 60 🍴 📷 🅿 🚌 20, 21

Kłębowo - "**Świteź**" 11-107 Kłębowo k/Lidzbarka Warmińskiego. 📞 (8983) 1360 **FAX** (8983) 1381 🚲 220 ⊖ US$ 7.00 BB inc 🍴 US$ 8.00 (full board) 👪 🅿 🏊

Kletno Kletno, 57-550 Stronie Śl. 📞 (72) 141358 🚲 36 📷 🏊

Kłodzko ul Nadrzeczna 5, 57-300 Kłodzko. 📞 (74) 672524 🚲 50 📷 👪

Kobylnica ul Poznańska 50, 62-006 Kobylnica. 📞 (61) 150103 🚲 50 📷 👪 🅿

Konin-Gosławice ul Leopolda Staffa 5, 62-505 Konin Gosławice. 📞 (63) 427235 🚲 60 📷 👪 🅿 🏊

Koronowo ul Sobieskiego 16, 86-010 Koronowo. 📞 (52) 822929 **Open:** 1.7-25.8 🚲 50 📷 👪 🏊

Koszalin - "**Gościniec**" ul Gnieźnieńska 3, 75-735 Koszalin. 📞 (94) 426068 **Open:** 1.1-23.12; 27-31.12 🚲 80 📷 👪 🚌 13, 16

KRAKÓW (3 Hostels)

Kraków - Oleandry ul Oleandry 4, 30-060 Kraków. 📞 (12) 338822 **FAX** (12) 338920 🚲 350 ⊖ US$ 7.00-10.00 BB inc 🍴 US$ 8 (full board) 📷 👪 ♿ 🅿 A🚌 Balice 152 🚌 119 🚋 15

Kraków - Kościuszki ul Kościuszki 88, 30-114 Kraków. 📞 (12) 221951 🚲 110 📷 A🚌 Balice 209 🚌 119 🚋 2

Kraków - Szablowskiego ul Szablowskiego 1C, 30-127 Kraków. 📞 (12) 372441 🚲 50 (1.7-31.8; 230) 🍴 📷 A🚌 Balice 208 🚋 4 or 12

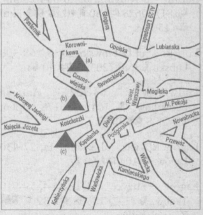

KRAKÓW - (a) Oleandry, (b) Kościuszki, (c) Szablowskiego

Kudowa Zdrój ul.Łąkowa 12, 57-350 Kudowa Zdrój 📞 (72) 661708, 661627

45 ● US$ 4.00-6.00 |O| ☻ ŧŧŧ ▣ ⚒
P ⚲ Alt 700m ✈ Wrocław 140km
▦ Kudowa Zdrój 600m

Kuraszków Kuraszków 50, 55-120
Oborniki Śląskie ☎ (71) 102571 ☒ 50
☻ P ▦ Oborniki Śląskie 3km

Lądek 57-540 Lądek Stójków. ☎ 645 ☒
30 ☻ ŧŧŧ ⚲

Lanckorona ul.Kazimierza Wielkiego
1, 34-143 Lanckorona. ☎ (33) 763589
☒ 80 |O| ☻ ŧŧŧ ▦ Kalwaria
Zebrzydowska 5km

Lębork ul Kossaka 103, 84-300 Lębork.
☎ (59) 621905 **Open:** 5.7-26.8 ☒ 50
☻

Legnica ul Jordana 17, 59-220 Legnica.
☎ (76) 25412 ☒ 62 |O|(B) ☻ ŧŧŧ

Lidzbark Warmiński ul Szkolna 3,
11-100 Lidzbark Warmiński. ☎ (8983)
2444 **Open:** 3.7-28.8 ☒ 60 ☻ P

Lidzbark Welski ul Garbuzy 9, 13-230
Lidzbark Welski. ☎ (84) 515178 **Open:**
1.7-30.8 ☒ 30 ☻

Lublin ul Długosza 6, 20-054 Lublin.
☎ (81) 30628 ☒ 80 ☻ ŧŧŧ P ▦ 3km
▦ 150

Lubsko ul.Dąbrowskiego 6, 68-300
Lubsko ☎ (68) 720398 ☒ 40 ☻

Ludwików 63-422 Antonin
Ludwików. ☎ (64) 336178 **Open:**
1.7-25.8 ☒ 30 ☻

Łagów k/Kielc ul Szkolna 1a, 27-430
Łagów. ☎ 104 ☒ 60 ☻

Łagów - "Łużyce" ul. Leśna 4, 59-910
Tagów. ☎ (797) 15908 ☒ 32 ☻ ▦
Zgorzelec 4km

Łańcut ul.Kościuszki 17, 37-100 Łańcut
☎ (17) 252822 **Open:** 3.7-25.8 ☒ 60
☻ ⚒ ▦

Łazy Łazy, 32-048 Jerzmanowice. **FAX**
(12) 338920 ☒ 61 ☻ ŧŧŧ P

Łeba - "Chaber" ul.Turystyczna 1,
84-360 Łeba ☎ (59) 661435 **Open:**
15.5-15.9 ☒ 120 ● US$ 8.00 ŧŧŧ P
⚲ ▲ Ⓡ (YH, 2 months in advance)

Łódź ul Legionów 27, 91-069 Łódź. ☎
(42) 330365 ☒ 83 ☻ ŧŧŧ ▣ ▦ 12, 22,
54 from Fabryczna ap ▦, 8 from
Kaliska, 2 from Chojny, 15 from Północ

Łubowo 62-260 Łubowo 12. ☎ (61)
275118 ☒ 50

Mąchocice Mąchocice- Scholasteria,
26-001 Masłów. ☎ (41) 112165, (41)
112171 ☒ 32 ☻ ŧŧŧ

Malbork ul Żeromskiego 45, 82-200
Malbork. ☎ (55) 2511 ☒ 55 |O| ☻ ŧŧŧ
P

Michałowice - "Złoty Widok"
ul.Kolonijna 14, 58-572 Michałowice
☎ (75) 53344 ☒ 33 (1.7-31.8; 61) ☻

Międzyzdroje ul Kolejowa 33, 72-610
Międzyzdroje. ☎ (97) 80344 **Open:**
1.7-15.8 ☒ 70 ☻

Mikołajki 11-730 Mikołajki. ☎ (878)
16434 **Open:** 1.7-31.8 ☒ 66 ▣ P ▲

Mosina ul Topolowa 2, 62-060 Mosina.
☎ (61) 132734 **Open:** 1.7-25.8 ☒ 44
☻ ŧŧŧ P ▲ ▦ 400m ▦ 400m

Mrągowo ul.Wojska Polskiego 2,
11-700 Mrągowo. ☎ (89) 842712
Open: 1.7-31.8 ☒ 60 ☻ ▦

Myczków Myczków, 38-610 Polańczyk
☎ Polańczyk 5 **Open:** 5.7-25.8 ☒ 45

Myślenice 32-400 Myślenice ☎ (115)
20677 **Open:** 1.7-25.8 ☒ 70 ☻

Myślibórz 59-422 Piotrowice,
Myślibòrz. ☎ (76) 708876 ☒ 42 ☻ P
▦ Jawor 7km

Narty - "Na Skarpie" Narty, 12-122 Jedwabno. ✆ (885) 43992 ⇤ 22 ♂ ♙ ⚓ 🚆 Szczytno 16km

Nieborów 96-416 Nieborów ✆ (46) 385694 **Open:** 1.7-30.9 ⇤ 54 ♂

Nowa Kaletka - "Kłobuk" Nowa Kaletka, 11-032 Butryny. ✆ (89) 130883, 130821 **Open:** 1.1-23.12, 27-31.12 ⇤ 250 ● US$ 15.00 (full board) 🍴 ♙ 🍽 🅿 ⚓

Nowa Słupia Świętokrzyska 64, 26-006 Nowa Słupia. ✆ (41) 177016 ⇤ 60 ♂ ♙ 🅿

Nowy Jaromierz Nowy Jaromierz, 64-220 Kargowa. ⇤ 25 ♂ ⚓

Nowy Sącz Al.Batorego 72, 33-300 Nowy Sącz. ✆ (18) 423241 ⇤ 50 ♂ ♙ 🅿

Nysa - "Pod Ziębickim Lwem" ul Boh Warszawy 7, 48-300 Nysa. ✆ (77) 333731 ⇤ 72 ♂ ♙ 🅿 ⚓ 🚆 1.5km

Oława ul Kutrowskiego 31a, 55-200 Oława. ✆ (71) 133156 ⇤ 50 ♂ ♙ 🅿

OLSZTYN (3 Hostels)

Olsztyn - **Kopernika** ul Kopernika 45, 10-512 Olsztyn. ✆ (89) 276650 ⇤ 70 ♂ ♙ 🅿 ⚓ 🚆 1km

Olsztyn - "Relaks" ul.Żołnierska 13a, 10-558 Olsztyn. ✆ (89) 277534 **Open:** 1.1-23.12; 27-31.12 ⇤ 210 ● US$ 5.00-22.00 🍴 ♙ 🍽 🅿 ⚓

Olsztyn - "Stadion" ul. Piłsudskiego 69A, Olsztyn. ✆ (89) 274510 **Open:** 1.1-23.12; 27-31.12 ⇤ 52 ● US$ 5.00-22.00 BB|inc 🍴 ♙ 🍽 ⚓

Opole ul Struga 16, 45-073 Opole. ✆ (77) 543352 **Open:** 5.7-25.8 ⇤ 50 ♂ ♙ 🅿

Osieczna - "Morena" ul Kopernika 4, 64-113 Osieczna. ✆ (65) 350134 ⇤ 60 🍴(B) ♂ ♙ 🅿 ⚓

Ostróda ul.Kościuszki 5, 13-100 Ostróda. ✆ (88) 465563 **Open:** 1.7-31.8 ⇤ 80 ♂ ⚓ 🚆

Paczków - "Pod Basztą" ul Kołłątaja 9, 48-370 Paczków. ✆ (77) 316441 ⇤ 78 ♂ ⚓

Pawełki Pawełki, 42-718 Kochcice. ✆ (34) 533648, 533100, 533102 **FAX** (34) 533105 ⇤ 40 ♂ ♙

Piła - "Staszicówka" Al WP 45, 64-920 Piła. ✆ (67) 132583 ⇤ 40 ♂ ♙ 🅿 ⚓ 🚆 1km

Piotrków Trybunalski ul.Dąbrowskiego 13, 97-300 Piotrków Trybunalski. ✆ (44) 470905 ⇤ 50 ♂ 🍽 🚆

Pisz ul Gizewiusza 4, 12-200 Pisz. ✆ (117) 32027 **Open:** 1.7-31.8 ⇤ 44 ♂ ⚓ R

Pobierowo ul Mickiewicza 19, 72-404 Pobierowo. ✆ (931) 64243 ⇤ 60 ♂ ♙ ⚓

Polanica Zdrój - "Nasz Dom" ul Cicha 1, 57-320 Polanica Zdrój. ✆ (74) 681212, 681406 **FAX** (74) 681053 ⇤ 150 ● US$ 8.00-12.00 BB|inc 🍴 ♙ 🔲 🅿 🌲 Alt 590m ✈ Wrocław 100km 🚆 Polanica Zdrój 1.5km

POZNAŃ (3 Hostels)

Poznań - **Berwińskiego** (*see town plan on next page*) ul Berwińskiego 2/3, 60-765 Poznań. ✆ (61) 663680 ⇤ 56 ♂ ♙ 🚆 Główny 200m 🚌 10,11 or 14

Poznań - **Biskupińska** ul Biskupińska 27, 60-463 Poznań. ✆ (61) 221063 ⇤ 59 ● US$ 8.00-12.00 🍴(B D) ♂ 🔲 🅿 ⚓ 🚐 60 or 95

Poznań - **Głuszyna** ul Głuszyna 127, 61-329 Poznań. ✆ (61) 788461 ⇤ 71 ● US$ 6.00-10.00 🍴 ♂ ♙ 🅿 🚆 Główny 8km 🚌 58 🚐 14

POZNAŃ - Berwińskiego

Przechlewo ul Szkolna, 77-320 Przechlewo. ☎ 25 Open: 1.7-30.8 🚉 50 ♂ ♔ 🔲

Przemków ul.Głogowska 37, 59-320 Przemków. ☎ 465 🚉 62 ♂ ♔ 🄿 🚌 🚌

Przemyśl - "Matecznik" ul.Lelewela 6, 37-700 Przemyśl. ☎ (10) 706145 🚉 52 ▥(B D) ♂ ♔ 🏤 🄿 🚌

Puławy ul Włostowicka 27, 24-100 Puławy. ☎ (81) 863367 🚉 110 ▥ ♂ ♔ 🄿 🚌 5km

Radom ul Miła 18, 26-600 Radom. ☎ (48) 40560 🚉 40 ♂ ♔

Radomsko ul.Piastowska 21, 97-500 Radomsko. ☎ (457) 34495 Open: 1.7-31.8 🚉 50 ♂ 🄿 🚌

Radziejowice ul.Sienkiewicza 6, 96-325 Radziejowice. ☎ (493) 504111 🚉 30 ♂ 🚌

Rozdziele Rozdziele, 32-731 Żegocina. ☎ Żegocina 87 🚉 54 ♂

Rybnica Leśna Rybnica Leśna, 58-352 Unisław Śląski. 🚉 44 ♂ 🄿

Rzeszów Rynek 25, 35-064 Rzeszów. ☎ (17) 34430 🚉 100 ♂ ♔ 🏤

Sandomierz ul Krępianki 6, 27-600 Sandomierz. ☎ (15) 322652 Open: 1.7-25.8 🚉 44 ♂ ♔

Sanok Konarskiego 10, 38-500 Sanok. ☎ (137) 30925 Open: 5.7-25.8 🚉 60 ♂

Sępólno Krajeńskie ul Hallera 29, 89-400 Sępólno Krajeńskie. ☎ (52) 882686 Open: 1.7-25.8 🚉 50 ♂ 🄿 ⬥

Sieradz ul 23 Stycznia 18, 98-200 Sieradz. ☎ (43) 5652 Open: 5.7-25.8 🚉 45 ♂ 🚌

Sławków Niwa ul Niwa 45, 42-533 Sławków. ☎ (32) 1931100 🚉 60 ▥ ♂ ♔ 🄿

Słupsk ul Deotymy 15a, 76-200 Słupsk. ☎ (59) 424631 Open: 1.7-30.8 🚉 88 ♔ 🛁 🄿

Śmigiel ul M Konopnickiej 4, 64-030 Śmigiel. ☎ (65) 180111 ext.143 🚉 30 ♂ ♔ ♿ ▥ 🄿

Smołdzino 76-214 Smołdzino. ☎ (59) 117321 Open: 1.7-31.8 🚉 25 ▥ ♂ ♔ ⬥

Stalowa Wola ul Rozwadowska 10, 37-464 Stalowa Wola. ☎ (16) 420429 Open: 1.7-25.8 🚉 52 ♂ ♔

Strzelno Parkowa 10, 88-320 Strzelno. ☎ (533) 89568 Open: 1.7-28.8 🚉 35 ♂ ⬥

Szamotuły ul.Obornicka 12, 64-500 Szamotuły. ☎ (668) 21165 🚉 44 ♂ 🄿

SZCZECIN (2 Hostels)

Szczecin - **"Elka- Sen"** ul.3 Maja 1a, 70-214 Szczecin. ☎ (91) 889272 **FAX** (91) 889272 🚉 44 ● US$ 8.00-20.00 ♂ ♔ 🛁 🚌 Dw.Główny 700m

Szczecin - **Monte Cassino** (*see town plan on next page*) ul Monte Cassino 19a, 70-467 Szczecin. ☎ (91) 224761 **FAX** (91) 224761 🚉 115 ♂ ♔ 🄿

SZCZECIN - Monte Cassino

Szczyrk - "Hondrasik" ul Sportowa 2, 43-370 Szczyrk. ☎ (30) 178933 ✉ 66 ♂ ⍤ 🅿 ⚲

Szczytno - "Pod Kasztanem" ul Pasymska 7, 12-100 Szczytno. ☎ (885) 43992 ✉ 60 ♂ ⍤ 🅿

Szklarska Poręba - "Wojtek" ul Piastowska 1, 58-585 Szklarska Poręba. ☎ (75) 172141 ✉ 75 ♂ ⍤

Szydłowiec ul Kilińskiego 2, 26-500 Szydłowiec. ☎ (48) 171374 ✉ 30 ♂

Święta Katarzyna 26-013 Święta Katarzyna. ☎ (41) 112206 ✉ 50 ♂ ⍤

Świnoujście ul.Gdyńska 26, 76-200 Świnoujście. ☎ (97) 3270613 ✉ 120 ♂ ⍤ ⛪ ⚓ 🚆

Tarnobrzeg ul Jachowicza 4, 39-400 Tarnobrzeg. ☎ (15) 233212 **Open:** 1.7-25.8 ✉ 52 ♂ ⍤

Tarnòw ul Konarskiego 17, 33-100 Tarnòw ☎ (14) 216916 ✉ 44 ♂

Toruń ul Rudacka 15, 87-100 Toruń. ☎ (56) 27242 **Open:** 1.7-31.8 ✉ 36 ♂ 🅿 🚆 3km

Trzemeszno ul Wyszyńskiego 3, 88-340 Trzemeszno. ☎ (533) 54031 **Open:** 1.5-30.9 ✉ 50 ♂ 🅿 ⚓

Ustka ul.Jagiellońska 1, 76-270 Ustka. ☎ (59) 145081 ✉ 25 ♂ ⛪ ⚓ 🚆

Ustroń - "Wiecha" ul.Stroma 5, 43-450 Ustroń-Jaszowiec. ☎ (3354) 3501, 2741 ✉ 180 ⊖ US$ 7.00 🆎 ⁱⁿᶜ 🍽 US$ 9.00 (full board) ♂ ⍤ 🅿 ⚲ Ⓡ (1.12-31.3)

Wałbrzych - "Daisy" ul Marconiego 1, 58-302 Wałbrzych. ☎ (74) 77942 ✉ 60 ♂ ⍤ ⚲

Wałcz Al.Zdobywców Wału Pomorskiego 76, 78-600 Wałcz. ☎ (67) 582749 **Open:** 1.7-25.8 ✉ 31 ♂ ⚓ 🚆 5km

Wapnica 72-617 Wapnica ☎ (97) 84106 **Open:** 1.7-15.8 ✉ 70 ♂ ⚓

WARSZAWA (3 Hostels)

Warszawa - Karolkowa ul Karolkowa 53a, 01-197 Warszawa. ☎ (22) 6328829 ✉ 160 🍽 ♂ ⍤ 🅿 🚆 Warszawa Centralna 🚌 24

Warszawa - Smolna ul Smolna 30, 00-375 Warszawa. ☎ (22) 278952 **Open:** 1.1-24.12; 27-31.12 ✉ 100 ♂ A🚌 175 🚆 Warszawa Centralna 🚌 101, 517, 521

WARSZAWA - (a) Karolkowa, (b) Smolna

Warszawa - Solidarności Al Solidarności 61, 03-402 Warszawa. ☎ (22) 184989 **FAX** (22) 185314 ✉ 60

⊜ US$ 12.00-20.00 ⒝Ⓑinc ⓨⓞⓛ ♦♦♦ ⌗ ⛨
🅿 ✈ Warszawa- Okęcie 35km 🚊
Warszawa Centralna 15km 🚋 512,
517, 160 🚋 4 Ⓡ (YH)

Włocławek ul Mechaników 1, 87-800
Włocławek. ☏ (54) 362410 🛏 48 ⓨⓞⓛ
♂ ♦♦♦ 🅿

Wolin ul Spokojna 1, 72-500 Wolin. ☏
(97) 61790 **Open:** 5.7-20.8 🛏 50 ♂
Ⓘ ⚓ 🚢 Świnoujście 30km 🚊
Wolin 600m

WROCŁAW (4 Hostels)

Wrocław - "Grand" ul.Piłsudskiego
100/102, 50-014 Wrocław. ☏ (71)
3436071 **FAX** (71) 3437893 🛏 204
⊜ US$ 12.00-16.00 ⒝Ⓑinc ⓨⓞⓛ ♦♦♦ ⛨ 🚊
Dw.Główny 400m

Wrocław - Kiełczowska ul Kiełczowska
43, 51-315 Wrocław. ☏ (71) 253076
(ext.17) 🛏 111 ⓨⓞⓛ ♂ ♦♦♦ 🅿 🚊 Psie
Pole 1km 🚋 N, 131

Wrocław - Kołłątaja ul.Kołłątaja 20,
50-007 Wrocław. ☏ (71) 3438856 🛏
47 ♂ ♦♦♦ ⛨ 🚊 Główny 500m

Wrocław - "Piast" ul.Piłsudskiego 98,
50-017 Wrocław. ☏ (71) 3430033,
3430034 **FAX** (71) 3437893 🛏 142
⊜ US$ 8.00-15.00 ⒝Ⓑinc ⓨⓞⓛ(B D) ♦♦♦ ⛨
🚊 Dw.Główny 500m

Zakopane - "Szarotka" ul Nowotarska
45, 34-500 Zakopane. ☏ (165) 13618
FAX (165) 66203 🛏 270 ⊜ US$
6.00-10.00 ⒝Ⓑinc ⓨⓞⓛ ♦♦♦ ⛨ 🅿 ♇

Zamość -"Osir" ul Kr Jadwigi 8, 22-400
Zamość. ☏ (84) 6011, 6012 🛏 100 ⊜
US$ 5.00-7.00 ⒝Ⓑinc ♦♦♦ ♿ 回 🅿 🚊
Zamość 400m

Zaniemyśl ul Poznańska 28, 63-020
Zaniemyśl. ☏ (667) 57289 🛏 45 ♂ ♦♦♦
🅿

Zawoja 34-223, Zawoja- Wilczna. ☏
Zawoja 106 🛏 45 ♂ ♦♦♦ ♇ Alt 1200m

Zduńska Wola ul.Dolna 21, 98-220
Zduńska Wola. ☏ (4388) 2440 🛏 81
♂ ♦♦♦ 🚊

Zieleniec Zieleniec 68, 57-340
Duszniki 🛏 29 ♂ ♇

Zielona Góra ul Wyspiańskiego 58,
65-036 Zielona Góra. ☏ (68) 270840
🛏 133 (1.4-31.10; 208) ♂ ♦♦♦

Złotoryja ul Kolejowa 2, 59-500
Złotoryja. ☏ (76) 873674 🛏 62 ♂ ♦♦♦

Żagań ul.X Lecia 19, 68-100 Żagań ☏
(68) 773235 🛏 40 ♂ 🚊

Żerków ul Cmentarna 1, 63-210
Żerków. ☏ (62) 471900 🛏 38 ♂

Żywiec ul Słonki 4, 34-300 Żywiec. ☏
(38) 612939 🛏 80 ♂ ♦♦♦ ⚓

PORTUGAL
PORTUGAL
PORTUGAL
PORTUGAL

Movijovem - Cooperativa de Interesse Público e
Responsabilidade Lda,
Av Duque de Ávila 137, 1050 Lisboa, Portugal

☎ (351) (1) 313 88 20
FAX (351) (1) 352 14 66

Travel Section/Central Booking: Movijovem

Opening Hours: Monday-Friday, 09.30-18.00hrs

Av Duque de Ávila 137, 1050 Lisboa, Portugal

☎ (351) (1) 313 88 20
FAX (351) (1) 352 86 21

E-Mail: movijovem@mail.telepac.pt

IBN Booking Centre for outward bookings:
■ Lisbon, *via National Office above*

Capital:	Lisboa
Language:	Portuguese
Currency:	$ (escudos)
Population:	9,962,670
Size:	92,082 sq km

PORTUGAL

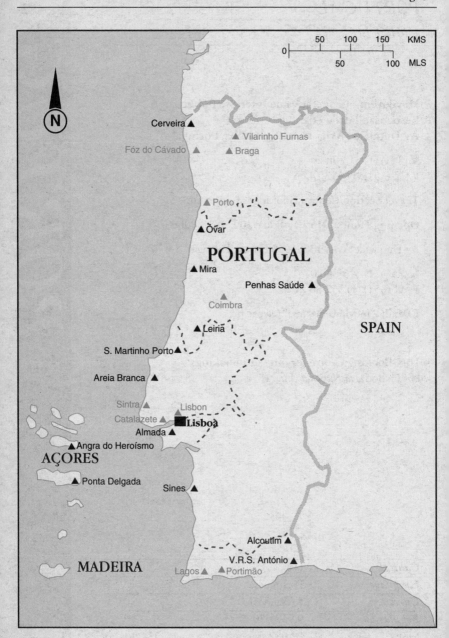

ENGLISH

PORTUGUESE HOSTELS

Hostels are generally open 24hrs although most usually close during part of the day for cleaning. Receptions are normally open 09.00-12.00; 18.00-24.00hrs. If telephoning the hostel please only do so during the reception opening times. The maximum length of stay at any one hostel is 8 consecutive nights, although this rule can be waived at the discretion of the warden. Expect to pay in the region of 1200-2350 escudos per night including bedlinen and breakfast. Meals are available, with prices ranging from 250 escudos for a snack to 900 escudos for lunch or dinner. All advance bookings should be made through the Portuguese Association national office.

PASSPORTS/VISAS

Many foreign visitors do not require a visa to visit Portugal provided they do not intend to stay for longer than 60-90 days. Please check before travelling.

HEALTH

Principal residential areas have hospitals and clinics which provide a 24 hour emergency service. Other places usually have clinics open 08.00-20.00hrs.

In Portugal, look for the word 'Farmácia'. They are open 09.00-13.00hrs and 15.00-19.00hrs weekdays and 09.00-13.00hrs on Saturdays. There is always a chemist on duty for emergencies and details can be found in the local press, from telephone operators and in chemists shop windows.

BANKING HOURS

Money changing is exclusive to banks, open to the public 08.30-15.00hrs, Monday to Friday. During the summer, Christmas and Easter, you can change money throughout the day in main tourist areas, frontiers and airports. Travellers cheques and credit cards are accepted in Portugal.

POST OFFICES

Post Offices are normally open 09.00-18.00hrs, Monday to Friday.

TRAVEL

Rail

Eurail and Inter-Rail cards are valid but a supplement must be paid on express trains. The Portuguese Railway Information Desks at Lisbon, Porto and Coimbra are open between 08.00 and 20.00hrs.

Bus

Portugal's bus network provides a fast and frequent service.

Ferry

There are frequent fast services in 4 major locations: Tagus River (from Lisbon to several localities); Setubal to Troia, Vila Nova de Cerveira to Spain and Vila Real de Santo António to Spain.

Driving

The rule of the road in Portugal is drive on the right. When driving seat belts must be worn. Unless otherwise indicated, vehicles coming from the right have priority. Sign posting conforms to the international code. Speed limits are 50 kmph in built up areas, 90 kmph on the open road and 120 kmph on motorways.

The legal alcohol limit for drivers is below 0.5 grammes per litre. Penalties can be either a heavy fine, confiscation or withdrawal of licence.

PUBLIC HOLIDAYS

New Year's Day, 1 January; Shrove Tuesday; Good Friday, 28 March; Liberation Day, 25 April; May Day, 1 May; Corpus Christi, 15 June; Camões Day, 10 June; Assumption of our Lady, 15 August; Republic Day, 5 October; All Saints Day, 1 November; Independence Day, 1 December; Immaculate Conception, 8 December; Christmas Day, 25 December.

TELEPHONE INFORMATION

International Code	Country Code	Main City Area Codes
00	351	Faro 89
		Lisbon 1
		Porto 2
		Coimbra 39

FRANÇAIS

AUBERGES DE JEUNESSE PORTUGAISES

Les auberges sont en général ouvertes 24h sur 24 bien que la plupart soient fermées une partie de la journée pour nettoyage. L'accueil est d'ordinaire ouvert de 9h à 12h et de 18h à 24h. Si vous téléphonez à une auberge, veuillez ne le faire que pendant les heures d'ouverture de la réception. La durée maximale d'un séjour dans une auberge est de 8 nuits consécutives, bien que ceci reste à la discrétion du directeur. Une nuit vous coûtera entre 1200 et 2350 ESC, draps et petit déjeuner compris. Les repas sont servis, dont les prix varient entre 240 ESC pour un casse-croûte et 900 ESC pour le déjeuner ou le dîner. Toutes les réservations d'avance doivent être faites auprès du bureau national de l'Association portugaise.

PASSEPORTS ET VISAS

De nombreux visiteurs étrangers n'ont pas besoin de visa pour visiter le Portugal, du moment où ils ne comptent pas y rester plus de 60 à 90 jours. Veuillez vérifier avant votre départ.

SOINS MEDICAUX

Les zones résidentielles principales sont équipées d'hôpitaux et de cliniques qui assurent un service d'urgences jour et nuit. Les autres zones ont en principe des cliniques ouvertes de 8h à 20h.

Au Portugal, cherchez le mot "Farmácia". Les pharmacies sont ouvertes de 9h à 13h et de 15h à 19h en semaine et de 9h à 13h le samedi. Il y a toujours une pharmacie de garde pour les urgences et vous trouverez leur adresse dans la presse locale, en appelant les standardistes du service téléphonique et en regardant la notice dans la vitrine des pharmacies.

HEURES D'OUVERTURE DES BANQUES

Les transactions monétaires ne se font que dans les banques, qui sont ouvertes au public de 8h30 à 15h, du lundi au vendredi. En été, à Noël et à Pâques, il est possible de changer de l'argent tout au long de la journée dans les principales régions touristiques, aux frontières et dans les aéroports. Les chèques de voyage et les cartes de crédit sont acceptées au Portugal.

BUREAUX DE POSTE

Les bureaux de poste sont normalement ouverts de 9h à 18h du lundi au vendredi.

DEPLACEMENTS

Trains
Les cartes Eurail et Inter-Rail sont valides mais il faut payer un supplément pour les trains express. Les bureaux de renseignements des chemins de fer portugais à Lisbonne, Porto et Coimbra sont ouverts entre 8h et 20h.

Autobus
Le réseau d'autobus portugais assure un service rapide et fréquent.

Ferry-boats
Il y a des services rapides et fréquents dans 4 endroits principaux: sur le Tage (de Lisbonne vers plusieurs régions); à Setubal à destination de Troia, Vila Nova de Cerveira à destination de l'Espagne at à Vila Real de Santo António à destination de l'Espagne.

Automobiles
La conduite se fait à droite au Portugal. Le port des ceintures de sécurité est obligatoire. Sauf indication contraire, les véhicules venant de la droite ont priorité. Les panneaux de signalisation routière sont conformes à la signalisation internationale. Les limites de vitesse sont de 50 km/h dans les agglomérations, 90 km/h à l'extérieur des agglomérations et 120 km/h sur les autoroutes.

La limite légale d'alcool dans le sang pour les conducteurs est de 0,5 grammes par litre. Les contraventions peuvent être soit une forte amende, soit la confiscation ou le retrait du permis.

JOURS FERIES

Nouvel an, 1er janvier; Mardi gras; Vendredi saint, 28 mars; Fête de la Libération, 25 avril; Fête du travail, 1er mai; Corpus Christi, 25 juin; Fête de Camões 10 juin; Assomption, 15 août; Fête de la République, 5 octobre; Toussaint, 1er novembre; Fête de l'Indépendance, 1er décembre; Immaculée Conception, 8 décembre; Noël, 25 décembre.

TELEPHONE

Indicatif International	Indicatif du Pays	Indicatifs régionaux des Villes principales	
00	351	Faro	89
		Lisbonne	1
		Porto	2
		Coimbra	39

DEUTSCH

PORTUGIESISCHE JUGENDHERBERGEN

Die Herbergen sind normalerweise 24 Stunden geöffnet. Einige Häuser sind aus Reinigungszwecken tagsüber geschlossen. Der Empfang ist normalerweise von 09.00-24.00 Uhr geöffnet. Telefonisch sollte man sich nur während der Empfangszeiten an eine Jugendherberge wenden. Der Höchstaufenthalt in einer Herberge ist auf 8 aufeinanderfolgende Nächte beschränkt. Es liegt jedoch im Ermessen des Verwalters, auf die Einhaltung dieser Vorschrift zu verzichten. Es ist mit einem Preis von 1200-2350 Esc pro Nacht, einschließlich Bettwäsche und Frühstück, zu rechnen. Mahlzeiten sind auch erhältlich. Die Preise variieren zwischen 250 Esc für einen Imbiß und 900 Esc für das Mittag- oder Abendessen. Alle Voranmeldungen sind über die Geschäftsstelle des portugiesischen Verbandes vorzunehmen.

PÄSSE UND VISA

Die meisten ausländischen Reisenden brauchen für den Besuch Portugals kein Visum, sofern sie nicht länger als 60-90 Tage im Land bleiben wollen. Bitte erkundigen Sie sich vor der Abreise.

GESUNDHEIT

In den wichtigsten Wohnbereichen gibt es Krankenhäuser und Kliniken, die einen 24-stündigen Notdienst bieten. An anderen Orten sind Kliniken von 08.00-20.00 Uhr geöffnet.

Schauen Sie sich in Portugal nach dem Wort 'Farmácia' um. Sie sind werktags von 09.00-13.00 Uhr und von 15.00-19.00 Uhr und samstags von 09.00-13.00 Uhr geöffnet. Für Notfälle hat immer ein Apotheker Notdienst. Nähere Einzelheiten stehen in der Ortspresse oder sind im Schaufenster von Apotheken angeschlagen. Auch die Fernsprechvermittlung erteilt Auskunft.

GESCHÄFTSSTUNDEN DER BANKEN

Geld kann nur auf Banken umgetauscht werden, die für die Öffentlichkeit montags bis freitags von 08.30-15.00 Uhr geöffnet sind. Im Sommer, an Weihnachten und an Ostern kann Geld in den wichtigsten Fremdenverkehrsgebieten, an den Grenzen und auf Flughäfen den ganzen Tag über umgetauscht werden. Reiseschecks und Kreditkarten werden in Portugal ebenfalls angenommen.

POSTÄMTER

Postämter sind gewöhnlich montags bis freitags von 09.00-18.00 Uhr geöffnet.

REISEN

Eisenbahn

Eurail- und Inter-Rail-Karten gelten in Portugal, aber für Expreßzüge muß ein Zuschlag bezahlt werden. Die Informationsstellen der portugiesischen Eisenbahn in Lissabon, Porto und Coimbra sind zwischen 08.00 und 20.00 Uhr geöffnet.

Busse

Das Busnetz von Portugal bietet einen schnellen und häufigen Verkehr.

Fähren

Von 4 Hauptorten aus gibt es einen schnellen und häufigen Fährenverkehr: auf dem Tajo (von Lissabon an mehrere Orte); von Setúbal nach Troia ; von Vila Nova de Cerveira nach Spanien und von Vila Real de Santo António nach Spanien.

Autofahren

In Portugal herrscht Rechtsverkehr. Sicherheitsgurt müssen getragen werden. Wenn nichts anderes angegeben, haben Fahrzeuge, die von rechts kommen, Vorfahrt. Die Beschilderung entspricht den internationalen Gepflogenheiten. Das Tempolimit beträgt in geschlossenen Ortschaften 50 Stundenkilometer, auf Landstraßen 90 Stundenkilometer und auf Autobahnen 120 Stundenkilometer.

Die zulässige Alkoholgrenze liegt für Fahrer unter 0,5 g pro Liter. Zuwiderhandlungen werden entweder mit einer hohen Geldstrafe, Beschlagnahme oder Entzug des Führerscheins bestraft.

FEIERTAGE

Neujahr, 1. Januar; Faschingsdienstag; Karfreitag, 28. März; Tag der Befreiung, 25. April; Maitag, 1. Mai; Fronleichnam, 15. Juni; Camões-Tag, 10. Juni; Mariä Himmelfahrt, 15. August; Tag der Republik, 5. Oktober; Allerheiligen, 1. November; Unabhängigkeitstag, 1. Dezember; Tag der unbefleckten Empfängnis, 8. Dezember; Weihnachten, 25. Dezember.

FERNSPRECHINFORMATIONEN

Internationale Kennzahl	Landes-Kennzahl	größere Städte -Ortsnetzkennzahlen	
00	351	Faro	89
		Lissabon	1
		Porto	2
		Coimbra	39

ESPAÑOL

ALBERGUES DE JUVENTUD PORTUGUESES

Los albergues abren generalmente las 24 horas del día, pero la mayoría suelen cerrar parte del día para la limpieza. La recepción suele estar abierta de 09.00 a 12.00 horas y de 18.00 a 24.00 horas. Si desea llamar al albergue, se ruega lo haga solamente durante el horario de apertura de la recepción. La estancia máxima en cualquier albergue es de 8 noches consecutivas, si bien esta norma puede no aplicarse a discreción del encargado. Se paga alrededor de 1200-2350 escudos por noche incluyendo ropa de cama y desayuno. Se sirven comidas, cuyos precios varían entre 250 escudos por un bocadillo hasta 900 escudos por el almuerzo o la cena. Todas las reservas anticipadas deben hacerse a través de la oficina nacional de la Asociación Portuguesa.

PASAPORTES Y VISADOS

Los ciudadanos de numerosos países no necesitan visado para entrar en Portugal siempre que no tengan previsto quedarse en el país más de 60-90 días. Se ruega confirmarlo antes de viajar.

SANIDAD

Las principales áreas residenciales tienen hospitales y clínicas con un servicio de urgencias de 24 horas. Otros lugares suelen tener clínicas abiertas de 08.00 a 20.00 horas.

En Portugal busque la palabra 'Farmácia'. Están abiertas de 09.00 a 13.00 horas y de 15.00 a 19.00 horas los días laborables, y de 09.00 a 13.00 horas los sábados. Siempre hay una farmacia de guardia para urgencias. Para información sobre farmacias de guardia, consultar la prensa local, telefonistas y carteles colocados en los escaparates de las farmacias.

HORARIO DE LOS BANCOS

El cambio de moneda sólo puede hacerse en los bancos, abiertos al público de 08.30 a 15.00 horas de lunes a viernes. En verano, Navidad y Semana Santa se puede cambiar moneda durante todo el día en las principales zonas turísticas, fronteras y aeropuertos. En Portugal se aceptan los cheques de viajero y las tarjetas de crédito.

OFICINAS DE CORREOS

Las oficinas de correos suelen abrir de 09.00 a 18.00 horas de lunes a viernes.

DESPLAZAMIENTOS

Tren

Las tarjetas Eurail e Inter-Rail son válidas pero hay que pagar un suplemento en los expresos. Los Mostradores de Información de CP (compañía ferroviaria portuguesa), de Lisboa, Porto y Coimbra abren entre 08.00 y 20.00 horas.

Autobús

La red de autobuses de Portugal presta un servicio rápido y frecuente.

Ferry

Hay servicios rápidos y frecuentes en 4 puntos del país: río Tajo (de Lisboa a varias localidades); Setubal a Troia, Vila Nova de Cerveira a España y Vila Real de Santo António a España.

Coche

La regla para conducir en Portugal es circular por la derecha. Hay que llevar puesto el cinturón de seguridad. A menos que se indique lo contrario, se da prioridad a los vehículos que vengan por la derecha. La señalización de tráfico es de conformidad con el código internacional. Los límites de velocidad son de 50 km/h en zonas edificadas, 90 km/h en carretera y 120 km/h en autopistas.

El límite legal de alcohol para conductores es menos de 0,5 gramos por litro. La sanción por infringir esta norma puede ir desde una multa importante, a la confiscación o retiro del permiso de conducir.

DIAS FESTIVOS

Año Nuevo, 1 enero; Martes de Carnaval; Viernes Santo, 28 marzo; Día de la Liberación, 25 abril; Fiesta de Mayo, 1 mayo; Corpus Christi, 15 junio; Día de Camões, 10 junio; Día de la Asunción de Nuestra Señora, 15 agosto; Día de la República, 5 octubre; Día de Todos los Santos, 1 noviembre; Día de la Independencia, 1 diciembre; Inmaculada Concepción, 8 diciembre; Navidad, 25 diciembre.

INFORMACION TELEFONICA

Código Internacional	Código Nacional	Indicativo de área de las Ciudades principales
00	351	Faro 89
		Lisboa 1
		Porto 2
		Coimbra 39

Hostels in this country may also display this symbol.

Les auberges de ce pays pourront également afficher ce symbole.

Jugendherbergen in diesem Land können auch dieses Symbol zeigen.

Es posible que los albergues de este país exhiban además este símbolo.

Alcoutim 8970 Alcoutim. ☎ (81) 46004 **FAX** (81) 46004 **Open:** 09.00-14.00hrs, 18.00-24.00hrs ⊅ 54 ⊜ $1200-1450 BBinc ⦀ 📷 🚻 ⬛ P 🚲 ⛵ 🍴 Vila Real de Santo António 40km 🚌 ap Alcoutim

Angra Do Heroísmo 1 SW CC Negrito, S.Mateus, 9700 Angra Do Heroísmo, Ilha Terceira-Açores, Portugal ☎ (095) 642095 **FAX** (095) 642096 **Open:** 06.00-24.00hrs (reception 08.00-12.00hrs, 18.00-24.00hrs) ⊅ 60 ⊜ $1550-1900 BBinc 🚻 ① P ⛵ ✈ Angra Do Heroísmo 3km ⛴ Angra Do Heroísmo Ⓡ (Central booking or YH)

Almada 2E Pragal, 2800 Almada. **Open:** Jun '97 ⊅ 164 ⊜ $1750-2350 BBinc

🍴 🚻 ♿ 📷 P ✈ Portela de Sacavém 20km ⛴ Cacilhas 4km 🚆 53 1km ap Centro Sul 1km

Areia Branca Praia da Areia Branca, 2530 Lourinhã. ☎ (61) 422127 **FAX** (61) 422127 **Open:** 09.00-14.00hrs, 18.00-24.00hrs ⊅ 116 ⊜ $1200-1500 BBinc 🍴 📷 🚻 ⬛ P 🚲 ⛵ 🚆 Torres Vedras 22km 🚌

Braga IBN Rua de Santa Margarida 6, 4700 Braga. ☎ (53) 616163 **FAX** (53) 616163 **Open:** 09.00-12.00hrs, 18.00-24.00hrs ⊅ 62 ⊜ $1300-1550 BBinc 📷 🚻 P 🚆 Braga 4km 🚌 Gualtar 100m ap Rua do Raio

Coimbra IBN Rua Henriques Seco 12-14, 3000 Coimbra. ☎ (39) 22955 **FAX** (39) 22955 **Open:**

09.00-12.00hrs, 18.00-24.00hrs ⚡85
⊜ $1300-1500 BBinc ♂ ♟ ⊡ 🚌
Coimbra- A 4km 🚌 7,29,46 100m
ap Liceu José Falcão

Fóz do Cávado IBN Fão; Esposende,
4740 Esposende. ☎ (53) 981790 **FAX**
(53) 981790 **Open:** 08.00-24.00hrs ⚡
83 ⊜ $1400-1700 BBinc ⏷ ♂ ♟ ⚡ 🅿
⛵ 🚌 Barcelos 13km 🚌 2km

Lagos 0.5N IBN Rua de Lancerote de
Freitas No 50, 8600 Lagos. ☎ (82)
761970 **FAX** (82) 761970 **Open:**
08.00-24.00hrs ⚡ 62 ⊜ $1400-1900
BBinc ♂ ♟ ⚡ ⊡ ⛵ 🚌 Lagos 1km 🚌
1km

Leiria Largo Cândido dos Reis 7D, 2400
Leiria. ☎ (44) 31868 **FAX** (44) 31868
Open: 09.00-12.00hrs, 18.00-24.00hrs
⚡56 ⊜ $1300-1600 BBinc ♂ 🏠 ⊡ 🚌
Leiria 3km 🚌 Leiria (A) 100m ap Sé

Lisbon IBN Pousada de Juventude de
Lisboa, Rua Andrade Corvo 46, 1050
Lisbon. ☎ (1) 3532696 **FAX** (1)
3532696 **Open:** 24hrs (Reception
08.00-24.00hrs) ⚡ 164 ⊜
$1900-2350 BBinc ⏷ ♟ ⚡ ⊡ ✈ Lisbon
5km A🚌 Green-Line (Direct to YH)
Picoas 200m ⛴ Lisbon 4km 🚌
Sta.Apolónia 4km 🚌 1,21,36,44,45
Green Line 100m Ⓤ Campo Grande;
Picoas 50m

LAGOS

LISBON

Lisbon - Catalazete IBN Catalazete, Estrada Marginal, 2780 Oeiras. ☎ (1) 4430638 **FAX** (1) 4430638 **Open:** 09.00-14.00hrs, 18.00-24.00hrs **Shut:** Until Feb '97 ⚓ 102 ● $1400-1700 BBinc ⊙ ♦♦♦ ⌂ ⊡ 🅿 ⚓ ✈ Lisbon 20km A🚌 83 Cais Sodré- Railway Station 15km ⚓ Lisbon 15km 🚊 Oeiras 2km

Lisboa ☞ **Lisbon**

MIRA (2 Hostels)

Mira - PJ de Mira 7E Pousada de Juventude de Mira, Parque de Campismo de Jovens, 3070 Praia de Mira. ☎ (31) 471275 **FAX** (31) 471275 **Open:** 08.00-24.00hrs ⚓ 58 ● $1200-1700 BBinc ⊙ Su (BB Wi) ♦♦♦ 🅿 ♣ ⚓ 🚊 Cantanhede 20km 🚌 1km ap Praia de Mira

Mira - Mira Youth Camping Park Parque de Campismo de Jovens, 3070 Praia de Mira. ☎ (31) 471275 **FAX** (31) 471275 **Open:** 1.6-15.9 ⚓ 500 ⊙ ⊙ ⊡ ⚫ 🅿 ♣ ⚓ 🚊 Cantanhede 20km 🚌 1km ap Praia de Mira

Oporto ☞ **Porto**

Ovar - Av D Manuel I (Est Nac 327) 3880 Ovar. ☎ (56) 591832 **FAX** (56) 591832 **Open:** 08.00-24.00hrs ⚓ 84 ● $1400-1700 ⊙ ⊙ ♦♦♦ ⌂ ⊡ 🅿 ⚓ 🚊 Ovar 2km

Penhas da Saude - Serra da Estrela, 6200 Covilhã. ☎ (75) 25375 **FAX** (75) 25375 **Open:** 09.00-14.00hrs, 18.00-24.00hrs; Apr '97 ⚓ 124 ● $1500-1750 BBinc ⊙ ⊙ ♦♦♦ 🅿 ⛷ 🚊 Covilhã 12km 🚌 Penhas

Ponta Delgada - 0.2E Rua S.Francisco Xavier, 9500 Ponta Delgada, Ilha S.Miguel- Acores Portugal ☎ (096) 629431 **FAX** (096) 629672 **Open:** 06.00-24.00hrs ⚓ 92 ● $1900-2200 BBinc ♦♦♦ ⌂ ① 🅿 ⚓ ✈ Ponta Delgada

3km ⚓ Ponta Delgada 1km Ⓡ (Central booking or YH)

Portimão - IBN Lugar do Coca Maravilhas, 8500 Portimão. ☎ (82) 491804 **FAX** (82) 491804 **Open:** 08.00-24.00hrs ⚓ 180 ● $1400-1800 BBinc ⊙ ⊙ ⊡ 🅿 ⚓ 🚊 Portimão 1km 🚌

Porto 4W IBN Rua Paulo Gama, 4150 Porto. **Open:** 24hrs (reception 08.00-24.00hrs) ⚓ 164 ● $1750-2350 BBinc ⊙ ⊙ ♦♦♦ ♿ ⊡ ✈ SÁ Carneiro 8km 🚊 São Bento 8km, Campanhã 4km 🚌 35 100m

São Martinho- Alfeizerão Estrada Nacional 8, 2460 Alfeizerão. ☎ (62) 999506 **FAX** (62) 999506 **Open:** 09.00-14.00hrs, 18.00-24.00hrs ⚓ 60 ● $1200-1450 BBinc ⊙ ⊙ ♦♦♦ ⌂ 🅿 ⚓ 🚊 São Martinho do Porto 4km 🚌 ap Alfeizarão

Sines 1NE Estrada da Floresta - Edificio E, 7520 Sines. ☎ (69) 635361 **FAX** (69) 635361 **Open:** 09.00-14.00hrs, 18.00-24.00hrs **Shut:** for renovation until May '97 ⚓ 114 ● $1400-1600 BBinc ⊙ ♦♦♦ ♿ ⊡ 🅿 ⚓ ✈ Portela de Sacavém 200km 🚌 Sines 1km ap Sines

Sintra IBN Stª Eufémia, S. Pedro de Sintra, 2710 Sintra. ☎ (1) 9241210 **FAX** (1) 9241210 **Open:** 09.00-14.00hrs, 18.00-24.00hrs ⚓ 55 ● $1300-1600 BBinc ⊙ ♦♦♦ 🅿 🚊 Sintra 🚌

Vila Nova de Cerveira Largo 16 de Fevereiro 21, 4920 Vila Nova de Cerveira. ☎ (51) 796113 **FAX** (51) 796113 **Open:** 09.00-12.00hrs, 18.00-24.00hrs ⚓ 56 ● $1200-1450 BBinc ⊙ ♦♦♦ ⊡ 🅿 ⚓ ⚓ 500m 🚊 Vila Nova de Cerveira 500m 🚌

Vila Real de Santo António R Dr Sousa Martins 40, 8900 Vila Real de Santo António (Algarve). ☎ (81) 44565 **FAX**

(81) 44565 **Open:** 09.00-12.00hrs, 18.00-24.00hrs ⚡ 56 ⊖ $1200-1450 BB|inc ✆ ♦♦♦ ☙ ⚓ 🚌 Vila Real de Santo António 400m 🚌

Vilarinho das Furnas [IBN] Parque Nacional do Geres, São João do Campo,

4840 Terras do Bouro. ☎ (53) 351339 FAX (53) 351339 Open: 09.00-14.00hrs, 18.00-24.00hrs Shut: for renovation until Apr '97 ⚡ 180 ⊖ $1300-1600 BB|inc ❄ ♦♦♦ ▣ P ☙ ⚓ 🚌 Braga 46km 🚌 500m ap Campo do Gerês

Standards will be monitored by Hostelling International and you, the user. If you are dissatisfied, let us know and we assure you that we will investigate and, where necessary, ensure appropriate action is taken. There are comment forms within this guide to help you contact us.

SCOTLAND
ECOSSE
SCHOTTLAND
ESCOCIA

ASSURED STANDARD

Scottish Youth Hostels Association,
7 Glebe Crescent, Stirling,
FK8 2JA, Scotland.

☎ (44) (1786) 891400
FAX (44) (1786) 450198

Office Hours: Monday-Friday, 08.45-17.00hrs

Travel Section: c/o Scottish Youth Hostels Association
7 Glebe Crescent, Stirling,
FK8 2JA, Scotland.

☎ (44) (1786) 451181

IBN Booking Centres for outward bookings:
■ **Edinburgh-SYHA** Regional Office,
  161 Warrender Park Road, Edinburgh EH9 1EQ.
  ☎ (44) (131) 2298660, **FAX** (44) (131) 2292456.
■ **Glasgow-SYHA** Regional Office,
  12 Renfield Street, Glasgow G2 5AL.
  ☎ (44) (141) 2263976, **FAX** (44) (141) 2042619.

Capital:	Edinburgh
Language:	English
Currency:	£ (Sterling)
Population:	5,112,100
Size:	78,781 sq km

SCOTLAND

SCOTTISH HOSTELS

More than 80 Scottish Youth Hostels offer a wonderful selection of places to stay, from a castle in the Highlands to remote loch-side or island locations. There are hostels in all the major cities, generally in historic buildings.

Whether you travel alone, as a family or with a group, Scottish hostels offer an ideal base for all the activities this varied country can offer; from walking the glens to exploring ancient celtic ruins, many hostels offer activity programmes - in winter you can ski Youth Hostel style too.

As you might expect, Scottish hostels offer excellent value for money - from £3.65-£11.95 bed linen included.

The Scottish Youth Hostel Association are among the first to offer assured standards at their hostels, and the entries in this section are graded accordingly (see page 6 for details).

All standard grade hostels ▲ are open from 07.00-23.45hrs although some may only offer access to limited facilities between 11.00-17.00hrs i.e. a common room and toilets. Check when booking.

Higher grade hostels ▲ have more facilities and are open all day from 07.00-02.00hrs (latest booking-in time 23.15hrs). Simple hostels △ generally in remote and beautiful locations have less facilities and are usually closed between 10.30-17.00hrs to economise on staff costs.

Hostels will have lots of information about what to do in the area, and at a considerable number you can even make your next night's booking by **FAX** if you are touring around. Most offer discounts on local attractions/facilities, which you can claim with your Hostelling International card.

PASSPORTS AND VISAS

You will need a valid passport. Not many visitors now require visas but do check in advance.

HEALTH

An international Certificate of Vaccination is not required to enter the UK, but you should check if one is needed on your re-entry into your own country.

Medical Insurance is essential because visitors are only eligible for free **emergency** treatment at National Health Service Accident and Emergency departments of hospitals. If you are admitted to hospital as an in-patient, even from an accident and emergency department, or referred to an out-patient clinic, you will be asked to pay unless you are a national of an EC country, resident in any member country, or a national or resident of a country which has a reciprocal health care agreement with the UK. You are strongly advised to take out adequate insurance cover before travelling to Britain.

BANKING HOURS

Banks are generally open weekdays 09.30-16.30hrs. Closed on Saturdays, Sundays and Public Holidays.

POST OFFICES

Open weekdays 09.00-17.30hrs and Saturdays 09.00-12.30hrs. They are closed on Sundays and Public Holidays.

SHOPPING HOURS

Most shops are open Monday-Saturday 09.00-17.30hrs. Some newsagents and food stores open from as early as 07.30hrs until as late as 20.00hrs, and in well populated areas some can remain open until 22.00hrs.

TRAVEL

Rail

There are main railway stations in Edinburgh and Glasgow with services to most parts of mainland Scotland.

Bus

Travel by national bus services is economical and there is access to all parts. In more remote areas the Royal Mail operates Postbuses which carry passengers as well as delivering post.

Ferry

There are ferry services to all populated Scottish islands. The two main operators are Caledonian MacBrayne on the west coast and P&O Ferries on the north coast.

Driving

Driving is on the left side. The national speed limit is 60 mph, increasing to 70mph on motorways. A typical speed limit in built up areas is 30mph. In remote areas single track roads with passing places can be expected, and drivers should not impede other road users.

PUBLIC HOLIDAYS

New Year, 1/3 January; Easter Monday, 31 March; Spring Bank Holiday, 5 May; May Bank Holiday, 26 May; Summer Bank Holiday, 4 August; Christmas, 25/27 December.

TELEPHONE INFORMATION

International Code	Country Code	Main City Area Codes	
00	44	Edinburgh	131
		Glasgow	141
		Inverness	1463
		Stirling	1786

FRANÇAIS

AUBERGES DE JEUNESSE ECOSSAISES

Les plus de 80 auberges écossaises offrent un choix fabuleux d'endroits où séjourner, qu'il s'agisse d'un château dans les Highlands ou d'un endroit isolé sur les bords d'un loch ou sur une île. Il existe des auberges dans toutes les grandes villes, généralement dans des monuments historiques.

Que vous voyagiez seul, en famille ou en groupe, les auberges écossaises vous proposent une base idéale pour toutes les activités que ce pays varié est en mesure d'offrir; de randonnées à travers les glens (vallées) jusqu'à l'exploration de ruines celtiques, de nombreuses auberges proposent des programmes d'activités - en hiver, vous pouvez même partir faire du ski dans un style 'ajiste'.

Comme vous vous en doutez, les auberges écossaises offrent un excellent rapport qualité-prix - les prix vont de £3.65 à £11.95 draps compris.

L'Association Ecossaise des Auberges de Jeunesse est parmi les premières à offrir des normes garanties dans ses auberges et chacune d'entre elles a été classée en conséquence (voir page 15 pour plus de détails).

Toutes les auberges de catégorie normale ▲ sont ouvertes entre 7h00 et 23h45 bien que certains établissements ne permettent l'accès qu'à un nombre limité d'installations (c.à.d. une salle commune et des toilettes) entre 11h00 et 17h00. Vérifiez à la réservation.

Les Auberges de catégorie supérieure ⚠ ont des installations plus sophistiquées et sont ouvertes toute la journée, de 7h00 à 2h00 (dernier délai pour l'enregistrement: 23h15). Les auberges 'simples' △, généralement situées dans des endroits aussi isolés que beaux sont moins équipées et sont habituellement fermées entre 10h30 et 17h00 pour économiser sur les frais de personnel.

Nos auberges auront toute sorte de renseignements à votre disposition sur ce qu'il y à faire dans la région et dans bon nombre d'entre elles, il vous sera même possible de réserver votre prochaine nuitée par fax si vous faites un circuit dans la région. La plupart offrent des réductions sur les attractions et animations locales qu'il vous sera possible d'obtenir grâce à votre carte d'adhérent Hostelling International.

PASSEPORTS ET VISAS

Les voyageurs doivent être munis d'un passeport valide. De nos jours, peu de visiteurs doivent avoir un visa mais vérifiez à l'avance.

SOINS MEDICAUX

Il n'est pas nécessaire de détenir un certificat international de vaccination pour rentrer au Royaume-Uni, mais il est conseillé de vous assurer qu'il ne vous en faudra pas un pour rentrer dans votre propre pays.

Il est essentiel que vous ayez une assurance maladie car les visiteurs ne peuvent bénéficier que d'un traitement **d'urgence** gratuit dans les services d'urgence et d'accidents des hôpitaux gérés par la Sécurité Sociale. Si vous êtes hospitalisé, même sur l'avis d'un service d'urgence et d'accidents, ou si vous êtes envoyé dans un service de consultation externe, vous aurez à payer à moins d'être un citoyen d'un pays du Marché commun, ou de résider dans un pays membre, ou à moins d'être un citoyen d'un pays ayant passé un accord de soins réciproque avec le Royaume-Uni. Il vous est fortement conseillé de souscrire à une assurance maladie avant de vous rendre en Grande-Bretagne.

HEURES D'OUVERTURE DES BANQUES

Les banques sont en général ouvertes en semaine de 9h30 à 16h30. Elles sont fermées le samedi le dimanche et les jours fériés.

BUREAUX DE POSTE

Ils sont ouverts en semaine de 9h à 17h30 et le samedi de 9h à 12h30. Ils sont fermés le dimanche et les jours fériés.

HEURES D'OUVERTURE DES MAGASINS

La plupart des magasins sont ouverts du lundi au samedi de 9h à 17h30. Certaines maisons de la presse et certains magasins d'alimentation sont ouverts à partir de 7h30 jusqu'à 20h, et dans les secteurs très peuplés, certains restent ouverts jusqu'à 22h.

DEPLACEMENTS

Trains
Les gares principales d'Edimbourg et de Glasgow assurent des services qui desservent la plupart des régions de l'Ecosse continentale.

Autobus

Les services nationaux de bus sont bon marché et desservent toutes les régions. Dans les régions plus isolées, le Royal Mail (service des postes) utilise des "bus postaux" (Postbuses) qui transportent des passagers tout en assurant la distribution du courrier.

Ferry-boats

Les bateaux desservent toutes les îles peuplées d'Ecosse. Les deux compagnies principales sont Caledonian MacBrayne sur la côte ouest et P & O Ferries sur la côte nord.

Automobiles

La conduite est à gauche. La limite de vitesse nationale est 95km/h et 110km/h sur les autoroutes. La limite de vitesse dans les agglomérations est en principe 45km/h. Dans les régions isolées, il est fréquent de trouver des chemins à une seule voie où il a été aménagé des aires de croisement pour véhicules; les conducteurs doivent donc être courtois envers les autres usagers de la route.

JOURS FERIES

Nouvel an, du 1er au 3 janvier; Lundi de Pâques, 31 mars; Fête de printemps, 5 mai; Fête de mai, 26 mai; Fête d'été, 4 août; Noël, 25-27 décembre.

TELEPHONE

Indicatif International	Indicatif du Pays	Indicatifs régionaux des Villes principales
00	44	Edimbourg 131
		Glasgow 141
		Inverness 1463
		Stirling 1786

DEUTSCH

SCHOTTISCHE JUGENDHERBERGEN

Mehr als 80 SYHA-Jugendherbergen bieten Reisenden eine große Auswahl an Unterkunftsmöglichkeiten (von einem Schloß im schottischen Hochland bis zu einer abgelegenen Herberge am See oder auf einer Insel). Es gibt Jugendherbergen in allen Großstädten, meist in historischen Gebäuden.

Ob Sie allein, mit der Familie oder mit einer Gruppe reisen, SYHA-Jugendherbergen sind ein idealer Ausgangspunkt für die Freizeitgestaltung in diesem verschiedenartigen Land; man kann in den Tälern wandern und auf Entdeckungsreise in alten keltischen Ruinen gehen. Viele Jugendherbergen bieten Aktivprogramme an, im Winter können Sie 'auf Jugendherbergsweise' Ski laufen.

Wie Sie vielleicht wissen, sind SYHA-Jugendherbergen Ihr Geld wert: £3.65-£11.95 einschließlich bettwäsche. Ausleihen von Bettwäsche, falls erforderlich.

Der Schottische Jugendherbergsverband gehört zu den ersten Verbänden, deren Häuser in Kategorien mit 'Garantierten Standards' eingeteilt wurden. Die Kategorie ist aus der jeweiligen Eintragung ersichtlich (siehe Seite 24 für Einzelheiten).

Alle Jugendherbergen des normalen Standards ▲ sind von 07.00-23.45 Uhr geöffnet, obwohl manche nur Zugang z.B. zu Toiletten und Unterstellplätzen bieten. Erfragen Sie dies bitte bei Ihrer Buchung.

Jugendherbergen mit höherem Standard ▲ bieten zusätzliche Leistungen an und sind ganztägig geöffnet. 07.00-02.00 Uhr (Anmeldungen spätestens um 23.15 Uhr).

Jugendherbergen des einfachen Standards △ sind meist in entlegenen doch landschaftlichen schönen Standorten anzutreffen, sie verfügen über eine einfache Ausstattung und sind gewöhnlich zwischen 10.30-17.00 Uhr, geschlossen.

In den Jugendherbergen erhalten die Gäste Informationen über die Umgebung. Wenn man eine Rundreise plant, kann man auch die Übernachtung für die nächste Herberge per Fax reservieren. Mit der Hostelling International Mitgliedskarte sind auch häufig Vergünstigungen bei verschiedenen örtlichen Einrichtungen verbunden.

PÄSSE UND VISA

Sie brauchen einen gültigen Reisepaß. Ein Visum wird nur noch von wenigen Reisenden benötigt. Sie sollten sich aber im voraus erkundigen.

GESUNDHEIT

Für die Einreise nach Großbritannien braucht man keine internationale Impfbescheinigung. Sie sollten sich aber erkundigen, ob eine solche Bescheinigung bei der Wiedereinreise in Ihr Heimatland verlangt wird.

Eine Krankenversicherung ist notwendig, da Besucher nur **im Notfall** Anspruch auf kostenlose Krankenhausbehandlung durch die Unfall- oder Notfallabteilung des Staatlichen Gesundheitsdienstes haben. Wenn Sie zur stationären Behandlung in ein Krankenhaus eingeliefert oder an eine ambulante Abteilung überwiesen werden, müssen Sie bezahlen, es sei denn, Sie sind Staatsbürger eines EG-Landes, oder Sie sind Staatsbürger eines Landes, welches mit Großbritannien einen reziproken Vertrag über die Gesundheitspflege hat. Das gilt sogar, wenn die Überweisung von einer Unfall- oder Notfallabteilung veranlaßt wird. Wir raten Ihnen daher sehr, vor Antritt Ihrer Reise nach Großbritannien, eine angemessene Versicherung abzuschließen.

GESCHÄFTSSTUNDEN DER BANKEN

Die Banken sind im allgemeinen werktags von 09.30-16.30 Uhr geöffnet, samstags, sonntags und feiertags geschlossen.

POSTÄMTER

Werktags von 09.00-17.30 Uhr und samstags von 09.00-12.30 Uhr geöffnet, sonntags und feiertags geschlossen.

LADENÖFFNUNGSZEITEN

Die meisten Geschäfte sind montags-samstags von 09.00-17.30 Uhr geöffnet. Einige Zeitungshändler und Lebensmittelgeschäfte sind schon ab 07.30 Uhr geöffnet und schließen erst um 20.00 Uhr. In dicht besiedelten Gebieten sind einige sogar bis 22.00 Uhr geöffnet.

REISEN

Eisenbahn
Hauptbahnhöfe gibt es in Edinburgh und Glasgow. Von hier aus verkehren Züge in die meisten Teile des schottischen Festlands.

Busse
Fahrten mit den landesweit verkehrenden Bussen sind sehr preisgünstig. In abgelegenen Gegenden werden Postbusse der Royal Mail eingesetzt, die Passagiere und Post befördern.

Fähren
Alle besiedelten schottischen Inseln sind mit der Fähre erreichbar. Die beiden Hauptbetreiber sind "Caledonian MacBrayne" an der Westküste und "P&O Ferries" an der Nordküste.

Autofahren

In Schottland herrscht Linksverkehr. Das Tempolimit beträgt 60 Meilen/Stunde (95 km/Stunde) und auf den Autobahnen 70 Meilen/Stunde (110 km/Stunde). In geschlossenen Ortschaften beträgt das Tempolimit gewöhnlich 30 Meilen/Stunde (45 km/Stunde). In abgelegenen Gegenden muß man mit einspurigen Straßen mit Ausweichstellen rechnen. Autofahrer sollten andere Verkehrsteilnehmer nicht behindern.

FEIERTAGE

Neujahr, 1./3. Januar; Ostermontag, 31. März; Frühlings-Feiertag, 5. Mai; Mai-Feiertag, 26. Mai; Sommer-Feiertag, 4. August; Weihnachten, 25./27. Dezember.

FERNSPRECHINFORMATIONEN

Internationale Kennzahl	Landes-Kennzahl	größere Städte - Ortsnetzkennzahlen	
00	44	Edinburgh	131
		Glasgow	141
		Inverness	1463
		Stirling	1786

ESPAÑOL

ALBERGUES DE JUVENTUD ESCOCESES

Más de 80 albergues juveniles escoceses ofrecen una estupenda selección de alojamiento, desde castillos en las tierras altas hasta albergues situados en remotos lagos o islas. Hay albergues juveniles en todas las principales ciudades, los cuales generalmente están situados en edificios históricos.

Ya sea que Ud viaje sólo, en familia o en grupo, los albergues juveniles escoceses proveen un lugar ideal para ejercer todas las diversas actividades que el país ofrece, desde excursiones por cañadas hasta exploraciones en las antiguas ruinas celtas. Muchos albergues ofrecen programas de actividades - a saber, en invierno, esquiar al estilo alberguista.

Como era de esperarse, los albergues juveniles escoceses ofrecen una excelente relación de calidad/precio por su dinero de £3,65-£11,95 se incluye ropa de cama.

La Asociación Escocesa de Albergues Juveniles fue entre las primeras en ofrecer normas garantizadas en los albergues juveniles y la información dada en esta sección está calificada apropiadamente (véase la página 33 para mayores detalles).

Todos los albergues juveniles de categoría estándar ▲ están abiertos de 7.00 a 23.45 horas, pero es posible que algunos limiten el acceso de 11.00 a 17 horas, por ejemplo, a la sala común y servicios. Confirmar esto al hacer la reserva.

Los albergues juveniles de categoría superior ▲ ofrecen mejores servicios y están abiertos todo el día de 07.00 a 02.00 horas (se puede firmar el registro hasta las 23.15 horas). Los albergues juveniles sencillos, △ que generalmente se encuentran en lugares remotos y famosos por su belleza, ofrecen un nivel de servicios inferior y, generalmente, están cerrados de 10.30 a 17.00 horas para economizar en gastos de personal.

Los albergues disponen de mucha información sobre actividades en la zona y, en la mayoría de ellos, incluso puede reservar por fax para la noche siguiente si está recorriendo el país. La mayor parte de los albergues ofrecen descuentos en el precio de los servicios y atracciones locales, los cuales conseguirá presentando su tarjeta Hostelling International.

PASAPORTES Y VISADOS

Se necesita un pasaporte válido. En la actualidad, muy pocos visitantes requieren visado, pero se recomienda confirmarlo con antelación.

SANIDAD

Para entrar en el Reino Unido no se precisa un Certificado Internacional de Vacunación, pero se aconseja verificar la necesidad de presentar uno al regresar a su país de origen.

Un seguro médico es fundamental porque los visitantes sólo tienen derecho a tratamiento gratuito de **urgencia** en el departamento de Accidentes y Urgencias de los hospitales del Servicio Nacional de Sanidad. Si se le ingresa en un hospital como paciente interno, aunque venga del departamento de urgencias, o se le manda a una consulta para paciente externos, se le pedirá que pague el coste del servicio a menos que sea ciudadano de un país de la CE, residente en cualquier país miembro, o ciudadano o residente en un país que tenga un acuerdo de asistencia sanitaria mutua con el Reino Unido. Se recomienda encarecidamente suscribir un seguro adecuado antes de viajar al Reino Unido.

HORARIO DE BANCOS

Por lo general, los bancos abren los días laborables de 09.30 a 16.30 horas y están cerrados los sábados, los domingos y festivos.

CASAS DE CORREO

Las casas de correo abren los días laborables de 09.00 a 17.30 horas y los sábados de 09.00 a 12.30 horas. Cierran los domingos y días festivos.

HORARIO COMERCIAL

La mayor parte de las tiendas abren de lunes a sábado de 09.00 a 17.30 horas. Algunas papelerías/kioscos y tiendas de comestibles abren desde las 07.30 horas hasta las 20.00 horas, y en áreas de mayor población algunas permanecen abiertas hasta las 22.00 horas.

DESPLAZAMIENTOS

Tren
Glasgow y Edimburgo tienen estaciones ferroviarias con servicios a la mayor parte de Escocia peninsular.

Autobús
Viajar en los servicios nacionales de autobús resulta económico y da acceso a todo el país. En las zonas más remotas, el servicio de correos Royal Mail dispone de autobuses que a la vez que sirven para el reparto de correo también pueden llevar pasajeros.

Ferry
Hay servicios de ferry a todas las islas escocesas habitadas. Las dos compañías principales son Caledonian MacBrayne en la costa oeste y P&O Ferries en la costa norte.

Coche
La conducción es por la izquierda. El límite de velocidad es de 60 millas/hora (aproximadamente 95 km/h), y de 70 millas/hora (unos 110 km/h) en las autopistas. El límite de velocidad habitual en zonas edificadas es de 30 millas/hora (unos 45 km/h). En las áreas más remotas se suelen encontrar carreteras de un solo carril con lugares especiales para pasar, en las que los conductores no deben estorbar a los demás usuarios de la vía.

DIAS FESTIVOS

Año Nuevo, 1-3 enero; Lunes de Pascua, 31 marzo; Fiesta de Primavera, 5 mayo; Fiesta de Mayo, 26 mayo; Fiesta de Verano, 4 agosto; Navidad, 25-27 diciembre.

INFORMACION TELEFONICA

Código Internacional	Código Nacional	Indicativo de área de las Ciudades principales
00	44	Edimburgo 131
		Glasgow 141
		Inverness 1463
		Stirling 1786

DISCOUNTS AND CONCESSIONS

Many hostels offer discounts off attractions, tours etc in their area. In addition your membership card entitles you to a number of national travel discounts:

National Trust for Scotland: 1/3 off entry fees
Wildfowl Trust: Reduction on entry fees
Arnold Clark Car Rental: 10% off basic tariffs except economy class
Sealink: 10% off, except Friday and Saturday sailings during July and August. Tickets only from port sailing office.

Hostels in this country may also display this symbol.

Les auberges de ce pays pourront également afficher ce symbole.

Jugendherbergen in diesem Land können auch dieses Symbol zeigen.

Es posible que los albergues de este país exhiban además este símbolo.

Aberdeen ⚠ 2W ‑CC‑ The King George VI Memorial Hostel, 8 Queen's Rd, Aberdeen AB15 4ZT. ☎ (1224) 646988 **Open:** 07.00-02.00hrs, 1-2.1; 3.2-31.12 ⇌ 108 ⊖ from £8.15, from £6.75 ‖◑|(B D) 1.7-31.8 ☞ ⅲ ▢ ⊞ P ⅙ ⅲ Aberdeen 2km 🚌 14, 15 2km ap YH ⓡ

Achininver △ Achiltibuie, Ullapool, Ross-shire N26 2YL. ☎ (1854) 622254 **Open:** 07.00-11.00hrs, 17.00-23.00hrs, 15.5-1.10 ⇌ 19 ⊖ £4.40, £3.65 ☞ 🚌 Achiltibuie-Ullapool 2.5km

Achmelvich △ Recharn, Lairg, Sutherland IV27 4JB. ☎ (1571) 844480

Open: 07.00-11.00hrs, 17.00-23.00hrs, 22.3-1.10 ⇌ 38 ⊖ £4.40, £3.65 ☞ P ⅙ ⅲ Lairg 79km 🚌 Drumbeg-Lochinver 2.4km ⓡ

Ardgartan ▲ Arrochar, Dunbartonshire G83 7AR. ☎ (1301) 702362 **Open:** 07.00-23.45hrs, 1-2.1; 3.2-31.12 ⇌ 82 ⊖ £7.35, £6.15 ‖◑|(B D) 17.4-30.9 ☞ ⅲ ▢ ⊞ P ⅲ Arrochar 4.8km 🚌 Glasgow-Campbeltown 2km ⓡ

Armadale ▲ Ardvasar, Sleat, Isle of Skye. ☎ (1471) 844260 **Open:** 07.00-23.45hrs, 15.3-1.10 ⇌ 42 ⊖ £5.75, £4.70 ☞ ① P ⛴ Armadale 2km ⅲ Mallaig (⛴) 2km ⓡ

Aviemore ⚠ IBN CC Inverness-shire, PH22 1PR. ☎ (1479) 810345 **Open:** 07.00-02.00hrs, 1.1-14.11; 23-31.12 🛏 115 ⊖ From £8.15, from £6.75 ♂ 🛉 🗊 🏛 🅿 ⚲ 🚃 Aviemore 2km 🚌 Inverness, Perth, Grantown Ⓡ

Ayr ▲ Craigweil Rd, Ayr KA7 2XJ. ☎ (1292) 262322 **Open:** 07.00-23.45hrs, 23.2-28.10 🛏 60 ⊖ £7.35, £6.15 ⦿(B D) 17.4-30.9 ♂ 🛉 🗊 🏛 🅿 ⚲ ✈ Prestwick 15km 🚃 Ayr 1.5km 🚌 2km ap Bus Station Ⓡ

Braemar ▲ Corrie Feragie, Braemar, Aberdeenshire AB35 5YQ. ☎ (1339) 741659 **Open:** 07.00-23.45hrs, 1.1-31.10; 23-31.12 🛏 70 ⊖ £7.35, £6.15 ♂ 🗊 🏛 🅿 ⚲ ⚲ 🚌 Braemar-Aberdeen 1km

Broadford ▲ Isle of Skye IV49 9AA. ☎ (1471) 822442 **Open:** 07.00-23.45hrs, 23.2-2.12 🛏 70 ⊖ £7.35, £6.15 ♂ ⓪ 🗊 🏛 🅿 ⚲ 🚌 UIG-Glasgow/Edinburgh, Portree-Kyleakin/Armadale + Postbus 1.5km Ⓡ

Broadmeadows △ Old Broadmeadows, Yarrowford, Selkirk TD7 5LZ. ☎ (1750) 76262 **Open:** 07.00-11.00hrs, 17.00-23.00hrs, 29.3-1.10 🛏 28 ⊖ £4.40, £3.65 ♂ 🅿 🚌 Galashiels-Peebles 1.5km

Cannich ▲ Beauly, Inverness-shire IV4 7LT. ☎ (1456) 415244 **Open:** 17.00-23.00hrs, 15.3-28.10 🛏 66 ⊖ £5.75, £4.70 ♂ 🛉 🅿 🚌 Cannich-Inverness/Beauly 1km

Carbisdale Castle ⚠ IBN CC Carbisdale, Culrain, Ardgay, Ross-shire IV24 3DP. ☎ (1549) 421232 **Open:** 07.00-02.00hrs, 24.2-5.5; 17.5-28.10 🛏 225 ⊖ From £10.05, from £8.65 BB inc ⦿(D) 17.4-30.9 ♂ 🛉 🛉 🗊 🗊 🏛 🅿 ⚲ 🚌 Culrain 800m 🚌 Ardgay-Strathoykel Postbus, Ardgay-Inverness 6.4km ap YH

Carn Dearg ▲ Gairloch, Ross-shire IV21 2DJ. ☎ (1445) 712219 **Open:** 07.00-23.45hrs 15.5-1.10 🛏 50 ⊖ £5.75, £4.70 ♂ 🏛 🅿 ⚲ 🚃 Achnasheen 51km 🚌 Strath-Achnasheen Postbus 3km Ⓡ

Coldingham ▲ The Mount, Coldingham, Eyemouth, Berwicks TD14 5PA. ☎ (1890) 771298 **Open:** 07.00-23.45hrs, 22.3-1.10 🛏 63 ⊖ £5.75, £4.70 ♂ 🏛 🅿 🚃 Berwick 19km 🚌 Edinburgh-Berwick 1.5km

Craig △ Diabaig, Achnasheen, Ross-shire IV22 2HE. **Open:** 07.00-11.00hrs, 17.00-23.00hrs, 15.5-1.10 🛏 16 ⊖ £4.40, £3.65 ♂ 🚃 Achnasheen 48km 🚌 Diabaig Achnasheen Postbus 5km

Crianlarich ▲ Perthshire FK20 8QN. ☎ (1838) 300260 **Open:** 07.00-23.45hrs, 23.2-28.10 🛏 78 ⊖ £7.35, £6.15 ♂ 🛉 ♿ 🗊 🏛 🅿 🚃 Crianlarich 🚌 Crianlarich-Glasgow, Oban, Fort William, Killin Ⓡ

Durness △ Smoo, Durness, Lairg, Sutherland IV27 4QA. ☎ (1971) 511244 **Open:** 07.00-11.00hrs, 17.00-23.00hrs, 15.5-1.10 🛏 40 ⊖ £4.40, £3.65 ♂ 🅿 🚃 Lairg 90km 🚌 Durness-Lairg/Inverness (Thurso in Su) Ⓡ

EDINBURGH (3 Hostels)

Edinburgh - Bruntsfield (*see town plan on next page*) ▲ 4W IBN CC 7 Bruntsfield Crescent, Edinburgh EH10 4EZ. ☎ (131) 4472994 **Open:** 1.1; 2.2-31.12 🛏 170 ⊖ From £8.15, from £6.75 ♂ 🗊 🏛 ⚲ ✈ Edinburgh/Turnhouse A 🚌 10km 🚃 Edinburgh Waverley 3.2km 🚌 11, 15, 16, 17, C1, C11 ap Forbes Rd Ⓡ

Edinburgh - Central ⚠ 0.1 W
Edinburgh YH, 7 Roberston Lane,
Cowgate, Edinburgh EH1 **Open:**
07.00-02.00hrs, 30.6-11.9 ⚡ 100 ●
From £9.15, from £7.75 ☞ � ▤ ✈
Edinburgh 6km A🚊 Waverley
Railway Station 500m 🚌 Waverley
500m **R** (Edinburgh District Office,
161 Warrender Park Rd, Edinburgh)

Edinburgh - **Eglinton** ⚠ 2W IBN CC
18 Eglinton Crescent, Edinburgh EH1
25DD. ☎ (131) 3371120 **Open:**
3.1-30.11 ⚡ 184 ● From £10.95,
from £9.45 BBinc ▮○▮(B D) ☞ ▤ ⚏ 🚲 ✈
Edinburgh/Turnhouse 10km 🚊
Haymarket 4km, Waverley 2km 🚌
3, 4, 12, 13, 22, 26, 28, 31, 33, 44
ap Palmerston Place **R**

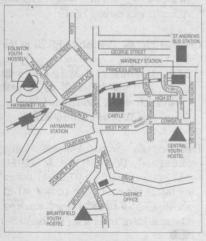

EDINBURGH -
(a) Bruntsfield, (b) Eglington

Falkland △ Back Wynd, Falkland, Fife
KY7 7BX. ☎ (1337) 857710 **Open:**
07.00-11.00hrs, 17.00-23.00hrs,
21.3-1.10 ⚡ 38 ● £4.40, £3.65 ☞ ⚏
▣ 🚌 Ladybank and Markinch 8km
🚌 Stirling, Cupar, Perth and
Kirkcaldy

Glasgow ⚠ 2W IBN CC 7/8 Park
Terrace, Glasgow G3 6BY. ☎ (141)
3323004 **Open:** 07.00-02.00hrs ⚡

158 ● From £10.95, from £9.45 BBinc
▮○▮(L D) ☞ ♦♦♦ ▤ ⚏ ▣ ✈
Glasgow/Abbotsinch 25km 🚌
Glasgow Central 2km, Glasgow Queen
Street 10km 🚌 11 from Queen St or
Buchanan Bus St, 44, 59 Central 1km
ap Woodlands Rd U Kelvinbridge
2km **R**

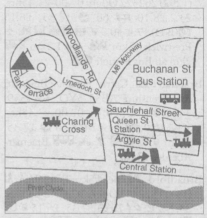

GLASGOW

Glen Affric △ Allt Beithe, Glen Affric,
Cannich, by Beauly, Inverness-shire IV4
7ND. **Open:** 07.00-11.00hrs,
17.00-23.00hrs, 21.3-27.10 ⚡ 26 ●
£5.40, £4.65 ☞ 🚌 Inverness 80km
🚌 Cannich-Beauly/Inverness 32km,
Cluanie- Inverness/Kyle/ Glasgow
11km **R**

Glenbrittle ▲ Isle of Skye IV47 8TA.
☎ (1478) 640278 **Open:**
07.00-23.45hrs, 21.3-1.10 ⚡ 48 ●
£5.75, £4.70 ☞ ① ⚏ ▣ 🚌 Kyle of
Lochalsh (via Kyleakin) 64km 🚌
Glenbrittle-Sligachan (Su), Sligachan-
Uig/Kyleakin/Glasgow 13km

Glencoe ▲ Ballachulish, Argyll PA39
4HX. ☎ (1855) 811219 **Open:**
07.00-23.45hrs ⚡ 62 ● £7.35, £6.15
☞ ♦♦♦ ▤ ⚏ ▣ 🚌 Glasgow, Oban, Fort
William 2.4km **R**

Glendevon △ Dollar,
Clackmannanshire FK14 7JY. ☎ (1259)

781206 **Open:** 07.00-11.00hrs, 17.00-23.00hrs, 21.3-1.10 🏁 42 ⊖ £4.40, £3.65 👢 🚿 🍴 Gleneagles 13km 🚌 Stirling-St Andrews 3.2km

Glendoll ▲ Clova, Kirriemuir, Angus DD8 4RD. 📞 (1575) 550236 **Open:** 07.00-23.45hrs, 21.3-1.10 🏁 60 ⊖ £5.75, £4.70 👢 🏃 🚿 🅿 🍴 Dundee 58km 🚌 Kirriemuir- Glendoll Postbus, Kirriemuir-Dundee

Glen Nevis ⚠ (IBN) Fort William, Inverness- shire PH33 6ST. 📞 (1397) 702336 Open: 07.00-02.00hrs, 1.1-27.10; 1-31.12 🏁 127 ⊖ From £8.15, from £6.75 👢 🔟 🚿 🅿 🍴 Fort William 5km 🚌 Fort William-Skye/Glasgow 5km ⓡ

Helmsdale △ Sutherland KW8 6JR. 📞 (1431) 821577 **Open:** 07.00-11.00hrs, 17.00-23.00hrs, 16.5-1.10 🏁 38 ⊖ £4.40, £3.65 👢 🐾 🍴 Helmsdale 2km 🚌 Inverness, Wick

Inveraray ▲ Argyllshire PA32 8XD. 📞 (1499) 302454 **Open:** 07.00-23.45hrs, 21.3-27.10 🏁 40 ⊖ From £5.75 from £4.70 👢 🚿 🅿 🚌 Glasgow-Campbeltown 1km

Inverey △ by Braemar, Aberdeenshire AB35 5YB. **Open:** 07.00-11.00hrs, 17.00-23.00hrs, 6.6-1.9 🏁 17 ⊖ £4.40, £3.65 👢 🅿 🚌 Braemar Postbus, Braemar/Aberdeen, Braemar/Pitlochry/Aviemde ⓡ

Inverness ⚠ 1S (IBN) CC 1 Old Edinburgh Rd, Inverness IV2 3HF. 📞 (1463) 231771 Open: 07.00-02.00hrs 🏁 128 ⊖ From £8.15, from £6.75 👢 🔟 🚿 🅿 🍴 Inverness 2km 🚌 Inverness- Aberdeen, Edinburgh, London, Wick 2km ⓡ (1.7-31.8)

Islay ▲ Port Charlotte, Island of Islay PA48 7TX. 📞 (1496) 850385 **Open:** 07.00-23.45hrs, 22.3-28.10 🏁 42 ⊖

£5.75, £4.70 👢 🏃 1 🅿 ⛴ Port Ellen 32km, Port Askaig 21.5km 🚌 500m ⓡ (1-31.10)

John o' Groats ▲ Canisbay, Nr John o'Groats, Wick, Caithness KW1 4YH. 📞 (1955) 611424 **Open:** 07.00-23.45hrs, 29.3-28.10 🏁 42 ⊖ £5.75, £4.70 👢 🅿 ⛴ Scrabster 32km, John o'Groats 2km, Thurso + Wick 29km 🚌 Wick/Thurso

Kendoon △ Dalry, Castle Douglas, Kircudbrightshire DG7 3UD. **Open:** 07.00-11.00hrs, 17.00-23.00hrs, 15.5-1.10 🏁 40 ⊖ £4.40, £3.65 👢 🚌 Ayr-Castle Douglas

Killin ▲ Perthshire FK21 8TN. 📞 (1567) 820546 **Open:** 07.00-23.45hrs, 15.3-28.10 🏁 49 ⊖ £5.75, £4.70 👢 🚿 🅿 🚌 Crianlarich, Stirling, Callander, Trossachs Postbus 1km

Kirkwall ▲ Old Scapa Rd, Kirkwall, Orkney KW15 1BB. 📞 (1856) 872243 **Open:** 07.00-23.45hrs, 22.3-28.10 🏁 90 ⊖ £7.35, £6.15 👢 🏃 1 🔟 🚿 🅿 ⛴ Stromness 24km, Kirkwall 2km 🚌 Stromness + South Ronaldsay for John o'Groats 2km ⓡ

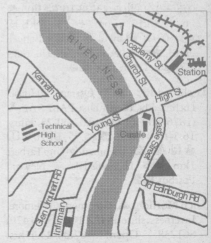

INVERNESS

Kirk Yetholm ▲ Kelso, Roxburghshire TD5 8PG. ☎ (1573) 420631 **Open:** 07.00-23.45hrs, 21.3-1.10 ⊘ 35 ⊖ £5.75, £4.70 ♂ ♚ ℙ 🚌 Kelso ®

Kyleakin ⚠ [IBN] Isle of Skye. ☎ (1599) 534585 **Open:** 07.00-02.00hrs ⊘ 78 ⊖ From £8.15, from £6.75 ⏀(B D) 17.4-30.9 ♂ ♚ ① ▣ ⚒ ℙ ⚲ ⛴ Kyle-Kyleakin 200m 🚌 Kyle (⛴) 1km 🚌 Inverness, Uig, Glasgow, Edinburgh, Armadale ® (1.7-31.8)

Lerwick ▲ Islesburgh House, King Harald St, Lerwick, Shetland ZE1 0EQ. ☎ (1595) 692114 **Open:** 07.00-23.45hrs, 1.4-1.10 ⊘ 60 ⊖ £7.35, £6.15 ♂ ♚ ① ▣ ⚒ ℙ ⚲ ⚓ ✈ Sumburgh 48km ⛴ Lerwick 2km ®

Loch Lochy ▲ South Laggan, Loch Lochy, Spean Bridge, Inverness- shire PH34 4EA. ☎ (1809) 501239 **Open:** 07.00-23.45hrs, 21.3-27.10 ⊘ 68 ⊖ £5.75, £4.70 ♂ ⚒ ℙ ⚲ 🚌 Spean Bridge 19km 🚌 Inverness, Fort William, Skye ap YH

Loch Lomond ⚠ [IBN] Loch Lomond Arden, Alexandria, Dumbartonshire G83 8RB. ☎ (1389) 850226 Open: 07.00-02.00hrs, 6.3-28.10 ⊘ 200 ⊖ From £8.15, from £6.75 ⏀(B D) 9.3-30.9 ♂ ♚ ⚏ ▣ ⚒ ℙ 🚌 Balloch 4km 🚌 Glasgow, Balloch, Fort William, Oban 1km ®

Lochmaddy ▲ Ostram House, Lochmaddy, North Uist PA82 5AE. ☎ (1876) 500368 **Open:** 07.00-23.45hrs, 16.5-1.10 ⊘ 36 ⊖ £5.75, £4.70 ♂ ① ⚒ ℙ ⚲ ⛴ Lochmaddy-Uig/Tarbert 1km 🚌 Lochboisdale + Newton Postbus ®

Loch Morlich ▲ Glenmore, Aviemore, Inverness-shire PH22 1QY. ☎ (1479) 861238 **Open:** 07.00-23.45hrs, 1.1-30.9; 16.11-31.12 ⊘ 92 ⊖ £7.35, £6.15 ⏀(B D) 1.1-30.9 ♂ ♚ ▣ ⚒ ℙ ⚓ ⛵ 🚣 Aviemore 11km 🚌 Aviemore ® (24.12-30.4, 1.7-31.8)

Loch Ness ▲ Glenmoriston, Inverness-shire IV3 6YD. ☎ (1320) 351274 **Open:** 07.00-23.45hrs, 21.3-28.10 ⊘ 59 ⊖ £5.75, £4.70 ♂ ♚ ⚒ ℙ 🚣 Inverness 38km 🚌 Inverness, Fort William, Skye ap YH

Loch Ossian △ Corrour, Inverness-shire PH30 4AA. ☎ (1397) 732207 **Open:** 07.00-11.00hrs, 17.00-23.00hrs, 21.3-1.10 ⊘ 20 ⊖ £4.40, £3.65 ♂ 🚣 Corrour 2km, Rannoch 14km 🚌 Pitlochry 14km ap Rannoch Station

Lochranza ▲ Isle of Arran KA27 8HL. ☎ (1770) 830631 **Open:** 07.00-23.45hrs, 23.2-28.10 ⊘ 74 ⊖ £7.35, £6.15 ♂ ♚ ① ⚒ ℙ ⚲ ⛴ Lochranza 1, Brodick 22.5km ®

Melrose ▲ Priorwood, Melrose, Roxburghshire TD6 9EF. ☎ (1896) 822521 **Open:** 07.00-23.45hrs ⊘ 86 ⊖ £7.35, £6.15 ⏀(B D) ♂ ♚ ▣ ⚒ ℙ 🚌 Edinburgh, Newcastle, Carlisle + Borders

Minnigaff ▲ Newton Stewart, Wigtownshire DG8 6PL. ☎ (1671) 402211 **Open:** 07.00-23.45hrs, 21.3-1.10 ⊘ 36 ⊖ £5.75, £4.70 ♂ ℙ ⚲ 🚌 Stranraer, Dumfries, Ayr, Glasgow 1km ap Newton St

New Lanark ▲ Wee Row, Rosedale St, New Lanark ML11 9DJ. ☎ (1555) 666710 **Open:** 07.00-23.45hrs ⊘ 64 ⊖ £9.25, £8.05 [BB]inc ⏀(B D) ♂ ♚ ▣ ⚒ ℙ ⛵ 🚣 Lanark 2.4km 🚌 ap New Lanark/Lanark ®

Oban ⚠ [IBN] [CC] Esplanade, Oban, Argyll PA34 5AF. ☎ (1631) 562025 Open: 07.00-23.45hrs, 23.2-28.10 ⊘ 114 ⊖ From £8.15, from £6.75 ♂ ♚ ▣ ⚒ ℙ ⛴ Oban 3km 🚣 Oban 3km

🚌 Oban-Glasgow/Inverness/Glencoe 3km **R**

Papa Westray ▲ Beltane House, Papa Westray, Orkney KW17 2BU. ☎ (1857) 644267 **Open:** 07.00-23.45hrs ⇌ 16 ⊖ £7.35, £6.15 ♂ ① ♿ ⛴ Papa Westray-Kirkwall 3km **R**

Perth ▲ 2W 107 Glasgow Rd, Perth PH2 0NS ☎ (1738) 623658 **Open:** 07.00-23.45hrs, 23.2-28.10 ⇌ 64 ⊖ £7.35, £6.15 ♂ ♚♚♚ 🖥 🚿 **P** ♿ ⛴ Perth 3km 🚌 Aberdeen, Edinburgh, Glasgow, Inverness, London 3km **R**

Pitlochry ▲ Braeknowe, Knockard Rd, Pitlochry PH16 5HJ. ☎ (1796) 472308 **Open:** 07.00-23.45hrs ⇌ 76 ⊖ £7.35, £6.15 ⛌(B D) 17.4-30.9 ♂ ♚♚♚ 🖥 🚿 **P** ⛴ Pitlochry 3km 🚌 Inverness/Perth, Braemar/Ballater (Su) 2km **R** (1.7-31.8)

Raasay △ Creachan Cottage, Raasay, Kyle, Ross-shire IV40 8NT. ☎ (1478) 660240 **Open:** 07.00-11.00hrs, 17.00-23.00hrs, 16.5-1.10 ⇌ 34 ⊖ £4.40, £3.65 ♂ ① **P** ♿ ⛴ Raasay 4.8km ⛴ Kyle of Lochalsh 36km **R**

Ratagan ▲ Glenshiel, Kyle, Ross-shire IV40 8HT. ☎ (1599) 511243 **Open:** 07.00-23.45hrs, 17.3-30.10; 21.3-27.10 (check before arrival) ⇌ 44 ⊖ £7.35, £6.15 ♂ ♚♚♚ ♿ 🖥 🚿 **P** ♿ ⛴ Glenelg to Skye 14.5km ⛴ Kyle of Lochalsh 29km 🚌 Shiel Bridge to Inverness/Glasgow daily 4km

Rowardennan ▲ Rowardennan by Drymen, Glasgow G63 0AR. ☎ (1360) 870259 **Open:** 07.00-23.45hrs, 28.2-27.10 ⇌ 80 ⊖ £7.35, £6.15 ⛌(B D) 17.4-30.9 ♂ ♚♚♚ 🖥 🚿 **P** ⛴ Balloch- Rowardennan ⛴ Balloch 29.5km 🚌 Balmaha to Drymen through to Balloch/Glasgow 11km **R**

Snoot △ Roberton, Hawick, Roxburghshire TD9 7LY. ☎ (1450) 880259 **Open:** 07.00-11.00hrs, 17.00-23.00hrs, 21.3-1.10 ⇌ 20 ⊖ £4.40, £3.65 ♂ ♿ ⛴ Hawick to Borthwick Water + Postbus 9km **R**

Stirling △ IBN CC St John St, Stirling FK8 1DU ☎ (1786) 473442 **Open:** 07.00-02.00hrs ⇌ 120 ⊖ From £10.95, from £9.45 BB inc ⛌(B D) ♂ ♚♚♚ ♿ 🖥 🚿 **P** ♿ ⛴ 3km 🚌 Stirling 1km 🚌 3km **R**

Stockinish △ Kyles, Stockinish, Tarbert, Harris HS3 3EN. ☎ (1859) 530373 **Open:** 07.00-11.00hrs, 17.00-23.00hrs, 21.3-1.10 ⇌ 32 ⊖ £4.40, £3.65 ♂ ① **P** ⛴ Tarbert 11km 🚌 Rodel-Leverburgh-Tarbert-Stornaway ap YH **R** (16.7-16.8)

Strathpeffer ▲ Ross-shire IV14 9BT. ☎ (1997) 421532 **Open:** 07.00-23.45hrs, 21.3-1.10 ⇌ 70 ⊖ £5.75, £4.70 ♂ 🚿 **P** ⛴ Dingwall 8km 🚌 Dingwall, Ullapool, Inverness 1km

Stromness ▲ Mainland, Orkney. ☎ (1856) 850589 **Open:** 07.00-23.45hrs, 21.3-27.10 ⇌ 40 ⊖ £5.75, £4.70 ♂ ① ♿ ⛴ Stromness 2km 🚌 Stromness/Kirkwall 2km

Tighnabruaich ▲ Argyll PA21 2BD. ☎ (1700) 811622 **Open:** 07.00-23.45hrs, 21.3-1.10 ⇌ 40 ⊖ £5.75, £4.70 ♂ 🚿 **P** ♿ ⛵ ⛴ Gourock 🚌 Dunoon

Tobermory △ Isle of Mull, Argyll PA75 6NU. ☎ (1688) 302481 **Open:** 07.00-23.45hrs, 21.3-27.10 ⇌ 51 ⊖ £5.75, £4.70 ♂ ① 🚿 ⛴ Craignure for Oban 35km ⛴ Oban (⛴) 35km 🚌 Craignure **R**

Tomintoul △ Main St, Tomintoul, Ballindalloch, Banffshire AB3 9HA. **Open:** 07.00-11.00hrs, 17.00-23.00hrs,

16.5-1.10 ✉ 38 ● £4.40, £3.65 ⛽ **P**
⛫ 🚌· Keith, Ballater, Tomintoul,
Aviemore (Su) **R**

Tongue ▲ Lairg, Sutherland IV27
4XH. ☎ (1847) 611301 **Open:**
07.00-23.45hrs, 21.3-1.10 ✉ 52 ●
£5.75, £4.70 ⛽ 🏠 **P** 🚌 Lairg 61km
🚌 Durness, Lairg, Thurso

Torridon ▲ Achnasheen, Ross- shire
IV22 2EZ. ☎ (1445) 791284 **Open:**
07.00-23.45hrs, 7.2-27.10 ✉ 80 ●
£7.35, £6.15 ⛽ 👬 🗄 🏠 **P** 🚌
Achnasheen 32km 🚌 Diabaig,
Kinlochewe/Achnasheen Postbus

Uig ▲ Isle of Skye IV51 9YD. ☎ (1470)
542211 **Open:** 07.00-23.45hrs,
21.3-27.10 ✉ 60 ● £5.75, £4.70 ⛽
👬 ① 🏠 **P** ⛴ Uig 3km 🚌 Kyle
of Lochalsh 80km 🚌 Skye, Glasgow,
Fort William, Edinburgh 3km

Ullapool ▲ Shore St, Ullapool, Ross-
shire IV26 2UJ. ☎ (1854) 612254
Open: 07.00-23.45hrs, 21.3-27.10 ✉
72 ● £7.35, £6.15 ⛽ 🗄 🏠 ⛫ ⛴
Ullapool 200m 🚌 Garve 51km 🚌
Ullapool/Inverness, Lochinver,
Achiltibuie **R**

Wanlockhead ▲ Lotus Lodge,
Wanlockhead, Biggar, Lanarkshire
ML12 6UT. ☎ (1659) 74252 **Open:**
07.00-23.45hrs, 21.3-27.10 ✉ 28 ●
£5.75, £4.70 ⛽ **P** 🚌 Kirkconnel
19km 🚌 Edinburgh/Glasgow-
Dumfries, Abington/Biggar Postbus
12km

Whiting Bay ▲ Brodick, Isle of Arran
KA27 8QW. ☎ (1770) 700339 **Open:**
07.00-23.45hrs, 28.2-27.10 ✉ 60 ●

£5.75, £4.70 ⛽ 👬 ① **P** ⛫ ⛴
Brodick 14.5km **R**

SUPPLEMENTARY ACCOMMODATION OUTSIDE THE ASSURED STANDARDS SCHEME

Berneray Isle of Berneray, North Uist,
HS6 5BQ. ✉ 16 ● £4.40, £3.65 ⛽ ①
⛴ Newton- Berneray- Leverburgh
3km

Eday London Bay, Eday, Orkney KW17
2AB. ☎ (18572) 622283 **Open:**
07.00-11.00hrs, 17.00-23.00hrs,
15.3-1.10 ✉ 24 ● £4.40, £3.65 ⛽ ①
⛫ ⛴ Eday-Kirkwall 6.4km **R**

Garenin Carloway, Isle of Lewis, HS2
9AL. **Open:** 07.00-11.00hrs,
17.00-23.00hrs ✉ 14 ● £4.40, £3.65
⛽ ⛪ ① ⛴ Stornoway-Ullapool 37km
🚌 Carloway-Stornoway 1.5km

Hoy Stromness, Orkney KW16 3NJ. ☎
(1856) 873535 **Open:** 07.00-23.45hrs,
1.5-10.9 ✉ 26 ● £5.75, £4.70 ⛽ ①
⛴ Moaness 500m, Lyness 16km **R**
(County Youth Service, Education
Office, Kirkwall, Orkney)

Rackwick Rackwick Outdoor Centre,
Hoy, Stromness, Orkney, KW16 3NJ.
☎ (1856) 873535 **Open:**
07.00-23.45hrs, 15.3-4.9 ✉ 8 ●
£5.75, £4.70 ⛽ ① ⛴ Moaness/Lyness
R (County Youth Service, Education
Office, Kirkwall, Orkney)

Rhenigidale Isle of Harris, HS3 3BD.
Open: 07.00-23.45hrs ✉ 11 ● £4.40,
£3.65 ⛽ ① ⛴ Tarbert 21km 🚌
Tarbert/South Harris/Stornoway

SLOVENIA
SLOVENIE
SLOWENIEN
ESLOVENIA

Počitniška Zveza Slovenije,
Parmova 33, 61000 Ljubljana, Slovenia.

☎ (386) (61) 312156
FAX (386) (61) 1332219.

Capital:	Ljubljana
Language:	Slovene
Currency:	Slovene Tolar (SIT)
Population:	1,965,986
Size:	20,254 sq km

SLOVENIA

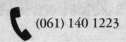

Bled - "Bledec" [0.5 NE] Grajska 17, 4260 Bled ☎ (64) 78230 **FAX** (64) 78230, (61) 1332219 ✉ 58 [BB][inc] ⛄ ⚄ 🏢 ⊡ ⛪ **P** 🚲 ⚓ ✈ Brnik 32km 🚃 Bled 2km 🚐 ap Bled Avtobusna Postaja 200m **R** (Central Office: ☎ (61) 312156, **FAX** (61) 1332219)

Koper Dijaški dom Koper, Cankarjeva 5, 6000 Koper. ☎ (66) 391150, 391154 **FAX** (66) 391150 ✉ 35 21.8-30.6 ✉ 300 1.7-20.8 ⊖ 18 DEM [BB][inc] ⛄ ⊡ ⛪ **P** 🚲 ⚓ ✈ Portorož 30km A🚐 Koper 1.5km ⛴ Luka Koper 500m 🚃 Koper 1.5km 🚐 1-3 200m **R** (☎/FAX YH)

LJUBLJANA (2 Hostels)

Ljubljana - Bežigrad Kardeljeva ploščad 28, 1000 Ljubljana. ☎ (61) 342867 **FAX** (61) 342864 **Open:** 24hrs ✉ 400 (28.6-28.8) ⊖ 16-18 DEM ⛄ (B. Grps) 🏢 ⊡ ⛪ **P** ✈ Brnik 17km A🚐 Bus station 2km 🚃 Ljubljana 2km 🚐 6, 8, 21 500m ap near YH **R** (☎/FAX YH)

Ljubljana - Tabor Vidovdanska 7, 1000 Ljubljana. ☎ (61) 321067, 321060 **FAX** (61) 321060 **Open:** 24hrs, 28.6-28.8 ✉ 200 ⊖ 17 DEM [BB][inc] 🏢 ⛪ **P** ✈ Ljubljana-Brnik 20km A🚐 Ljubljana- Brnik 1km 🚃 Ljubljana 1km 🚐 5 50m **R** (☎/FAX YH)

Maribor Dijaški dom 26 Junij Maribor, Železnikova 12, 2000 Maribor. ☎ (62) 511800 **Open:** 07.00-10.00, 19.00-23.00hrs, 1.7-20.8 ✉ 50 ⊖ 16 DEM [BB][inc] **P** 🚲 ✈ Ljubljana 134km A🚐 Ljubljana-Maribor 🚃 Maribor 3km 🚐 3, 3/1, 9 3km ap 0.300m **R**

Zreče RTC Rogla, Depandansa Jelka, 3214 Zreče. (Alt 1517m) ☎ (63) 754322 **FAX** (63) 754096 **Open:** 1.12-15.4; 28.5.15.10 ✉ 58 ⊖ 21 DEM [BB][inc] ⛄ ⊡ ⛪ **P** 🎿 🚲 ✈ Ljubljana 100km 🚃 Celje 40km 🚐 Zreče 16km ap Rogla **R** (Prodajna Služba ☎ (63) 7681105, 7681106, 7.681107 **FAX** (63) 762446)

SPAIN
ESPAGNE
SPANIEN
ESPAÑA

Instituto de la Juventud/Red Española de Albergues
Juveniles,
c/ José Ortega y Gasset 71,
Madrid 28006, Spain.

☎ (34) (1) 3477700
FAX (34) (1) 4018160

Office Hours: Monday-Friday, 09.00-14.00hrs
                    Saturday, 09.00-12.00hrs

Travel Section: TIVE,
c/ José Ortega y Gasset 71,
28006 Madrid, Spain.

☎ (34) (1) 3477700

IBN Booking Centres for outward bookings
- Barcelona - ICSJ Central Reservation,
  c/ Calabria 147, 08015 Barcelona.
  ☎ (34) (3) 4838363, **FAX** (34) (3) 4838350.
- Barcelona - ICSJ Youth Tourism Office,
  c/ Calabria 147, 08015 Barcelona, Catalunya.
  ☎ (34) (3) 4838378, **FAX** (34) (3) 4838370.
- Madrid - TIVE Office,
  c/ Fernando el Católico 88, 28015 Madrid.
  ☎ (34) (1) 5437412, **FAX** (34) (1) 5440062.

Capital:	Madrid
Language:	Spanish
Currency:	Ptas (pesetas)
Population:	39,433,942
Size:	504,782 sq km

SPAIN

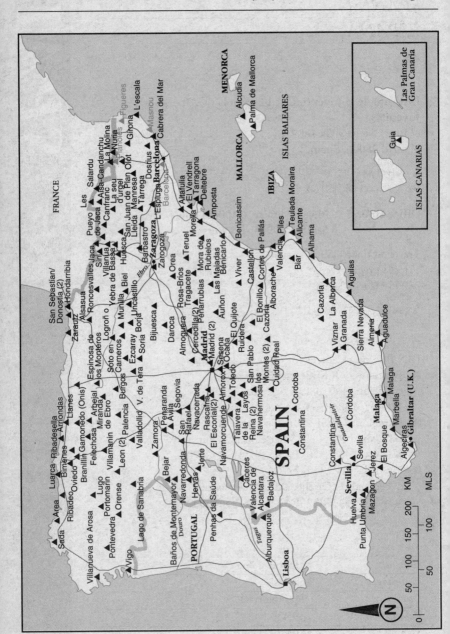

ENGLISH

SPANISH HOSTELS

Whether on the coast or in the mountains, Spain has 184 Youth Hostels to choose from, including several specialist ski hostels, one in the Canary Islands and two in Majorca. Although there is no upper age limit, those under 26 years have priority. Under 13s are not accommodated except when accompanied by an adult.

Opening times vary but are generally 08.00-22.30hrs in winter, 23.30hrs in summer. You can usually check in any time between 09.30 and 19.00hrs. Prices vary depending on region, age and whether breakfast is included.

Reservations for hostels should be made directly to the Youth Hostel. For information on group reservations (minimum of 20, under 30 years of age) contact Red Española de Albergues Juveniles, ☎ (34) (1) 3477631.

PASSPORTS AND VISAS

A passport is required except in the case of EC citizens who only need their Identity Card. Some countries may require a visa so check before you travel.

HEALTH

Medical care is free to nationals of EC countries or those of countries which have a reciprocal agreement with Spain, otherwise it is advisable to take out insurance cover.

BANKING HOURS

Banks are open weekdays 08.30-14.00hrs.

POST OFFICES

Post offices are open weekdays 09.00-14.00hrs.

SHOPPING HOURS

Shops are normally open Monday-Saturday 10.00-13.30hrs and 17.00-20.30hrs.

TRAVEL

Rail
The Spanish railways, RENFE, offer a variety of discounts and reductions on their tickets, depending on the day of travel. Eurorail and Inter-Rail cards are valid subject to a supplement on certain fast trains.

Bus
The bus companies offer a special rate with a discount for young travellers under 26 years of age.

PUBLIC HOLIDAYS

Epiphany, 6 January; Good Friday, 28 March; Labour Day, 1 May; St James Apostle Day, 25 July; Our Lady of Paloma, 15 August; Columbus Day, Our Lady of Pilar, 12 October; All Saints Day, 1 November; Constitution Day, 6 December; Immaculate Conception, 8 December; Christmas, 25 December.

TELEPHONE INFORMATION

International Code	Country Code	Main City Area Codes	
07	34	Barcelona	3
		Bilbao	4
		Granada	58
		Madrid	1
		Sevilla	5
		Valencia	6

> FRANÇAIS

AUBERGES DE JEUNESSE ESPAGNOLES

Sur la côte ou dans les montagnes, l'Espagne a 184 auberges de jeunesse, y compris plusieurs auberges spécialisées dans le ski, une dans les îles Canaries et deux à Majorque. Bien qu'il n'y ait pas d'âge limite supérieur, priorité est donnée aux moins de 26 ans. Les enfants de moins de 13 ans ne sont pas admis à moins d'être accompagnés par un adulte.

Les heures d'ouverture varient mais en général vont de 8h à 22h30 en hiver et jusqu'à 23h30 en été. Vous pouvez en principe arriver entre 9h30 et 19h. Les prix varient selon la région, l'âge ou selon que le petit-déjeûner est compris ou non.

Pour réserver, adressez-vous directement à l'auberge en question. Pour plus d'informations sur les réservation de groupes (minimum de 20 personnes de moins de 30 ans), veuillez contacter la Red Española de Albergues Juveniles (REAJ) au numéro de téléphone suivant: (34) (1) 3477631.

PASSEPORTS ET VISAS

Les passeports sont nécessaires sauf pour les citoyens de la CE, qui n'ont besoin que d'une carte d'identité. Certains pays peuvent exiger un visa; il est donc prudent de vérifier avant votre départ.

SOINS MEDICAUX

Les citoyens de la CE et ceux venant de pays ayant passé un accord réciproque avec l'Espagne ont droit à des soins gratuits, sinon, il est conseillé de souscrire à une police d'assurance maladie.

HEURES D'OUVERTURE DES BANQUES

Les banques sont ouvertes en semaine de 8h30 à 14h.

BUREAUX DE POSTE

Les bureaux de poste sont ouverts en semaine de 9h à 14h.

HEURES D'OUVERTURE DES MAGASINS

Les magasins sont normalement ouverts du lundi au samedi de 10h à 13h30 et 17h à 20h30.

DEPLACEMENTS

Trains
Les chemins de fer espagnols, RENFE, offrent toute une variété de remises et réductions sur leurs billets, selon le jour du voyage. Les cartes Eurail et Inter-Rail sont valides, mais un supplément est à payer pour certains trains rapides.

Autobus

Les compagnies d'autobus offrent un tarif spécial avec une remise pour les jeunes voyageurs de moins de 26 ans.

JOURS FERIES

Fête des Rois Mages (Epiphanie), 6 janvier; Vendredi Saint, 28 mars; Fête du Travail, 1er mai; Apôtre St Jean, 25 juillet; Notre Dame de Paloma, 15 août; Fête du Monde Hispanique, Notre Dame de Pilar, 12 octobre; Toussaint, 1er novembre; Jour de la Constitution, 6 décembre; Immaculée Conception, 8 décembre; Noël, 25 december.

TELEPHONE

Indicatif International	Indicatif du Pays	Indicatifs régionaux des Villes principales	
07	34	Barcelone	3
		Bilbao	4
		Grenade	58
		Madrid	1
		Séville	5
		Valence	6

$$\boxed{\text{DEUTSCH}}$$

SPANISCHE JUGENDHERBERGEN

Spanien hat an der Küste und in den Bergen 184 Jugendherbergen, darunter mehrere Herbergen speziell für Skifahrer, eine Herberge auf den Kanarischen Inseln und zwei in Mallorca. Obwohl es keine obere Altersgrenze gibt, werden junge Leute unter 26 Jahren bevorzugt aufgenommen. Kinder unter 13 Jahren werden nicht aufgenommen, es sei denn, sie befinden sich in Begleitung einer erwachsenen Person.

Die Öffnungszeiten sind unterschiedlich, liegen aber im allgemeinen zwischen 08.00 und 22.30 Uhr im Winter und 23.30 im Sommer. Normalerweise kann man jederzeit zwischen 09.30 und 19.00 Uhr aufgenommen werden. Die Preise unterschieden sich je nach dem Gebiet, dem Alter und ob das Frühstück inbegriffen ist.

Man muß sich direkt mit der Jugendherberge voranmelden. Für Einzelheiten mit Bezug auf Gruppenreservierungen (mindestens 20 Leute, unter 30 Jahre) bitte sich mit dem Verband: Red Española de Albergues Juveniles in Verbindung setzen. ☎(34) (1) 3477631.

PÄSSE UND VISA

Außer im Falle von Staatsbürgern eines EG-Landes, die nur eine Kennkarte benötigen, braucht man für Spanien einen Reisepaß. Für Reisende aus gewissen Ländern könnte auch ein Visum erforderlich sein. Bitte erkundigen Sie sich deshalb vor der Abreise.

GESUNDHEIT

Für Staatsbürger eines EG-Landes und aus Ländern, mit denen Spanien einen reziproken Vertrag geschlossen hat, ist die ärztliche Behandlung kostenlos. In anderen Fällen ist es ratsam, eine Versicherung abzuschließen.

GESCHÄFTSSTUNDEN DER BANKEN

Banken sind werktags von 08.30-14.00 Uhr geöffnet.

POSTÄMTER

Postämter sind werktags von 09.00-14.00 Uhr geöffnet.

LADENÖFFNUNGSZEITEN

Die Geschäfte sind gewöhnlich montags bis samstags von 10.00-13.30 Uhr und 17.00-20.30 Uhr geöffnet.

REISEN

Eisenbahn

Die spanische Eisenbahn, RENFE, bietet je nach dem Reisetag verschiedene verbilligte Fahrkarten an. Eurail- und Inter-Rail-Karten sind in Spanien gültig, aber für gewisse Schnellzüge muß ein Zuschlag bezahlt werden.

Busse

Die Busunternehmen wenden für junge Reisende unter 26 Jahren einen Sondertarif mit verbilligten Fahrpreisen an.

FEIERTAGE

Erscheinungsfest, 6. Januar; Karfreitag, 28. März; Maifeiertag, 1. Mai; Tag des Heiligen James, 25. Juli; Unsere Liebe Frau von Paloma, 15. August; Kolumbustag, Unsere Liebe Frau von Pilar, 12. Oktober; Allerheiligen, 1. November; Tag der Verfassung, 6. Dezember; Tag der unbefleckten Empfängnis, 8. Dezember; Weihnachten, 25. Dezember.

FERNSPRECHINFORMATIONEN

Internationale Kennzahl	Landes-Kennzahl	größere Städte - Ortsnetzkennzahlen	
07	34	Barcelona	3
		Bilbao	4
		Granada	58
		Madrid	1
		Sevilla	5
		Valencia	6

$$\boxed{\text{ESPAÑOL}}$$

ALBERGUES DE JUVENTUD ESPAÑOLES

Ya sea en la costa o en la montaña, España tiene 184 albergues juveniles entre los que elegir, incluyendo varios albergues especializados en el esquí, uno en las Islas Canarias y dos en Mallorca. Aunque no existe un límite máximo de edad, tienen prioridad los menores de 26 años. No se admiten a menores de 13 años a menos que vayan acompañados de un adulto.

El horario durante el cual están abiertos los albergues varía, pero suele ser de 8.00 h. a 22.30 h. en invierno y hasta las 23.30 h. en verano. Normalmente, Ud. podrá registrarse entre las 9.30 y las 19 h. Los precios varían según la región, la edad y según si está incluido o no el desayuno.

Para reservar, póngase en contacto directamente con el albergue juvenil. Si desea informarse sobre las reservas de grupo (mínimo 20 personas menores de 30 años), contacte con la Red Española de Albergues Juveniles. ☎ (34) (1) 3477631.

PASAPORTES Y VISADOS

Es necesario un pasaporte, salvo para los ciudadanos de la Unión Europea, los cuales sólo necesitan su Documento Nacional de Identidad. Es posible que los ciudadanos de ciertos países necesiten visado. Por lo tanto, se recomienda hacer las averiguaciones pertinentes antes de viajar.

SANIDAD

Los tratamientos médicos son gratuitos para los ciudadanos procedentes de países de la Unión Europea y de otros países que tengan un acuerdo mutuo con España. En los demás casos, se recomienda hacerse un seguro.

HORARIO DE LOS BANCOS

Los bancos abren los días laborables de 8.30 h. a 14 h.

OFICINAS DE CORREOS

Las oficinas de correos abren los días laborables de 9 h. a 14 h.

HORARIO COMERCIAL

Las tiendas suelen abrir de lunes a sábado de 10 h. a 13.30 h. y de 17 h. a 20.30 h.

DESPLAZAMIENTOS

Tren

La red de ferrocarriles españoles RENFE ofrece un surtido de descuentos en el precio de sus billetes, dependiendo del día en que se viaje. Las tarjetas Eurorail e Inter-Rail son válidas, pero tendrá que pagar un suplemento para viajar en determinados trenes rápidos.

Autobús

Las compañías de autobuses ofrecen una tarifa especial con descuento para pasajeros menores de 26 años.

DIAS FESTIVOS

6 enero, Festividad de los Reyes Magos; 28 marzo, Viernes Santo (Semana Santa); 1 mayo, Fiesta del Trabajo; 25 julio, Santiago Apóstol; 15 agosto, Nuestra Sra. de la Paloma; 12 octubre, Día de la Hispanidad, Nuestra Sra. del Pilar; 1 noviembre, Día de Todos los Santos; 6 diciembre, Día de la Constitución; 8 diciembre, Inmaculada Concepción; 25 diciembre, Navidad.

INFORMACION TELEFONICA

Código Internacional	Código Nacional	Prefijos de las Ciudades Principales	
07	34	Barcelona	3
		Bilbao	4
		Granada	58
		Madrid	1
		Sevilla	5
		Valencia	6

DISCOUNTS AND CONCESSIONS

If you are under 26 years, your Hostelling International card entitles you to 25% off KLM Royal Dutch Airlines from Alicante, Barcelona, Madrid, Malaga and Palma to Amsterdam, New York, Atlanta, Chicago, Houston and Los Angeles, Montreal, Toronto, Calgary and Vancouver, Mexico, Tokyo, New Delhi.

A Penalba/Orense Nogueira de Ramuin, 32004 Orense ✆ (88) 200196 Open: 1.1-30.6; 1.9-31.12 ⊯ 30 ⁑(L) ▦ ▦ Orense

Aguadulce Campillo del Moro S/N, 04720 Aguadulce, Almeria. ✆ (50) 340346 FAX (50) 345855 ⊯ 108 ●

900-1300ptas ⁑ ✇ ⑂ ♿ 🅿 ⚙ ⚓ ✈ Almeria 25km ▦ Almeria 17km ▦ Almeria-Aguadulce 2km ⓡ (YH or ✆ (5) 4558293 FAX (5) 4558292, 09.00-19.30hrs)

Aguilas-Calarreona Ctra de Vera Km4, 30880 Aguilas. ✆ (68) 413029 ⊯ 80

⊜ 430-509ptas ⊺◎⊺ (1.7-31.8) ✈ Alicante 180km 🚃 Murcia- Aguilas 103km 🚌 Murcia- Aguilas 103km **R** (📞 (68) 413029 at least 7 days in advance)

Albarracín - **Rosa Bríos** c/ Santa María 5, Albarracín CP 44100, Teruel. 📞 (78) 710005, (78) 641033 **FAX** (78) 641030 **Open:** 08.00-23.00hrs, 1.1-30.6; 1.9-31.12 🛏 65 ⊺◎⊺ ☞ 🛉 🏠 ▣ ✈ Zaragoza 184km 🚃 Cella 27km 🚌 Albarracín **R** (**FAX** (74) 607754)

La Alberca "El Valle", Murcia. 📞 (68) 164429, 607185 **Open:** 08.00-24.00hrs 🛏 60 ⊜ 430-509ptas ⊺◎⊺ (1.7-31.8) ▣ ✈ Alicante 95km 🚃 Murcia 8km 🚌 Murcia- La Alberca 2km **R** (📞 (68) 164419, 607185 at least 7 days in advance)

Albergue Juvenil "El Quijote" ⟨CC⟩ Avda. Castilla-La Mancha, 12, 45820.- El Toboso (Toledo) 📞 (25) 197398 🛏 70 ⊺◎⊺ 🛉 ▣ ✈ Barajas-Madrid 120km 🚃 Alcazar de San Juan 15km 🚌 El Toboso

Albergue Juvenil "Navahermosa" c/Del Milagro, S/N 45150.- Navahermosa (Toledo) 📞 (25) 428547, (25) 428616 🛏 150 ⊺◎⊺ ▣ 🚃 Toledo 45km 🚌 Navahermosa

Albergue Juvenil "Peñarrubias" c/ Consuelo, 4, 16540.- Caracenilla (Cuenca) 📞 (69) 272711, (69) 272652 🛏 30 ⊺◎⊺ 🛉 ▣ 🅿 ☞ ✈ Barajas-Madrid 140km 🚃 Huete 12km 🚌 Carrascosa 20km **R**

Alborache "Torre D'Alborache", Cta de Macastre, CP 46369 📞 (6) 2508123, 2508124 **FAX** (6) 2508020 **Open:** 1.2-22.12 🛏 116 ⊺◎⊺ ♿ (toilets not adapted) ▣ ✈ Manises 30km ⛴ Puerto de Valencia 50km 🚃 Bunyol 4km 🚌 ap YH **R** (YH or 📞 (6) 3869252 **FAX** (6) 3869951)

Alburquerque "Castillo de Luna", Alburquerque, Badajoz. 📞 (24) 400041 **Open:** 1.6-30.9 (1.1-31.5; 1.10-31.12 weekends) 🛏 10 ⊺◎⊺ 🛉 🚃 3.7km

Alcudia Ctra Cabo Pinar, Alcudia, Mallorca 📞 (71) 545395 **FAX** (71) 545395 **Open:** 15.6-30.8 🛏 120 ⊺◎⊺ 🛉 ▣ 🚌 4km

Algeciras Parque Natural, "Los Alcornocales", Ctra Nacional 340 Km 95,600, 11390 El Pelayo- Algeciras (Cádiz). 📞 (56) 679060 **FAX** (56) 679017 🛏 100 ⊜ 900-1300pts ⊺◎⊺ ♿ 🅿 ☞ ⛵ 🚃 Algeciras 10km 🚌 Comes Algeciras- Tarifa ap YH **R** (YH or 📞 (5) 4558293 **FAX** (5) 4558292 09.00-19.30hrs)

Alhama de Murcia "Sierra Espuña", Murcia. 📞 (68) 630023 **Shut:** for renovation 🛏 100 ⊜ 430-509ptas ⊺◎⊺ (1.7-31.8) ✈ Alicante 135km 🚃 Murcia- Alhama 33km 🚌 Murcia- Alhama 33km **R** (📞(68) 630023 at least 7 days in advance)

Alicante "La Florida", Avda Orihuela 59, 03007 Alicante. 📞 (6) 5113044 **FAX** (6) 5282754 🛏 204 (1.7.30.9) 25 (1.10-30.6) ⊺◎⊺ (except 1-30.9) ▣ ⛵ ✈ Alicante 12km ⛴ Alicante 3km 🚃 Central 1km 🚌 Central 2km **R** (YH or 📞 (6) 3869252 **FAX** (6) 3869951)

Almería c/ Isla de Fuerteventura S/N, 04007 Almería. 📞 (50) 269788 **FAX** (50) 271744 🛏 171 ⊜ 900-1300pts ⊺◎⊺ ♿ ☞ ⛵ ✈ Almería 11km A🚌 city centre ⛴ Almería 300m 🚃 Almería 1km 🚌 1, 4A **R** (YH or 📞 (5) 4558293 **FAX** (5) 4558292, 09.00-19.30hrs)

Almoguera AJ "La Cabaña", 19115 Almoguera, Guadalajara. 📞 (49) 380037, (49) 380038 **FAX** (49) 380038 🛏 110 ⊜ 1100-1500pts ⟨BB⟩ⁱⁿᶜ

¶⚙️&🛬 Madrid-Barajas 76km 🚌 Almoguera 1km **R** (**℡** (1) 5333474 (C/Cea Bermúdez 14 2°D, 28013 Madrid)

Almorox "Granja Escuela Pradoluengo", Camino Cadalso- Pinar, 45900 Almorox, Toledo. **℡** (1) 8623265, 8623303 **Open:** 16.1-14.2 ✉ 58 ● 1100-1500pts BB|inc ¶ 🚌 Almorox 3km **R**

Alsasua CC Zelai 91, Alsasua, Navarra. **℡** (48) 562304 **FAX** (48) 467584 **Shut:** 1-30.9 ✉ 70 ¶ ♦♦♦ & P 🛬 Noain/Pamplona 50km 🚌 Alsasua 1km 🚌 Pamplona-Alsasua#0.3 **R** (**FAX**)

Altafulla "Casa Gran", Placeta 12, 43893 Altafulla, Tarragona: Tarragona 12km W. **℡** (77) 650779 **FAX** (77) 650588 ✉ 65 ¶ ♦♦♦ 🏠 ⚙️⛴🛬 Barcelona 90km ⛴ Tarragona 12km 🚌 Altafulla 800m 🚌 Altafulla 100m **R** (**℡** (3) 4838363, **FAX** (3) 4838350)

Andorra ☞ **La Seu d'Urgell**

Arbejal Cta Arbejal- Palencia, Arbejal. **℡** (88) 870174, 747300 ✉ 70 ¶ 🚌 Ciudad

Arriondas c/ el Barco S/N, 33540 Ariondas (Asturias). **℡** (8) 5840334 ✉ 12 ¶(L) 🚌 Arriondas 🚌 Arriondas

Auñon "Entrepeñas", Poblado de Entrepeñas, Auñon, Guadalajara. **℡** (49) 350120 **Open:** 1.1-30.10, 10-31.12 ✉ 64 ● 1100-1500pts BB|inc ¶ (Not available Sat, Sun + holidays) 🚌 Guadalajara 60km 🚌 Sacedon 4km **R** (Grps)

Avila "Profesor Arturo Duperier", Av de Juventud s/n, Avila. **℡** (20) 221716, 355092 **Open:** 1.7-31.8 ✉ 90 ¶

Aviles "El Foco", c/Santa Apolonia 126 33400 Aviles **℡** (8) 5576008 **FAX** (8) 5511772 ✉ 8 ¶(L) & ⚙️⛴🚌 Aviles 33m 🚌 Aviles

Barbastro "Joaquin Costa", Paseo de Los Pinos 9-13, 22300 Barbastro, Huesca. **℡** (74) 293025, 311834, 313310 **FAX** (74) 293040, 313527 **Open:** 1-31.7 ✉ 120 ● 1000-1400pts ¶ ♦ ♦♦♦ & ⚙️🛬 Zaragoza 120km 🚌 Monzón 16km 🚌 ap Barbastro **R** (**℡FAX** (74) 313527)

BARCELONA (4 Hostels)
(*see town plan on next page*)

Barcelona - **Mare de Déu de Montserrat** IBN Passeig Mare de Déu del Coll 41-51, CP 08023 Barcelona. **℡** (3) 2105151 **FAX** (3) 2100798 ✉ 180 ¶ ♦♦♦ & 🏠 ⚙️P 🛬 Barcelona 12km ⛴ Barcelona 🚌 Barcelona 4km 🚌 25, 28 2m ap Mare de Déu del Coll U III-Green; Vallcarca 100m **R** (**℡** (3) 4838363 **FAX** (3) 4838350)

Barcelona - **Hostal de Joves** Passeig Pujades 29, CP 08018 Barcelona. **℡** (3) 3003104 ✉ 68 ¶(B) ♦ 🛬 Barcelona 12km ⛴ Barcelona 4km 🚌 Terminus 300m 🚌 41, 141 50m U 1 - Red; Arc de Triomf 200m

Barcelona - **Pere Tarrés** Numancia 149-151, CP 08029 Barcelona. **℡** (3) 4102309 **FAX** (3) 4196268 ✉ 90 ¶(B) ♦ ♦♦♦ ⚙️P 🛬 Barcelona 12km ⛴ Barcelona 4km 🚌 Barcelona-Sants 🚌 34, 33, 6, 7, 63, 68, 59, 15 50m U III - Green; Les Corts/Maria Cristina 500m **R** (**FAX**)

Barcelona - **Studio** Duquesa d'Orleans 58, CP 08034 Barcelona. **℡** (3) 2050961 **FAX** (3) 2050900 **Open:** 1.7-30.9 ✉ 40 ¶ ♦♦♦ ⚙️🛬 BarcelonA 12km ⛴ Barcelona 4km 🚌 Barcelona Sants 🚌 66, 34 100m U Ferrocarrils Generalitat; Reina Elisenda 200m

Los Batanes (Frente al Monasterio de "El Paular"), Rascafria, Madrid. **℡** (1) 8691511 **FAX** (1) 8690125 **Open:** 09.00-20.00hrs ✉ 110 ● 950-1300pts BB|inc ¶ ♦♦♦ P 🚌

Continental 2.5km  (Grps to Central Reservations)

BARCELONA - (a) Hostal de Joves, (b) Montserrat, (c) Pere Tarrés, (d) Studio

Béjar "Llano Alto", El Castañar, Béjar, Salamanca: Salamanca 65km. ☎ (23) 400702, 296000 ⇌ 200 ⵏⵟ ⵏⵟⵏ ⵎⵎ 3.5km

Benicarló "Sant Crist del Mar", Avda de Yecla 29, Benicarló, CP 12580 Castellón. ☎ (64) 470836, 470500 **FAX** (64) 460225 **Open:** 1.1-23.12; 28-31.12 ⇌ 80 (8 1.8-30.6) ⵏⵟ ⵏⵟⵏ ✈ Manises Valencia 140km ⛴ de Pesca ⵎⵎ Benicarló 1km ⵎⵎ 1km ⓡ

Benicasim "Argentina", Av Ferrándiz Salvador 40, Benicasim, CP 12560 Castellón. ☎ (64) 300949, 302709 **FAX** (64) 300473, (6) 3869951 **Open:** 1.2-22.12 ⇌ 140 ⵏⵟ ⵏⵟⵏ ⵖ (toilets not adapted) ⵖ ⛵ ✈ Manises, Valencia 65km ⛴ Valencia 60km ⵎⵎ Benicasim/Castellón 1.5km ⵎⵎ from Castellón 100m ⓡ (YH or ☎ (6) 3869252 **FAX** (6) 3869951)

Biar Llomes de la Mare de Deu 6, CP 03410 Biar, Alicante. ☎ (6) 5810875 **FAX** (6) 5810875 ⇌ 68 ⵏⵟ ⵖ ✈ El Altet Alicante 60km ⛴ Alicante 60km ⵎⵎ Villena 1.5km ⓡ

Biel Av. de la Mina s/n, 50619 Biel, Zaragoza. (Ctra N- 1202, direction Ayerbe 40KM) ☎ (76) 669001 **Open:** Mon-Fri 09.00-14.00hrs ⇌ 26 ⵐ ⵏⵟ ⵖ ⵖ ✈ Zaragoza 95km ⵎⵎ Ayerbe-(Huesca) 30km ⵎⵎ Zaragoza- Biel 95km ⵎⵎ "Agreda Automovil" 95km ⓡ (☎ (76) 224300)

Bijuesca c/Virgen III, 12, 50316 Bijuesca (Zaragoza). ☎ (76) 847292 **Open:** 24 hrs ⇌ 63 ⵏⵟ ⵖ ⵎⵎ Torrijo 12km ⓡ (☎ (76) 847292)

Bocamar - San Esteban De Pravia Muros de Nalon (Asturias) ☎ (8) 5580127 **Open:** Christmas, Easter, 1.7-30.9 ⇌ 4 ⵏⵟ(L) ⵖ ⵎⵎ San Esteban Pravia 500m ⵎⵎ San Esteban Pravia 500m

Borja Santuario de la Misericordia, 50540 Borja, Zaragoza. ☎ (76) 714967 **FAX** (76) 714986 **Open:** 1.1-30.9; 1-30.11; 1-31.12 ⇌ 45 ⊖ 700Pts ⵖ ✈ Zaragoza 65km ⵎⵎ Borja ⓡ (**FAX** (76) 714986)

El Bosque (Cadiz) c/Molino de Enmedio S/N, 11670 El Bosque, Cadiz. ☎ (5) 4558293 **FAX** (5) 4558292 ⇌ 76 ⊖ 900-1300pts ⵏⵟ ⵖ ⵖⵔ ⵎⵎ Cadiz 105km ⵎⵎ Los Amarillos from Cadiz + daily Seville to El Bosque 500m ⓡ (**FAX** 09.00-19.30hrs)

Burgos "Gil de Siloe", Avda General Vigón s/n, Burgos. ☎ (47) 220362, 265642 **Open:** 1.7-31.8 ⇌ 120 ⵏⵟ

Buslone - "El Cabanin" Busloñe-33162 Morcin (Asturias) ☎ (8) 5783178 **FAX** (8) 5783192 ⇌ 10 ⵖ ⵖ ⵎⵎ Santa Eulalia 5km ⵎⵎ Busloñe

Cabrera de Mar "Torre Ametller", Veïnat de Sta Elena d'Agell, Cabrera del Mar, CP 08349 Barcelona: Barcelona 30km. ☎ (3) 7594448 **FAX** (3) 7500495 ⇌ 150 ⵏⵟ ⵏⵟⵏ ⵖ ⵎ ⵖ ⵔ ✈ Barcelona 42km ⵎⵎ Vilassar de Mar

4km 🚌 Sta Elena d'Agell 200m **®**
(☎ (3) 4838363 **FAX** (3) 4838350)

Candanchu Albergue Aisa Candanchu,
Puerto Del Somport, Aisa-Candanchu
(Huesca) ☎ (74) 373023 **Open:**
1.1-31.5; 1.7-31.12 🛏 30 ● 1695pts
🍴 ♟ ✈ Pamplona 165km 🚆
Canfranc 8km 🚌 Candanchu

Canfranc Estación, Plaza del Pilar 2-3,
22880 Canfranc, Huesca. ☎ (74)
293025 **FAX** (74) 293040 🛏 35 ●
500-700pts 🍴 ☎ ▣ ♟ ✈ Zaragoza
170km 🚆 Canfranc 🚌 Canfranc
® (☎ (74) 293025 **FAX** (74) 293040)

Carbes - "Guillermo Mañana" Carbes
33558 Amieva (Asturias) ☎ (8)
5848916 **FAX** (8) 5848561 🛏 2 🍴(L)
▣ 🚆 Arriondas 20km 🚌 Onis
Cangas de 15km

Carlos V Jerte 5S CTRA-Plasencia-Avila
☎ (27) 470062 **Open:** 1.6-30.9
(31.9-31.5.98 Weekends) 🛏 10 🍴 ♟
🚆 Plasencia 50km 🚌 5km ap Jerte

CASTELLÓN (2 Hostels)

Castellón - "El Maestrat" Av Hnos Bou
26, CP 12003 Castellón. ☎ (64) 220457,
223543 **FAX** (64) 237600 🛏 90 (Su
only) 🍴 ♟ ✈ Manises Valencia 65km
🚢 Pesquero 6km 🚆 Castellón 1km
🚌 1km **®** (☎ (6) 3869252 **FAX**
(6) 3869951)

Castellón - "Mare de deu del Lledó" c/
Orfebres Santalínea 2, CP 12005
Castellón. ☎ (64) 254096, 254392
FAX (64) 216677 🛏 90 (Su only) 🍴
✈ Manises Valencia 65km 🚢
Pesquero 🚆 Castellón 5km 🚌 1km
® (☎ (6) 3869252 **FAX** (6) 3869951)

Cazorla Pza Mauricio Martínez 6, 23470
Cazorla, Jaén. ☎ (53) 720329 **FAX** (53)
720203 🛏 97 ● 900-1300 ptas 🍴 ♿
♟ 🚆 Los Propios/Cazorla 30km,
Linares/Baeza 60km 🚌 Jaen-Cazorla

® (YH or ☎ (5) 4558893 **FAX** (5)
4558892)

CERCEDILLA (2 Hostels)

Cercedilla - "Villa Castora" Cta de las
Dehesas s/n, Cercedilla, Madrid. ☎ (1)
8520334 **FAX** (1) 8522411 **Open:**
09.00-20.00hrs 🛏 80 ● 950-1300pts
BB inc 🍴 ♟ 🚆 Cercedilla 600m 🚌
Larrea 500m **®** (**FAX**) (Grps to
Central Reservation)

Cercedilla - "Las Dehesas" Cta de las
Dehesas s/n, Cercedilla, Madrid. ☎ (1)
8520135 **FAX** (1) 8521836 **Open:**
09.00-20.00hrs 🛏 75 ● 950-1300pts
BB inc 🍴 ▣ 🚆 Cercedilla 2km 🚌
Larrea 3km **®** (Grps to Central
Reservation)

Columbiello Columbiello 33637 Lena
(Asturias) ☎ (8) 5490617 **FAX** (8)
5493536 **Open:** 1.4-30.6; 1-30.9 🛏 5
♟ ▣ ♟ 🚆 Pola De Lena 3km 🚌
Pola De Lena 3km

Constantina c/ Cuesta Blanca S/N,
41450 Constantina, Sevilla. ☎ (5)
5881589 **FAX** (5) 5881619 🛏 93 ●
900-1300pts 🍴 ♿ ♟ ✈ Seville 125km
🚆 Cazalla-Constantina 11km 🚌
Seville-Constantina 100m **®** (YH or
☎ (5) 4558293 **FAX** (5) 4558292,
09.00-19.30hrs)

Coma Ruga CC "Sta Maria del Mar", Av
Palfuriana 80, Coma-Ruga CP 43880
Tarragona 18km. ☎ (77) 680008 **FAX**
(77) 682959 🛏 180 🍴 ♟ ▣ ▣ ♟
🚆 St.Vicens de Calders 1.5km 🚌
Coma-Ruga 100m **®** (☎ (3) 4838363
FAX (3) 4838350)

Cordoba Plaza Judá Leví S/N, 14003
Cordoba. ☎ (57) 290166 **FAX** (57)
290500 🛏 94 ● 900-1300pts 🍴 ♿
♟ 🚆 Cordoba 1.5km 🚌 12, 50m
® (YH or ☎ (5) 4558293 **FAX** (5)
4558292, 09.00-19.30hrs)

Cortes de Pallas "La Peña", Crta Cortes de Pallas, 46199 Cortes de Pallas, Valencia. ☎ (6) 2517134 **Open:** Su, weekends + Christmas ✉ 130 ⍟ ♟ ⌂ 🅿 🚌 Buñol- Cortes 500m ℝ (Silvia Villareal, Albergue Peña, c/Ingeniero Rafael Janini 23-12a, 46022 Valencia ☎ (6) 3721577)

LA CORUÑA (3 Hostels)

La Coruña - Bergondo "Playa de Gandarío", Gandarío Sada, Bergondo, La Coruña. ☎ (81) 791005 **FAX** (81) 794217 ✉ 300 ⍟ (L: 1.7-15.9) 🅿 ⚓ ✈ Santiago 12km A🚌 city centre 70km ♆ La Coruña 20km 🚌 La Coruña-Sada-Betanzos 1.5km

La Coruña - "Marina Española" Gorbeiroa-Bergondo, La Coruña. ☎ (81) 620118, 624202

La Coruña - Monte de Gozo Carretera de Santiago-Aeropuerto KM 3, 15820 Santiago ☎ (81) 558942 **FAX** (81) 562892 ✉ 300 ⍟(L) ▣ ⚓ ♆ Santiago

Daroca "El Hospitalillo", c/ Cortes de Aragón, 13 Ctra, N- 234 direction of Teruel- Zaragoza, 50360 Daroca (Zaragoza) ☎ (76) 801268 ✉ 60 ⍟ ⊞ ▣ ⌂ 🅿 ✈ Zaragoza 65km A🚌 Daroca 200m ♆ Daroca 🚌 Daroca-Zaragoza

Deltebre Avda de les Goles de l'ebres s/n, 43580 Deltebre, Tarragona. ☎ (77) 480136 **FAX** (77) 481284 ✉ 120 ⍟ ⌀ ♟ ⚒ ▣ 🅿 ⚙ ⚓ ♆ L'Aldea 8km 🚌 Deltebre 500m ℝ (☎ (3) 4838363, **FAX** (3) 4838350)

DONOSTIA-SAN SEBASTIAN (2 Hostels)

Donostia-San Sebastian - "La Sirena" ⌷⌷ Igeldo Pasealekua 25, Donostia, San Sebastian. ☎ (43) 310268, 311293 **FAX** (43) 214090 **Shut:** 11.00-15.00hrs, 24.00-08.00hrs(Sun-Thurs), (Wi- Fri/Sat 11.00-15.00hrs, 02.00-08.00hrs, Su 11.00-15.00hrs, 02.00-08.00hrs) ✉ 96 ◗ 1475-2000pts ᴮᴮⁱⁿᶜ ⍟ ⌀ ♟ ⚒ ▣ ✈ Hondarribia 20km, Miarritze 40km, Sondika 100km ⛴ Santurtzi 120km ♆ Donostia 🚌 5,6,16,24 ℝ (FAX)

Donostia-San Sebastian - "Ulia-Mendi" Parque de Ulia, Pasco de Ulia, 299 Donostia, San Sebastian. ☎ (43) 310268, 311293 **FAX** (43) 214090 **Open:** 1.1-31.8; 1.10-31.12 ✉ 60 ᴮᴮⁱⁿᶜ ⍟ ▣ 🅿 ✈ Hondarribia 20km, Miarritze 40km, Sondika 100km ⛴ Santurtzi 120km ♆ Donostia- San Sebastian 6km ℝ (FAX) (Grps)

Dosrius "Mas Silvestre", Veïnat d'en Rimbles 14, 08319 Dosrius, Barcelona. ☎ (3) 7955014 **FAX** (3) 7955199 ✉ 160 ⍟ 🅿 ✈ Prat (Barcelona) 45km ♆ Mataro 20km 🚌 Canyamars 8km ℝ (☎ (3) 4838363 FAX (3) 4838350)

L'Escala "Empúries", Les Coves, 41, 17130 L'Escala, Girona. ☎ (72) 771200 **FAX** (72) 771572 ✉ 50 ⍟ 🅿 ⚓ ♆ Figueres 20km 🚌 L'Escala 2km ℝ ☎ (3) 4838360 **FAX** (3) 4838350

EL ESCORIAL (2 Hostels)

El Escorial - "Santa Maria del Buen Aire" Finca de la Herreria s/n, San Lorenzo de el Escorial, Madrid. ☎ (1) 8903640 **FAX** (1) 8903640 **Open:** 09.00-20.00hrs ✉ 88 ◗ 950-1300pts ᴮᴮⁱⁿᶜ ⍟ 🅿 ♆ El Escorial 3km 🚌 Herranz 1.5km ℝ (FAX) (Grps to Central Reservations)

El Escorial - c/ Residencia 14, San Lorenzo de El Escorial, Madrid. ☎ (1) 8905924 **FAX** (1) 8905925 **Open:** 09.00-20.00hrs ✉ 100 ◗ 950-1300pts ᴮᴮⁱⁿᶜ ⍟ ♟ ♆ El Escorial 3km 🚌 Herranz 1.5km ℝ (FAX) (Grps to Central Reservations)

L'Espluga de Francolí "Jaume I", Les Masies s/n, 43440 L'Espluga de Francolí, Tarragona: (Tarragona 45km). ☎ (77) 870356 **FAX** (77) 870414 ✉ 160 ⚏ ⚏ ⚏ ⚏ ⚏ Reus 35km ⚏ L'Espluga de Francolí 3km ⚏ Poblet 1km **Ⓡ** (☎ (3) 4838363 **FAX** (3) 4838350)

El Floran El Floran-Blimea (Asturias) ☎ (8) 5670050 ✉ 10 ⚏(L) ⚏ Blimea ⚏ Blimea

Espinosa "Espinosa de los Monteros", Espinosa, Burgos. ☎ (47) 120449, 265642 ✉ 60 ⚏

Ezcaray "Molino Viejo", Camino de los Molinos s/n, Ezcaray, La Rioja. ☎ (41) 354197 ✉ 49 ⚏ ⚏ Logroño, Haro ⚏ Ezcaray 500m ap YH **Ⓡ** (☎ (41) 291100 **FAX** (41) 256120)

Fayacaba Melendreros- Bimanes (Asturias) ☎ (8) 5700162 ✉ 4 ⚏ Nava 15km ⚏ Nava 15km

Felechosa Felechosa, 33688 Aller (Asturias). ☎ (8) 5487341 ✉ 4 ⚏ ⚏ ⚏ Collanza 5km ⚏ Felechosa **Ⓡ** (☎ (85) 235054)

Figueres Ⓘ ⓑ Ⓝ "Tramuntana", Anicet de Pages 2, Figueres, CP 17600 Girona. ☎ (72) 501213 **FAX** (72) 673808 ✉ 56 ⚏ ⚏ ⚏ ⚏ Figueres 800m ⚏ Figueres 100m **Ⓡ** (☎ (3) 4838363 **FAX** (3) 4838350)

Fonte del Cai Carretera General, Poo de Llanes (Asturias) ☎ (8) 5400205 ✉ 10 ⚏ ⚏ Poo de Llanes ⚏ Poo de Llanes

Genestaza Genestaza- Tineo (Asturias) ☎ (8) 5800187 ✉ 2 ⚏

Girona "Cerverí de Girona", Ciutadans 9, CP 17004 Girona. ☎ (72) 218003 **FAX** (72) 212023 ✉ 103 (1.7-20.8), 8 (academic year) ⚏ ⚏ ⚏ ⚏ ⚏ Vilobi d'onyar 15km ⚏ Girona 800m ⚏ Girona 800m **Ⓡ** (☎ (3) 4838363 **FAX** (3) 4838350)

Granada c/Ramon y Cajal 2, 18003 Granada. ☎ (58) 284306 **FAX** (58) 285285 ✉ 126 ⚏ 900-1300pts ⚏ ⚏ ⚏ ⚏ Granada 20km ⚏ Granada 1.5km ⚏ 11, ap YH **Ⓡ** (YH or ☎ (5) 4558293 **FAX** (5) 4558292, 09.00-19.30hrs)

Guía Alberge Juvenil "San Fernando", Santa María de Guía, Av Juventud, Guía, Gran Canaria. ☎ (28) 550685, 550827 **FAX** (28) 882728 **Open:** 08.00-23.00hrs ✉ 87 ⚏ 350-400pts ⚏ ⚏ ⚏ ⚏ ⚏ 40km ⚏ Las Palmas 19km **Ⓡ** (**FAX**)

Hondarribia "Juan Sebastián Elcano", Faroko Igoera No.7, Hondarribia, Gipuzkoa. ☎ (43) 641550 **FAX** (43) 640028 **Open:** 1.1-14.8, 17.9-31.12; 08.00-24.00hrs, (+01.00-02.00hrs) ✉ 20 ⚏ ⚏ ⚏ ⚏ Hondarribia 1km, Miarritze 20km, Sondika 130km ⚏ Irun 3km

Huelva Avenida Marchena Colombo 14, 21004 Huelva. ☎ (59) 253793 **FAX** (59) 253499 ✉ 130 ⚏ 900-1300pts ⚏ ⚏ ⚏ ⚏ ⚏ Sevilla 100km ⚏ Huelva 1.7km ⚏ Huelva Line No 6 ap YH **Ⓡ** (YH or ☎ (5) 4558293 **FAX** (5) 4558292, 09.00-19.30hrs)

Jaca "Escuelas Pias", Avda Perimetral s/n, 22700 Jaca, Huesca. ☎ (74) 360536 **Open:** 1.1-30.9; 1-31.12 (Grps 1.10-30.11) ✉ 150 ⚏ 1000-1300pts ⚏ ⚏ ⚏ ⚏ Zaragoza 139km ⚏ Jaca **Ⓡ** (☎ (74) 360536)

Jerez de la Frontera Avda Carrero Blanco 30, Jerez de la Frontera, 11408 Cádiz. ☎ (56) 143901 **FAX** (56) 143263 ✉ 120 ⚏ 900-1300pts ⚏ ⚏ ⚏ ⚏ ⚏ La Parra Jerez 5km ⚏ Jerez 2km ⚏ Federico Mayo ap YH **Ⓡ** (☎ YH or (5) 4558293, 09.00-19.30hrs)

Lago de Sanabria "San Martín de Castañeda", Cta de San Martín de Castañeda, Galende, Lago de Sanabria,

Zamora. ☎ (80) 622083, 521700 ✉ 80 ⓘⓄⅢ 15km 🚌 500m

Layos "El Castillo de Layos", c/ Conde de Mora s/n, Layos, Toledo. ☎ (25) 376585 **FAX** (1) 3572564 **Open:** Grps only ✉ 120 ● 1100-1500pts BB|inc ⓘⓅⅢ Toledo 10km 🚌 Layos ®

Leitariegos Puerto de Leitariegos (Cangas del Narcea) ☎ (8) 5810514 for information ✉ 2 ⓘ(L) ⓢⓄⅡ 🚌 Puerto de Leitariegos ® ☎(87) 471325

Lekároz Albergue Juvenil Baztan- 31795 Lekároz, Navarra. ☎ (48) 580655 **FAX** (48) 581036 **Open:** 1.6-10.12 **Shut:** 1-30.11 ✉ 80 ⓘⅢ& ✈ Noain-Pamplona 56km Ⅲ Pamplona 56km 🚌 Elizondo 2km

León - Europa "Consejo de Europa", Paseo del Parque 2, León. ☎ (87) 200206, 236500 **Open:** 1.7-31.8 ✉ 97 ⓘ

Lés "Matacabos", Sant Jaume s/n, CP 25540 Lés, Val D'Aran, Lleida. ☎ (73) 648048 **FAX** (73) 648352 ✉ 45 ⓘ ⓘⅡ 🚌 Lés 200m ® (☎ (9) 4838363 **FAX** (9) 4838350)

Llanes "Juventudes", c/ Celso Amieva, 7, 33500 Llanes (Asturias). ☎ (8) 5400770 **FAX** (8) 5400770 ✉ 16 ⓘ & ✈ Ranon Aviles 160km AⅢ Llanes/Oviedo Ⅲ Llanes 3km 🚌 Llanes 3km

Lleida "Sant Anastasi", Rambla d'Aragó 11, CP 25003 Lleida. ☎ (73) 266099 **FAX** (73) 261865 ✉ 120 ⓘⓘⅡ Ⅲ Lleida 3km 🚌 Lleida 500m ap Line 1, YH ® (☎ (3) 4838363 **FAX** (3) 4838350)

Logroño Residencia Universitaria, c/ Caballero de la Rosa 38, 26004 Logroño. ☎ (41) 291145 **Open:** Su ✉ 92 ⓘⓄ Ⅲ Logroño 🚌 Logroño ® (☎ (41) 291162, 291100 **FAX** (41) 256120)

Luarca "Fernán Coronas", El Villar S/N, 33700 Luarca (Asturias). ☎ (8) 5640676 **FAX** (8) 5640557 ✉ 16 ⓘⓄ ✈ Ranon Aviles 160km AⅢ Luarca/Oviedo Ⅲ Luarca 2km 🚌 Luarca 500m

LUGO (3 Hostels)

Lugo - "Eijo Garay" c/ Pintor Corredoira 4, CP 15900 Lugo, Galicia. ☎ (82) 220450 **FAX** (82) 230524 **Open:** 1.7-30.9 ✉ 100 ⓘⓘⓄⓅ ✈ Santiago 199km AⅢ Lugo 400m Ⅲ Lugo 800m 🚌 Lugo 400m ® (Maximum 2 days in advance)

Lugo - "Area" Playa de Area - Viveiro, CP 15900 Lugo, Galacia. ☎ (82) 560851 **Open:** 1.7-30.8 ✉ 120 ⓘⓘ ✈ Coruña 121km, Santiago 153km AⅢ Viveiro - Coruña- Santiago 6km Ⅲ Viveiro 6km ® (☎ At least 2 days in advance)

Lugo - "Hermanos Pedrosa" Pintor Corredoira 2, Lugo, Galacia. ☎ (82) 221090 **Open:** 1.7-30.9 ✉ 100 ⓘⓄ ✈ Santiago 110km AⅢ 300m Ⅲ Lugo 1.5km 🚌 Lugo 1.5km

MADRID (2 Hostels)
(*see townplan on next page*)

Madrid - "Santa Cruz De Marcenado" Calle Sta Cruz de Marcenado No 28, Madrid. ☎ (1) 5474532 **FAX** (1) 5481196 **Open:** 09.00-20.00hrs ✉ 72 ● 950-1300pts BB|inc Ⓞ ✈ Barajas 12km Ⅲ Chamartin 8km 🚌 Circular 1, 2, 44, 133 500m Ⓤ Argüelles 500m

Madrid - Richard Schirrmann Casa de Campo, Madrid. ☎ (1) 4635699 **FAX** (1) 4644685 **Open:** 09.00-20.00hrs ✉ 134 ● 950-1300pts BB|inc ⓘⓄⓅ ✈ Barajas 20km Ⅲ Norte 3.5km 🚌 33 500m ap Plaza Isabel II-Campo Ⓤ Lago 1km ® (to Central Reservations)

Las Majadas Plaza Mayor s/n, Cuenca. ☎ (69) 283050 **FAX** (69) 283050 ✉

60 😑 -26/1100pts, +26/1500pts BBinc
¶O¶ ⛩ Cuenca 36km 🚌 Cuenca 36km ®

MADRID - (a) Marcenado,
(b) Richard Schirrmann

Málaga Plaza Pio XII 6, 29007 Málaga. 📞 (5) 2308500 **FAX** (5) 2308504 ✉ 107 😑 900-1300pts ¶O¶ 👣 ♿ ⚓ ✈ Málaga 10km 🚍 Málaga 700m 🚌 18 ap YH ® (YH or 📞 (5) 4558293 **FAX** (5) 4558292, 09.00-19.30hrs)

Mallorca "Playa de Palma", Calle Costa Brava, 13 Sometimes, 07610 Palma de Mallorca. 📞 (71) 260892 **FAX** (71) 262012 **Open:** 1.6-30.9 ✉ 65 ¶O¶ 👫 ✈ 6km 🚢 18km 🚌 15 ap Plaza de España Arenal

Manresa "Del Carme", Pl del Milcentenari de Manresa, s/n 08240 Manresa. (Barcelona 60km) 📞 (3) 8750396 **FAX** (3) 8726838 ✉ 64 ¶O¶ 👣 👫 ♿ 🅿 🚍 Manresa 320m 🚌 Manresa 500m ® (📞 (3) 4838363 **FAX** (3) 4838350)

Marbella Calle Trapiche 2, 29600 Marbella, Málaga. 📞 (5) 2771491 **FAX** (5) 2863227 ✉ 101 😑 900-1300pts ¶O¶ 👣 ♿ 🅿 ⚓ ✈ Málaga 40km 🚌 Marbella 500m ® (YH or 📞 (5) 4558293 **FAX** (5) 4558292, 09.00-19.30hrs)

El Masnou IBN "Josep M Batista i Roca", Av dels Srs Cusí i Furtunet 52, El Masnou, CP 08320 El Masnou: Barcelona 15km. 📞 (3) 5555600 **FAX** (3) 5400552 ✉ 96 ¶O¶ ♿ 🅿 ⚓ ✈ Barcelona 12km 🚢 Barcelona 15km 🚍 Ocata 1km 🚌 El Masnou 25m ® (📞 (3) 4838363 **FAX** (3) 4838350)

Mazagon Cuesta de la Barca S/N, 21130 Mazagon, Huelva. 📞 (59) 536262 **Open:** 15.6-15.9 (Grps 1.1-31.12) ✉ 100 😑 900-1300pts ¶O¶ 👣 ♿ 🚲 ⚓ 🚍 Huelva 24km 🚌 Huelva- Mazagon 2.5km ® (YH or 📞 (5) 4558293 **FAX** (5) 4558292, 09.00-19.30hrs)

Miranda de Ebro "Fernán González" c/ Andua s/n, Miranda de Ebro, Burgos. 📞 (47) 320932, 265642 ✉ 110 ¶O¶

La Molina "Mare de Déu de les Neus", Ctra de Font Canaleta, 17537 La Molina, Girona. 📞 (72) 892012 **FAX** (72) 892050 **Shut:** 25.12 ✉ 152 ¶O¶ 👫 ◻ 🅿 🏂 Alt 1450m 🚍 La Molina 300m ® (📞 (3) 4838363 **FAX** (3) 4838350)

Mora de Rubielos c/San Esteban, 28 44400 Mora De Rubielos 📞 (78) 800311 **FAX** (78) 806050 **Open:** 08.00-23.00hrs, 1-31.12 ✉ 59 BBinc ¶O¶ 👣 ◻ 🅿 ✈ Zaragoza 229km 🚍 Rubielos de Mora 17km 🚌 Mora de Rubielos ® (📞 (78) 800311)

Morella "**Fábrica Giner**" Crta Morella-Forcall KM 4'5 📞 (6) 3869252 **FAX** (6) 3869951 ✉ 60 ¶O¶ 👫 ♿ 🎪 🅿 ✈ Manises 176km 🚢 Valencia 170km 🚍 Vinarós 60km

Munilla "Hayedo de Santiago", c/ Cipriano Martinez 29, Munilla. 📞 (41) 394213 ✉ 50 ¶O¶ 🚍 Logroño y Calahorra 🚌 Munilla ® (📞 (41) 291100 **FAX** (41) 256120)

Navamorcuende "El Chortalillo", Camino de la Tablada s/n, 45630 Navamorcuende, Toledo. 📞 (25) 811186 **Open:** Grps only ✉ 150 😑 -

26/1100pts, +26/1500pts [BB]inc |O| ▯
🚆 Talavera de la Reina 25km 🚌 Talavera de la Reina 25km (R)

Navarredonda de Gredos Avila. (Rd C 500, Barco de Avila 64km) ☎ (20) 348005, 355092 ✉ 60 |O|

Nuria "Pic de Áliga", Núria, 17534 Queralbs. ☎ (72) 732048 **FAX** (72) 732048 ✉ 138 |O| ♦♦♦ ♜ Alt 2120m 🚆 RENFE: Ribes de Freser/Cremallera a Núria 🚌 Ripoll 15km (R) (☎ (3) 4838363 **FAX** (3) 4838350)

Ocaña Convento Santo Domingo, c/Santo Domingo, 45300 Ocaña, Toledo, Castilla- La- Mancha. ☎ (25) 130055, 120180, 120871 **FAX** (25) 120871 **Open:** 09.00-24.00hrs (Grps 15+) ✉ 50 ● 1100-1500pts [BB]inc |O| ♦♦ ♣ Madrid-Barajas 100km 🚆 Ocaña 500m 🚌 Aranjuez 15km (R)

Olot [CC] "Torre Malagrida", Passeig de Barcelona 15, 17800 Olot, Girona. ☎ (72) 264200 **FAX** (72) 271896 **Shut:** 1-25.9 ✉ 76 [BB]inc |O| ♦♦♦ ♿ 14 ♣ ▯ ⛵ 🚌 Olot 250m (R) (☎ (3) 4838363 **FAX**(3) 4838350)

Onis "Gamonedo", Gamonedo De Onis 33556, Asturias. ☎ (8) 5844005 ✉ 2 ⛵ ♣ Ranon Aviles 165km A🚌 Benia/Onis- Oviedo 10km 🚆 Arriondas 25km 🚌 Benia-Onis 6km

OREA (2 Hostels)

Orea - "Aula de la Naturaleza El Autillo" Llano Hoz Seca, Orea, Guadalajara. ☎ (1) 5593050 **FAX** (1) 5417034 ✉ 60 ● 1100-1500pts [BB]inc |O| 🚆 Santa Eulalia/Teruel 🚌 Orea 6km

Orea - "Granja- Escuela Orea" Cuidad Real, Ctra Toledo, s/n ☎ (26) 690241 ✉ 90 ● 1100-1500pts [BB]inc |O| ♦♦♦ ♿ ▣ ⛵ ♣ Aeropuerto de Barajas 200km

🚆 Ciudad Real 2km 🚌 Ciudad Real 2km

ORENSE (2 Hostels)

Orense - **"Florentino López Cuevillas"** Arturo Perez Serantes 2, CP 32004 Orense. ☎ (88) 252412, 252451 **Open:** 1.7-30.9 ✉ 60 |O| ♣ ♣ La Vacolla Santiago/Peinador Vigo 120km A🚌 5km 🚆 Orense 1km 🚌 Urbano 50m

Orense - **"Monasterio de San Estovo de Rivas do Sil"** Nogueira de Romuin, 32004 Orense ☎ (88) 221054 **Open:** 1.1-30.6; 1.9-31.12 ✉ 32 ▯ 🚆 Orense

Oviedo "Ramón Menéndez Pidal", Avda Julián Clavería S/N, 33006 Oviedo (Asturias) ☎ (8) 5232054 **FAX** (8) 5233393 ✉ 6 (1.7-30.9, 12) |O| ♣ Ranon Aviles 50km A🚌 Oviedo 1km 🚆 Oviedo 🚌 Oviedo

Palacio de San Andrés de Cornellana Camino de Los Caleros S/N Contrueces- Gijón (Asturias). ☎ (8) 5160673, (8) 5171855 ✉ 6 🚆 A 3km 🚌 A 3km

Palacio Fontela c/Eduardo Sierra 10, Grado (Asturias) ☎ (8) 5753424 ✉ 5 |O|(L) ⛵ ▯ 🚆 Grado 🚌 Grado

PALENCIA (2 Hostels)

Palencia - **"Escuela Castilla"** Avda de Burgos s/n, Palencia. ☎ (79) 721475, 747300 **Open:** 1.7-31.8 ✉ 57 |O|

Palencia - **"Victorio Macho"** Avda Cardenal Cisneros 12, Palencia. ☎ (79) 720462, 747300 **Open:** 1.7-31.8 ✉ 42 |O|

Las Palmas ☞ **Guía**

Pamplona [0.5 SE] Goroare S/N; 31002 Pamplona, Navarra ☎ (48) 107832 **FAX** (48) 151764 **Open:** 12.1-10.12 **Shut:** 1-15.7 ✉ 15 |O| ♿ ▯ ⛪ [P] ♣ Noain- Pamplona 6km 🚆 Pamplona 4km 🚌 3, 1km

Peñaranda de Bracamonte Colegio "Diego de Torres y Villarroel", c/ Elisa Muñoz Rodríguez 34, Peñaranda de Bracamonte. (Salamanca 40km) ✆ (23) 540988, 296000 **Open:** 1.7-31.8 ✉ 50 🍴 👥

Piles "Mar i Vent", Doctor Fleming s/n, Playa de Piles s/n, 46712 Valencia. ✆ (6) 2831748 **FAX** (6) 2831121, 3869951 **Open:** 15.1-30.11 ✉ 84 🍴 👥 ♿ 📷 🚲 ⚓ ✈ Manises 80km ⛴ Valencia 70km 🚌 Gandia-Oliva 6km 🚌 ap YH ⓡ (YH or ✆ (6) 38669252 **FAX** (6) 3869951)

Planoles IBN "Pere Figuera", Ctra de Neva Prat Cap Riu S/N, 17535 Planoles, Girona. ✆ (72) 736177 **FAX** (72) 736431 ✉ 170 🍴 👥 ♿ 📦 🏃 Alt 1120m 🚌 Planoles 100m 🚌 Ripoll 22km ⓡ (✆ (3) 4838363 **FAX** (3) 4838350)

Poble Nou Del Delta "L'Encanyissada", Poble Nou Del Delta, 43549 Amposta, Tarragona. ✆ (77) 742203 **FAX** (77) 742709 ✉ 46 🍴 👥 🚲 ⚓ 🚌 Amposta, L'Aldea 27km 🚌 Amposta 18km ⓡ (✆ (3) 4838363 **FAX** (3) 4838350)

Pontevedra "As Sinas", Vilanova de Arousa, Pontevedra, Galicia. ✆ (86) 554081 ✉ 144 🍴 (1.7-15.9) 👥 📦 ⚓ ✈ Santiago 45km, Vigo 53km A 🚌 Vilanova de Arousa 🚌 Villagarcia de Arousa 5km 🚌 5km ap Villagarcia de Arousa ⓡ (✆ At least 3 days in advance)

Portomarín "Benigno Quiroga", Portomarín, Lugo. ✆ (82) 545022 ✉ 25 🍴 📦 ✈ Santiago 110km A 🚌 500m 🚌 Lugo-Portomarin

Pravia La Tienda, Pravia (Asturias) ✆ (8) 5820015 ✉ 4 🍴(L) 📦 🚌 Pravia 11km 🚌 Pravia 11km

Puerto de Navacerrada - "Alvaro Iglesias" 28470 Puerto de Navacerrada, Madrid. ✆ (1) 8523887 **FAX** (1) 8523891 **Open:** 09.00-20.00hrs ✉ 92 ● 950-1300pts BB inc 🍴 📦 🚌 Funicular- Puerto Navacerrada 🚌 "La Sepulvedana" 300m ⓡ (Grps to Central Reservations: Oficina Central de Albergues Juveniles de Madrid, c/ Alcalá 32, 28013 Madrid. ✆ (1) 5804216 **FAX** (1) 5804215)

Punta Umbría Avenida Océano 13, Punta Umbría, 21100 Huelva. ✆ (59) 311650 **FAX** (59) 314229 ✉ 90 ● 900-1300pts 🍴 ♿ 🚲 ⚓ 🚌 Huelva 25km 🚌 Damas, Huelva- Punta Umbria ap YH ⓡ (YH or ✆ (5) 4558293 **FAX** (5) 4558292, 09.00-19.30hrs)

Rellanos Rellanos- 33873 Tineo (Asturias) ✆ (8) 5801669 **FAX** (8) 5800233 ✉ 4 🍴(L) 📦 🚌 Luarca 38km 🚌 Navelgas 8km

Residencia de Plentzia Marinell S/N, 48620 Plentzia. ✆ (4) 6771866 **FAX** (4) 6773041 **Open:** 09.00-23.00hrs ✉ 12 ● 1110-1625pts BB inc 👥 ♿ ✈ Bilbao/Sondika 30km 🚌 Plentzia 500m ⓡ (States Sports Council ✆ (4) 4208746)

Residencia Juvenil "Joaquin Sama" Baños de Montemayor ✆ (23) 428003 **Open:** 1.6-30.9 (+ weekends) ✉ 10 🍴 👥 🚌 Plasencia 50km 🚌 Baños Montemayor

Ribadeo Campamento Xuvenil "A Devesa", 27700 Ribadeo, Lugo, Galicia. ✆ (82) 123300 **Open:** 15.6-30.8 ✉ 75 👥 📦 📦 ✈ Coruña 163km, Santiago 177km A 🚌 A Devesa-Ribadeo 🚌 Ribadeo 6km 🚌 ap A Devesa- Ribadeo ⓡ (✆ At least 2 days in advance)

Ribadesella "Roberto Frasinelli", c/ Ricardo Cangas S/N, la Playa, 33560

Ribadesella (Asturias). ☎ (8) 5861380 ⚑ 12 ♂ ♣ ✈ Ranon Aviles 135km A🚌 Ribadesella- Oviedo 🚃 Ribadesella 1km 🚌 Ribadesella

Robledo Alto de Robledo, Lugo de Llanera (Asturias) ☎ (8) 5770007 **FAX** (8) 5771045 ⚑ 3 ♂ 🔳 🚃 Lugo de Llanera 2km 🚌 Lugo de Llanera 2km

Roncesvalles ⟨CC⟩ Real Colegiata, Roncesvalles, Navarra. ☎ (48) 790403 **FAX** (48) 760015 **Open:** 1.1-30.9; 1-31.12 **Shut:** 1-30.11 ⚑ 65 🍴🏤🏨 ✈ Noain Pamplona 50km 🚃 Pamplona 50km 🚌 "La Montañesa" Pamplona-Burguete 2km ⟨R⟩ By FAX

Ruidera "Alonso Quijano", Crtra de las Lagunas s/n, Osa de Montiel, Albacete. ☎ (26) 528053 **Open:** 1.1-15.9; 20.10-31.12 ⚑ 80 ⊖ 1100-1500pts 🆚inc 🍴 (Not available Sat, Sun + holidays) 👪 🚃 Manzanares 52km 🚌 Ossa de Montiel 14km

Sabiñanigo- Yebra de Basa. Santa Orosia c/La Iglesia, 22610 Yebra de Basa (Huesca) ☎ (74) 480823 ⚑ 26 👪 🅿 🚃 Sabiñanigo 10km 🚌 Sabiñanigo 10km ⟨R⟩ (74) 483311

Sada "Marina Española", Corbeiroa, Bergondo, Sada, La Coruña. ☎ (81) 620118 ⚑ 110 🍴 ✈ La Coruña 12km, Santiago 70km 🚢 La Coruña 23km 🚃 La Coruña 20km 🚌 Coruña-Sada-Betanzos 1km

Salardú ⟨CC⟩ "Era Garona", Cta de Vielha, 25598 Salardú, Lleida. ☎ (73) 645271 **FAX** (73) 644136 ⚑ 180 👪 ♿ 🔳 🅿 ⚓ 🚲 🚌 Salardú 250m ⟨R⟩ (☎ (3) 4838363 **FAX** (3) 4838350)

San Juan del Plan "El Molino Viejo", 22367 San Juan del Plan, Huesca. ☎ (74) 506149 ⚑ 22 ⊖ 600-800pts ✈ Zaragoza 240km 🚌 Huesca-Barbastro-Plan ⟨R⟩ (Grps)

San Martin La Plaza- 33111 Teverga (Asturias) ☎ (8) 5764454 ⚑ 16 🍴(L) 🚌 La Plaza

SAN PABLO DE LOS MONTES (2 Hostels)

San Pablo de los Montes - "**Baños del Robledillo**" San Pablo de los Montes, Toledo. ☎ (25) 415300, 415025, 415001 **FAX** (25) 415300 **Open:** 1.1-31.5; 1.10-31.12 ⚑ 50 🍴 Grps +20 persons (-20 persons B only) 🚃 Los Yebenes 55km 🚌 San Pablo de Los Montes 5km

San Pablo de los Montes - "**Baños del Sagrario**" San Pablo de los Montes, Toledo. ☎ (25) 416057; 415453; 415411 ⚑ 300 ⊖ 1100-1500pts 🆚inc 🍴 ♂ 🔳 🚃 Toledo/Sonseca 47km 🚌 San Pablo de los Montes ⟨R⟩ (☎(1) 5333474)

San Rafael Cta Madrid-La Coruña S/N, San Rafael, Segovia. (Segovia 30km) ☎ (21) 171457, 417384 ⚑ 55 🍴 🚃 San Rafael 1km 🚌 San Rafael 1km

San Sebastian ☞ **Donostia**

Segovia "Emperador Teodosio, Avda Conde de Sepúlveda s/n, 40006 Segovia. ☎ (21) 420027, 417384 **Open:** 1.7-31.8 ⚑ 80 🍴 🚃 Segovia ⟨R⟩

Serandinas Serandinas- 33726 Boal (Asturias) ☎ (8) 5978146 ⚑ 5 🍴(L) 🚃 Navia 14km 🚌 Serandinas

Seseña "Sta Maria del Sagrario", Ctra de Andalucía K 36, 200 Seseña, Toledo. ☎ (1) 8936152 **Open:** 1.1-30.7; 1.9-31.12 ⚑ 55 ⊖ 1100-1500pts 🆚inc 🍴 🚃 Seseña 3km 🚌 Seseña 500m

La Seu d'Urgell "La Valira", Joaquim Viola 57, 25700 La Seu d'Urgell. Andorra 9km. ☎ (73) 353897 **FAX** (73) 353874 **Shut:** 24-26.12, Sun except 1.7-31.8 ⚑ 100 🍴(B) (1-30.9 only)

♿ ▣ 🅿 ⚒ 🚐 La Seu d'Urgell 700m
ⓡ (📞 (3) 4838363 **FAX** (3) 4838350)

Sevilla Isaac Peral 2, 41012 Sevilla. 📞
(5) 4613150 **FAX** (5) 4613158 **Shut:**
for renovation ✉ 198 ⊖ 1100-1300pts
🍽 ✈ Seville 14km 🚎 "Santa Justa"
7km 🚐 6, 34 ap YH **ⓡ** (YH or 📞
(5) 4558293 **FAX** (5) 4558292)

Sierra Nevada Estacion de Prado Llano
S/N, Sierra Nevada, 18193 Granada. 📞
(58) 480305 **FAX** (58) 481377 **Open:**
1.1-30.4 ✉ 206 ⊖ 900-1300pts 🍽
♿ 🅿 ⚒ 🚲 ✈ Granada 66km 🚎
Granada 46km 🚐 Granada- Sierra
Nevada 500m ap YH **ⓡ** (YH or 📞(5)
4558293 **FAX** (5) 4558292,
09.00-19.30hrs

Soncillo Cta de Soncillo a Logrono,
Soncillo, Burgos. 📞 (47) 120449,
217521 **FAX** (47) 265642 ✉ 50 🍽

Soria - "Antonio Machado" Plaza José
Antonio 1, Soria. 📞 (75) 221789,
223100 **Open:** 1.7-31.8 ✉ 100 🍽 🚎
Soria-Cañuelo 1km 🚐 300m ap Adda
de la Victoria

Soto de Cameros "Hospital San Jose",
c/ San Jose s/n, Soto de Cameros, La
Rioja. 📞(41) 291100 **FAX** (41) 256120
✉ 46 🍽 🚐 ap Parada de Autobus

TALAVERA DE LA REINA (2 Hostels)

**Talavera de la Reina - "Fernando de
Rojas"** c/Capitan Cortes 125-Talavera
de la Reina 📞 (25) 805666 **FAX** (25)
801111 **Open:** Grps only ✉ 200 🍽
👫 ✈ Barajas (Madrid) 120km 🚎
Talavera de la Reina 🚐 Talavera de la
Reina

Talavera de la Reina - "Grijalba" ⬚35S⬚
Carretera de Cervera km 35 📞 (25)
709482, 810409 **FAX** (25) 810409 ✉
160 ⬚BB⬚inc 🍽 👫 ▣ 🏛 🅿 🚲 ⚓ ✈ Barajas
Madrid 115km A🚐 direct to YH 🚎
Talavera 🚐 ap YH

Tarragona "Sant Jordi", Avda President
Companys 5, CP 43005 Tarragona. 📞
(77) 240195 **FAX** (77) 243134 ✉ 192
(1.7-31.8), 🍽 👫 ▣ 🚎 Tarragona 1km
🚐 Tarragona 100m **ⓡ** (📞 (3)
4838363 **FAX** (3) 4838350)

Tàrrega "Ca N'Aleix", Plaça Del Carme,
5, Tarrega, Lleida 📞 (73) 313053 **FAX**
(73) 500037 ✉ 107 (1.7-30.9) 🍽 👫
🚎 Tàrrega 🚐 Tàrrega **ⓡ** (📞 (3)
4838363 **FAX** (3) 4838350)

Tella- Sin "Tella Sin" (Huesca) 📞 (74)
506212 ✉ 48 🍽 👫 ✈ Zaragoza
212km 🚎 Huesca 135km

Teruel "Luis Buñel" Ciudad Escolar s/n,
44003 Teruel. 📞 (78) 601712, 602223
Open: 1-31.7; 1-30.9 ✉ 192 ⊖
1000-1400pts 🍽 👫 ✈ Zaragoza
180km 🚎 Teruel 🚐 Teruel **ⓡ**
(**FAX** (74) 607754)

Teulada-Moraira "La Marina" Camino
Campamento 31, CP 03725 📞 (6)
6492030, 6492044 **FAX** (6) 6491051
✉ 130 🍽 👫 ♿ ▣ 🏛 ⚓ ✈ Altet
(Alicante) 95km 🚎 Teulada 8km **ⓡ**
(YH or 📞 (6) 3869252 **FAX** (6)
3869951)

Toledo "San Servando", Castillo de San
Servando, Toledo. 📞 (25) 224554
Open: 1.1-15.8; 15.9-31.12 **Shut:**
Easter + Christmas ✉ 46 ⊖
1100-1500pts ⬚BB⬚inc 🍽 ▣ 🚎 500m
🚐 200m

Tragacete "San Blas", Tragacete,
Cuenca: Cuenca 73km. 📞 (69) 289131
Open: Grps only ✉ 64 ⊖
1100-1500pts ⬚BB⬚inc 🍽 🚎 Cuenca
70km 🚐 Tragacete 3km **ⓡ**

Uncastillo "Ayllon", c/ Mediavilla 30,
50678 Uncastillo, Zaragoza. 📞 (76)
679400 **FAX** (76) 679497 ✉ 50 ⊖
1000pts 🍽 🚻 ▣ ✈ Zaragoza 111km
🚐 Uncastillo 3km **ⓡ** (📞 (76)
699400)

Valdeavellano de Tera Soria. ☎ (75) 271211, 223100 ✉ 60 ⑩ 🚌 desde Soria

Valencia Colegio Mayor "La Paz", Avda del Puerto 69, Valencia. ☎ (6) 3617459 **Open:** 1.7-15.9 ✉ 130 🖃 ✈ Manises 15km A🚌 Bus station 4km ⛴ Valencia 2km 🚃 Norte 2km 🚌 from city EMT; from ⛴ 1, 2, 3, 4, 19 Ⓡ (☎ (6) 3617459)

Valencia de Alcántara "Sta Mª de Guadalupe", Puerto Roque, Valencia de Alcántara, Cáceres. ☎ (27) 580041 **Open:** 1.6-30.9 (1.1-31.5; 1.10-31.12 weekends) ✉ 10 ⑩ ⅲ 🚌 8km ap Valencia de Alcántara

Valladolid "Rio Esgueva", c/ Cementerio 2, Valladolid. ☎ (83) 251550, 340044 **Open:** 1.7-31.8 ✉ 80 ⅲ

Vic ⒸⒸ Avda D'Olimpia S/N, 08500 Vic, Barcelona. ☎ (3) 8894938 ✉ 156 ⑩ ⅲ ♿ 🖃 🚃 Vic 800m 🚌 800m Ⓡ (☎(3) 4838363 **FAX**(3) 4838350)

Vigo "Altamar" c/ Cesáreo González 4, CP 36210 Vigo CP, Pontevedra. ☎ (86) 290808 ✉ 80 ⑩ ⅲ ✈ Vigo 5km A🚌 5km ⛴ Vigo 2km 🚃 Vigo 1.5km 🚌 800m

Villabre Villabre- 33826 Yernes y Tameza (Asturias) ☎ (8) 5972303 ✉ 6 ⑩(L) 🖃 🚃 Grado 24km 🚌 Grado 24km Ⓡ

Villamanín León. ☎ (87) 598243, 236500 ✉ 54 ⑩ Ⓡ

Villanúa Afueras o Camino de la Selva S/N, 22870 Villanúa, Huesca. ☎ (74) 378016, 293025 **FAX** (74) 378016, 293040 ✉ 100 ⊖ 1000-1400pts ⑩ ⅲ 🅿 🛏 ✈ Zaragoza 149km 🚃 Jaca 10km 🚌 Villanúa Ⓡ

Vitoria- Gasteiz./ Carlos Abaitua Aterpetxea. Escultor Isaac Diez, S/N 01007 Vitoria-Gasteiz. ☎ (45) 148100 **FAX** (45) 148100 **Open:** 08.00-24.00hrs **Shut:** 15-31.1; 1-15.9 ✉ 20 ⊖ 1110-1650pts ⒷⒷⁱⁿᶜ ✈ Vitoria-Gasteiz / Foronda 10 km. Bilbao / Sondika 70km 🚃 Vitoria- Gasteiz 750m 🚌 1.5km Ⓡ (Grps of 12+ ☎ (45) 231782)

Viver c/ Molino 1, CP 12460 Viver, Castellón. ☎ (64) 141101 **FAX** (6) 3869951 **Open:** 1.1-23.12; 28-31.12 ✉ 90 ⑩ (1.7-31.8) 🖃 ✈ Manises Valencia 80km ⛴ Valencia 75km 🚃 Viver 2.5km 🚌 200m Ⓡ (☎ (6) 3869252 **FAX** (6) 3869951)

Viznar Camino de Fuente Grande S/N, 18179 Viznar, Granada. ☎ (58) 543307 **FAX** (58) 543448 ✉ 108 ⊖ 900-1300pts ⑩ 🗄 ♿ 🅿 🛏 ✈ Granada 25km 🚃 Granada 17km 🚌 Martin Prez, Granada-Viznar 500m Ⓡ (YH or ☎ (5) 4558293 **FAX** (5) 4558292, 09.00-19.30hrs)

Zaragoza "Baltasar Gracian", c/ Franco y López 4, 50005 Zaragoza. ☎ (76) 551387, 714967 **FAX** (76) 553432 **Open:** 1.1-31.7; 19-31.12 ✉ 55 ⊖ 1000pts ⑩ (B) 🗄 ⅲ ♿ ✈ Zaragoza 🚃 Zaragoza 🚌 Zaragoza Ⓡ (☎ (76) 224300 **FAX** (76) 553432)

Zarautz San Inazio 25, Zarautz, Guipuzkoa ☎ (43) 132910 **FAX** (43) 130006 **Open:** 1.1-31.8; 1.10-31.12 **Shut:** 24.00-08.00hrs but you can enter at 01.00hrs and 02.00hrs ✉ 25 ⒷⒷⁱⁿᶜ ⑩ ⅲ ♿ 🖃 ⊞ 🅿 ✈ Hondarribia, Miarritze, Sondika 🚃 Zarautz 🚌 16 ap opposite Ice-Cream Shop

SWEDEN
SUEDE
SCHWEDEN
SUECIA

ASSURED STANDARD

**Svenska Turistföreningen (STF),
Kungsgatan 2/Stureplan 4C, PO Box 25,
101 20 Stockholm, Sweden.**

☎ (46) (8) 4632100
FAX (46) (8) 6781958

Office Hours: Monday-Friday, 09.00-17.00hrs

Travel Section: Svenska Turistföreningen (STF),
Kungsgatan 2, PO Box 25,
10 120 Stockholm, Sweden.

☎ (46) (8) 4632100

IBN Booking Centre for outward bookings
■ **Stockholm,** *via National Office above*

Capital:	Stockholm
Language:	Swedish
Currency:	1 crown (SEK) - 100 öre
Population:	8.6 million
Size:	449,964 sq km

SWEDEN - NORTH

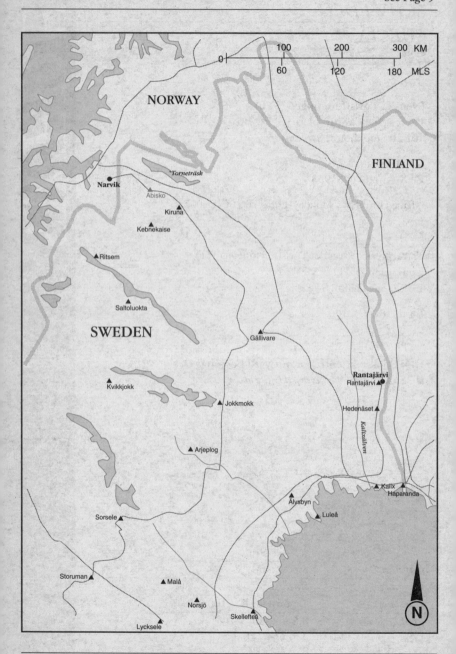

SWEDEN - CENTRAL

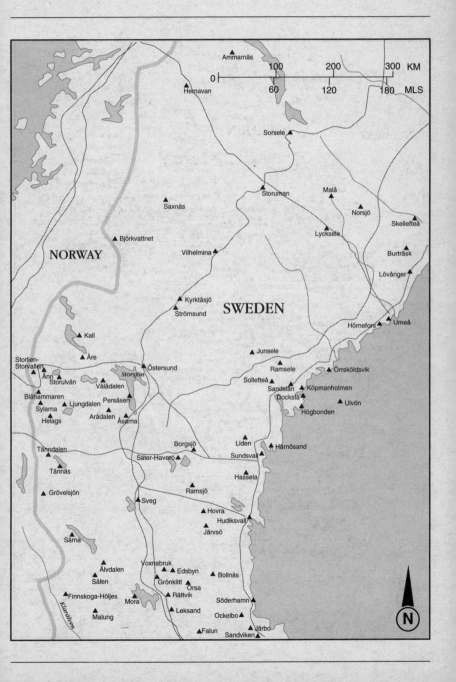

SWEDEN - SOUTH

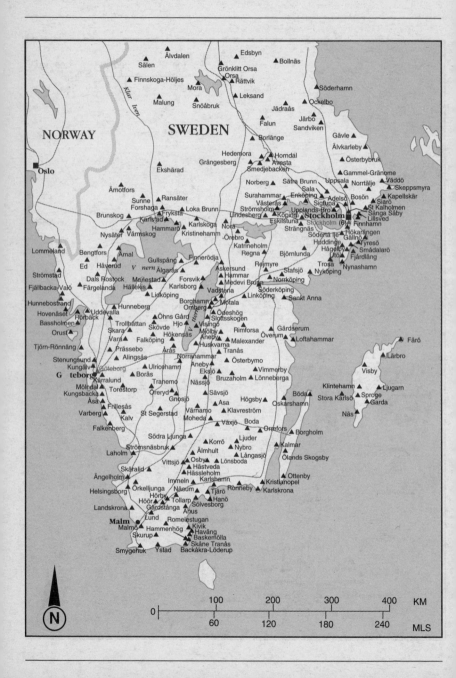

ENGLISH

SWEDISH HOSTELS

Most Scandinavian hostels have excellent facilities for families, and Sweden is no exception. In addition your Hostelling International card gives you access to networks of mountain accommodation in Lappland and other areas.

All Swedish hostels are participating in Hostelling International's new Assured Standards Scheme (see page six for details).

Most hostels are shut 10.00-17.00hrs. Always telephone if you are going to arrive after 18.00hrs. Members should expect to pay in the region of 75-140 SEK per night, less for children.

PASSPORTS AND VISAS

Citizens from many countries may visit Sweden and stay for up to three months without any special permits provided they have a valid passport, enough money to support themselves during their stay in Sweden and money to buy their return ticket.

If you are a national of a Nordic country you do not need a passport to enter Sweden.

Citizens of most Eastern European, African and Asian countries must have a special permit/visa before they are allowed to enter Sweden. Apply for your visa at the Swedish Embassy or Consulate in your country of residence.

HEALTH

If you become ill or have an accident whilst in Sweden and have to call a doctor, make sure that the doctor is affiliated to försäkringskassan (the Swedish National Health Service). You can also go to the casualty ward at a hospital.

Don't forget your passport! The charge for a visit to a casualty unit is approximately SEK 180. If you need medicine you have to obtain a prescription from a doctor and take it to the chemist's for dispensing. The minimum you normally have to pay for medicine is SEK 120.

BANKING HOURS

Banks are normally open Monday to Friday between 09.30 and 15.00hrs. In some larger cities a few banks stay open until 17.30hrs. There are also offices to change money near the railway stations and airports of key cities.

POST OFFICES

Post offices are generally open during normal shopping hours, 09.00-18.00hrs on weekdays and 10.00-13.00hrs on Saturdays. Some branches may be closed on Saturdays during July.

SHOPPING HOURS

Most shops are open 09.00-18.00hrs on weekdays and 09.00-13.00hrs on Saturdays (some shops stay open until 16.00hrs). In some larger towns department stores remain open until 20.00hrs or even 22.00hrs, some are also open on Sundays between 12.00 and 16.00hrs.

TRAVEL

Air
Major cities and towns throughout Sweden are linked by an efficient network of services operated mainly by SAS (Scandinavian Airlines) and some other domestic airlines.

Rail

Swedish State Railways (SJ) provides a highly efficient network of train services covering the entire country. On virtually all long distance trains you will find a dining car or buffet for meals, drinks and snacks. On longer overnight journeys, sleeping-cars and couchettes are provided in both first and second class sections.

The Scanrail pass is a 21 day ticket which entitles you to unlimited journeys in Sweden, Norway, Denmark and Finland. "Reslust" is a travel card which entitles you to a 25% discount on the full price of second-class services on Tuesdays, Wednesdays, Thursdays and Saturdays.

Coach

Sweden has an excellent network of express coach connections between larger towns and cities in southern and central Sweden and between Stockholm and the coastal towns in the north. The main operator is Swebus but several other companies operate a network of weekend coach services. Eurolines 10% discount from Swedish cities to cities abroad.

Ferry

It is easy to get to Sweden by ferry. The journey between Helsingborg (Sweden) and Helsingör (Denmark) only takes 20 minutes. There are also ferry services between Sweden and Germany, Great Britain, Denmark, Norway, Finland, Poland, Estonia and Russia.

Driving

The road network in Sweden is extensive and well maintained with toll-free motorways. Seat belts must be worn by the driver and all passengers. Dipped headlights are obligatory when driving, both by day and by night.

Swedish regulations on drinking and driving are strictly enforced, and costly fines are imposed on any motorists who are found to be driving under the influence of alcohol or other stimulants.

TELEPHONE INFORMATION

International Code	Country Code	Main City Area Codes	
009	46	Helsingborg	42
		Malmö	40
		Stockholm	8
		Göteborg	31

When dialling within Sweden dial "0" before the area code.

FRANÇAIS

AUBERGES DE JEUNESSE SUEDOISES

La plupart des auberges scandinaves sont très bien équipées pour les familles, et la Suède ne fait pas exception à la règle. En outre, votre carte internationale vous permettra d'utiliser d'autres types d'hébergement en Laponie et dans d'autres régions.

Toutes les auberges suédoises participent au nouveau Plan Hostelling International pour la Garantie des Normes - voir page 15 pour un complément d'information.

La plupart des auberges sont fermées entre 10h et 17h et vous êtes prié de bien vouloir téléphoner si vous devez arriver après 18h. Une nuit vous coûtera entre 75 et 140KRS, moins pour les enfants.

PASSEPORTS ET VISAS

Les citoyens de nombreux pays peuvent se rendre en Suède et y rester pendant un maximum de trois mois sans permis spécial, pourvu qu'ils soient munis d'un passeport valide, d'assez d'argent pour subvenir à leurs besoins pendant leur séjour dans le pays et pour acheter leur billet retour.

Si vous êtes citoyen d'un pays scandinave, vous n'avez pas besoin de passeport pour entrer en Suède.

Les citoyens de la plupart des pays d'Europe de l'est, ainsi que des pays d'Afrique et d'Asie doivent être munis d'un permis/visa spécial pour entrer en Suède. Pour obtenir un visa, adressez-vous à l'Ambassade ou au Consulat de Suède dans votre pays.

SOINS MEDICAUX

Si vous tombez malade ou êtes victime d'un accident en Suède, et que vous deviez appeler un médecin, assurez-vous qu'il est affilié à försäkringskassan (la sécurité sociale suédoise). Vous pouvez aussi vous rendre au service des urgences d'un hôpital.

N'oubliez pas votre passeport! Une visite à un service d'urgences vous coûtera environ 180KRS. Si vous avez besoin de médicaments, il vous faudra obtenir une ordonnance auprès d'un docteur et vous rendre chez un pharmacien. Normalement, cela vous coûtera 120KRS minimum.

HEURES D'OUVERTURE DES BANQUES

En principe, les banques sont ouvertes du lundi au vendredi de 9h30 à 15h. Dans certaines grandes villes, quelques banques restent ouvertes jusqu'à 17h30. Il y a aussi des bureaux où l'on peut changer de l'argent, près des gares et des aéroports des grandes villes.

BUREAUX DE POSTE

Les bureaux de poste sont en principe ouverts pendant les heures d'ouverture normales des magasins, de 9h à 18h en semaine et de 10h à 13h le samedi. Certains bureaux ferment le samedi en juillet.

HEURES D'OUVERTURE DES MAGASINS

La plupart des magasins sont ouverts de 9h à 18h en semaine et de 9h à 13h le samedi (certains magasins restent ouverts jusqu'à 16h). Dans certaines grandes villes, les grands magasins restent ouverts jusqu'à 20h ou même 22h. Certains ouvrent également le dimanche, de 12h à 16h.

DEPLACEMENTS

Avions
Les villes et grandes villes de Suède sont reliées par un réseau de services aériens très efficaces assurés en majeure partie par SAS (Scandinavian Airlines) et par d'autres compagnies.

Trains
Les chemins de fer suédois (SJ) gèrent un réseau ferroviaire extrêmement efficace dans tout le pays. Pratiquement tous les trains couvrant de longues distances sont équipés d'un wagon-restaurant ou d'un buffet offrant des repas, des snacks et des boissons. Pour les voyages de nuit plus longs, les trains sont équipés de wagons-lits et de couchettes en première et en deuxième classe.

Le 'Scanrail pass' est un billet valable 21 jours qui vous permet de faire des voyages illimités en Suède, en Norvège, au Danemark et en Finlande. "Reslust" est une carte qui vous donne droit à une remise de 25% sur le plein tarif de voyages en deuxième classe les mardi, mercredi, jeudi et samedi.

Cars
La Suède a un excellent réseau de services express reliant les grandes villes du sud et du centre du pays, ainsi qu'entre Stockholm et les villes côtières du nord. La compagnie principale est Swebus, mais d'autres compagnies assurent un service de cars pendant le weekend. La compagnie Eurolines offre une remise de 10% sur tout trajet reliant une ville suédoise à toute autre ville à l'étranger.

Ferry-boats
Il est facile de se rendre en Suède par bateau. La traversée entre Helsingborg (Suède) et Helsingör (Danemark) ne dure que 20 minutes.

Il y a aussi des traversées entre la Suède et l'Allemagne, la Grande-Bretagne, le Danemark, la Norvège, la Finlande, la Pologne, l'Estonie et la Russie.

Automobiles

Le réseau routier est étendu et bien entretenu, et les autoroutes sont gratuites. Le port des ceintures de sécurité est obligatoire pour tous les occupants du véhicule. Il est obligatoire de rouler en codes, de jour comme de nuit.

Les lois concernant l'alcool au volant sont appliquées de façon très stricte et de très fortes amendes sont imposées aux conducteurs appréhendés sous l'influence de l'alcool ou d'autres stimulants.

TELEPHONE

Indicatif International	Indicatif du Pays	Indicatif régional des Villes principales	
009	46	Helsingborg	42
		Malmö	40
		Stockholm	8
		Göteborg	31

Pour téléphoner à l'intérieur du pays, ajoutez un zéro devant l'indicatif régional.

DEUTSCH

SCHWEDISCHE JUGENDHERBERGEN

Die meisten skandinavischen Herbergen haben ausgezeichnete Einrichtungen für Familien, Schweden ist keine Ausnahme. Außerdem werden Sie mit Ihrer Hostelling International-Karte in allen Bergunterkünften in Lappland und anderen Gebieten aufgenommen.

Alle Jugendherbergen sind an dem 'Zugesicherten Standard-Plan' des Hostelling Internationals beteiligt (siehe Seite 24 für Einzelheiten).

Die meisten Herbergen sind zwischen 10.00 und 17.00 Uhr geschlossen. Rufen Sie immer an, wenn Sie erst nach 18.00 Uhr ankommen. Mitglieder haben mit einem Preis von ca skr 75-140 pro Nacht, für Kinder weniger, zu rechnen.

PÄSSE UND VISA

Staatsbürger vieler Länder können ohne besondere Genehmigung nach Schweden einreisen und bis zu drei Monate lang im Land bleiben, sofern sie im Besitz eines gültigen Reisepasses sind und genügend Geld für ihren Unterhalt während ihres Aufenthaltes bzw. zum Kauf Ihrer Rückfahrkarte haben.

Wenn Sie Staatsbürger eines nordischen Landes sind, brauchen Sie für die Einreise nach Schweden keinen Paß.

Staatsbürger der meisten osteuropäischen, afrikanischen und asiatischen Länder müssen sich eine spezielle Genehmigung bzw. ein Visum beschaffen, ehe Ihnen die Einreise nach Schweden gestattet wird. Ihr Visum beantragen Sie bei der Schwedischen Botschaft oder beim Schwedischen Konsulat in Ihrem Heimatland.

GESUNDHEIT

Wenn Sie in Schweden krank werden oder einen Unfall erleiden und einen Arzt rufen müssen, sollten Sie sich vergewissern, daß der Arzt der 'försäkringskassan' (der allgemeinen Krankenkasse in Schweden) angeschlossen ist. Sie können sich auch in der Ambulanz eines Krankenhauses behandeln lassen.

Vergessen Sie nicht Ihren Paß! Für einen Besuch der Ambulanz werden Ihnen ca skr 180 berechnet. Wenn Sie Arzneimittel brauchen, müssen Sie sich vom Arzt ein Rezept geben lassen, mit dem Sie dann zur Apotheke gehen. Für Arzneimittel müssen Sie gewöhnlich mindestens skr 120 bezahlen.

GESCHÄFTSSTUNDEN DER BANKEN

Die Banken sind montags bis freitags von 09.30 bis 15.00 Uhr geöffnet. In einigen größeren Städten bleiben einige Banken bis 17.30 Uhr geöffnet. In der Nähe von Bahnhöfen und Flugplätzen gibt es in größeren Städten auch Wechselstuben.

POSTÄMTER

Postämter sind im allgemeinen während der normalen Geschäftszeit, d.h. werktags von 09.00-18.00 Uhr und samstags von 10.00-13.00 Uhr, geöffnet. Einige Filialen sind im Juli samstags geschlossen.

LADENÖFFNUNGSZEITEN

Die meisten Geschäfte sind werktags von 09.00-18.00 Uhr und samstags von 09.00-13.00 Uhr geöffnet (einige Geschäfte schließen erst um 16.00 Uhr). In einigen größeren Städten sind Warenhäuser bis 20.00 Uhr oder sogar bis 22.00 Uhr geöffnet. Einige sind auch sonntags von 12.00 bis 16.00 Uhr geöffnet.

REISEN

Flugverkehr

Größere Städte sind über ein effizientes Flugverkehrsnetz, das hauptsächlich von SAS (Scandinavian Airlines) und anderen inländischen Fluggesellschäften betrieben wird, miteinander verbunden.

Eisenbahn

Die Schwedische Staatliche Eisenbahn (SJ) bietet im ganzen Land einen überaus leistungsfähigen Eisenbahnverkehr. So gut wie alle Fernverkehrszüge haben einen Speisewagen oder ein Buffet für Mahlzeiten, Getränke und Snacks. Auf längeren Nachtfahrten werden in Abteilen der ersten und zweiten Klasse Schlaf- und Liegewagen eingesetzt.

Der Scanrailpaß ist ein 21 Tage lan gültiges Ticket, das zu unbegrenztem Fahren in Schweden, Norwegen, Dänemark und Finnland berechtigt. "Reslust" ist eine Reisekarte, die dienstags, mittwochs, donnerstags und samstags Anspruch auf einen Nachlaß von 25% auf den vollen Zweite-Klasse-Preis gewährt.

Busse

Schweden verfügt über ein ausgezeichnetes Expreßbusnetz, das größere Städte in Süd- und Mittelschweden miteinander verbindet und Stockholm an die Küstenstädte im Norden anbindet. Der Hauptbetreiber ist "Swebus". Es gibt aber noch mehrere andere Unternehmen, die am Wochenende einen Busverkehr anbieten. Auslandsreisen, die in Schwedischen Städten beginnen, gewährt Eurolines den Reisenden einen Rabatt von 10%.

Fähren

Es ist leicht, mit der Fähre nach Schweden zu gelangen. Die Fahrt zwischen Helsingborg (Schweden) und Helsingör (Dänemark) dauert nur 20 Minuten.

Auch zwischen Schweden und Deutschland, Großbritannien, Dänemark, Norwegen, Finnland, Polen, Estland und Rußland gibt es einen Fährenverkehr.

Autofahren

Schweden hat ein sehr umfangreiches und gutes Straßennetz mit gebührenfreien Autobahnen. Der Fahrer und alle Mitfahrer müssen einen Sicherheitsgurt tragen. Man muß sowohl bei Tag als auch bei Nacht mit Abblendlicht fahren.

Die schwedischen Vorschriften über Alkohol am Steuer werden streng eingehalten. Wer unter dem Einfluß von Alkohol oder anderen Stimulanzien ein Kraftfahrzeug führt, hat mit einer hohen geldstrafe zu rechnen.

FERNSPRECHINFORMATIONEN

Internationale Kennzahl	Landes-Kennzahl	größere Städte-Ortsnetzkennzahlen	
009	46	Helsingborg	42
		Malmö	40
		Stockholm	8
		Göteborg	31

Innerhalb Schwedens ist vor der Ortsnetzkennzahl eine "0" zu wählen.

ESPAÑOL

ALBERGUES DE JUVENTUD SUECOS

Casi todos los albergues escandinavos cuentan con estupendas instalaciones para familias y Suecia no es ninguna excepción. Además, su tarjeta de Hostelling International le dará derecho a utilizar la red de albergues de montaña de Laponia y de otras zonas.

Todos los albergues juveniles suecos participan en el nuevo Plan Hostelling International de Normas Garantizadas ver página 33 para más información.

Casi todos los albergues están cerrados de 10.00 a 17.00 horas. Llame por teléfono si va a llegar más tarde de las 18.00 horas. Los huéspedes tendrán que pagar entre 75 y 140 coronas suecas por noche. Hay precios reducidos para los niños.

PASAPORTES Y VISADOS

Los ciudadanos de muchos países pueden visitar Suecia y permanecer allí hasta tres meses sin necesidad de ningún permiso especial, siempre que tengan el pasaporte en regla, dinero suficiente para vivir durante su estancia en Suecia y dinero para comprar el billete de vuelta.

Si es de algún país nórdico, no necesitará pasaporte para entrar en Suecia.

Los ciudadanos de casi todos los países de Europa del Este, de Africa y de Asia deben conseguir un permiso especial/visado para entrar en Suecia. Solicite su visado en la embajada o el consulado sueco del país donde vive.

SANIDAD

Si enferma o tiene un accidente mientras está en Suecia y tiene que acudir al médico, asegúrese de que esté afiliado al "försäkringskassan" (servicio nacional de salud sueco). También puede acudir al departamento de accidentes de cualquier hospital.

No olvide el pasaporte: el precio de una visita a la unidad de accidentados es aproximadamente de 180 coronas suecas. Si necesita algún medicamento, la receta deberá extenderla un médico y tendrá que llevarla a la farmacia. El precio mínimo que normalmente deberá pagar por un medicamento es de 120 coronas suecas.

HORARIO DE BANCOS

Los bancos suelen abrir de lunes a viernes de 09.30 a 15.00 horas. En las ciudades más grandes, algunos bancos siguen abiertos hasta las 17.30 horas. También hay sucursales para cambiar dinero cerca de las estaciones de ferrocarril y los aeropuertos de las ciudades más importantes.

CASAS DE CORREO

Las casas de correo por lo general abren con el mismo horario que las tiendas: de 09.00 a 18.00 horas de lunes a viernes y de 10.00 a 13.00 horas los sábados. Es posible que algunas casas de correo cierren los sábados durante el mes de julio.

HORARIO COMERCIAL

Casi todas las tiendas abren de 09.00 a 18.00 horas de lunes a viernes y de 09.00 a 13.00 horas los sábados (algunas tiendas, hasta las 16.00 horas). En algunas de las ciudades más importantes hay grandes almacenes que están abiertos hasta las 20.00 horas e incluso hasta las 22.00 horas; también algunos abren los domingos de 12.00 a 16.00 horas.

DESPLAZAMIENTOS

Avión

Las grandes ciudades de Suecia están unidas por una eficaz red de vuelos, atendidos fundamentalmente por SAS (Scandinavian Airlines) y por otras compañías de vuelos nacionales.

Tren

Los ferrocarriles nacionales de Suecia (SJ) ofrecen una excelente red de servicios de tren por todo el país. Prácticamente en todos los trenes para largos recorridos encontrará un vagón restaurante o un bufé para comidas, bebidas y aperitivos. En los viajes más largos que se hacen de noche, hay coches cama y literas tanto en primera como en segunda clase.

El Scanrailpass es un billete para 21 días con el que podrá viajar sin límite por Suecia, Noruega, Dinamarca y Finlandia. "Reslust" es una tarjeta de viaje con la que podrá beneficiarse de un descuento del 25% sobre el precio de los billetes de segunda clase los martes, miércoles, jueves y sábados.

Autobús

Suecia cuenta con una excepcional red de autobuses directos que unen las ciudades y centros urbanos más importantes del sur y el centro de Suecia, así como Estocolmo y las ciudades costeras del norte. La principal agencia es Swebus, aunque también hay otras empresas que ofrecen un servicio de autobuses para los fines de semana. Eurolines ofrece un descuento del 10% para viajes desde ciudades suecas a ciudades de otros países.

Ferry

Es muy fácil llegar a Suecia por ferry. De Helsingborg (Suecia) a Helsingör (Dinamarca) sólo se tarda veinte minutos. También hay servicio de ferry entre Suecia y Alemania, Gran Bretaña, Dinamarca, Noruega, Finlandia, Polonia, Estonia y Rusia.

Coche

La red de carreteras de Suecia es muy amplia y está en perfecto estado. Las autopistas no tienen peaje. El conductor y todos los pasajeros tienen que llevar el cinturón de seguridad. Es obligatorio circular con las luces encendidas, de día y de noche.

La normativa sueca sobre conducción y alcohol se cumple al pie de la letra, y se imponen fuertes multas a todos los conductores que conduzcan bajo la influencia del alcohol o de otros estimulantes.

INFORMACION TELEFONICA

Código Internacional	Código Nacional	Indicativo de área de las Ciudades principales	
009	46	Helsinborg	42
		Malmö	40
		Estocolmo	8
		Göteborg	31

Para las llamadas dentro de Suecia, marque el "0" antes del prefijo.

DISCOUNTS AND CONCESSIONS

Many good travel and excursion deals are available through the travel offices in Stockholm, Göteborg and Malmö.

Hostels in this country may also display this symbol.

Les auberges de ce pays pourront également afficher ce symbole.

Jugendherbergen in diesem Land können auch dieses Symbol zeigen.

Es posible que los albergues de este país exhiban además este símbolo.

Adelsö ▲ Adelsögården, 17892 Ekerö. ☎ (8) 56051450 **FAX** (8) 56051400 **Open:** 15.6-31.8 ⊠ 30 ⍩ ♂ ♦♦♦ ① ⊡ ♟ ⛴ 1km 🚌 311, 312 from Brommaplan 30km ℝ

Åhus ▲ Stavgatan 3, 29631 Åhus, Skåne. ☎ (44) 248535 **FAX** (44) 243898 ⊠ 34 ♂ ♦♦♦ ⅑ ⊡ ✈ 20km 🍴 Kristianstad 18km 🚌 300m ℝ (1.9-1.6: Turistbyrån, Box 63, 29621 Åhus ☎ (44) 240106, 243246)

Älgarås ▲ Box 102, 54502 Älgarås, Västergötland. ☎ (506) 40450 ⊠ 26 ♂ ♦♦♦ 🍴 18km 🚌 2km ℝ (17.8-9.6)

Alingsås ▲ ⅭⅭ Villa Plantaget, 44134 Alingsås, Västergötland. ☎ (322) 36987 **FAX** (322) 36987 ⊠ 42 ⍩(B) ♂ ♦♦♦ ♟ 🍴 700m 🚌 700m

Älmhult ▲ Sjöstugan, 34394 Älmhult, Småland. ☎ (476) 71600 **FAX** (476) 12632 **Open:** 1.5-1.9 ⊠ 24 ⍩ ♂ ♦♦♦ ⊡ ♟ 🍴 2km

Älvdalen ▲ Tre Björnar, Dalgatan 31, 79631 Älvdalen. ☎ (251) 10482 **FAX** (251) 10482 ⊠ 32 ⍩(B) ♂ ♦♦♦ ♟ 🍴

Mora 40km 🍴 Mora-Älvdalen ap YH ℝ (1.9-15.6)

Älvkarleby ▲ Laxön, 81070 Älvkarleby, Uppland. ☎ (26) 82122 **FAX** (26) 72861 **Open:** 2.1-19.12 ⊠ 66 ♂ ♦♦♦ 🚌 838, 200m

Älvsbyn ▲ Nyfors 1, 94236 Älvsbyn, Norrbotten. ☎ (929) 55630 **FAX** (929) 10527 **Open:** 1.6-31.8 ⊠ 56 ⍩(B) ♂ ♦♦♦ ⊡ ♟ 🍴 2km

Åmål ▲ Gerdinsgatan 7, 66237 Åmål, Dalsland. ☎ (532) 10205 **FAX** (532) 10205 **Shut:** 21.12-5.1 ⊠ 48 ⍩(B) ♂ ♦♦♦ ⅑ ♟ 🍴 1.5km

Ammarnäs ▲ STF Vandrarhem, Ammarnäs Fack 88, 92075 Ammarnäs ☎ (952) 60045 **FAX** (952) 60251 ⊠ 44 ⍩ ♂ ♦♦♦ 🚌 Sorsele 90km

Åmotfors ▲ Norra Mon, 67040 Åmotfors, Värmland. ☎ (571) 22008 **FAX** (571) 30146 ⊠ 102 ⍩(B) ♂ ♦♦♦ ⅑ ♟ 🍴 Charlottenberg 6km ℝ (15.9-15.5)

Aneby ▲ Ralingsåsgården, Kronobergs-missionen, Box 143, 57891

Aneby. ✆ (380) 40295 **FAX** (380) 40218 **Open:** 1.7-15.8 ⌫ 25 ✿ ⊞ ⊡ ⚓ ☵ Eksjö

Ängelholm ▲ Magnarp 174, 26083 Vejbystrand, Skåne. ✆ (431) 52364 **FAX** (431) 52364 **Open:** 1.4-31.10 ⌫ 60 ▣(B L) ✿ ⊞ ⊡ ⬛ ☵ 10km 🚌 50m

Ånn ▲ Ånn 2467, 83015 Duved, Jämtland. ✆ (647) 71070 **FAX** (647) 71070 ⌫ 46 ▣(B) ✿ ⊞ ⚲ ☵ Ånn 50m

Arådalen ▲ Västra Arådalen, 84031 Åsarna, Jämtland. ✆ (687) 14054 **Open:** 22.6-27.8 ⌫ 18 ✿ ⊞ ☵ Svenstavik 65km

Arjeplog STF Vandrarhem ▲ Arjeplog, Lyktan, Lugnetvägen 4, 93090 Arjeplog ✆ (961) 61210 **FAX** (961) 10150 **Open:** 1.5-30.11 ⌫ 30 ▣(B) ✿ ⬥ ⚲ 🚌 200m

Årås ▲ **CC** Kölingared, 56593 Mullsjö. ✆ (515) 91151 **Open:** 8.6-17.8 ⌫ 28 ▣(B) ✿ ⚲ **R** J Böhn, Kölinksholm, 565 93 Mullsjö

Åre ▲ Brattlandsgården, 83010 Undersåker, Jämtland. ✆ (647) 30138 ⌫ 70 ✿ ⊞ ⬥ ☵ Undersåker 4km **R** (Grps 1.10-1.1)

Asa- Lammhult ▲ STF Vandrarhem Asa, 36030 Lammhult, Småland. ✆ (472) 63110 ⌫ 35 ✿ ⊞ ⬥ ⊡ ☵ Växjö 40km 🚌 Lammhult 15km **R** (1.10-30.4: Borensved, Asa, 36030 Lammhult ✆ (472) 63003, 63110)

Åsarna ▲ **CC** 84031 Åsarna, Jämtland. ✆ (687) 30230 **FAX** (687) 30360 ⌫ 60 /30 ▣ ✿ ⊞ ⊡ 🚌 500m

Askersund ▲ Lindbogården, 69601 Askersund, Närke. ✆ (583) 81087 **Open:** 2.6-20.8 ⌫ 40 ▣(B) ✿ ⊞ ⊡ ☵ Hallsberg 25km 🚌 1km

Avesta ▲ Älvbrovägen 33, 77435 Avesta. ✆ (226) 80623 **Open:** 8.1-22.12 ⌫ 36 ✿ ⊞ ⊡ ☵ 4km

Backåkra- Löderup ▲ STF Vandrarhem Backåkra, Kustvägen, 27645 Löderup, Skåne. ✆ (411) 26080 **Open:** 15.5-1.9 ⌫ 70 ▣(B) ✿ ⊞ ☵ Ystad 🚌 322 from Ystad **R** (2.9-14.5 **FAX** (411) 555585 Tourist Office, St Knuts Torg, 27142 Ystad)

Baskemölla ▲ Baskemölla Simrishamn, Tjörnedalavägen 81, 27294 Simrishamn. ✆ (414) 26173 **FAX** (414) 26054 ⌫ 56 ▣(B) ✿ ⊞ ⬥ ⊡ ☵ Simrishamn 5km 🚌 100m

Bassholmen ▲ c/o Fritidskontoret, 45181 Uddevalla. ✆ (522) 651308 **FAX** (522) 16080 **Open:** 17.6-11.8 ⌫ 38 ▣(B) ✿ ⊞ ① ⚓ ⛴ from Uddevalla, Lysekil **R**

Bengtsfors ▲ Gammelgården, 66631 Bengtsfors, Dalsland. ✆ (531) 61075 **Open:** 15.5-17.8 ⌫ 50 ▣(B) ✿ ⊞ ☵ 300m 🚌 400m

Björkvattnet ▲ Björkvattnet 1425, 83090 Gäddede, Jämtland. ✆ (672) 23024 **FAX** (672) 23024 ⌫ 38 ✿ ⊞ 🚌 Gäddede 20km **R** (30.8-31.5)

Björnlunda ▲ Hembygdsgården, Box 81, 64050 Björnlunda, Södermanland. ✆ (158) 20014 **Open:** 1.6-31.8 ⌫ 13 ✿ ⊞ ⚲ 🚌 1km

Böda ▲ **CC** Mellböda, 38074 Löttorp, Öland. ✆ (485) 22038 **FAX** (485) 22198 **Open:** 2.5-24.8 ⌫ 173 ▣(B) ✿ ⊞ 🚌 Borgholm **R** (1.9-30.4)

Boda ▲ Box 136, 36065 Boda Glasbruk, Småland. ✆ (481) 24230 **Open:** 1.4-31.10 ⌫ 49 ▣ ✿ ⊞ ☵ Nybro 16km 🚌 Nybro 16km

Bollnäs ▲ Lenninge 6003, 82191 Bollnäs, Hälsingland. ✆ (278) 23092

FAX (278) 23092 ✉ 50 ▯①(B) ♂ ♜♜♜
▯ ⚒ 5km 🚐 70, 26

Borås ▲ Box 440 22 Sjöbo 4, 50004
Borås, Västergötland. ☎ (33) 121434
FAX (33) 140582 **Open:** 1.1-22.12;
30-31.12 ✉ 44 ♂ ♜♜♜ ⚒ 2km 🚐
400m

Borghamn ▲ Borghamnsskolan,
59293 Borghamn Vättern,
Östergötland. ☎ (143) 20220 **Open:**
12.6-6.8 ✉ 50 ▯①(B) ♜♜♜ ⚙ 🚐 610
Vadstera, 650 Linköping 500m

Borgholm ▲ Rosenfors, 38736
Borgholm, Öland. ☎ (485) 10756 **FAX**
(77878) **Open:** 30.4-15.9 ✉ 90 ▯①(B)
♂ ♜♜♜ ⚒ Kalmar 🚐 200m

Borgsjö ▲ 4177 Borgsjöbyn, 84105
Erikslund. ☎ (690) 20075 **Open:**
1.6-1.9 ✉ 30 ▯① ♂ ♜♜♜ ⚒ 15km 🚐
100m

Borlänge ▲ ㏄ Kornstigen 23A,
78452 Borlänge, Dalarna. ☎ (243)
227615 **FAX** (243) 16411 ✉ 75 ▯①(B)
♂ ♜♜♜ ▯ ⚒ 3km 🚐 602

Bosön ▲ 18147 Lidingö, Stockholm. ☎
(8) 6056605-06 **FAX** (8) 7671644
Open: 19.6-13.8 ✉ 26 ▯① ♜♜♜ ▯ ⚓ Ⓤ
Ropsten 🚐 202, 204, 212

Brunskog ▲ Bergamon, 67194 Edane,
Värmland. ☎ (570) 52141 **FAX** (570)
52149 ✉ 70 ▯①(B) ♂ ♜♜♜ ⚒ Edane
7km 🚐 Arvika 18km Ⓡ (1.9-1.6)

Bruzaholm ▲ ㏄ Wäduren AB,
Eksjövägen 13, Box 25, 57034
Bruzaholm. ☎ (381) 20200 **Open:**
15.5-15.8 ✉ 24 ▯① ♂ ♜♜♜ ⚙ ▯ 🏠 ⚙
⚒ Eksjö 300m 🚐 Eksjö

Burträsk ▲ Hembygdsgården, Box 72,
93721 Burträsk, Västerbotten. ☎ (914)
11013, 10287 **Open:** 15.6-15.8 ✉ 52
♂ ♜♜♜ ✈ 30km ⚒ 40km 🚐 400m
Ⓡ (Burträskik, Box 62, 93721
Burträsk)

Dals Rostock ▲ STF Vandrarhem, Dals
Rostock, Kroppefjälls Fritidscenter,
46450 Dals Rostock ☎ (530) 20360
FAX (530) 20345 ✉ 54 ▯①(B) ♂ ♜♜♜
▯ ⚙ ⚓ 🚐 1.4km

Docksta ▲ Dockstavägen 47, 87033
Docksta, Ångermanland. ☎ (613)
13064 **FAX** (613) 40391 ✉ 80 ▯①(B)
♂ ♜♜♜ ▯ ✈ 40km ⚒ Kramfors 50km
🚐 3km

Ed ▲ Strömstadsvägen 18, 668 31 Ed,
Dalsland. ☎ (534) 10191 **FAX** (534)
10550 **Shut:** 20.12-10.1 ✉ 46 ♂ ♜♜♜
▯ ⚒ 700m 🚐 700m Ⓡ (1.9-30.5)

Edsbyn ▲ Hogagatan 15, 82804
Edsbyn. ☎ (271) 34462 **FAX** (271)
34176 ✉ 36 ▯①(B) ♂ ♜♜♜ ⚒ 27km
🚐 400m Ⓡ (20.8-15.6)

Ekshärad ▲ Pilgrimen, Box 105,
68050 Ekshärad. ☎ (563) 40590 ✉ 22
▯① ♂ ♜♜♜ 🚐 100m

Eksjö ▲ Österlånggatan 31, 57531
Eksjö, Småland. ☎ (381) 36180 **FAX**
(381) 17755 ✉ 55 ♂ ♜♜♜ ⚒ 500m

Enköping ▲ ⑥S Bredsand, 74591
Enköping, Uppland. ☎ (171) 80066 ✉
48 ♂ ♜♜♜ ♿ ⚒ 6km Ⓡ (Grps
1.9-31.5)

Eskilstuna ▲ ㏄ Vilsta Camping,
63229 Eskilstuna. ☎ (16) 513080 **FAX**
(16) 513086 ✉ 40 ♂ ♜♜♜ ♿ ▯ ⚒
Eskilstuna 2km 🚐 ap YH

Falkenberg ▲ ⑥SE Näset, c/o
Turistbyrån, Box 293, 31123
Falkenberg, Halland. ☎ (346) 17111
FAX (346) 14526 ✉ 40 ▯①(B) ♂ ♜♜♜
⚙ ⚒ 6km

Falköping ▲ Mössebergsparken
Lidgatan 4, 52132 Falköping,
Västergötland. ☎ (515) 85020 **FAX**
(515) 10043 **Open:** 15.1-15.12 (Grps
16.12-14.1) ✉ 46 ▯①(B) ♂ ♜♜♜ ▯ ⚒
1km

Falun ▲ 4E Haraldsboskolans elevhem, Hälsinggårdsv. 7, 79143 Falun, Dalarna. ✆ (23) 10560 **FAX** (23) 14102 **Open:** 2.1-19.12 ✉ 190 ⦿(B) ♂ ⁙ ⛁ ⟟ ⚲ ⛻ 3km ⛍ 701, 704

Färgelanda ▲ Dagsholm, 45892 Färgelanda. ✆ (528) 20350 ✉ 60 ⦿(B) ♂ ⁙ ♿ ▣ ⛍ 200m ⓡ (1.9-15.5)

Fårö ▲ Fårögården, 62035 Fårösund, Gotland. ✆ (498) 223639 **Open:** 20.5-31.8 ✉ 46 ⦿ ♂ ⁙ ① ⚲ ⛴ 17km ⓡ

Finnerödja ▲ Sandbäcken, 69030 Finnerödja, Västergötland. ✆ (584) 440074 **FAX** (584) 440047 ✉ 54 ♂ ⁙ ♿ ▣ ⛍ 23km ⓡ (1.11-1.4)

Finnhamn ▲ Finnhamns Friluftsområde, Box 84, 13025 Ingmarsö, Uppland. ✆ (8) 54246212 **FAX** (542) 54246212 ✉ 76 ♂ ⁙ ① ⛴ Waxholmsbolaget, Cinderella, Lagnö Sjötaxi ⓡ

Finnskoga-Höljes ▲ STF Vandrarhem Finnskoga, Värdshuset, 68065 Höljes, Värmland. ✆ (564) 20100 **Open:** 22.1-21.12 ✉ 24 ⦿ ♂ ⁙ ⟟ ⛍ 400m

Fjällbacka Valö ▲ STF Vandrarhem Fjällbacka, Valö, 45071 Fjällbacka, Bohuslän. ✆ (525) 31234 **Open:** 2.5-25.8 ✉ 12 ♂ ⁙ ① ▣ ⓡ

Fjärdlång ▲ STF Vandrarhem, Fjärdlång, 13054 Dalarö. ✆ (8) 50156092 **FAX** (8) 50156634 **Open:** 10.6-29.9 ✉ 47 ♂ ⁙ ① ⛁ ⛴ from Stockholm + Dalarö ⛻ Haninge + ⛍ 839 Dalarö ⓡ

Forshaga ▲ CC STF Vandrarhem Forshaga, Slottet, Folkets Hus, Slottsvägen 9, Box 76, 66722 Forshaga ✆ (54) 873040 **FAX** (54) 873053 **Open:** 1.5-15.9 ✉ 20 ⦿(B) ♂ ⛻ N Karlstad 20km ⛍ 500m

Forsvik ▲ STF Vandrarhem Forsvik, Bruksvägen 11, 54673 Forsvik ✆ (505) 41137 **Open:** 1.6-1.9 ✉ 55 ♂ ⁙ ⚲ ⛴

Frillesås ▲ Vallersvik, Box 64, 43030 Frillesås. ✆ (340) 650028, 653000 **FAX** (340) 653551 **Open:** 26.4-28.9 ✉ 30 ⦿ ♂ ⁙ ⛻ 25km ⛍ 1km

Fryksta- Kil ▲ STF Vandrarhem, Fryksta, 66525 Kil, Värmland. ✆ (554) 40850 **FAX** (554) 13772 **Open:** 1.1-30.11 ✉ 30 ⦿(B) ♂ ⁙ ♿ ▣ ⛻ Kil 4km

Gällivare ▲ Barnhemsv 2, Andra Sidan, 98239 Gällivare. ✆ (970) 14380 **FAX** (970) 16586 ✉ 100 ⦿(B) ♂ ⁙ ▣ ⟟ ✈ 9km ⛻ 400m ⛍ 300m

Gammel- Gränome ▲ Stavby, 74050 Alunda, Uppland. ✆ (174) 13108 ✉ 27 ♂ ⁙ ⛍ 811, 886 from Uppsala 26km

Garda ▲ Kommunhuset, 62016 Ljugarn, Gotland. ✆ (498) 491391 **FAX** (498) 491181 **Open:** 11.1-21.12 ✉ 48 ♂ ⁙ ① ▣ ⚲ ⛍ 200m ⓡ (15.8-1.6 ✆ (498) 491220)

Gärdserum ▲ STF Vandrarhem, Gärdserum, 59797 Åtvidaberg, Småland. ✆ (120) 20134 **FAX** (120) 20037 **Open:** 15.5-15.9 ✉ 24 ♂ ⁙ ⛻ Falerum 3km ⛍ from Linköping + Valdemarsvik

Gårdstånga ▲ Pl 263 Gårdstånga, 24032 Flyinge. ✆ (46) 52087 **FAX** (46) 52666 **Open:** 3.1-21.12 ✉ 34 ⦿(B) ♂ ⁙ ⛻ Eslöv, Lund 10km ⛍ 120 from Lund, 157 from Eslöv ⓡ (1.9-1.5)

GÄVLE (2 Hostels)

Gävle - Södra Rådmansgatan ▲ STF Vandrarhem Gävle, Södra Rådmansgatan 1, 80251 Gävle, Gästrikland. ✆ (26) 621745 **FAX** (26)

615990 Open: 9.1-22.12 (Arrive before 19.00hrs Wi) ⚥ 72 ♂ ♦♦♦ ⑁ ▣ 🍴
600m

Gävle - Engeltofta Bönavägen ▲ STF Vandrarhem Gävle Engeltofta, Bönavägen 118, 80595 Gävle, Gästrikland. ☎ (26) 96160, 96063, FAX (26) 96055 Open: 1.5-31.8 ⚥ 74 ♂ ♦♦♦ ▣ 🍴 Gävle 7km

Gnosjö ▲ Fritidsgården Träffpunkten, 33580 Gnosjö, Småland. ☎ (370) 331115 ⚥ 33 ♂ ♦♦♦ 🍴 500m 🚌 500m ⓡ (15.8-5.6)

GÖTEBORG (4 Hostels)

Göteborg - ▲ ⟨CC⟩ STF Vandrarhem, Slottsskogen Vegagatan 21, 41311 Göteborg ☎ (31) 426520 FAX (31) 142102 Open: 9.1-21.12 ⚥ 92 🍴(B) ♂ ♦♦♦ 🚋 🚌 210, 703, 705 🚆 1, 2

Göteborg - ▲ ⟨CC⟩ STF Vandrarhem, Stigbergsliden, Stigbergsliden 10, 41463 Göteborg ☎ (31) 241620 FAX (31) 246520 ⚥ 90 🍴(B) ♂ ♦♦♦ 🚋 Ⓟ 🍴 3km 🚆 4, 3, 9 200m

Göteborg - **Kärralund** ▲ ⟨CC⟩ Olbersgatan, 41655 Göteborg. ☎ (31) 840200 FAX (31) 840500 Open: 8.1-21.12 ⚥ 48 ♂ ♦♦♦ ▣ 🍴 5km 🚆 5 ap Welandergatan

Göteborg - Mölndal ▲ ⟨IBN⟩ ⟨CC⟩ Torrekulla Turiststation, 42835 Kållered ☎ (31) 7951495 FAX (31) 7955140 Open: 7.1-21.12 ⚥ 140 / 110 🍴(B) ♂ ♦♦♦ ⑁ ▣ Ⓟ 🚌 705,711, fron Heden

Gothenburg ☞ Göteborg

Grängesberg ▲ Bergmansgården, Hårdtorpsvägen 15, 77240 Grängesberg, Dalarna. ☎ (240) 21830 FAX (240) 21830 Open: 9.6-24.8 ⚥ 46 ♂ ♦♦♦ 🍴 3km 🚌

Grönklitt ▲ ⟨CC⟩ 79498 Orsa Dalarna. ☎ (250) 46200 FAX (250) 46111 ⚥ 40 🍴 ♂ ♦♦♦ ▣ �) ⚲ 🍴 Orsa 13km

Gullspång ▲ Alhöjden, 54700 Gullspång, Västergötland. ☎ (551) 20786 FAX (551) 20694 ⚥ 36 🍴(B) ♂ ♦♦♦ ▣ 🍴 20km 🚌 100m ⓡ (20.8-15.6 ☎ (551) 20021, 22620)

Hågelby ▲ Hågelbygård, 14743 Tumba. ☎ (8) 53062020 FAX (8) 53031100 ⚥ 28 🍴(B) ♂ ♦♦♦ 🚌 🚌 ap Tumba station 🚌 707, 708, 723 ⓡ (10.8-7.6)

Hällekis ▲ Falkängen, Falkängsvägen, 53374 Hällekis, Västergötland. ☎ (510) 40653 FAX (510) 40085 ⚥ 72 🍴(B) ♦♦♦

Hammar ▲ Hargebaden, 69694 Hammar, Närke. ☎ (583) 770556 Open: 15.4-15.9 ⚥ 40 🍴(B) ♂ ♦♦♦ ▣ 🚌

Hammarö ▲ Djupsundsvägen 1, 66334 Skoghall, Värmland. ☎ (54) 510440 Open: 19.6-6.8 ⚥ 84 🍴(B) ♂ ♦♦♦ ▣ ⚲ 🚌 Karlstad

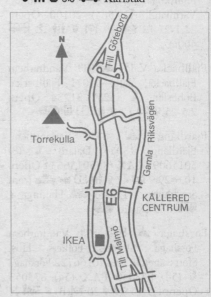

GÖTEBORG - Mölndal

Hammenhög ▲ STF Vandrarhem Hammenhög, Skolgatan 20, 27650 Hammenhög ℓ (414) 440095 **FAX** (414) 440041 **Open:** 15.6-15.8 ☒ 72 �🍴(B) ☞ ⅲ 🚌 300m

Hanö ▲ STF Vandrarhem, Hanö, 29400 Sölvesborg, Blekinge. ℓ (456) 53000 ☒ 24 ☞ ⅲ ① ⌂ ® (1.9-22.5 ℓ (456) 53022)

Härnösand ▲ Volontären 14, Box 107, 87123 Härnösand. ℓ (611) 10446 **Open:** 11.6-6.8 ☒ 70 🍴(B) ☞ ⅲ 🚻 2km 🚌

Haparanda ▲ Strandgatan 26, 95331 Haparanda, Norrbotten. ℓ (922) 61171 **FAX** (922) 61784 ☒ 45 🍴 ☞ ⅲ ♿ 🚻 1km 🚌 from Boden, Luleå, Kalix

Hassela ▲ Franshammars Kraftstation, Bjuråkersvägen 2216, 82078 Hassela. ℓ (652) 40444 ☒ 21 ☞ ⅲ ⚡ Alt 6000m 🚻 Sundsvall 🚌 1.4km Hudiksvall 60km, Ljusdal 65km, Sundsvall 50km

Hässleholm ▲ Hässleholmsgården 303, 28135 Hässleholm, Skåne. ℓ (451) 68234 **FAX** (451) 68232 ☒ 60 ☞ ⅲ 🍴 🚻 1.5km 🚌 500m

Hästveda ▲ Hembygdsparken, Box 97, 28023 Hästveda, Skåne. ℓ (451) 30273 **Open:** 1.4-31.10 ☒ 30 ☞ ⅲ ♿ 🍴 🚻 Hässleholm 🚌 536 400m ® (1.4-31.5; 1.9-31.10: Grönegatan 6, 28023 Hästveda ℓ (451) 30211)

Haväng STF Vandrarhem Haväng ▲ Skepparpsgården, 27737 Kivik, Skåne. ℓ (414) 74071 **FAX** (414) 74073 **Open:** 1.5-15.9 ☒ 50 🍴(B) ☞ ⅲ 🚻 Kristianstad 47km 🚌 Ravlunda ® (1-30.4; 15-30.9)

Håverud ▲ Museiv 3, 46400 Mellerud, Dalsland. ℓ (530) 30275, 30745 ☒ 38 ☞ ⅲ 🍴 ♻ 🚻 200m 🚌 100m ® (31.8-30.4)

Hedemora ▲ Hälla Härbärge, Hällavägen, 77630 Hedemora, Dalarna. ℓ (225) 711350 **FAX** (225) 34124 ☒ 47 🍴(B) ☞ ⅲ 🍴 🚻 900m 🚌 400m

Hedenäset ▲ Skolbacken 25, 95795 Hedenäset. ℓ (927) 30350 **FAX** (927) 30268 **Open:** 1.6-31.8 ☒ 90 🍴(L) ☞ ⅲ ⌂ ♻ ⛵ ✈ Kallax 130km 🚌 500m

HELSINGBORG (2 Hostels)

Helsingborg - Villa Thalassa ▲ STF Vandrarhem Helsingborg, Villa Thalassa, Dag Hammarskjölds väg, 25433 Helsingborg, Skåne. ℓ (42) 210384 **FAX** (42) 128792 **Open:** 16.1-30.11 ☒ 138 🍴(B) ☞ ⅲ 🚻 4km 🚌 7 Pålsjöboden

Helsingborg - KFUM ▲ STF Vandrarhem Helsingborg II, KFUM Nyckelbo Scoutstigen, 25284 Helsingborg, Skåne. ℓ (42) 92005 **FAX** (42) 91050 ☒ 30 🍴(B) ☞ ⅲ ♿ ⌂ 🚻 7km 🚌 252 300m ® (1.9-30.4; KFUM, Karl X Gustavst gata 68, 25440 Helsingborg ℓ (42) 211312)

Hemavan ▲ FBU- gården, 92066 Hemavan. ℓ (954) 30002 **FAX** (954) 30510 **Open:** 15.6-30.9 ☒ 48 🍴 ☞ ♻ ✈ 380km A🚌 30m 🚌 30m

Hjo ▲ Stadsparken, 54433 Hjo, Västergötland. ℓ (503) 10085 **Open:** 1.5-31.8 ☒ 48 🍴 ☞ ⅲ ♿ ⌂ ♻ 🚌 30m

Högbonden ▲ Fyrvaktarbostaden, c/o Mitt Sverige Turism, Box 77, 87122 Härnösand, Ångermanland. ℓ (613) 23005, (611) 29030 **Open:** 15.5-30.9 ☒ 27 ☞ ⅲ ① ⛴ Högbonden 🚌 Bönhamn ® (Grps 15.5-14.6; 15.8-30.9)

Högsby ▲ Stavbygården, Tingshusplan 1, 57992 Högsby, Småland. ℓ (491)

21600 **FAX** (491) 21242 ⚐ 55 📞(B) ♂ ♔ 🚌 from Kalmar, Växjö ap YH ⓡ (9.1-8.6; 11.8-31.12)

Hökarängen ▲ Martinskolan, Munstycksvägen 18, 12357 Farsta. ☎ (8) 941765 **Open:** 24.6-11.8 ⚐ 50 📞(B) ♂ ♔ 🅿 Ⓤ 18 from Stockholm Central Hökarängen

Hökensås ▲ 🆔 Kyrkbyn, 56693 Brandstorp. ☎ (502) 50350, 50013 **FAX** (502) 50024 **Open:** 21.6-10.8 ⚐ 25 ♂ ♔ 🚋 Skövde 🚌 from Hjo, Habo or Jönköping ap Brandstorp ⓡ (**Shut:** ☎ (502) 50013, **FAX** (502) 50024)

Hörby ▲ Studieförbundet Vuxenskolans-Kursgård, 24292 Hörby, Skåne. ☎ (415) 14830 **FAX** (415) 14328 **Open:** 9.6-15.8 ⚐ 60 📞(B) ♔ 🚋 Eslör 🚌 3km

Horndal ▲ Rossgården, Sibirienv 1, 77060 Horndal, Dalarna. ☎ (226) 40815 ⚐ 25 ♂ ♔ 🚌 Avesta 25km

Höör ▲ 🆔 Backagården, Stenskogen, 24391 Höör. ☎ (413) 25510 **FAX** (413) 25956 ⚐ 48 📞(B) ♂ ♔ 🔲 🚌 5km ⓡ (1.9-1.6)

Hörnefors ▲ Sundelinsvägen 62, 91020 Hörnefors. ☎ (930) 20480 **Open:** 1.6-31.8 ⚐ 40 ♂ ♔ ♿ 🔲 ✈ Umeå 28km 🚌 300m

Hovenäset ▲ Box 110, 45601 Kungshamn, Bohuslän. ☎ (523) 37463 **Open:** 10.6-13.8 ⚐ 34 ♂ ♔ ♿ 🔲 🚌 100m ⓡ (Ulrika Granander Kungsg 11, 46131 Trollhättan)

Hovra ▲ STF Vandrarhem, Hovra, 82042 Korskrogen Hälsingland: 12km NW of Färila. ☎ (651) 26055 **FAX** (651) 26055 ⚐ 34 ♂ ♔ 🚋 Ljusdal 30km 🚌

Huddinge ▲ Sundbygård, Sundbygårdsv, 14191 Huddinge. ☎ (8)

7469480 **Open:** 22.6-19.8 (Grps 18.8-22.6) ⚐ 32 📞(B) ♂ ♔ 🅿 ✈ Stockholm ⓡ (18.8-22.6)

Hudiksvall ▲ 🆔 Malnbaden, Box 3023, 82403 Hudiksvall. ☎ (650) 13260 ⚐ 36 ♂ ♔ 🔲 ♿ 🚋 4km 🚌 4km

Hunneberg ▲ Bergagårdsvägen 9B, 46831 Vargön, Västergötland. ☎ (521) 220340 **FAX** (521) 68497 **Open:** 13.1-16.12 ⚐ 60 📞(B) ♂ ♔ ♿ ♿ ✈ 7km 🚋 1.5km 🚌 400m

Hunnebostrand ▲ Gammelgården, 45046 Hunnebostrand, Bohuslän. ☎ (523) 58730 **Open:** 1.5-30.9 ⚐ 86 ♂ ♔ 🚌 100m ⓡ (Grps 1.5-1.6; 21.8-30.9)

Huskvarna ▲ 🆔 Odengatan 10, 56132 Huskvarna, Småland. ☎ (36) 148870 **FAX** (36) 148840 ⚐ 112 📞(B) ♂ ♔ ♿ 🚋 Huskvarna 🚌 100m

Immeln ▲ 🆔 Pl 2338, 28063 Sibbhult, Skåne. ☎ (44) 96090, 96332 **FAX** (44) 96090 ⚐ 30 ♂ ♔ ♿ 🔲 ⛪ 🚋 Kristianstad 25km

Jädraås ▲ Gammelboningsvägen 6, 81691 Jädraås, Gästrikland. ☎ (297) 45317, 45140 **FAX** (297) 45335 ⚐ 45 📞(B) ♂ ♔ 🚋 Ockelbo, Sandviken 🚌 from Ockelbo ap YH ⓡ (1.9-31.5)

Järbo ▲ Britta Zachrisson, Box 1194, Vreten 81028 Järbo, Gästrikland. ☎ (290) 70151 ⚐ 30 /16 ♂ ♔ 🔲 🚋 Sandviken 15km 🚌 800m ⓡ (1.10-30.4)

Järvsö ▲ Harsagården, Harsa, 82040 Järvsö. ☎ (651) 49511 **FAX** (651) 49590 ⚐ 28 📞 ♂ ♔ ⚡ ♿ 🚋 Järvsö 18km 🚌 14km

Jokkmokk ▲ Åsgård, Åsgatan 20, 96231 Jokkmokk, Lappland. ☎ (971)

55977 **FAX** (971) 55977 ✉ 50 🍴 (B Su) ☕ 👪 🛁 300m 🚌 1km ⓡ (☎ (10) 6642299)

Junsele ▲ Kullberg 3031, 88037 Junsele, Ångermanland. ☎ (621) 32010 **FAX** (621) 32010 ✉ 46 🍴(B) ☕ 👪 🛁 Sollefteå 🚌 12km ap Junsele

Kalix ▲ Grytnäs Herrgård, Box 148, 95222 Kalix, Norrbotten. ☎ (923) 10733 **Open:** 15.6-20.8 ✉ 37 ☕ 👪 ⚙ 🚌 Boden, Luleå, Haparanda

Kall ▲ Kalls Gästgiveri, Kall 2220, 83005 Järpen, Jämtland. ☎(647) 41012 **FAX** (647) 41012 **Open:** 1.1-30.4; 1.6-31.12 ✉ 26 🍴 ☕ 👪 ⚙ 🏊 🛁 19km 🚌 200m ⓡ (15.8-15.6)

Kalmar ▲ 1N 💳 Rappeg 1C, 39230 Kalmar, Småland. ☎ (480) 12928 **FAX** (480) 88293 **Open:** 8.1-21.12 ✉ 71 /50 🍴(B) ☕ 👪 ⚙ 🛁 1.5km

Kalv ▲ STF Vandrarhem, Kalv, Erikslund 2, 51261 Kalv, Västergötland. ☎ (325) 51000 **Open:** 15.5-15.8 ✉ 27 ☕ 👪

Kapellskär ▲ Pl 985, Riddersholm, 76015 Gräddö, Uppland. ☎ (176) 44169 ✉ 34 ☕ 👪 ⛴ from Nybrokajen 🚌 from Stockholm, Uppsala, Norrtälje ⓡ (Grps 15.8-1.6)

Karlsborg ▲ Ankarvägen, 54630 Karlsborg, Västergötland. ☎ (505) 44600 **FAX** (505) 44600 **Open:** 1.6-31.8 ✉ 74 ☕ 👪 🛁 Skövde 🚌 Skövde ⓡ (15.8-13.6)

Karlshamn ▲ 6NE STF Vandrarhem Karlshamn, Surbrunnsvägen 1C, 37439 Karlshamn ☎ (454) 14040 **FAX** (454) 14040 **Open:** 1.4-30.9 ✉ 72 🍴(B) ☕ 👪 🛁 500m 🚌 100m

Karlskoga ▲ Grönfeldtsudden, 69141 Karlskoga, Värmland. ☎ (586) 56780 ✉ 84 🍴(B) ☕ 👪 ♿ ⚙ 🛁 10km 🚌 2km

Karlskrona ▲ STF Vandrarhem Karlskrona, Ruthensparre, Borgmästaregatan 8, 37122 Karlskrona ☎ (455) 83481 **Open:** 15.6-15.8 ✉ 48 ☕ 👪 ⚙ 🛁 500m 🚌 500m ⓡ (Turistbyrån **FAX** (455) 82255)

Karlstad ▲ Ulleberg, 65342 Karlstad, Värmland. ☎ (54) 566840 **FAX** (54) 566042 **Open:** 16.1-14.12 ✉ 102 🍴(B) ☕ 👪 ♿ ⚙ 🅿 🛁 3.5km 🚌 11, 21, 32

Katrineholm ▲ 2S Stora Djulö, 64192 Katrineholm, Södermanland. ☎ (150) 10225 **FAX** (150) 10225 **Open:** 30.5-31.8 ✉ 45 🍴(B) ☕ 👪 ⚙ 🛁 3km ⓡ (Grps 30.4-30.5)

Kiruna ▲ Skyttegatan 20A, 98137 Kiruna, Lappland. ☎ (980) 17195 **Open:** 16.6-22.8 ✉ 94 🍴(B) ☕ 👪 🛁 2km ⓡ (Write to: National office)

Kivik, STF Vandrarhem ▲ Tittutvägen, 277 30 Kivik ☎ (414) 71195 **Open:** 1.5-30.8 ✉ 35 🍴(B) ☕ 👪 ✈ Everöd 45km 🛁 Simrishamn 18km

Klavreström ▲ Malmgatan 1, 36072 Klavreström, Småland. ☎ (474) 40944 **FAX** (474) 40944 **Open:** 15.5-27.8 ✉ 70 🍴(B) ☕ 👪 ♿ ⚙ ☢ 🛁 Växjö 40km 🚌 Växjö

Klintehamn ▲ Pensionat Warfsholm, Box 56, 62020 Klintehamn, Gotland. ☎ (498) 240010 **FAX** (498) 241411 ✉ 50 ☕ 👪 ⚜ 🚌 200m ⓡ (1.9-1.5)

Köping ▲ Ågärdsg 2D, 73132 Köping, Västmanland. ☎ (221) 24495 **FAX** (221) 24495 **Open:** 10.1-10.12 ✉ 40 / 20 ☕ 👪 ⚙

Köpmanholmen ▲ Box 18, 89014 Köpmanholmen. ☎ (660) 33496, 33764 **Open:** 15.5-31.8 ✉ 36 ☕ 👪 ⚙ 🛁 25km 🚌 1km ⓡ (1.9-15.5)

Korrö ▲ 36024 Linneryd, Småland: (5km S Linneryd on route 122). ☎ (470) 34249 FAX (470) 34556 Open: 1.4-30.9 ✉ 87 ⎮⊙⎮(B) ♂ ⅲ 🚂 🚲 🚃 Växjö 🚌 500m

Kristinehamn ▲ Kvarndammen, 68100 Kristinehamn, Värmland. ☎ (550) 14771 Open: 15.5-30.8 ✉ 16 ⎮⊙⎮ ♂ ⅲ ⑥ 🚲 🚃 5km 🚌 100m

Kungälv ▲ Färjevägen 2, 44231 Kungälv, Bohuslän. ☎ (303) 18900 FAX (303) 19295 ✉ 50 ⎮⊙⎮(B) ♂ ⅲ ♿ 🚌 Göteborg 19km

Kungsbacka ▲ Klóvsten, Box 10106, 43422 Kungsbacka, Halland. ☎ (300) 19485 Open: 19.6-13.8 ✉ 58 ⎮⊙⎮(B) ⅲ ♿ ⑥ 🚃 1.6km 🚌 500m ®
(Shut: Kungsbacka Turistbyrån ☎ (300) 34595)

Kyrktåsjö ▲ Tåsjödalens Pl 1525, 83080 Hoting, Ångermanland. ☎(671) 20004 ✉ 20 ⎮⊙⎮(B) ♂ ⅲ 🚂 ⛵ 🚃 Hoting 23km ® (1.10-31.5)

Laholm ▲ ⒸⒸ Tivolivägen 4, 31230 Laholm, Halland. ☎ (430) 13318 FAX (430) 15325 ✉ 68 ⎮⊙⎮(B) ♂ ⅲ ⑥ 🚃 300m 🚌 300m ® (19.12-9.1)

Landskrona ▲ St Olovsgatan 15, 26136 Landskrona, Skåne. ☎ (418) 12063 FAX (418) 13075 Open: 27.1-30.11 ✉ 45 ⎮⊙⎮(B) ♂ ⅲ 🚃 1.2km

Långasjö ▲ Stallgatan, 36195 Långasjö, Småland. ☎ (471) 50310 ✉ 43 ♂ ⅲ ♿ 🚃 10km 🚌 300m ® (1.9-14.5)

Lärbro ▲ Gutegården, 620 34 Lärbro, Gotland. ☎ (498) 225786 Open: 15.5-31.8✉39 ♂ ⅲ ① 🚲 ⛵ Visby 🚌 700m

Leksand ▲ ⎮25S⎮ Parkgården, Box 3051, 79335 Leksand, Dalarna. ☎(247)

Liden ▲ Larmvägen 2, Box 35, 86041 Liden. ☎ (692) 10567 Open: 1.6-31.8 ✉ 50 /20 ♂ ♿ ⑥ ✈ 50km 🚃 50km 🚌 500m

Lidköping ▲ Gamla Stadens Torg Nicolaigatan 2, 53132 Lidköping, Västergötland. ☎ (510) 66430 ✉ 52 ♂ ⅲ ⑥ 🚲 ✈ 4km 🚃 500m 🚌 500m

Lindesberg ▲ Fritidsbyn, Fotbollsgatan 11, Box 88, 71122 Lindesberg, Västmanland. ☎ (581) 81175, 81170 FAX (581) 81169 ✉ 58 ♂ ⅲ ⑥ 🚃 3km ® (1.9-31.5)

Linköping ▲ Klostergatan 52A, 58223 Linköping, Östergötland. ☎ (13) 149090 FAX (13) 148300 ✉ 90 /56 ⎮⊙⎮(B) ♂ ⅲ ♿ 🚃 700m 🚌 50m

Ljuder ▲ Grimsnäs Herrgård, 36053 Skruv, Småland. ☎ (478) 20400 FAX (478) 20400 ✉ 70 ⎮⊙⎮(B) ♂ ⅲ ⑥ 🚲 🚃 Lessebo 🚌 1km ® (1.10-1.4)

Ljugarn ▲ Strandridaregården, 62016 Ljugarn, Gotland. ☎ (498) 493184 Open: 1.5-30.8 ✉ 31 ♂ ⅲ ⛴ Visby 🚌 200m ® (1-31.5; 1-31.8)

Ljungdalen ▲ Dunsjögården, Box 15, 84035 Ljungdalen, Härjedalen. ☎ (687) 20285 (21.6-15.10), 20364 (15.10-23.6) ✉ 40 ♂ ⅲ ⑥ 🚂 🚌 100m

Löderup ☞ Backåkra-Löderup

Loftahammar ▲ Trillin, Trillinvägen 3, Box 57, 59095 Loftahammar, Småland. ☎ (493) 61110 FAX (493) 61929 ✉ 16 ⎮⊙⎮(B) ♂ ⅲ 🚲 🚌 24 50m

Loka Brunn ▲ ⒸⒸ STF Vandrarhem, Loka Brunn, 71294 Grythyttan, Västmanland. ☎ (591) 13570 FAX (591) 30000 Open: 1.5-30.9 ✉ 44 ⎮⊙⎮

♂ ⚥ ♿ ⚓ ₩ Degerfors 50km ₩
13km ap Grythyttan

Lommeland ▲ Pl 3146A Råsshult,
45200 Strömstad, Bohuslän. ☎ (526)
42027 **Open:** 20.5-1.9 ✍ 57 ♂ ⚥ ◙
♻ ₩ 20km ℞ (15.9-1.5)

Lönneberga ▲ Ånggården, Lönneberga
vägen, 57794 Silverdalen, Småland. ☎
(495) 40036 **FAX** (495) 40451 ✍ 55
◖◙(B) (15.6-15.8) ♂ ⚥ ♻ ₩ 600m
℞ (15.8-15.6)

Lönsboda ▲ Tranebodavägen 12,
28070 Lönsboda, Skåne. ☎ (479) 21525
Open: 15.6-31.8 ✍ 16 ◖◙(B) ♂ ⚥ ♻
₩ Osby ₩ 400m

Lövånger ▲ ⒸⒸ Lövångers, Kyrkstad,
Box 13, 93010 Lövånger. ☎ (913)
10395 **FAX** (913) 10759 **Open:**
2.1-24.12 ✍ 30 ◖◙(B) ♂ ⚥ ✈ 35km
₩ Skellefteå 50km, Umeå 80km

Luleå ▲ ⒸⒸ N:a Gäddvik,
Örnviksvägen 87, 97594 Luleå. ☎ (920)
52325 **FAX** (920) 52419 ✍ 62 ◖◙ ♂
⚥ ♻ ₩ 6 from Luleå 400m

Lund ▲ Tåget Vävaregatan 22,
Bjeredsparken, 22237 Lund. ☎ (46)
142820 **FAX** (46) 320568 **Open:**
10.1-19.12 ✍ 108 ◖◙(B) ♂ ⚥ 🚲 ♻
✈ 30km A₩ 300m ₩ 300m ₩
300m

Lycksele ▲ Duvan i Lycksele AB, Storg
47, 92132 Lycksele. ☎ (950) 14670
FAX (950) 10233 **Open:** 10.6-14.8 ✍
40 ◖◙ ♂ ⚥ ✈ 5km ₩ 500m ₩
500m

Malå ▲ STF Vandrarhem Malå,
Hotellgatan 10, 93070 Malå ☎ (953)
14291 **FAX** (953) 14291 **Open:**
11.5-30.8 ✍ 48 ♂ ✈ Lycksele 90km
₩ Bastuträsk 80km ₩ 50km

Malexander ▲ Sommarhagen, 59010
Boxholm, Östergötland. ☎ (142) 30037
Open: 1.4-30.9 ✍ 15 ◖◙ ⚥ ₩
Boxholm, Kisa 25km

Malmö ▲ Backavägen 18, 21432
Malmö, Skåne. ☎ (40) 82220 **FAX** (40)
510659 **Open:** 16.1-14.12 ✍ 157 ♂
⚥ ◙ ₩ Malmö 4km ₩ 21A

Malung ▲ Vallerås Turistgård, PL
1448, 78233 Malung. ☎ (280) 14040
FAX (280) 41057 ✍ 46 ◖◙(B) ♂ ⚥
₩ 4km ₩ 100m

Mariefred ☞ Strängnäs 18km

Mariestad ▲ Hamngatan 20, 54230
Mariestad, Västergötland. ☎ (501)
10448 ✍ 60 ♂ ⚥ ♻ ₩ 250m ℞
(20.8-10.6)

Medevi ▲ ⒸⒸ Medevi Brunn, 59197
Motala, Östergötland. ☎ (141) 91100
FAX (141) 91532 **Open:** 13.6-11.8 ✍
50 ◖◙ ♂ ⚥ ⛪ ₩ 17km ₩

Mjölby ▲ Hembygdsgården,
Norrgårdsgatan 14, 59541 Mjölby,
Östergötland. ☎ (142) 10016 **Open:**
8.1-23.12 ✍ 48 ♂ ⚥ ◙ ₩ 1km ℞
(15.9-30.4)

Moheda ▲ Kursgården
Kronobergshed, 34036 Moheda,
Småland. ☎ (472) 40052 **FAX** (472)
40135 ✍ 46 ♂ ⚥ ◙ ₩ 6km ₩
300m

Motala ▲ Skogsborgsgatan 1, 59152
Motala, Östergötland. ☎ (141) 57436
FAX (141) 57436 **Open:** 15.5-15.8 ✍
60 ◖◙(B) ♂ ⚥ ♿ ₩ 4km ₩ 400m
℞ (Turistbyrån ☎ (141) 57436,
225285)

Mölndal ☞ Göteborg

Mora ▲ STF Vandrarhem Mora,
Målkull Ann's, Vasagatan 19, 79232
Mora ☎ (250) 38196 **FAX** (250) 38195
✍ 62 ◖◙(B) ♂ ⚥ ♿ ◙ ⛪ ✈ 6km ₩
200m ₩ 200m ● Su: Säbbenbo,
Fredsgatan 6

Näs ▲ Näs Skola, 62011 Havdhem,
Gotland. ☎ (498) 489116 **Open:**
8.6-18.8 ✍ 36 ◖◙(B) ♂ ⚥ ⛴ Visby

Nässjö ▲ Sörängens Folkhögskola, Rågången 4, 571 38 Nässjö ☎ (380) 10645 **FAX** (380) 19076 **Open:** 10.6-20.8 ✉ 50 ⦿(B) ♂ ⅲ 🅾 🅿 🚋 3km 🚌 500m

Näsum ▲ STF Vandrarhem Näsum, Klagstorpsvägen 80-20, 29594 Näsum ☎ (456) 20188 **Open:** 1.6-31.8 ✉ 22 ⦿(B) ♂ ⅲ ♿ 🚋 1.5km 🚌 300m

Nora ▲ Tåghem, Box 52, 71322 Nora. ☎ (587) 14676 **FAX** (587) 10538 **Open:** 1.5-30.9 ✉ 64 ⦿(B) ♂ ⅲ 🅾 🚌 100m ⓇR (☎ (10) 2906060)

Norberg ▲ STF Vandrarhem Norberg, Gruvbyn Klackberg, 73891 Norberg ☎ (223) 20247 ✉ 50 ♂ ⅲ 🅾 🚋 Fagersta 🚌 1km

Norrahammar ▲ Spånhult, 56231 Norrahammar. ☎ (36) 61075 **Open:** 10.6-14.8 ✉ 33 ⦿(B) ♂ ⅲ ♿ 🚋 Jönköping 2km

NORRKÖPING (2 Hostels)

Norrköping - Turistgården ▲ ⒸⒸ STF Vandrarhem Norrköping, Turistgården, Ingelstadsgatan 31, 60223 Norrköping, Östergötland. ☎ (11) 101160 **FAX** (11) 186863 **Open:** 9.1-21.12 ✉ 87 ⦿(B) ♂ ⅲ ♿ 🚋 800m

Norrköping - Abborreberg ▲ ⑤Ｅ STF Vandrarhem Norrköping, Abborreberg, Lindö, Box 7100, 60007 Norrköping, Östergötland. ☎ (11) 319344 **Open:** 10.6-18.8 ✉ 30 ⦿(B) ♂ ⅲ 🚌 111

Norrtälje ▲ Brännäsgården Bältartorpsgatan 6, Box 814, 76128 Norrtälje. ☎ (176) 71569 **FAX** (176) 71589 **Open:** 10.6-18.8 ✉ 32 ⦿(B) ♂ ⅲ ✈ 40km 🚌 500m

Norsjö ▲ Prästudden, Prästudden 6, 93591 Norsjö, Västerbotten. ☎ (918) 10181 **Open:** 10.6-11.8 ✉ 24 ⦿(B)

♂ ⅲ 🅾 ♿ 🚋 Bastuträsk 30km 🚌 3km

Nybro ▲ Vasagatan 22, 38232 Nybro, Småland. ☎ (481) 10932 **FAX** (481) 10932 **Open:** 8.1-20.12 ✉ 100 ⦿(B) ♂ ⅲ ♿ 🅾 ♿ 🚋 2km

Nyköping ▲ Brunnsgatan 2, 61132 Nyköping, Södermanland. ☎ (155) 211810 **Open:** 16.5-14.9 ✉ 56 ♂ ⅲ 🚋 1km

Nynäshamn ▲ Nickstabadsvägen 15, 14943 Wynäshamn ☎ (8) 52020834 ✉ 42 ♂ ⅲ 🚋 Nynäshamn from Stockholm ⓇR (1.9-31.5)

Nysäter ▲ Rönngården, 66102 Värmlands Nysäter. ☎ (533) 30030 **Open:** 13.6-10.8 ✉ 25 ⦿(B) ♂ ⅲ 🚋 Karlstad 50km 🚌 200m

Ockelbo ▲ c/o Ockelbo Basket, N Åsgatan 32, 81631 Ockelbo, Gästrikland. ☎ (297) 40201, 42320 **FAX** (297) 42320 ✉ 28 /18 ⦿(B) ♂ 🚿 🚋 Ockelbo 100m 🚌 50m ⓇR (15.9-15.5)

Ödeshög ▲ Hembygdsgården, Södra Vägen 63, 59931 Ödeshög, Östergötland. ☎ (144) 10700 **Open:** 15.5-31.8 ✉ 55 ♂ ⅲ ♿ 🅾

Öhns Gård ▲ Odensåker, 54015 Väring. ☎ (500) 441317 **FAX** (500) 441210 ✉ 50 ⦿(B) ♂ ⅲ ♿ 🅾 🚋 35km 🚌 510 50m ap YH

Ölands Skogsby ▲ 38693 Färjestaden, Öland. ☎ (485) 38395 **Open:** 28.4-31.8 ✉ 70 ⦿(B) ♂ ⅲ 🅾 🚌 103, 413 Kalmar 17km

Omberg ▲ Stocklycke, 59993 Ödeshög, Östergötland. ☎ (144) 33044 **FAX** (144) 33045 ✉ 53 ⦿ ♂ ⅲ 🚌 3km ⓇR (Grps 1.10-31.3)

Örebro ▲ ③Ｓ Fanjunkarevägen 5, 70365 Örebro. ☎ (19) 310240 **FAX**

(19) 310256 ⊷ 118 ▯⊙|(B) ♂ ♦♦♦ ⬚ ⌷⌷⌷⌷
1km

Öreryd Hestra ▲ ⊡CC⊡ STF
Vandrarhem Öreryd, 33027 Hestra. ☎
(370) 337035 **FAX** (370) 337035 ⊷
27 ♂ ♦♦♦ ♿ ⬚ ⊞ ⌷⌷⌷⌷ Hestra 7km ⊞⊞⊞
300m ❽ (2.9-15.6)

Örkelljunga ▲ Eket, 28600
Örkelljunga, Skåne. ☎ (435) 53123
FAX (435) 53660 **Open:** 1.5-31.8 ⊷
16 ▯⊙|(B) ♦♦♦ ⬚ ✈ Ängelholm 20km
⊞⊞⊞ 300m

Örnsköldsvik ▲ Pl 1980, 89027
Överhörnäs, Ångermanland. ☎ (660)
70244 ⊷ 30 ▯⊙|(B) ♂ ♦♦♦ ⊞⊞⊞
Örnsköldsvik 9km ❽ (20.8-10.6)

Orrefors ▲ Backabyggningen,
Silversparregatan 14, 38040 Orrefors.
☎ (481) 30020 **FAX** (481) 30020
Open: 1.5-1.9⊷64 ♂ ♦♦♦ ⬚ ⌷⌷⌷⌷ Nybro
⊞⊞⊞ ap YH

Orsa ▲ Box 95, 79422 Orsa. ☎ (250)
42170 **FAX** (250) 42365 **Open:**
1.12-13.4; 8.5-2.11 ⊷ 68 ▯⊙|(B) ♂ ♦♦♦
⬚ ⌷⌷⌷⌷ Orsa 900m ⊞⊞⊞ 900m

Orust ▲ Tofta gård, Stocken, 47492
Ellös, Bohuslän. ☎ (304) 50380 **Open:**
1.4-1.10 ⊷ 56 ♂ ♦♦♦ ⬚ ❽ (1.4-1.6;
1.9-1.10)

Osby ▲ ⊡CC⊡ Järnvägsgatan 17 (c/o Stora
Hotellet), 28331 Osby, Skåne. ☎ (479)
31830 **FAX** (479) 16222 **Open:**
24.6-7.8 ⊷ 30 ▯⊙|(B) ♂ ♦♦♦ ♿ ⌷⌷⌷⌷
100m ⊞⊞⊞ 100m

Oskarshamn ▲ Åsavägen 8, 57235
Oskarshamn, Småland. ☎ (491) 88198
FAX (491) 81045 ⊷ 130 ♂ ♦♦♦ ⬚ ⌷⌷⌷⌷
200m

Österbybruk ▲ Stråkvägen 3, Box 76,
74063 Österbybruk, Uppland: 43km
NE Uppsala. ☎ (295) 21570 **FAX** (295)
20050 ⊷ 36 ♂ ♦♦♦ ⊞⊞⊞ 823 from
Uppsala 200m ❽ (19.8-10.6)

Österbymo ▲ Ydregården, 57060
Österbymo, Östergötland. ☎ (381)
60103 **Open:** 15.5-31.8 ⊷ 20 ▯⊙| ♦♦♦

Östersund ▲ Södra Gröngatan 34,
83135 Östersund, Jämtland. ☎ (63)
139100 **Open:** 12.6-7.8 ⊷ 100 ♂ ♦♦♦
⌷⌷⌷⌷ 600m ❽ (☎ (63) 102343)

Ottenby ▲ Näsby, 38065 Degerhamn,
Öland. ☎ (485) 62062 **FAX** (485)
62161 ⊷ 146 ▯⊙|(B) ♂ ♦♦♦ ♿ ⬚ ♠ ⌷⌷⌷⌷
Kalmar ap YH ❽ (3.8-24.6)

Överum ▲ Källarbacken 2, Box 19,
59096 Överum, Småland. ☎ (493)
30302 ⊷ 20 ♂ ♦♦♦ ⌷⌷⌷⌷ 100m ⊞⊞⊞
200m

Persåsen ▲ ⊡CC⊡ 84044 Oviken,
Jämtland. ☎ (643) 40180 **FAX** (643)
40105 **Open:** 17.6-18.8 ⊷ 27 ▯⊙| ♂
♦♦♦ ♿ ⬚ ♠ ⌷⌷⌷⌷ 18km

Prässebo ▲ Pl 3606, 46010 Lödöse,
Västergötland. ☎ (520) 667024 **Open:**
15.5-31.8 ⊷ 33 ♂ ♦♦♦ ⊞⊞⊞ Göteborg
50km, Trollhättan 30km ❽ (**Shut:**
☎ (520) 667175)

Ramsele ▲ Turistgården, Box 95,
88040 Ramsele, Ångermanland. ☎
(623) 10510 **Open:** 1.6-31.8 ⊷ 36
▯⊙|(B) ♂ ♦♦♦ ♿ ⌷⌷⌷⌷ Långsele 57km ⊞⊞⊞
1km ❽ (1.1-31.5 ☎ (623) 72580,
10167)

Ramsjö ▲ Viken, 82046 Ramsjö,
Hälsingland. ☎ (651) 50373 **Open:**
15.6-15.8⊷20 ♦♦♦ ⊞⊞⊞ Ljusdal 56km
ap 100m

Ransäter ▲ Geijersgården 1, 68493
Ransäter, Värmland. ☎ (552) 30050
Open: 1.5-31.8 ⊷ 18 ♂ ♦♦♦ ⊞⊞⊞ 1km

Rättvik ▲ Centralgatan, 79530
Rättvik, Dalarna. ☎ (248) 10566 **FAX**
(248) 70394 ⊷ 104 ▯⊙|(B) ♂ ♦♦♦ ♿ ⬚
⌷⌷⌷⌷ 1km ⊞⊞⊞ 1km

Rantajärvi, STF Vandrarhem ▲
Rantajärvi 78, 957 94 Övertorneå ☎

(927) 23000 **FAX** (927) 23123 **Open:**
1.6-31.8 ⊠ 38 ⏉ ⏉ ⏉ ⏉

Regna ▲ Regnagården, 64010 Högsjö.
☎ (151) 70127 **FAX** (151) 70127 ⊠
40 ⏉ ⏉ ⏉ ⏉ ⏉ 100m

Rejmyre, STF Vandrarhem ▲
Metallvägen 9, 610 14 Rejmyre ☎ (11)
86118 **FAX** (11) 87521 **Open:** 1.5-1.9
⊠ 32 ⏉(B) ⏉ ⏉ Norrköping 40km
⏉ 410, 416

Rimforsa ▲ STF Vandrarhem
Rimforsa, Kalvudden, 59041 Rimforsa
☎ (494) 20137 **Open:** 1.5-30.9 ⊠ 25
⏉(B) ⏉ ⏉ ⏉ 2km ⓡ (1.10-30.4
☎ (8) 56032361)

Romelestugan ▲ Box 47, 24013
Genarp, Skåne. ☎ (46) 55073, 55138
⊠ 26 ⏉(B) ⏉ ⏉ ⏉ 3km ⓡ
(1.9-30.4)

Ronneby ▲ Övre Brunnsvägen 54,
37236 Ronneby, Blekinge. ☎ (457)
26300 **FAX** (457) 26300 **Open:**
8.1-16.12 ⊠ 104 ⏉(B) ⏉ ⏉ ⏉ 5km
⏉ 1km

Rörbäck ▲ Bokenäs, PL 15705, 451 96
Uddevalla. ☎ (522) 650190 **Open:**
1.5-30.9 ⊠ 47 ⏉(B) ⏉ ⏉ ⏉ ⏉ ⓡ
(☎ (31) 402740)

Sala ▲ Sofielund, Mellandammen,
73336 Sala, Västmanland. ☎ (224)
12730 ⊠ 28 ⏉ ⏉ ⏉ ⏉ 2km ⓡ
(Grps 15.11-1.2)

Sälen ▲ Gräsheden, Box 58, 78067
Sälen, Dalarna. ☎ (280) 82040 **FAX**
(280) 82045 ⊠ 60 ⏉(B) ⏉ ⏉ ⏉ ⏉
from Malung, Mora

Sandslån ▲ Sandslån 3144, 87052
Nyland. ☎ (612) 50541 **FAX** (612)
50006 **Open:** 15.5-15.9 ⊠ 80 ⏉ ⏉
⏉ ⏉ ⏉ 3km ⏉ 2km ⏉ 200m

Sandviken ▲ Svarvaregatan 26, 81136
Sandviken ☎ (26) 259865 **Open:**

13.6-15.8 ⊠ 69 ⏉(B) ⏉ ⏉ ⏉ 2km
⏉ 1.5km

Sankt Anna ▲ Gamla Färjeläget, 61402
St Anna, Östergötland. ☎ (121) 51312
Open: 1.6-1.9 ⊠ 32 ⏉(B) ⏉ ⏉ ⏉ ⏉
⏉ from Söderköping ap Lagnöbron

SÄRNA (2 Hostels)

Särna - Björkhagen ▲ STF Vandrarhem
Särna, Björkhagen, Box 535, 79090
Särna, Dalarna. ☎ (253) 10308 ⊠ 25
⏉(B) ⏉ ⏉ ⏉ Mora 120km ⏉
Mora/Grövelsjön

Särna - Turistgården ▲ STF
Vandrarhem Särna, Turistgården,
Sjukstugev 4, 79090 Särna, Dalarna. ☎
(253) 10437 ⊠ 37 ⏉(B) ⏉ ⏉ ⏉ ⏉
⏉ Mora 120km ⏉
Mora/Grövelsjön

Säter- Haverö ▲ Hembygdsgården,
84193 Östavall, Medelpad. ☎ (690)
30137 **Open:** 1.6-18.8 ⊠ 14 ⏉ ⏉

Sätra Brunn ▲ ⏉ STF Vandrarhem,
Sätra Brunn 73326, Sala ☎ (224) 54600
FAX (224) 54601 **Open:** 1.5-30.9 ⊠
43 ⏉ ⏉ ⏉ ⏉ Sala 13km ⏉ Sala
13km, Västerås 30km

Sävsjö ▲ Eksjöhovgård, 57691 Sävsjö,
Småland. ☎ (382) 12280 **FAX** (382)
61760 ⊠ 24 ⏉ ⏉ ⏉ ⏉ 1.5km ⓡ
(1.9-15.5)

Saxnäs ▲ ⏉ STF Vandrarhem,
Saxnäs, Kultsjögården Box 6, 91088
Marsfjäll, Lappland. ☎ (940) 70044. ⊠
52 ⏉ ⏉ ⏉ ⏉ Vilhelmina 90km ⏉

Sigtuna ▲ Kyrkans
utbildningscentrum, Manfred
Björkquists allè 12, Box 92, 19322
Sigtuna, Uppland. ☎ (8) 59258478
FAX (8) 59258384 **Open:** 22.6-7.8 ⊠
60 ⏉(B) ⏉ ⏉ ⏉ Märsta (from
Stockholm) + ⏉ 570, 575

Skåne Tranås ▲ Helgonavägen, 27392
Tomelilla, Skåne ☎ (417) 20330 **FAX**

(417) 20330 ✄ 54 ⦿(B) ♂ ♿ 8km
🚌 200m ⓡ (1.9-1.6: Per Ingvar
Carlsson Diligensv 8, 27392 Tomelilla)

Skara ▲ ⟦CC⟧ Vasaparken, 53232 Skara,
Västergötland. ☏ (511) 12165 **FAX**
(511) 20085 ✄ 65 ⦿(B) ♂ ♦♦♦ ♿ ♿
Skövde 🚌 700m

Skäralid-Klippan ▲ STF Vandrarhem,
Skäralid, PL 750, 26070 Ljungbyhed,
Skåne. ☏ (435) 42025 **FAX** (435)
42383 **Open:** 16.4-14.9 (Grps
1.1-31.12) ✄ 29 ♂ ♦♦♦ ♿ 18km 🚌
200m

Skellefteå ▲ Elevhemsgatan 13, 93156
Skellefteå, Västerbotten. ☏ (910) 37283
FAX (910) 37283 **Open:** 15.6-15.8 ✄
40 ⦿(B) ♂ ♦♦♦ ▣ ♿ 3km 🚌 2km
ⓡ (Shut: Skellefteå Camping,
Mossgatan, 93140 Skellefteå ☏ (910)
18855)

Skeppsmyra ☞ Stockholm
(Archipelago)

Skövde ▲ Billingens Stugby &
Camping, Alphyddevägen 54133
Skövde. ☏ (500) 471633 **FAX** (500)
471044 ✄ 18 ♂ ♦♦♦ ▣ ✈ 10km ♿
2km 🚌 250m

Skurup ▲ Bruksgatan 3, 27435
Skurup, Skåne. ☏ (411) 36061 **Open:**
6.6-14.8 ✄ 32 ⦿(B) ♂ ♦♦♦ ▣ ⚙ ♿
600m 🚌 600m

Smådalarö ▲ 13054 Dalarö. ☏ (8)
50153073 **FAX** (8) 50153383 ✄ 40
⦿ ♂ ♦♦♦ ℗ ♿ Haninge 🚌 839
ap Smådalarö ⓡ (1.9-1.6)

Smedjebacken ▲ ⟦CC⟧ Mogavägen 4,
Box 65, 77722 Smedjebacken, Dalarna.
☏ (240) 76645 **FAX** (240) 76645 ✄
70 ⦿(B) ♂ ♦♦♦ ♿ ▣ ⚓ ♿ 2km 🚌
70m

Smygehuk STF Vandrarhem ▲
Kustvägen, P1 314, 23178 Smygehuk
☏ (410) 24583 **FAX** (410) 24509 ✄

43 ⦿(B) ♂ ♦♦♦ ▣ ⛴ Trelleborg 🚌
146, 183 ⓡ (15.9-15.5)

Snöå Bruk ▲ 78051 Dala Järna. ☏ (281)
24018 **FAX** (281) 24018 ✄ 91 ⦿(B)
♦♦♦ ▣ ♨ ♿ Dala Järna 5km 🚌 1km

Söderhamn ▲ ⟦15W⟧ ⟦CC⟧ Mohedsvägen
59, 82692 Söderala Hälsingland ☏
(270) 45233 **FAX** (270) 45326 **Open:**
29.5-1.9 ✄ 35 ♂ ♦♦♦ ♨ ♿ 15km 🚌
100m

Söderköping ▲ Mangelgården, 61430
Söderköping, Östergötland. ☏ (121)
10213 **Open:** 1.6-31.8 ✄ 36 ♂ ♦♦♦ ⚙
🚌 1km

Södertälje ▲ ⟦6SW⟧ Tvetagården, 15192
Södertälje, Södermanland. ☏ (8)
55098025 **FAX** (8) 55098471 ✄ 60
⦿(B) ♂ ♦♦♦ ♿ Södertälje 6km 🚌
784 from ♿

Södra Ljunga ▲ STF Vandrarhem,
Södra Ljunga, 34191 Ljungby,
Småland. ☏ (372) 16011 ✄ 53 ⦿(B)
♂ ♦♦♦ ▣ ⚙ ♿ 14km 🚌 14km

Sollefteå ▲ Hundhotellet, Övergård
7006, 88193 Sollefteå. ☏ (620) 15817
Open: 11.1-20.12 ✄ 26 ⦿(B) ♂ ♦♦♦
⚙ ✈ 35km ♿ Sollefteå 2.5km

Sölvesborg ▲ Ynde Byväg 22, 29492
Sölvesborg. ☏ (456) 19811 **FAX** (456)
19449 **Open:** 8.1-16.12 ✄ 60 ⦿(B)
♂ ♦♦♦ ▣ ⚙ ♿ 3km 🚌 3km

Sorsele ▲ Torggatan 1-2, 92070
Sorsele, Lappland. ☏ (952) 10048
Open: 10.6-9.8 ✄ 24 ⦿(B) ♂ ♦♦♦ ♿
1km 🚌 600m ⓡ (Sorsele
Turistbyrån, Stationsgatan 19, 92070
Sorsele ☏ (952) 10900)

Sproge ▲ Mattsarve Sommargård,
Sproge, 62020 Klintehamn, Gotland. ☏
(498) 241097 **FAX** (498) 241097
Open: 1.5-31.8 ✄ 48 ⦿(B) ♂ ♦♦♦ 🚌
3km

Stafsjö ▲ STF Vandrarhem Stafsjö, Störningsväg 8, 61895 Stavsjö ☎ (11) 393384 🛏 28 👕 🍴 Norrköping 25km 🚌 20m

Stenungsund ▲ Tollenäs, Pl 6109, 44491 Stenungsund. ☎ (303) 82120 **Open:** 15.4-15.10 🛏 50 🍽(B) 👥 ♿ 🚴 ⛵ 🍴 Stenungsund 2km 🚌 500m **ℝ** (1.9-15.10; 15.4-1.6)

STOCKHOLM (4 Hostels)

Stockholm - "af Chapman/ Skeppsholmen" ▲ IBN CC STF Vandrarhem 'af Chapman', Skeppsholmen, 11149 Stockholm. ☎ (8) 6795015 **FAX** (8) 6119875 **Open:** 1.4-15.12 **Shut:** 02.00hrs 🛏 136 🍽(B) 👥 🏢 ✈ Stockholm 🚌 65 **ℝ**

Stockholm - **Skeppsholmen Västra Brobänken** ▲ CC STF Vandrarhem, Skeppsholmen Västra Brobänken, 11149 Stockholm. ☎ (8) 6795017 **FAX** (8) 6117155 **Open:** 5.1-22.12 🛏 152 🍽(B) 👥 ♿ ✈ Stockholm 🚌 65 **ℝ**

STOCKHOLM -
(a) af Chapman, (b) Skeppsholmen"

Stockholm - **Zinkensdamm** ▲ CC Zinkensväg 20, 11741 Stockholm. ☎ (8) 6168100 **FAX** (8) 6168120 🛏 466 🍽(B) 👕 👥 🔲 🅿 🚴 ✈ Stockholm 🆄

T-Centralen; Zinkensdamm (go down stairs from Hornsgatan 103-107) **ℝ** (Grps ☎ (8) 6168118)

STOCKHOLM - Zinkensdamm

Stockholm - **Långholmen** ▲ CC Kronohäktet, Box 9116, 10272 Stockholm. ☎ (8) 6680510 **FAX** (8) 7208575 🛏 254 🍽 👕 👥 ♿ 🏢 🔲 🅿 🚌 40, 54, 66 🆄 Hornstull **ℝ**

STOCKHOLM - Långholmen

Hostels in the Archipelago / *AJ dans l'archipel* / JH im Archipel / *Albergues en el archipiélago*

Bosön ☞ **Bosön**

Finnhamn ▲ Finnhamns Friluftsområde, Box 84, 13025 Ingmarö. ☎ (8) 54246212 **FAX** (8) 54246212 ✉ 76 ♂ � ① ⛴ from Grand Hotell, Stockholm ℝ

Fjärdlång ☞ Fjärdlång

Gällnö ▲ 130 33 Gällnö by, Uppland. ☎ (8) 57166117 **FAX** (8) 57166288 **Open:** 1.5-30.9 ✉ 31 ♂ � ① 🏠 ⚓ ⛴ from Grand Hotell, Stockholm ℝ

Kapellskär ☞ Kapellskär

Lillsved ▲ STF Vandrarhem, Lillsved 13990, Värmdö ☎ (8) 54138530 **FAX** (8) 54138316 **Open:** 1.6-30.8 ✉ 49 ✗|(B) ♂ � ⛴ Waxholmsbolaget 🚌 from Slussen

Siarö ▲ STF Vandrarhem Siarö, Siaröfortet, 18495 Ljusterö ☎ (8) 54242149 **Open:** 1.5-30.9 ✉ 30 ♂ � ① ⚓ ⛴ Waxholmsbolaget ℝ 1-31.5; 1-31.9

Skeppsmyra ▲ **CC** Pensionat Lyckhem, 76042 Björkö. ☎ (176) 94027 **FAX** (176) 94044 ✉ 40 /20 ♂ � ⊡ 🏠 🚲 ⚓ ⛴ Nybrokajen-Stockholm 🚌 636 from Stockholm ℝ (7.8-20.6)

St Kalholmen ▲ c/o Rubin, 13042 Stavsudda, Uppland. ☎ (8) 54246023 **Open:** 11.6-14.8, (Grps 15.8-10.6) ✉ 22 ♂ (no electricity) � ① ⛴ Stockholm ℝ

Utö ☞ Utö

Väddö ☞ Väddö

Stora Karlsö ▲ 62020 Klintehamn. ☎ (498) 240500, 240567 **FAX** (498) 245260 **Open:** 5.5-31.8 ✉ 28 ✗| � ① ⛴ Klintehamn 🚌 Visby ap Klintehamn ℝ

Stora Segerstad ▲ 33021 Reftele. ☎ (371) 23200, 23209 **FAX** (371) 23210

Open: 13.6-8.8 ✉ 52 ✗|(B) ♂ � ⊡ 🚌 Reftele 5km 🚌 Reftele 5km

Storuman ▲ Fack 3, 92321 Storuman, Lappland. ☎ (951) 10428 **Open:** 17.6-11.8 ✉ 57 ♂ � 🚲 🚌 400m ℝ (Shut: ☎ (951) 77730)

Storvallen-Storlien STF Vandrarhem Storvallen ▲ Box 119, 83019 Storlien Jämtland ☎ (647) 70050 ✉ 46 ♂ � ♿ ⊡ ℙ 🚌 Storlien 4km

Strängnäs ▲ Benningeskolan, Solstigen 4, 64540 Strängnäs. ☎ (152) 16861 **FAX** (152) 16862 ✉ 50 ✗|(B) ♂ � ♿ ⊡ 🚌 500m 🚌 500m ℝ (1.9-1.6)

Strömsholm ▲ Sofielund, 73040 Kolbäck, Västmanland. ☎ (220) 43774 **Open:** 15.6-15.8 ✉ 32 ♂ � ♿ 🚌 Kolbäck 4km 🚌

Strömsnäsbruk ▲ **CC** Fågelvägen 2, 28733 Strömsnäsbruk, Småland. ☎ (433) 20050 **FAX** (433) 20050 ✉ 55 ♂ � ⊡ 🚲 🚌

Strömstad ▲ N Kyrkogatan 12, 45230 Strömstad, Bohuslän. ☎ (526) 10193 **Open:** 17.4-16.10 ✉ 76 ♂ � 🚲 🚌 300m ℝ (17.4-31.5; 1.9-16.10)

Strömsund ▲ Tullingsås, PL 6173, 83392 Strömsund, Jämtland. ☎ (670) 30088 ✉ 64 ✗|(B) ♂ � 🚌 9km 🚌 5km

Sundsvall ▲ Box 430, 85106 Sundsvall, Medelpad. ☎ (60) 612119 **FAX** (60) 617801 **Open:** 8.1-22.12 ✉ 150 ✗| ♂ � 🚌 2km

Sunne ▲ Hembygdsvägen 7, 68631 Sunne, Värmland. ☎ (565) 10788 **FAX** (565) 10567 ✉ 71 ✗|(B) ♂ � 🚌 2km

Surahammar ▲ **CC** Bruksgården, Stationsvägen 2, 73531 Surahammar, Västmanland. ☎ (220) 33008 **Open:**

1.6-31.8 ⌷ 68 ⓘ ⑄ ▣ 🚌 200m 🚐 from Västerås 200m

Sveg ▲ Hotell Härjedalen, Vallervägen 11, 82900 Sveg, Härjedalen. ☏ (680) 10338 ⌷ 50 ⓘ ⑄ ⚒ 🚌 1km 🚐 1km ⓡ (1.10-31.5)

Tännäs ▲ STF Vandrarhem Tännäs, Tännäsgården Box 4, 84094 Tännäs ☏ (684) 54067 ⌷ 30 ⓘ ⑄ ⚒ 🚐 100m

Tänndalen ▲ Skarvruets fjällhotel, 84098 Tänndalen. ☏ (684) 22111 FAX (684) 22311 ⌷ 45 🍽 ⓘ ⑄ ⚥ ✈ 140km 🚐 100m

Tjärö ▲ STF Turiststation Tjärö, 37010 Bräkne Hoby. ☏ (454) 60063 FAX (454) 39063 Open: 1.5-30.9 ⌷ 100 ⓘ ⑄ ① ⚒ 🚌 Bräkne Hoby 8km ⓡ (Grps 11-30.9)

Tjörn Rönnäng ▲ STF Vandrarhem Tjörn, Nyponv 5, 47141 Rönnäng Bohuslän. ☏ (304) 677198 ⌷ 38 🍽(B) ⓘ ⑄ ▣ 🚐 ap YH ⓡ (16.8-15.3: Hakefjordsvägen 14, 47141 Rönnäng. ☏ (304) 677419)

Tollarp ▲ Box 33, Lundgrensväg 2, 29010 Tollarp. ☏ (44) 310023 FAX (44) 312304 Open: 14.6-10.8 ⌷ 60 🍽(B) ⓘ ⑄ ✈ 20km 🚌 Kristianstad 20km 🚐 300m

Torestorp ▲ Solbergavägen 2, 51193 Torestorp ☏ (320) 55141 Open: 1.5-15.9 ⌷ 37 🍽(B) ⓘ ♿ 🚌 Kinna 16km 🚐 100m ⓡ (☏ (320) 55141 Per-Ove Esbjörnsson)

Tranås ▲ Hembygdsgården, Ekbergsparken, 57339 Tranås, Småland. ☏ (140) 15166 ⌷ 35 /30 ⓘ ⑄ 🚌 1.5km 🚐 1.5km ⓡ (15.12-15.1)

Tranemo ▲ Västergården, Smedsgatan 2, 51431 Tranemo, Västergötland. ☏ (325) 76710 ⌷ 42 ⓘ ⑄ ♿ ▣ 🚐 200m ⓡ (12.8-12.5)

Trollhättan ▲ ⊡3W ⊞CC STF Vandrarhem Trollhättan, Gulavillan, Tingvallavägen 12, 46132 Trollhättan, Västergötland. ☏ (520) 12960 FAX (520) 15600 ⌷ 40 🍽(B) (15.6-15.8) ⓘ ⑄ 🚴 ✈ 6km 🚌 3km

Trosa ▲ Stensunds folkhögskola, 61991 Trosa, Södermanland. ☏ (156) 53200 FAX (156) 53222 Open: 12.6-19.6; 23.6-19.8 ⌷ 15 ⓘ ⑄ ▣ 🚴 🚐 from Stockholm, Nyköping, Södertälje

Tyresö ▲ Prinsvillan, Kyrkvägen 3, 13560 Tyresö, Södermanland. ☏ (8) 7700304 Open: 1.6-25.9 ⌷ 52 🍽(B) ⓘ ⑄ 🚴 🚐 805, 815, 816 from Gullmarsplan ap Tyresö kyrka

Uddevalla ▲ ⊡6SW Gustafsberg 124, 45191 Uddevalla. Bohuslän. ☏ (522) 15200 FAX (522) 511798 Open: 15.6-16.8 ⌷ 55 🍽 ⓘ ⑄ ▣ ⚓ 🚢 4km 🚌 6km 🚐 4km

Ulricehamn ▲ ⊡2N Skotteksgården, 52390 Ulricehamn, Västergötland. ☏ (321) 13184 FAX (321) 14802 ⌷ 40 🍽 ⓘ ⑄ 🚌 15km 🚐 2km

Ulvön ▲ c/o Kai Näsström, 89015 Ulvöhamn. ☏ (660) 34068 Open: 1.6-31.8 ⌷ 30 ⓘ ⑄ ① 🚢 from Köpmanholmen ⓡ (1.1-31.5 Turistbyrån, Nygatan 18, 89188 Örnsköldsvik)

Umeå ▲ Västra Esplanaden 10, 90326 Umeå ☏ (90) 771650 FAX (90) 771695 ⌷ 87 🍽(B) ⓘ ⑄ ▣ 🚌 450m 🚐 350m

Upplands-Bro ▲ STF Vandrarhem 196 30 Bro, Säbyholm, Naturbruksgymnasiet, 19791 Bro, Uppland. ☏ (8) 58242781 FAX (8) 58242693 Open: 14.6-13.8 ⌷ 40 ⓘ ℗

Uppsala ▲ ⊡6S Sunnersta Herrgård, Sunnerstavägen 24, 75651 Uppsala,

Uppland. ✆ (18) 324220 **Open:** 1.5-31.8 🛏 84 ⛺(B) 🚻 ♿ 🚂 6km 🚌 20 6km

Utö ▲ 🆑 Gruvbyn, 13056 Utö, Södermanland. ✆ (8) 50157660 **FAX** (8) 50157265 **Open:** 9.1-15.12 🛏 44 ⛺ 🚻 ♿ ① 🗑 ⛴ 🚲 ⛴ Strömkajen 🚂 Västerhaninge + 🚌 846 Årsta + ⛴ 🆁 ● Military area, permission from Swedish police required

Väddö ▲ Älmsta, Box 9, 76040 Väddö, Uppland. ✆ (176) 50078 **Open:** 4.7-17.8 🛏 31 🚻 ♿ 🚲 🚌 from Norrtälje

Vadstena ▲ Skänningegatan 20, Box 28, 59221 Vadstena, Östergötland. ✆ (143) 10302 **FAX** (143) 10404 🛏 65 ⛺(B) 🚻 ♿ 🗑 🚂 Mjölby 22km 🚌 ap YH 🆁 (21.8-12.6)

Vålådalen ▲ 🆑 83012 Vålådalen. ✆ (647) 35110 **FAX** (647) 35191 🛏 37 ⛺ 🚻 ♿ ⚓ 🚂 Undersåker 27km 🚌 Undersåker 27km ap YH

Vänersborg ☞ Hunneberg

Vara ▲ Folkhögskolan, Badhusgatan, Box 145, 53481 Vara, Västergötland. ✆ (512) 10838 **FAX** (512) 12702 **Open:** 23.6-10.8 🛏 35 ⛺(B) 🚻 ♿ 🚂 800m 🚌 800m 🆁 (Turistbyrån, Torggatan, 53400 Vara ✆ (512) 31220)

Varberg ▲ 7S Vare Kommungård, Himle, 43200 Varberg, Halland. ✆ (340) 41173 **Open:** 1.4-30.9 🛏 43 🚻 ♿ 🚂 8km 🚌 1.5km

Värmskog ▲ 67195 Klässbol, Värmland. ✆ (570) 61134 **Open:** 16.5-31.8 🛏 28 🚻 ♿ 🚂 Grums 19km

Värnamo ▲ 🆑 Tättingvägen 1, 33142 Värnamo. ✆ (370) 19898 **FAX** (370) 18235 🛏 98 ⛺(B) 🚻 ♿ 🗑 🚂 1.5km 🚌 1.5km 🆁 (1.9-31.5)

Västerås ▲ 5SW 🆑 KFUK-KFUM, Lövuddens konferens och fritidscenter, 72591 Västerås, Västmanland. ✆ (21) 185230 **FAX** (21) 123036 **Open:** 2.1-23.12 🛏 62/76 ⛺ 🚻 ♿ 🚂 5km 🚌 25

Växjö ▲ 6NE Evedal, 35263 Växjö, Småland. ✆ (470) 63070 **FAX** (470) 63216 🛏 65 ⛺(B) 🚻 ♿ 🗑 ⚓ 🚂 6km 🚌 Su only 🆁 (1.9-31.5)

Vilhelmina ▲ Elevhemmet, Tallåsvägen 34, 91232 Vilhelmina, Lappland. ✆ (940) 14165 **Open:** 14.6-3.8 🛏 78 ⛺(B) 🚻 ♿ ♿ 🚲 🚂 1km 🚌 1km 🆁 (Turistbyrån, Volgsjövägen 29, 91232 Vilhelmina ✆ (940) 15270, 15271)

Vimmerby ▲ 4E Hörestadhult, 59800 Vimmerby, Småland. ✆ (492) 10225 **Open:** 12.6-14.8 🛏 32 ⛺(B) 🚻 ♿ 🚂 4km 🚌 5km

Visby ▲ Hus 55, Gamla A7 Området, 62182 Visby. ✆ (498) 269842 **Open:** 9.6-8.8 🛏 99 ⛺(B) 🚻 ♿ 🗑 ⛴ Visby 🚌 200m

Visingsö, STF Vandrarhem ▲ Kvarnlyckan, 560 34 Visingsö ✆ (390) 40191, (708) 794315 **Open:** 1.5-1.9 🛏 29 🚻 ♿ ①

Vittsjö ▲ STF Vandrarhem Vittsjö, EFS- Pensionat Lehultsväg 13, 28022 Vittsjö ✆ (451) 22087 **FAX** (451) 22087 **Open:** 1.5-30.9 🛏 30 ⛺(B) 🚻 🚻 🚌 From Markaryd or Hässleholm 700m

Voxnabruk ▲ Voxnadalens Kanot, Voxna 21, 82893 Voxnabruk ✆ (271) 41150 **FAX** (271) 43080 🛏 28 🚻 🚲 ⚓ 🚂 Bollnäs 🚌 300m 🆁 (Grps 1.11-30.4)

Ystad ▲ Kantarellen, Sandskog, Fritidsvägen, 27160 Ystad, Skåne. ✆ (411) 66566 **FAX** (411) 10913 🛏 80 ⛺(B) 🚻 ♿ 🗑 🚂 2km 🚌 304, 572, 573

MOUNTAIN CENTRES / CENTRES DE MONTAGNE / BERGZENTREN / CENTROS DE MONTAÑA

(For further information, contact STF / *Pour de plus amples renseignements, s'adresser à STF* / Nach weiteren Angaben STF fragen / *Si se desea informacion más amplia, es preciso dirigirse a STF*)

1 Lappland

Abisko 98107 Abisko. ☎ (980) 40200 Open: 22.2-14.9 🛏 400 ● 140-270 SEK 🍴 🚻 🚂🚃

Kebnekaise 98129 Kiruna. ☎ (980) 55000 Open: 8.3-3.5; 14.6-14.9 🛏 194 ● 240-290 SEK 🍴 🚻

Kvikkjokk 96202 Kvikkjokk. ☎ (971) 21022 Open: 15.3-3.5; 14.6-14.9 🛏 58 ● 150-220 SEK 🍴 🚻 🚂🚃

Ritsem 98299 Gällivare. ☎ (973) 42030 Open: 28.2-3.5; 28.6-27.9 🛏 40 ● 160 SEK 🚻 🚂🚃

Saltoluokta 98299 Gällivare. ☎ (973) 41010 Open: 9.3-5.5; 15.6-15.9 🛏 87 ● 170-250 SEK 🍴 🚻 🚂🚃

2 Jämtland

Blåhammaren 83015 Duved. ☎ (647) 70120 Open: 22.2-3.5; 28.6-14.9 🛏 46 ● 170-300 SEK 🍴 🚻

Storulvån 83015 Duved. ☎ (647) 72200 Open: 22.2-3.5; 28.6-14.9 🛏 144 ● 170-375 SEK 🍴 🚻 🚂🚃

Sylarna 83015 Duved. ☎ (647) 75010 Open: 24.2-5.5; 28.6-14.9 🛏 90 ● 170-285 SEK 🚻

Vålådalen 83012 Vålådalen. ☎ (647) 35110 Open: 21.12-20.4; 14.6-14.9 🛏 210 ● 140-400 SEK 🍴 🚻 🚂🚃

3 Härjedalen

Helags 84035 Ljungdalen. ☎ (687) 20150 Open: 22.2-3.5; 28.6-14.9 🛏 72 ● 170-195 SEK 🚻

4 Dalarna

Grövelsjön 79091 Idre. ☎ (253) 23090 Open: 22.12-5.1; 1.2-20.4; 14.6-14.9 🛏 150 ● 200-480 SEK 🍴 🚻 🚂🚃

MOUNTAIN HUTS / CABANES DE MONTAGNE / BERGHÜTTEN / CABAÑAS DE MONTAÑA

(For further information, contact STF / *Pour de plus amples renseignements, s'adresser à STF* / *Nach weiteren Angaben STF fragen* / *Si se desea información más amplia, es preciso dirigirse a STF*)

Most of these mountain huts are far from roads and railways and are situated near rough tracks; these tracks cover more than 4,700km, the best known being Kungsleden, in Lappland. ● 145-195 SEK. / *La plupart de ces cabanes de montagne sont loin des routes et des chemins de fer et se trouvent près de sentiers primitifs; ces sentiers couvrent plus de 4700km - le mieux connu est Kungsleden, en Laponie.* ● *145-195 SEK.* / Die meisten dieser Berghütten sind weit von einer Strasse oder Bahnlinie abseits an Wanderwegen gelegen; diese erstrecken sich über mehr als 4700km - der bekannteste ist Kungsleden, in Lappland. ● 145-195 SEK. / *La mayoría de las cabañas de montaña están alejados de las carreteras y de los ferrocarriles y se encuentran cerca de senderos agrestes que cubren más de 4.700km - el más conocido es el Kungsleden, en Laponia.* ● *145-195 SEK.*

1 Lappland	1 Lappland	1 Lappland	1 Lappland	3 Härjedalen
Pältsa	Tarfala	Sitojaure	Aigert	Helags
Pålnoviken	Hukejaure	Aktse	Servejokk	Fältjägarn
Jieprenjåkk	Sitasjaure	Pårte	Syterstugan	Skedbro
Kårsavagge	Singi	Pieskehaure	Viterskalet	Rogen
Abiskojaure	Kaitumjaure	Vaimok	Tärnasjöstugan	
Unna Allakas	Teusajaure	Såmmarlappa		4 Dalarna
Alesjaure	Vakkotavare	Tarrekaise	2 Jämtland	Storrödtjärn
Tjäktja	Vaisaluokta	Njunjes	Anaris	
Vistas	Akka		Lunndörren	
Nallo	Kutjaure		Vålåvalen	
Sälka			Stensdalen	
			Gåsen	

SWITZERLAND
SUISSE
SCHWEIZ
SUIZA

ASSURED STANDARD

**Schweizer Jugendherbergen, Schaffhauserstrasse 14,
Postfach 161,
8042 Zürich, Switzerland.**

☏ (41) (1) 3601414
FAX (41) (1) 3601460
Email: booking office@youthhostel.ch
Internet: http://www.youthhostel.ch

Office Hours: Monday-Friday, 08.00-12.00hrs and
13.00-18.00hrs

Travel Section: Jugi Tours, Schaffhauserstrasse 14,
Postfach 161, 8042 Zürich, Switzerland.

☏ (41) (1) 3601400
FAX (41) (1) 3601444

IBN Booking Centres for outward bookings:
■   Zurich-Jugi Tours, *via Travel Section above.*
Siège Romand, Av Léopold Robert 65.

Capital:	Bern
Language:	French/German/Italian/Romansh
Currency:	S Fr (franc)
Population:	7,021,200
Size:	41,288 sq km

SWITZERLAND

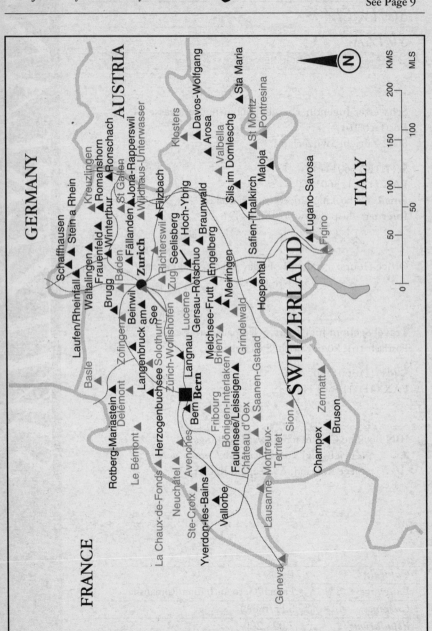

ENGLISH

SWISS HOSTELS

Swiss Youth Hostels are renowned for their quality and are all participating in Hostelling International's new Assured Standards Scheme see page six for details, whether a tranquil lakeside location or a base for your annual ski-ing trip. Most have family rooms.

In most Swiss Youth Hostels you must check out by 09.30hrs and have checked in by 20.00hrs. Opening times vary, so check with the hostel or get hold of a copy of the Swiss guide.

Expect to pay in the region of 17.50-30.00SFr per night including bed linen and breakfast. Breakfast is not included in hostels with prices below 17.50SFr. A second night reduction of 2.50SFr is offered. Where there are self-catering facilities a small charge is made for fuel.

PASSPORTS AND VISAS

Many visitors require only a valid passport to enter Switzerland, but you should contact the nearest Swiss embassy for details.

BANKING HOURS

Banks are open Monday to Friday 08.30-12.00hrs and 14.00-16.30hrs.

POST OFFICE

Post offices are open Monday to Friday 07.30-12.00hrs and 13.45-18.00hrs. They are also open on Saturdays 08.30-11.00hrs.

SHOPPING HOURS

Shops are open Monday to Friday 08.00-12.30hrs and 13.30-18.30hrs, Saturday 08.00-12.30hrs and 13.30-16.00hrs. In big cities shops do not tend to close at lunch time.

TRAVEL

Rail
Rail travel is regular and efficient. Eurail and Inter-Rail cards are valid, though only on state-run railways.

Bus
The Swiss bus service is both regular and efficient.

Ferry
50% reduction on steamers crossing Lake Constance and Lake Geneva for Inter-Rail holders, Eurail holders may be offered free passage.

Driving
An international driving licence is required.

TELEPHONE INFORMATION

International Code	Country Code	Main City Area Codes	
00	41	Basle	61
		Bern	31
		Geneva	22
		Lausanne	21
		Zurich	1

$$\boxed{\text{FRANÇAIS}}$$

AUBERGES DE JEUNESSE SUISSES

Les auberges de jeunesse suisses sont réputées pour leur qualité et participent toutes au nouveau Plan Hostelling International pour la Garantie des Normes en auberge (voir page 15 pour plus de détails), qu'elles soient situées au bord d'un lac tranquille ou qu'elles servent de base pour vos vacances de sports d'hiver annuelles. La plupart ont des chambres familiales.

Dans la plupart des auberges suisses, les visiteurs doivent quitter leur chambre à 9h30 et en prendre possession à 20h. Les heures d'ouverture varient; il est donc conseillé de vérifier auprès de l'auberge ou d'obtenir un exemplaire du guide suisse.

Une nuit vous coûtera entre 17,50 et 30,00 FS, petit déjeûner et draps compris. Le petit-déjeûner n'est pas compris lorsque la nuitée n'atteint pas les 17,50 FS. Une réduction de 2,50 FS est offerte pour une deuxième nuit. Dans les auberges offrant la possibilité de cuisiner, une petite contribution est demandée pour l'énergie consommée.

PASSEPORTS ET VISAS

Un passeport valide sera suffisant pour de nombreux visiteurs mais il est prudent de vérifier auprès de l'Ambassade suisse la plus proche pour plus de détails.

HEURES D'OUVERTURE DES BANQUES

Les banques sont ouvertes du lundi au vendredi de 8h30 à 12h et de 14h à 16h30.

BUREAUX DE POSTE

Les bureaux de poste sont ouverts du lundi au vendredi de 7h30 à 12h et de 13h45 à 18h. Ils sont aussi ouverts le samedi de 8h30 à 11h.

HEURES D'OUVERTURE DES MAGASINS

Les magasins sont ouverts du lundi au vendredi de 8h à 12h30 et de 13h30 à 18h30. Le samedi, ils ouvrent de 8h à 12h30 et de 13h30 à 16h. Dans les grandes villes, les magasins ont tendance à ne pas fermer pour midi.

DEPLACEMENTS

Trains
Le système ferroviaire fonctionne bien et les trains sont réguliers. Les cartes Eurail et Inter-Rail sont valides seulement sur les réseaux gérés par l'état.

Autobus
Le système d'autobus suisse fonctionne bien et les bus sont réguliers.

Ferry-boats
Les personnes munies de cartes Inter-Rail bénéficient d'une réduction de 50% sur les vapeurs assurant la traversée du lac de Constance et du lac de Genève. Les personnes munies de cartes Eurail pourront peut-être traverser gratuitement.

Automobiles
Les conducteurs doivent être munis d'un permis de conduire international.

TELEPHONE

Indicatif International	Indicatif du Pays	Indicatifs régionaux des Villes principales	
00	41	Bâle	61
		Berne	31
		Genève	22
		Lausanne	21
		Zurich	1

DEUTSCH

SCHWEIZER JUGENDHERBERGEN

Die Schweizer Jugendherbergen sind für ihre Qualität bekannt und sind an dem 'Zugesicherten Standardsplan' beteiligt (siehe Seite 24 für Einzelheiten). Das gilt sowohl für die Herbergen an ruhigen Seen als auch für die von Skiläufern benutzten Herbergen. Die meisten haben Familienzimmer.

Die meisten Schweizer Jugendherbergen muß man am Tag der Abreise bis 9.30 Uhr verlassen, und am Tag der Ankunft muß man vor 20.00 Uhr eintreffen. Die Öffnungszeiten sind unterschiedlich. Erkundigen Sie sich daher bei der jeweiligen Herberge, oder besorgen Sie sich ein Exemplar des Schweizer Verzeichnisses.

Es ist mit einem Preis von 17,50-30,00 sfr pro Nacht, einschließlich Bettwäsche und Frühstück, zu rechnen. In Jugendherbergen mit Preisen unter 17,50 sfr ist das Frühstück nicht eingeschlossen. Für die zweite Nacht wird meist ein Nachlaß von 2,50 sfr gewährt. Wo es Einrichtungen für Selbstversorger gibt, wird für Brennstoff nach abgelesenem Verbrauch eine kleine Gebühr erhoben.

PÄSSE UND VISA

Viele Besucher brauchen für die Einreise in die Schweiz nur einen gültigen Reisepaß. Erkundigen Sie sich aber bitte ausführlich bei der nächsten schweizerischen Botschaft.

GESCHÄFTSSTUNDEN DER BANKEN

Banken sind montags bis freitags von 8.30-12.00 Uhr und von 14.00-16.30 Uhr geöffnet.

POSTÄMTER

Postämter sind montags bis freitags von 7.30-12.00 Uhr und von 13.45-18.00 Uhr geöffnet. Sie sind auch samstags von 8.30-11.00 Uhr geöffnet.

LADENÖFFNUNGSZEITEN

Die Geschäfte sind montags bis freitags von 8.00-12.30 Uhr und von 13.30-18.30 Uhr und samstags von 8.00-12.30 Uhr und von 13.30-16.00 Uhr geöffnet. In Großstädten machen die Geschäfte im allgemeinen keine Mittagspause.

REISEN

Eisenbahn

Die Züge sind pünktlich, und die Eisenbahnverbindungen sind gut. Eurail- und Inter-Rail-Karten sind in der Schweiz nur auf staatlich betriebenen Strecken gültig.

Busse

In der Schweiz gibt es gute Busverbindungen und einen regelmäßigen Busverkehr.

Fähren

Inhaber einer Inter-Rail-Karte erhalten auf Dampfern über den Bodensee und den Genfer See 50 % Ermäßigung. Inhaber einer Eurail-Karte werden oft kostenlos mitgenommen.

Autofahren

Es wird ein internationaler Führerschein verlangt.

FERNSPRECHINFORMATIONEN

Internationale Kennzahl	Landes-Kennzahl	größere Städte - Ortsnetzkennzahlen	
00	41	Basel	61
		Bern	31
		Genf	22
		Lausanne	21
		Zürich	1

ESPAÑOL

ALBERGUES DE JUVENTUD SUIZOS

Los albergues juveniles suizos son reconocidos por su calidad y todos participan en el nuevo Plan de Hostelling International de Normas Garantizadas (véase la página 33 para más información), ya se encuentren junto a la tranquilidad de un lago o en estaciones de esquí. La mayoría disponen de habitaciones familiares.

En la mayor parte de los albergues juveniles suizos hay que dejar la habitación antes de las 09.30 horas y registrarse a la llegada antes de las 20.00 horas. El horario de apertura varía, por lo que se recomienda confirmarlo con el albergue deseado o hacerse con un ejemplar de la guía suiza.

Se paga alrededor de 17,50 - 30,00 SFr. por noche incluyendo ropa de cama y desayuno. Se ofrece un descuento de 2,50 SFr. para la segunda noche. El desayuno no está incluido en el precio de la estancia si éste es menos de 17,50 SFr. En los albergues que disponen de cocina para huéspedes se cobra una pequeña tarifa por el combustible que se haya gastado.

PASAPORTES Y VISADOS

En su mayor parte, los visitantes sólo necesitan un pasaporte válido para entrar en Suiza, pero se recomienda dirigirse a la embajada suiza más cercana para confirmarlo.

HORARIO DE BANCOS

Los bancos abren de lunes a viernes de 08.30 a 12.00 horas y de 14.00 a 16.30 horas.

CASAS DE CORREO

Las casas de correo abren de lunes a viernes de 07.30 a 12.00 horas y de 13.45 a 18.00 horas. También abren los sábados de 08.30 a 11.00 horas.

HORARIO COMERCIAL

Las tiendas abren de lunes a viernes de 08.00 a 12.30 horas y de 13.30 a 18.30 horas, los sábados de 08.00 a 12.30 horas y de 13.30 a 16.00 horas. En las grandes ciudades las tiendas tienden a no cerrar a la hora del almuerzo.

DESPLAZAMIENTOS

Tren
Los trenes son regulares y rápidos. Las tarjetas Eurail e Inter-Rail son válidas, pero sólo en los servicios estatales.

Autobús
El servicio de autobús suizo es regular y rápido.

Ferry
Descuento del 50% en los barcos a vapor que cruzan el lago de Constanza y el lago de Ginebra para los titulares de tarjetas Inter-Rail. Los titulares de tarjetas Eurail tienen la posibilidad de obtener pasaje gratuito.

Coche
Se necesita un permiso de conducir internacional.

INFORMACION TELEFONICA

Código Internacional	Código Nacional	Indicativo de área de las Ciudades principales	
00	41	Basilea	61
		Berna	31
		Ginebra	22
		Lausana	21
		Zurich	1

DISCOUNTS AND CONCESSIONS

Many hostels offer discounts off tourist attractions, transport fees, sports and leisure facilities etc.

Arosa ▲ Seewaldstr, 7050 Arosa (Graubünden). ☎ (81) 3771397 **FAX** (81) 3771397 **Open:** 1.1-12.4; 21.6-18.10; 14-31.12 ⊭ 155 ⠀⠀ ᵇᵇ inc ⠀ ✚✚✚ ⠀ ⠀ Alt 1800m ✈ Zürich 147km ⠀ Arosa 800m

Avenches ▲ IBN CC rue du Lavoir 5, 1580 Avenches (Vaud). ☎ (26) 6752666 **FAX** (26) 6752717 **Open:** 1.3-16.11 ⊭ 76 ᵇᵇ inc ⠀ ✚✚✚ ⠀ ⠀ ✈ Genève 138km ⠀ Avenches 1.5km ⠀ Rest. Croix Blanc

Baden ▲ IBN CC Kanalstr 7, 5400 Baden (Aargau). ☎ (56) 2216736 **FAX** (56) 2217660 **Open:** 14.3-23.12 ⊭ 84 ᵇᵇ inc ⠀ ✚✚✚ ⠀ ⠀ ✈ Zürich 19km ⠀ Baden 1km ⠀ 3, 4, 7 500m ap Kantonsschule

Basle ▲ 1 SE IBN CC St Alban-Kirchrain 10, 4052 Basle. ☎ (61) 2720572 **FAX** (61) 2720833 **Open:** 1.1-24.12 ⊭ 197 ᵇᵇ inc ⠀ ✚✚✚ ⠀ ⠀ ✈ Basel 7km ⠀ Basel 1km ⠀ 2100m ap Kunstmuseum

Beinwil am See ▲ CC Seestrasse 71, 5712 Beinwil am See (Aargau). ☎ (62) 7711883 **FAX** (62) 7716123 **Open:** 14.2-14.12 ⊭ 98 ᵇᵇ inc ⠀ ✚✚✚ ⠀ ⠀ ✈ Zürich 30km ⠀ Beinwil 800m

Le Bémont ▲ IBN CC 2877 Le Bémont (Jura). ☎ (32) 9511707 **FAX** (39) 9512413 **Open:** 2.2-1.12 ⊭ 96 ᵇᵇ inc ⠀ ✚✚✚ ⠀ ⠀ ✈ Basel 77km ⠀ Le Bémont 100m

BASLE

Bern ▲ 1 SE 'Jugendhaus',
Weihergasse 4, 3005 Bern. ☎ (31)
3116316 **FAX** (31) 3125240 **Open:**
1-12.1; 27.1-31.12 **Shut:** 24.00-07.00hrs
🛏 186 🍴 ♿ 🔲 ⛭ 🅿 ✈ Bern 10km,
Zürich 120km 🚂 Bern 800m

BERN

Bönigen- Interlaken ▲ IBN CC
Aareweg 21, Am See, 3806 Bönigen
(Bern). ☎ (33) 8224353 **FAX** (33)
8232058 **Open:** 15.3-15.12 🛏 150
BB inc 🍴 ♿ 🔲 ⛭ 🅿 ⛵ ✈ Zürich 170km
🚂 Interlaken-Ost 1.5km 🚌 1200m
ap Lütschinen Brücke

Braunwald ▲ CC 'Im Gyseneggli',
8784 Braunwald (Glarus). ☎ (55)
6431356 **FAX** (55) 6432435 **Open:**
1.1-31.3; 15.6-19.10; 12-31.12 🛏 82
BB inc 🍴 ♂ ♿ ⛭ ⛷ Alt 1400m ✈ Zürich
87km 🚂 Linthal 4km ● Cable Car
Standseilbahn 2km

Brienz ▲ IBN CC Strandweg 10, am
See, 3855 Brienz (Bern). ☎ (33)
9511152 **FAX** (36) 9512260 **Open:**
2.5-22.10 🛏 86 BB inc 🍴 ♂ ♿ ⛭
⛵ ✈ Zürich 201km 🚂 Brienz 1km

Brugg ▲ CC Im Hof 11, Schlösschen
Altenburg, 5200 Brugg (Aargau). ☎
(56) 4411020 **FAX** (56) 4423820
Open: 1.3-1.12 **Shut:** 23.00-06.30hrs

🛏 52 BB inc 🍴 ♂ ♿ 🏠 ⛭ 🅿 ✈ Zürich
25km 🚂 Brugg 1km

Bruson △ 1934 Bruson (Valais). ☎ (27)
7762356 **FAX** (27) 7761312 **Open:**
1.1-30.4; 1.6-31.10; 1-31.12 🛏 40
🍴 (B) ♂ ♿ ⛷ ✈ Genève 146km 🚂
Le Châble 2km 🚌 Bruson 500m

Château-d'Oex ▲ IBN CC Les Riaux,
1837 Château- d'Oex (Vaud). ☎ (26)
9246404 **FAX** (29) 9245843 **Open:**
1.1-19.10; 20-31.12 🛏 54 BB inc 🍴 ♿
♿ ⛭ 🅿 ⛷ ✈ Genève 148km 🚂
Château d'Oex 800m

La Chaux-de-Fonds ▲ IBN CC rue
du Doubs 34, 2300 La Chaux-de-Fonds
(Neuchâtel). ☎ (32) 9684315 **FAX** (32)
9682518 **Open:** 1.1-2.11; 27-31.12 🛏
80 BB inc 🍴 ♂ ♿ ♿ 🔲 ⛭ 🅿 ⛷ ✈ Genève
145km 🚂 La Chaux-de-Fonds 800m
🚌 4 ap Bois-du-Petit Château

Davos- Wolfgang △ CC 'Höhwald',
7265 Davos-Wolfgang (Graubünden).
☎ (81) 4161484 **FAX** (81) 4165055
Open: 1.1-20.4; 7.6-26.10; 13-31.12
🛏 75 BB inc 🍴 ♂ ♿ ⛭ 🅿 ⛷ Alt 1570m
⛵ ✈ Zürich 145km 🚂 Davos-
Wolfgang 1km 🚌 ap Wolfgang

Delémont ▲ IBN CC Route de Bâle
185, 2800 Delémont (Jura). ☎ (32)
4222054 **FAX** (32) 4228830 **Open:**
1.3-7.12 🛏 80 BB inc 🍴 ♂ ♿ ♿ 🔲 ✈
Genève 160km 🚂 Delémont 1.5km
🚌 Morepont 500m

Engelberg ▲ Berghaus, Dorfstr 80,
6390 Engelberg (Obwalden). ☎ (41)
6371292 **FAX** (41) 6374988 **Open:**
1.1-20.4; 18.5-15.11; 30.11-31.12 🛏
150 BB inc 🍴 ♿ ⛭ ⛷ ✈ Zürich 150km
🚂 Engelberg 800m

Figino ▲ IBN CC Via Casoro 2, 6918
Figino (Ticino) ☎ (91) 9951151 **FAX**
(91) 9951070 **Open:** 1.3-26.10 **Shut:**
23.00-06.00hrs 🛏 160 BB inc 🍴 ♂
individuals & families only ♿ ⛭ 🅿 ⛵

✈ Zürich 180km ⛴ Lugano 8km 🚂
Lugano 8km 🚌 100m ap Casoro

Filzbach ▲ 'Lihn' Blaukreuz Kurs-und Ferienzentrum, 8876 Filzbach (Glarus). ☎ (55) 6141342 **FAX** (55) 6141707 **Open:** 1.1-6.12; 25-31.12 ⊠ 50 BBinc
🍴 ♿ ⛪ 🅿 ⚲ ✈ Zürich 71km 🚂
Näfels - Mollis 6km 🚌 800m ap Post Filzbach

Frauenfeld ▲ Rüegerholz, Festhüttenstr 22, 8500 Frauenfeld (Thurgau). ☎ (52) 7213680 **Open:** 07.00-10.00hrs, 17.00-22.00hrs, 1-31.1; 1.3-31.10; 1-31.12 ⊠ 40 ⚲ 🅿 ✈ Zürich 50km 🚂 Frauenfeld 1km 🚌 Altersheim 200m

Fribourg ▲ IBN CC 2 rue de l'Hôpital, 1700 Fribourg. ☎ (26) 3231916 **FAX** (26) 3231940 ⊠ 90 BBinc 🍴 ⚲ ♿ 🅿 ✈ Genève 138km 🚂 Fribourg 500m 🚌 1, 3, 7 100m ap Place Phyton

Genève ▲ 1S IBN CC 30 rue Rothschild, 1202 Genève. ☎ (22) 7326260 **FAX** (22) 7383987 ⊠ 350 BBinc 🍴 ⚲ ♿ ⛪ ✈ Genève 2km 🚂 Genève-Cornavin 1km 🚃 1 100m ap Palais Wilson

GENÈVE

Gersau-Rotschuo ▲ CC PO Box 159, Rotschuo, 6442 Gersau (Schwyz). ☎

(41) 8281277 **FAX** (41) 8281277 **Open:** 2.3-30.11 **Shut:** From 22.30hrs ⊠ 120 BBinc 🍴 ⚲ ♿ ⛪ 🅿 ⚲ ✈ Zürich 60km ⛴ Vitznau 2km 🚂 Brunnen + Kussnacht 🚌 Rotschuo 500m Ⓡ

Grindelwald ▲ IBN CC Terrassenweg, 3818 Grindelwald (Bern). ☎ (33) 8531009 **FAX** (33) 8535029 **Open:** 1.1-19.4; 17.5-31.10; 19-31.12 ⊠ 125 BBinc 🍴 🔲 ⛪ 🅿 ⚲ ✈ Zürich 200km 🚂 Grindelwald 1km 🚌 Gaggi 100m Ⓡ

Gstaad ☞ **Saanen-Gstaad**

Herzogenbuchsee △ Gasthof/Hotel zum Kreuz, Kirchgasse 1, 3360 Herzogenbuchsee (Bern). ☎ (62) 9616031 **FAX** (62) 9616598 **Open:** 07.30-22.30hrs, (Mon- Sat) 07.30-17.30hrs (Sun), 4.1-24.12 ⊠ 33 BBinc 🍴 ⛪ 🅿 ✈ Zürich 100km 🚂 Herzogenbuchsee 800m

Hoch-Ybrig ▲ CC Fuederegg, 8842 Hoch-Ybrig (Schwyz). ☎ (55) 4141766 **FAX** (55) 4142065 **Open:** 1.1-14.4; 2.7-30.10; 5-31.12 ⊠ 80 BBinc 🍴 ⚲ ♿ ♿ ⛪ ✈ Zürich 80km 🚂 Einsiedeln 🚌 Weglosen ● Cable Car LSB 1km

Hospental ▲ Gotthardstrasse, 6493 Hospental (Uri). ☎ (41) 8871889, **Open:** 1.1-14.4; 16.5-14.10; 16-31.12 ⊠ 65 ⚲ ♿ 🅿 ✈ Zürich 190km 🚂 Hospental 800m 🚌 200m

Interlaken ☞ **Bönigen**

Jona-Rapperswil ▲ CC 'Busskirch', Hessenhofweg 10, 8645 Jona (St Gallen). ☎ (55) 2109927 **FAX** (55) 2109928 **Open:** 31.1-2.11 ⊠ 74 BBinc 🍴 ♿ ♿ ⛪ 🅿 ✈ Zürich 64km 🚂 Rapperswil 1.5km or Blumenau 500m 🚌 Obersee 200m 🚃 Busskirch

Klosters ▲ IBN CC 'Soldanella', Talstr 73, 7250 Klosters (Graubünden).

📞 (81) 4221316 **FAX** (81) 4225209
Open: 1.1-27.4; 20.6-26.10; 19-31.12
✉ 84 [BB]inc 🍽👨 ⛃ 🅿 ⏱ Alt 1250m
✈ Zürich 140km 🚆 Klosters 800m
Ⓡ

Kreuzlingen ▲ [IBN] [CC] Villa
Hörnliberg, Promenadenstr 7, 8280
Kreuzlingen (Thurgau). 📞 (71)
6882663 **FAX** (71) 6884761 Open:
1.3-30.11 ✉ 97 [BB]inc 🍽👨 🅿 ⛃ 🚘
♨ ✈ Zürich 70km 🚢 Kreuzlingen
🚆 Kreuzlingen-Hafen 800m

Langnau im Emmental ▲ Mooseggstr
32, 3550 Langnau (Bern). 📞 (34)
4024526 **Open**: 1.1-7.2; 17.2-19.9;
13.10-31.12 ✉ 45 ♂ 👨 ⛃ 🚘 ✈
Zürich 90km 🚆 Langnau 800m

Laufen △ [CC] Schloss Laufen am
Rheinfall, 8447 Dachsen (Zürich). 📞
(52) 6596152 **FAX** (52) 6596039
Open: 28.2-30.11 ✉ 87 [BB]inc 🍽 ♂ 👨
🚘 ⛃ 🚘 ✈ Zürich 60km 🚆
Dachsen/Neuhausen "Schloss Laufen"
🚊 1, 2, 9 800m ap Neuhausen

Lausanne ▲ [CC] Jeunotel, Ch.du Bois
de- Vaux 36, 1007 Lausanne. 📞 (21)
6260222 **FAX** (21) 6260226 ✉ 240
[BB]inc 🍽 ♂ 👨 ♿ 🅿 ⛃ 🚘 ♨ ✈ Geneva
62km 🚆 Lausanne 1.5km 🚊 2
500m ap Bois de- Vaux 🚊 Metro for
Ouchy 1km ap Station

Leissigen ▲ [CC] "La Nichée" am See,
3706 Leissigen (Bern). 📞 (33) 8471214
FAX (33) 8471497 **Open**: 2.5-22.10
✉ 40 [BB]inc 🍽 👨 ♨ ✈ Bern 37km,
Zürich 157km 🚢 Leissigen 800m
🚆 Leissigen 800m 🚊 Leissigen
800m

Lenzerheide ☞ **Valbella**

Liechtenstein ☞ **Schaan-Vaduz**

Locarno △ [CC] "Palagiovani", Via
Varenna 18, 6600 Locarno, (Ticino).
Open: From 28.3 ✉ 200 [BB]inc 🍽 👨

♿ 👻 ⛃ 🅿 ♿ ♨ ✈ Lugano 30km 🚆
Locarno 500m 🚌 Post Buses 100m
ap Main Station Ⓡ 📞 (1) 3601414;
FAX (1) 3601460

Lugano ▲ Via Cantonale 15, 6942
Savosa (Ticino). 📞 (91) 9662728 **FAX**
(91) 9682363 **Open**: 21.3-30.10 ✉
110 [BB]inc 🍽 ♂ 👨 🅿 ⛃ 🚘 ♨ ✈ Zürich
150km 🚆 Lugano 1.5km 🚌 5 200m
ap Crocifisso

LUGANO

Lucerne △ [2N] [IBN] [CC] am Rotsee,
Sedelstr 12, 6004 Lucerne. 📞 (41)
4208800 **FAX** (41) 4205616 ✉ 194
[BB]inc 🍽 👨 🅿 ⛃ 🚘 ♨ ✈ Zürich 60km
🚆 Luzern 2km 🚌 18 100m
ap Gopplismoos; 1 1km ap Schlossberg

LUCERNE

Maloja △ ⊞ 7516 Maloja (Graubünden). ✆ (81) 8243258 **FAX** (81) 8243571 **Open:** 1.1-13.4; 2.6-12.10; 3-31.12 (Grps from 30.5) ⚑ 90 ᴮᴮⁱⁿᶜ ⏐⚍⏐ ♂ ⏐ᵚⁱᵚ ⏐ 🏠 ⏐🅿 ⏐ 🚣 ⏐ ⛴ ⏐ ✈ Zürich 200km 🚌 St Moritz 16km 🚆 Maloja 200m Ⓡ (YH St. Moritz, Via Surpunt 60, 7500 St. Moritz ✆ (81) 8333969, **FAX** (81) 8338046)

Mariastein- Rotberg ▲ ⊞ Jugendburg, 4115 Mariastein (Solothurn). ✆ (61) 7311049 **FAX** (61) 7312724 **Open:** 1.-5.1; 17.3-31.12 ⚑ 86 ᴮᴮⁱⁿᶜ ⏐⚍⏐ ♂ ⏐ 🏠 ⏐ 🅿 ⏐ ✈ Basel 30km 🚌 Aesch 28km 🚆 Basel-Rotberg 800m 🚋 10 Flüh 2.5km

Melchsee-Frutt ▲ ⊞ Berggasthaus Tannalp, 6068 Melchsee- Frutt (Obwalden). ✆ (41) 6691241 **FAX** (41) 6691147 **Open:** 1.1-19.4; 21.6-19.10; 16-31.12 ⚑ 80 ᴮᴮⁱⁿᶜ ⏐⚍⏐ ⏐ᵚⁱᵚ ⏐ ✈ Zürich 130km 🚌 Sarnen 2km 🚌 Stöckalp + cable car to Melchsee-Frutt then to Tannalp 4km Ⓡ

Montreux-Territet ⚠ ⎙ⁱᵇⁿ⎙ ⊞ 'Haut Lac', Passage de l'auberge 8, 1820 Territet (Vaud). ✆ (21) 9634934 **FAX** (21) 9632729 **Open:** 4.1-22.12 ⚑ 112 ᴮᴮⁱⁿᶜ ⏐⚍⏐ ⏐ᵚⁱᵚ ⏐ ♿ ⏐ 🅿 ⏐ ⛴ ⏐ ✈ Genève 95km 🚢 Port du Territet 750m 🚌 Territet 750m 🚌 Montreux-Villeneuve 200m

Pontresina ▲ ⎙ⁱᵇⁿ⎙ ⊞ 'Tolais', 7504 Pontresina (Graubünden). ✆ (81) 8427223 **FAX** (81) 8427031 **Open:** 1.1-12.4; 13.6-18.10; 19-31.12 ⚑ 117 ᴮᴮⁱⁿᶜ ⏐⚍⏐ ⏐ᵚⁱᵚ ⏐ 🅿 ⏐ 🚣 ⏐ ✈ Zürich 203km 🚌 Pontresina 100m

Rapperswil-Jona ☞ **Jona-Rapperswil**

Rheinfall ☞ **Laufen & Schaffhausen**

Richterswil ▲ ⎙ⁱᵇⁿ⎙ ⊞ Richterswil "Horn", Hornstr 5, 8805 Richterswil (Zürich). ✆ (1) 7862188 **FAX** (1) 7862193 **Open:** 1.3-21.12 ⚑ 80 ᴮᴮⁱⁿᶜ

⏐⚍⏐ ⏐ᵚⁱᵚ ⏐ ♿ ⏐ 🏠 ⏐ 🅿 ⏐ ✈ Zürich 30km 🚢 Lake Zürich 300m 🚌 Richterswil 350m

Romanshorn ▲ Gottfried-Keller-Str 6, 8590 Romanshorn (Thurgau). ✆ (71) 4631717 **FAX** (71) 4611990 **Open:** 16.2-29.10 ⚑ 126 ᴮᴮⁱⁿᶜ ⏐⚍⏐ ⏐ᵚⁱᵚ ⏐ ♿ ⏐ 🏠 ⏐ 🅿 ⏐ ⛴ ⏐ ✈ Zürich 🚢 400m 🚌 Romanshorn 400m

Rorschach (2 Hostels)

Rorschach - YH Rorschach Berg "Im Ebnet" △ Rorschacherberg, 9400 Rorschach (St Gallen) ✆ (71) 8415411 **Open:** Grps only 31.3-29.10 ⚑ 20 ⛴ 🚌 Rorschach 🚌 350m ap JH

Rorschach - YH Rorschach "See" ▲ ⊞ Churerstrasse 4, 9400 Rorschach. ✆ (71) 8449712 **FAX** (71) 8449713 **Open:** 1.4-31.10 ⚑ 32 ᴮᴮⁱⁿᶜ ⏐⚍⏐ ⏐ᵚⁱᵚ ⏐ 🏠 ⏐ 🅿 ⏐ ⛴ ⏐ ✈ Zürich 80km 🚢 Romanshorn 8km 🚌 Rorschach 300m

Saanen-Gstaad ▲ ⎙ⁱᵇⁿ⎙ ⊞ Chalet Rüblihorn, 3792 Saanen (Bern). ✆ (33) 7441343 **FAX** (33) 7445542 **Open:** 1.1-6.4; 16.5-29.10; 6-31.12 ⚑ 80 ᴮᴮⁱⁿᶜ ⏐⚍⏐ ⏐ᵚⁱᵚ ⏐ 🏠 ⏐ 🚣 ⏐ ✈ Genève 158km 🚌 Saanen 800m

St Gallen ▲ ⎙ⁱᵇⁿ⎙ ⊞ Jüchstrasse 25, 9000 St Gallen. ✆ (71) 2454777 **FAX** (71) 2454983 **Open:** 7.3-15.12 ⚑ 104 ᴮᴮⁱⁿᶜ ⏐⚍⏐ ⏐ᵚⁱᵚ ⏐ 🔒 ⏐ 🏠 ⏐ 🅿 ⏐ ✈ Zürich 80km 🚌 St Gallen 1.5km 🚌 1 500m ap Singenberg 🚋 Speicher-Trogenbahn 500m ap Schülerhaus

Sta Maria im Münstertal ▲ ⊞ Chasa Plaz, 7536 Sta Maria im Münstertal (Graubünden). ✆ (81) 8585052 **FAX** (81) 8585496 **Open:** 1.1-31.3; 16.5-26.10; 19-31.12 **Shut:** 10.00-17.00hrs ⚑ 68 ♂ ⏐ᵚⁱᵚ ⏐ 🚣 ⏐ ✈ Zürich 240km 🚌 Zernez 5km 🚌 Sta Maria 350m Ⓡ (✆ (82) 85052)

St Croix ▲ IBN CC 16 rue Centrale, 1450 Ste Croix (Vaud). ☎ (24) 4541810 **FAX** (24) 4544522 **Open:** 1.1-13.4; 25.4-19.10; 27-31.12 ⇌ 64 BB inc ❙❉❙ ☞ ❙❉❙ ▣ ⊞ ⊉ ✈ Genève 92km ⊞⊞ Ste Croix 350m

St Moritz ▲ IBN CC Via Surpunt 60, 7500 St Moritz (Graubünden). ☎ (81) 8333969 **FAX** (81) 8338046 ⇌ 190 BB inc ❙❉❙ (D included in ☺) ❙❉❙ ▣ ⊞ ▣ ⊉ ⚓ ✈ Zürich 200km ⊞⊞ St Moritz 1.7km ⊞⊞ 350m ap Hotel Sonne

Schaan-Vaduz ▲ Untere Rütigasse 6, 9494 Schaan- Vaduz (Fürstentum Liechtenstein). ☎ (75) 2325022 **FAX** (75) 2325856 **Open:** 1.3-30.11 ⇌ 104 BB inc ❙❉❙ ❙❉❙ ⚿ ⊞ ▣ ✈ Zürich 108km ⊞⊞ Buchs 2km ⊞⊞ 5 350m ap Schaan, Mühleholz

Schaffhausen ▲ 1 NW Belair, Randenstr 65, 8200 Schaffhausen. ☎ (52) 6258800 **FAX** (52) 6245954 **Open:** 14.3-31.10 ⇌ 86 BB inc ❙❉❙ ☞ ❙❉❙ ⊞ ⊞ ▣ ✈ Zürich 40km ⊞⊞ Schaffhausen 1.5km ⊞⊞ 3 or 6 (direction Sommerwies) 100m ap Wiesli **R**

Seelisberg ▲ Gnadenhaus Stöck, beim Rütli 6377 Seelisberg (Uri) ☎ (1) 3601414 **FAX** (1) 3601460 **Open:** Grps only 28.3-16.11 ⇌ 25 ⚓ Rütli walking 30 mins, Treib walking 45 mins ⊞⊞ Brunnen

Sils im Domleschg △ Burg Ehrenfels, 7411 Sils im Domleschg (Graubünden) ☎ (81) 6511518 **Open:** Grps only 5.4-27.10 ⇌ 40 ⊞ ⊞⊞ Thusis ⊞⊞ 1km ap Sils **R**

Sion ▲ IBN CC rue de l'Industrie 2, 1950 Sion (Valais). ☎ (27) 3237470 **FAX** (27) 3237438 **Open:** 1-5.1; 17.1-19.10; 19-31.12 ⇌ 80 BB inc ❙❉❙ ☞ ❙❉❙ ⚿ ▣ ⊞ ▣ ✈ Genève 161km ⊞⊞ Sion 350m

Solothurn ▲ IBN CC Landhausquai 23, "Am Land", 4500 Solothurn. ☎ (32) 6231706 **FAX** (32) 6231639 **Open:** 4.1-30.11 ⇌ 92 BB inc ❙❉❙ ❙❉❙ ⚿ ⊞ ⊞ ✈ Zürich 100km ⊞⊞ Solothurn 500m

Stein am Rhein ▲ Niederfeld, Hemishoferstr 87, 8260 Stein am Rhein (Schaffhausen). ☎ (52) 7411255 **FAX** (52) 7415140 **Open:** 8.3-31.10 ⇌ 121 BB inc ❙❉❙ ❙❉❙ ⊞ ▣ ⚓ ✈ Zürich 60km ⚓ 700m ⊞⊞ Stein am Rhein 1.7km ⊞⊞ 350m ap Strandbad **R**

Unterwasser ☞ **Wildhaus**

Vaduz ☞ **Schaan**

Valbella- Lenzerheide ▲ IBN CC Voa Sartons 41, 7077 Valbella-Lenzerheide (Graubünden). ☎ (81) 3841208 **FAX** (81) 3844558 **Open:** 1.1-20.4; 13.6-26.10; 12-31.12 ⇌ 115 BB inc ❙❉❙ ☞ (Su not for Grps) ❙❉❙ ⊞ ▣ ⊉ ✈ Zürich 124km ⊞⊞ Chur + Tiefencastel 2km ⊞⊞ Valbella 1.7km

Vallorbe ▲ CC rue du Simplon 11, 1337 Vallorbe (Vaud). ☎ (21) 8431349 **FAX** (21) 8433249 **Open:** 1.1-20.4; 2.5-26.10; 27-31.12 ⇌ 75 BB inc ❙❉❙ ❙❉❙ ⊞ ▣ ✈ Genève 93km ⊞⊞ Vallorbe 600m

Wildhaus-Unterwasser ▲ IBN CC Befang 73, 9658 Wildhaus (St Gallen). ☎ (71) 9991270 **FAX** (71) 9991201 **Open:** 1.1-31.3; 1.5-31.10; 27-31.12 ⇌ 75 BB inc ❙❉❙ ☞ (not for Grps) ❙❉❙ ▣ ⊞ ▣ ⊉ ✈ Zürich 83km ⊞⊞ Nesslau + Buchs 4km ⊞⊞ Schönau-Wildhaus 900m

Winterthur- Hegi ▲ Schloss Hegi, Hegifeldstr 125, 8409 Winterthur (Zürich). ☎ (52) 2423840 **FAX** (52) 2425830 **Open:** 1.3-31.10 **Shut:** 10.00-14.00hrs; Mon+Fri-17.00hrs ⇌ 48 ☞ ⊞ ▣ ✈ Zürich 19km ⊞⊞ Oberwinterthur 800m ⊞⊞ 1

Oberwinterthur 1km ap Station 🚂 1
Oberwinterthur 1km ap Station ®

Yverdon-les-Bains △ ССС rue du Parc
14, 1400 Yverdon-les-Bains (Vaud). ℆
(24) 4251233 **FAX** (24) 4260096
Open: 1.3-15.12 ⊠ 40 BBinc ⦅ ⁜ ⅏
P ⚓ ✈ Genève 89km 🚃 1km 🚌
Yverdon-les-Bains 700m ®

Zermatt ▲ IBN CCC Winkelmatten,
3920 Zermatt (Wallis). ℆ (27) 9672320
FAX (27) 9675306 **Open:** 1.1-27.4;
6.6-8.11; 12-31.12 ⊠ 138 BBinc ⦅ (D
included in ☺) ⁜ ⦿ ⅏ ⅄ ✈ Genève
234km 🚌 Zermatt 800m 🚌 50m
ap Winkelmatten ®

Zofingen ▲ IBN CCC General
Guisan-Str 10, 4800 Zofingen (Aargau).
℆ (62) 7522303 **FAX** (62) 7522316
Open: 16.3-14.12 **Shut:**
09.30-17.00hrs ⊠ 60 ⦅ ⦆ ⁜ ⅏ P
✈ Zürich 60km 🚌 Zofingen 500m

Zug ▲ IBN CCC Allmendstr 8,
Sportstadion 'Herti', 6300 Zug. ℆ (41)
7115354 **FAX** (41) 7105121 **Open:**
1-26.1; 8.3-31.12 ⊠ 92 BBinc ⦅ ⦆ (use
charge) ⁜ ⅋ ⦿ ⅏ P ⚓ ✈ Zürich-
Kloten 42km 🚌 Zug 800m 🚌 11
+ 6 50m ap Stadion

Zürich- Wollishofen △ 3SW IBN
CCC Mutschellenstr 114, 8038 Zürich.
℆ (1) 4823544 **FAX** (1) 4801727
Open: 24hrs ⊠ 306 BBinc ⦆ ⁜ ⅋ ⦅
⅏ P ⚓ ✈ Zürich 10km 🚌 Zürich
4km 🚃 7 350m ap Morgental

**SUPPLEMENTARY
ACCOMMODATION
OUTSIDE THE ASSURED
STANDARDS SCHEME**

Fällanden 'Im Rohrbuck', Maurstr 33,
8117 Fällanden (Zürich). ℆ (1)
8253144 **FAX** (1) 8255480 **Open:**
Grps only 28.2-7.12 ⊠ 46 BBinc ⦆ ⁜
⅏ P ⚓ ✈ Zürich 19km 🚌 Stettbach
3km 🚌 753 100m ap YH

Langenbruck Haus Rosengarten,
Bärenwilerstr. 10 Postplatz 26, 4438
Langnbruck (BL) ℆ (62) 3901312 **FAX**
(1) 3601460 ⊠ 45 ⦆ 🚌 Waldenburg,
Olten, Balstal 5km 🚌 Langenbruck
500m ® (℆ (1) 3601414)

Safien- Thalkirch 7109 Safien-
Thalkirch (Graubünden). ℆ (81)
6471107 **Open:** 07.30-09.30hrs,
17.00-22.30hrs, Grps 1.1-19.10;
4-31.12 ⊠ 28 ⦆ ⁜ P ✈ Zürich
149km 🚌 Versam- Safien 5km 🚌
Thalkirch 350m ®

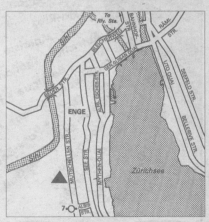

ZÜRICH - WOLLISHOFEN

DORS TRANQUILLE
RÉSERVE À L'AVANCE:
Écosse
Allemagne
Suisse
Australie • Russie
Canada
Nouvelle-Zélande
Afrique du Sud
République d'Irlande
Taïwan • Singapour
Suède • Argentine
Finlande
Portugal • Hongrie
Italie
Indonésie • Kenya
Espagne
Hong-Kong
Japon
Costa-Rica
Malaisie
Autriche • Thaïlande
Belgique • Norvège
République Tchèque • France
Grèce • Pays-Bas
Angleterre et Pays de Galles
Luxembourg
États-Unis d'Amérique
Danemark
Irlande Du Nord
Brésil
Corée du Sud
IBN
Réserve-toi une bonne nuit de sommeil dans les auberges du monde entier…
dans plus de 26 pays
jusqu'à six mois à l'avance
avec confirmation immédiate
HOSTELLING INTERNATIONAL
L'hébergement économique auquel tu peux te fier

FEDERAL REPUBLIC OF YUGOSLAVIA
RÉPUBLIQUE FÉDÉRALE DE YOUGOSLAVIE
BUNDESREPUBLIK JUGOSLAWIENS
REPUBLICA FEDERAL DE YUGOSLAVIA

Ferijalni savez Jugoslavije,
11000 Beograd, Obilićev venac 4/III,
Yugoslavia (Federal Republic of).

☎ (381) (11) 622-956, 622-584
FAX (381) (11) 322-07-62

Office Hours: Monday-Friday 09.00-17.00hrs

Travel Section:

"Mladost-turist" Beograd 11000, Terazije 3.
☎ (381) (11) 3222-131 FAX(381) (11) 3223-352

"Ferijal", 11000 Beograd, Oblićev venac 4/III.
☎ (381) (11) 622-956 FAX(381) (11) 628-733

"Junior", 11070 Novi Beograd, Bulevar Umetnosti 27.
☎ (381) (11) 222-45-56 FAX(381) (11) 144-828

Capital:	Belgrade, 2.000.000
Language:	Serbian
Currency:	Din. (dinar)
Population:	10.406.742

YUGOSLAVIA

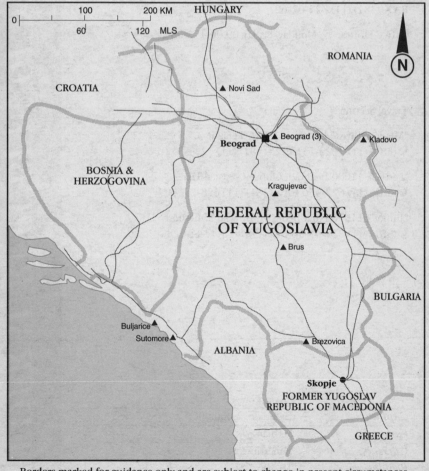

Borders marked for guidance only and are subject to change in present circumstances

ENGLISH

YOUTH HOSTELS IN YUGOSLAVIA

There are 10 Youth Hostels located in cities with many interesting monuments, museums and galleries, along the tourist trail from north-west to south-east, near the Danube river, in the national parks and mountain resort and around the coast. Information about events, festivals, popular attractions, recreation, sport and other facilities is available at Youth Hostels. Most are open 07.00-23.00hrs and there is no limit to the length of stay. Prices vary according to location and facilities, ranging from DEM 10-27 including breakfast. Family rooms are available at many Youth Hostels but it is essential that you book in advance.

PASSPORTS AND VISAS

You will need a valid passport. An entrance visa is necessary for some countries and do check in advance. Visas can be issued in Yugoslav Embassies and Consulates.

HEALTH

Vaccinations are not required. Reciprocal agreements on health care exist between Yugoslavia and certain countries, entitling visitors to treatment on the same basis as Yugoslav citizens. Enquire about obtaining a certificate before you travel. Other visitors are required to pay for treatment but charges are very moderate in most cases.

BANKING HOURS

Monday-Friday 08.00-19.00hrs. Saturday 08.00-15.00hrs. In Belgrade on Sunday there is one bank open 24hrs.

POST OFFICES

Monday-Friday 08.00-19.00hrs. Saturday 08.00-15.00hrs. In Belgrade on Sunday there is one post office open 24hrs.

SHOPPING HOURS

Generally Monday-Friday 08.00-20.00hrs. Saturday 08.00-15.00hrs. In larger cities some shops (drugstores) are open 24hrs.

TRAVEL

Air
It is possible to travel around by air to several places. JAT Jugoslav Airlines run international services linking Belgrade with Adriatic coast and major cities.

Rail
There is a reliable rail network linking the country. Rail travel is a good reasonably inexpensive way to travel.

Bus
An extensive bus network runs between all cities and villages, with frequent departures from Belgrade. Most towns are served with good local services.

Ferry
The ferry line Bar-Bari operates between Yugoslavia and the Italian Adriatic coast.

Driving
Driving is on the right side. All towns are connected with good roads. Car hire is available in bigger towns. Drivers should obtain an international driving licence. International motor insurance (green card) is compulsory. The Automobile and Motorcycle Club has organized service and towing stations along all major thoroughfares. For help and information dial 987.

TELEPHONE INFORMATION

International Code	Country Code	Main City Area Codes	
99	381	Belgrade	11
		Novi Sad	21
		Kruševac	37
		Priština	38
		Podgorica	81
		Bar	82
		Budva	86

FRANÇAIS

AUBERGES DE JEUNESSE EN YOUGOSLAVES

Il y a 10 auberges de jeunesse. Ces auberges sont situées dans des villes comprenant de nombreux monuments intéressants, des musées et des galeries, le long de la route touristique qui va du nord-ouest au sud-est, près du Danube, dans des parcs nationaux et des stations de montagne et le long de la côte.

Des renseignements sur les événements, festivals, attractions populaires, loisirs, sports et autres sont disponibles dans les auberges de jeunesse. La plupart sont ouvertes entre 7.00 et 23.00 heures et la durée de séjour n'est pas limitée.

Les prix, qui varient en fonction de l'emplacement et des installations, vont de 10 à 37 DEM, petit déjeuner compris.

Des chambres familiales sont disponibles dans les auberges de jeunesse mais il est essentiel de réserver à l'avance.

PASSEPORTS ET VISAS

Vous devez avoir un passeport en cours de validité. Un visa d'entrée est nécessaire pour certains pays, vérifiez à l'avance. Des visas peuvent être obtenus dans les ambassades et les consulats yougoslaves.

SOINS MEDICAUX

Aucune vaccination n'est requise. Des accords réciproques de soins médicaux existent entre la Yougoslavie et certains pays, donnant aux visiteurs le droit au traitement sur la même base que les citoyens yougoslaves. Demandez comment obtenir un certificat avant votre départ. D'autres visiteurs doivent payer pour leur traitement mais les frais sont modérés dans la plupart des cas.

HEURES D'OUVERTURE DES BANQUES

Lundi-Vendredi 8h-19h. Samedi 8h-15h A Belgrade le dimanche, vous trouverez une banque ouverte 24 heures sur 24.

BUREAUX DE POSTE

Lundi-Vendredi 8h-19h. Samedi 8h-15h A Belgrade le dimanche, vous trouverez une poste ouverte 24 heures sur 24.

HEURES D'OUVERTURE DES MAGASINS

Habituellement Lundi-Vendredi 8h-20h. Samedi 8h-15h. Dans les plus grandes villes, certains magasins (drugstores) sont ouverts 24h sur 24.

DEPLACEMENTS

Air

Il est possible de voyager par voie aérienne vers plusieurs destinations. JAT Jugoslav Airlines assurent des vols internationaux reliant Belgrade à la côte Adriatique et aux villes principales.

Train

Un réseau ferroviaire fiable couvre le pays. Voyager par train est un bon moyen de voyager raisonnablement bon marché.

Bus

Un réseau d'autobus étendu fonctionne entre tous les villages et les villes avec de fréquents départs de Belgrade. La plupart des villes sont desservies par de bons services locaux.

Ferry

Bar-Bari Ferry Line relie la Yougoslavie et la partie italienne de la côte Adriatique.

Conduire

La conduite est à droite. Toutes les villes sont reliées par de bonnes routes. Il est possible de louer des voitures dans les grandes villes. Les conducteurs doivent avoir un permis de conduire international. L'assurance automobile internationale est obligatoire (carte verte). Le Club Automobile et Motocycliste a organisé un service de dépannage le long des principales routes. Pour recevoir de l'aide ou des informations composer le 987.

TELEPHONE

Indicatif International	Indicatif du Pays	Indicatifs régionaux des Villes principales	
99	381	Belgrade	11
		Novi Sad	21
		Kruševac	37
		Priština	38
		Podgorica	81
		Bar	82
		Budva	86

DEUTSCH

JUGENDHERBERGEN IN JUGOSLAWIEN

Es gibt zehn Jugendherbergen, die sich in Städten mit vielen interessanten Denkmalen, Museen und Galerien befinden. Sie sind entlang der Nordwest/Südost-Touristenroute, entlang der Donau, in Nationalparks und Urlaubsorten im Gebirge sowie an der Küste gelegen.

Informationen bezüglich Veranstaltungen, Festivals, Touristenattraktionen, Freizeitgestaltungsmöglichkeiten, Sport- und anderen Einrichtungen, sind von den Jugendherbergen erhältlich.

Die meisten Herbergen sind von 7.00 bis 23.00 Uhr geöffnet und haben keine Aufenthaltsdauerbegrenzung.

Die Übernachtungspreise sind je nach Örtlichkeit und gebotenen Einrichtungen unterschiedlich, in einer Preislage von 10,00 bis 27,00 DEM einschließlich Frühstück. Viele Jugendherbergen bieten Familienzimmer an, diese müssen jedoch unbedingt im voraus gebucht werden.

PÄSSE UND VISA

Ein gültiger Reisepaß wird benötigt. Für manche Länder ist eine Einreisegenehmigung erforderlich, dies bitte vorher abklären. Einreisegenehmigungen können in jugoslawischen Konsulaten und Landesvertretungen ausgegeben werden.

GESUNDHEIT

Impfungen sind nicht erforderlich. Zwischen Jugoslawien und bestimmten anderen Ländern bestehen gegenseitige Vereinbarungen zur ärztlichen Versorgung, durch die Besuchern dieselbe Versorgung wie jugoslawischen Staatsangehörigen gestattet wird. Vor Reiseantritt muß eine Bescheinigung besorgt werden. Andere Besucher müssen für ärztliche Versorgung privat bezahlen, die Gebühren sind jedoch meist gering.

GESCHÄFTSSTUNDEN DER BANKEN

Montag bis Freitag 8.00 bis 19.00 Uhr. Samstag 8.00 bis 15.00 Uhr. In Belgrad gibt es eine Bank, welche sonntags 24 Stunden geöffnet ist

POSTÄMTER

Montag bis Freitag 8.00 bis 19.00 Uhr. Samstag 8.00 bis 15.00 Uhr. In Belgrad gibt es ein Postamt, welches sonntags 24 Stunden geöffnet ist

LADENÖFFNUNGSZEITEN

Normalerweise Montag bis Freitag 8.00 bis 20.00 Uhr. Samstag 8.00 bis 15.00 Uhr. In größeren Städten sind manche Geschäfte (Drugstores) 24 Stunden geöffnet.

REISEN

Flugzeug
Flugverbindungen bestehen zwischen mehreren Städten. JAT Jugoslav Airlines bieten internationale Verbindungen zwischen Belgrad und der Adriaküste sowie größeren Städten an.

Bahn
Es besteht ein landesweites, verläßliches Bahnnetz. Die Bahn ist eine gute, relativ kostengünstige Reisemöglichkeit.

Bus
Zwischen allen Städten und Dörfern bestehen ausgedehnte Busverbindungen, mit häufigen Abfahrten von Belgrad aus. Die meisten Städte haben gute lokale Busverbindungen.

Fähre
Die Bar-Bari Fährengesellschaft verbindet den jugoslawischen und italienischen Teil der Adriaküste miteinander.

Auto
Es wird rechts gefahren. Alle Städte haben gute Straßenverbindungen. In größeren Städten gibt es Autovermietungen. Autofahrer sollten sich einen internationalen Führerschein besorgen. Internationale Versicherung (Grüne Karte) ist Pflicht. Der Automobil- und Motorradclub hat Notruf- und Abschleppdienste entlang allen Hauptdurchgangsstraßen eingerichtet. Für Hilfe- und Informationsrufe bitte 987 wählen.

FERNSPRECHINFORMATIONEN

Internationale Kennzahl	Landes-Kennzahl	größere Städte - Ortsnetzkennzahlen	
99	381	Belgrade	11
		Novi Sad	21
		Kruševac	37
		Priština	38
		Podgorica	81
		Bar	82
		Budva	86

ESPAÑOL

ALBERGUES DE JUVENTUD YUGOSLAVOS

Existen 10 albergues de juventud situados en ciudades llenas de monumentos, museos y galerías, en la ruta turística que se extiende del noroeste al sureste, cerca del río Danubio, y que incluye parques nacionales y áreas de montaña o costeras.

En los albergues encontrará información sobre acontecimientos, festivales, atracciones populares, recreación, deporte y otras actividades.

La mayoría están abiertos entre 07.00-23.00 hrs y puede hospedarse el tiempo que quiera.

Los precios varían dependiendo de la ubicación y prestaciones, y van de DEM 10 - 27, incluyendo desayuno.

En muchos albergues hay habitaciones familiares, pero es fundamental que reserve.

PASAPORTES Y VISADOS

Necesitará un pasaporte vigente. Los ciudadanos de algunos países requerirán visado, por lo que le recomendamos que verifique por adelantado. Si lo requiere, podrá obtener el visado en las embajadas y consulados yugoslavos.

SANIDAD

No se requieren vacunas. Existen acuerdos sanitarios recíprocos entre Yugoslavia y algunos países, lo que le asegura al visitante que recibirá el mismo tratamiento que los ciudadanos yugoslavos. Solicite información antes de viajar sobre los certificados. Otros visitantes deberán pagar por su tratamiento, pero los precios son muy moderados en la mayoría de los casos.

HORARIO DE BANCOS

De lunes a viernes 08.00-19.00 hrs. Sábados 08.00-15.00 hrs. En Belgrado, los domingos, hay un banco abierto las 24 horas.

OFICINAS DE CORREOS

De lunes a viernes 08.00-19.00 hrs. Sábados 08.00-15.00 hrs. En Belgrado, los domingos, hay una oficina postal abierta las 24 horas.

HORARIO COMERCIAL

En general, las tiendas están abiertas de lunes a viernes 08.00-20.00 hrs y sábados 08.00-15.00 hrs. En las ciudades importantes, algunas tiendas (droguerías) están abiertas las 24 horas.

DESPLAZAMIENTOS

Avión
Es posible llegar en avión a diferentes lugares. JAT Líneas Aéreas Yugoslavas cuentan con servicios internacionales que enlazan Belgrado con la costa del Adriático y ciudades principales.

Tren
Existe una buena red férrea nacional. Los viajes por tren son baratos y razonables.

Autobús
Una extensa red de autobuses une muchas ciudades y pueblos, con salidas frecuentes desde Belgrado. La mayoría de las ciudades cuentan con buenos servicios locales.

Ferry
Bar-bari Ferry Line conecta Yugoslavia con la costa italiana del Adriático.

Coche

Se conduce en el lado derecho. Todas las ciudades están conectadas mediante buenas carreteras. En las ciudades más grandes podrá alquilar un coche. Los conductores deberán poseer un carnet internacional de conducir. Es obligatorio contar con un seguro internacional (carta verde).

El Club de Automóviles y Motos ha organizado estaciones de servicio y remolque a lo largo de las carreteras principales. Para solicitar ayuda e información, marque 987.

INFORMACION TELEFONICA

Código Internacional	Código Nacional	Indicativo de área de las Ciudades principales	
99	381	Belgrado	11
		Novi Sad	21
		Kruševac	37
		Priština	38
		Podgorica	81
		Bar	82
		Budva	86

Hostels in this country may also display this symbol.

Les auberges de ce pays pourront également afficher ce symbole.

Jugendherbergen in diesem Land können auch dieses Symbol zeigen.

Es posible que los albergues de este país exhiban además este símbolo.

BELGRADE (BEOGRAD) (3 Hostels)

Belgrade (Beograd) - "M" Beograd (*see town plan on next page*) 5 SE ⊂⊂▸ Bulevar JNA 56a, Beograd 11000 ☎ (11) 2372560, 2372561 **FAX** (11) 461236 ⚑ 150 ● $19.00 BB inc ⦿ ⋔ ▢ ⬚ P ⚓ ✈ Surčin-Beograd 25km A🚌 Bus Jat 5km ⛟ Belgrade-Glavna Stanica 5km 🚐 47,48 50m 🚐 9,10 100m Ⓡ ('Mladost- turist', Beograd, Terazije 3. ☎ (11) 3222131)

Belgrade (Beograd) - Lipovička Šuma 20 S Lipovica- Barajevo, Beograd. ☎ (11) 8302184 **FAX** (11) 3220762 **Open:** 08.00-23.00hrs ⚑ 40 ● US$10 ⦿ ⋔ ▢ ⬚ P 🚐 571 20km 🚐 12,13 20km

Belgrade (Beograd) - SRC "Pionirski Grad" (*see town plan on next page*) 5 S SRC (Sport and Recreation Centre), "Pionirski Grad" Kneza Višeslava 27, 11000 Belgrade ☎ (11) 542166 **FAX** (11) 559538 **Open:** 07.00-21.00hrs ⚑ 40 ● $7.00 ⦿ ⋔ ⬚ ▢ P ✈ Surčin-Beograd 25km A🚌 Bus Jat 5km ⛟ Belgrade Glavna Stanica 5km 🚐 23,53 50m

Brezovica 0.1 S "Junior Ski Klub", Brezovica Štrpce ☎ (290) 70155, 70162 **FAX** (11) 620437 ⚑ 50 ● $10 BB inc ⦿ ⋔ P ⚲ Alt 900m ✈ Priština 63km ⛟ Uroševac 28km 🚐 Štrpce 300m

Brus 2 SW YH 'Junior' Kopaonik, 37220 Brus. ☎ (37) 833176 **FAX** (37) 833193 **Open:** 24hrs ⚑ 150 ● 16 DEM ⦿

Alt 1100m ® (Travel agency "Junior" ✆ (11) 2224556)

BEOGRAD (BELGRADE) - (a) YGH, (b) SRC

Buljarice 'Toplica', Cara Lazara 49, Prokuplje, Buljarice. ✆ (27) 21035 Open: 1.7-30.8 ⊨ 200

Kladovo [2W] Omladinski Kamp "Djerdap" 19320 Kladovo ✆ (19) 87577, 87983 **FAX** (19) 81394 **Open:** 08.00-21.00hrs, 1.4-30.11 ⊨ 350 ● $10.00 [BB][inc] Tekija 12km Negotin 67km Karataš from Kladovo 100m

Kragujevac YGH, 'Sloboda', Ul Lenjinova 1, Kragujevac. ✆ (34) 63035 ⊨ 60

Novi Sad [3S] YH "Ribnjak" Donji Put 79, Novi Sad ✆ (21) 434846, 25339 **FAX** (21) 52543 **Open:** 09.00-21.00hrs ⊨ 52 ● $7.00 Novi Sad 2km Novi Sad Centar 3km 77, 84 500m ® (FS Novi Sad, Bulevar Mihazla 19, Novi Sad. ✆ (21) 25339)

Sutomore Ljetovalište FS "Bori i Ramiz", Naselje "Gorelac", Sutomore. ✆ (85) 72352 **Open:** 1.7-30.8 ⊨ 100 2km ● Information: (Priština **FAX** (38) 22824)

ASSOCIATE ORGANIZATIONS / ACCREDITED AGENTS

The International Youth Hostel Federation also has Associate Organizations and Accredited Agents in a number of other countries. These are not listed in the main body of the Guide as they do not fulfil the minimum requirements for full membership. In some instances approval has been given for the inclusion of details on their hostel network and/or other relevant information.

Those organizations which are in Europe are as follows:-

ORGANISATIONS ASSOCIEES / ACCREDITEES

La Fédération Internationale des Auberges de Jeunesse a également des organisations associées et des agents accrédités dans un certain nombre d'autres pays qui ne figurent pas sur la liste des pays dans le corps principal du Guide, car elles ne répondent pas aux exigences minimales régissant l'adhésion de membre à part entière. Dans certains cas, l'inclusion des renseignements concernant leurs auberges de jeunesse et/ou d'autres renseignements utiles a été approuvée.

Les organisations en question, en Europe sont les suivantes:-

ASSOZIIERTE / AKKREDITIERTEN ORGANISATIONEN

Der Internationale Jugendherbergsverband steht auch mit assoziierten/akkreditierten Organisationen in verschiedenen anderen Ländern in Verbindung, die jedoch nicht im Hauptverzeichnis angegeben sind, weil sie nicht vollberechtigt Mitgliedsverbände sind. In einigen Fällen konnten jedoch Angaben über JH solcher Verbände sowie andere wesentliche Angaben ins Verzeichnis aufgenommen werden.

Die Organisationen in Europa sind wie folgt:-

ORGANIZACIONES ASOCIADAS / AGENTES ACREDITADOS

La Federación Internacional de Albergues Juveniles (IYHF) también tiene Organizaciones Asociadas y Agentes Acreditados en otros países, pero éstos no se han incluido en la parte principal de la Guía, ya que no cumplen con los requisitos mínimos necesarios para ser miembros de pleno derecho. En algunos casos, se ha aprobado la inclusión de información sobre su red de albergues y/u otra información pertinente.

En Europa, estas organizaciones son las siguientes:

ASSOCIATE ORGANIZATIONS

ESTONIA: *Balti Puhkemajd, Estonian Youth Hostels Association,* Tatari 39-310, EE 0001 Tallinn.
☎ (372) (6) 461455
FAX (372) (6) 461595

LITHUANIA: *Lithuanian Youth Hostels,* PO Box 12, Kauno Str 1A-407, 2000 Vilnius-C.
☎ (370) (2) 262660 FAX (370) (2) 725453

MACEDONIA: *Macedonian Youth Hostel Association,* PO Box 499, Prolet 25, 91000 Skopje.
☎ (389) (91) 239947, 235029
FAX (389) (91) 235029

MALTA: *NSTS,* 220 St. Paul St, Valletta VLT 07.
☎ (356) 244983 FAX (356) 230330

SLOVAK REPUBLIC: *Ubytovne Mladých Na Slovensku (UMS),* Pražská 11, 81636 Bratislava.
☎ (42) (7) 417271, 498672
FAX (42) (7) 494715

ACCREDITED AGENTS

ESTONIA: *Noorte Reisiklubi, (Youth Travel Club)*, 59-234 Mustamae tee, Tallinn EE 0006.
☎ (372) (2) 528427, (372) 6503561
FAX (372) 6503563

LATVIA: *Latvian Youth Hostels Association*, 32-11 Kr. Barona St, Riga LV 1011.
☎ / FAX (371) (7) 217544

RUSSIA: *St Petersburg International Hostel*, PO Box 57, St Petersburg 193312.
☎ (7) (812) 2770569, 3298018
FAX (7) (812) 2775102, 3298019

Blue Chip Travel, Chistoprudny Blvd 12a, Suite 628, 101000 Moscow.
☎ (7) (095) 9169364/65
FAX (7) (095) 9244968

"STAR", 50 Bolshaya Perreyaskavskaya, 10th Floor, Moscow 129041.
☎ (7) (095) 9135952
FAX (7) (095) 2807686

TURKEY: *Gençtur Tourism & Travel Agency Ltd*, Prof K Ismail Gurkan Cad No.14 K.4, Cagaloglu-Sultanahmet, Istanbul.
☎ (90) (212) 5205274/5
FAX (90) (212) 5190864

7-TUR Tourism Ltd, Inonü cad 37/2, Gümüssuyu, Istanbul.
☎ (90) (212) 2525921
FAX (90) (212) 2525924

Yücelt Interyouth Hostel, Caferiye Sok No 6/1, Sultanahmet 34400, Istanbul.
☎ (90) (1) 5136150 FAX (90) (1) 5127628

UKRAINE: *Ukrainian Youth Hostel Association*, (c/o Bofarm), Dr I Fritsky, PO Box 547, 252001 Kiev.
☎ (38) (44) 2213273
FAX (38) (44) 2296946

ESTONIA

(Associate Organization)

Estonian Youth Hostels Association, Tatari 39-310, EE0001 Tallinn.
☎ (372) (6) 461457, **FAX** (372) (6) 461595, **Email:** puhkemajad@online.ee

NOTE: A Visa may be required for entering Estonia which is also valid in Latvia and Lithuania. A Visa is obtainable from an Estonian Embassy.

IBN Booking Centre - for outward bookings
■ **Tallinn** - *via National Office above.*

Gabriel 0.7SW Kallasmaa 3, Maardu. ☎ (2) 233 223 **Open:** 24hrs ⚲ 80 ⦿ ⛄ 🚾 ⬛ ⬚ P ✈ Tallinn 20km ⛴ Tallinn 22km 🚋 Tallinn 23km 🚌 186, 183

Kabli Häädermeeste Vald, Lepanina Suvemajad, Kalbi, Pärnu Maakond EE3634. ☎ (44) 40773 **FAX** (44) 40230 **Open:** 24hrs ⚲ 70 BBinc ⦿ ⬚ ⛄ ✈ Tallinn 185km ⛴ Tallinn 185km 🚋 Pärnu 55km 🚌 from Pärnu 100m ap Kabli

Laulasmaa 41W Keila vald, Harjumaa. ☎ (2) 715 521, 715 542 **FAX** (2) 718 474 **Open:** 24hrs ⚲ 130 BBinc ⦿ ⛄ ⬛ ⬚ P ✈ Tallinn 45km ⛴ Tallinn 42km 🚋 Tallinn 40km 🚌 300m ap Lohusalu

Otepää 1.5W Kastolatsi 3, Otepää. ☎ (76) 55 238 **FAX** (76) 55 238 **Open:** Reception 10.00-20.00hrs ⚲ 25 ⛄ P ⛷ Alt 120m ⛰ ✈ Tallinn 230km ⛴ Tallinn 230km 🚋 Palupea 10km

Pärnu/Aisa 0.3S 【CC】 Aisa 39, Pärnu. ☎ (44) 43 186 **FAX** (44) 43 186 **Open:** 24hrs ⚲ 50 BBinc ⦿ ⛄ ⬚ ⬛ P ✈ Tallinn 126km ⛴ Tallinn 126km 🚋 Pärnu 1km

Pühajarve 3SW Pühajärve puhkekodu, Pühajärve sjk, Valga County. **Open:** 24hrs ⚲ 200 BBinc ⦿ ⛄ ⬛ P ⛷ Alt 90m ⛰ ✈ Tallinn 225km ⛴ Tallinn 225km 🚋 Palupea 10km ⓡ (EYHA Office 2 weeks in advance)

Seedri 2W Seedri 4, Pärnu. **Open:** 24hrs ⚲ 86 ⦿ ⛄ ⬛ ⛰ ✈ Tallinn 126km ⛴ Tallinn 126km 🚋 Pärnu 1.5km ⓡ (EYHA office)

Taevaskoja 6S Taevaskoja puhkemaja, Taevaskoja sjk, Pölva County. ☎ (79) 92 067 **Open:** 24hrs ⚲ 30 ⦿(B) ⛄ ⬚ ⛷ ⛰ ⛰ ✈ Tallinn 215km ⛴ Tallinn 215km 🚋 Teavaskoja 300m 🚌 1.5km ⓡ (EYHA Office 2 weeks in advance)

TALLINN (3 Hostels)

Tallinn - Vikerlase Vikerlase 15, Tallinn EE0036. ☎ (6) 327781 **FAX** (6) 327715 **Open:** 08.00-22.00hrs, Sat 08.00-17.00hrs **Shut:** Sun ⚲ 48 ⦿(B) ⬚ ⛄ ⬚ ✈ Tallinn 5km ⛴ Tallinn 6km 🚋 Tallinn Balti 6km 🚌 25, 51, 500m ap Paternaki ⓡ (2 weeks)

Tallinn - "Merevaik" Söpruse Str 182, Tallinn EE0029. ☎ (2) 529604 ⚲ 70 ⦿ ⛄ ⬛ P ✈ Tallinn 15km ⛴ Tallinn 4km 🚋 Tallinn 4km 🚌 2, 3 100m ap Linnutee ⓡ (EYHA Office)

Tallinn - Mahtra Mahtra 44, Tallinn EE0038. ☎ (2) 218828 **FAX** (2) 586765 **Open:** 24hrs ⚲ 12 ⦿(B D) ⛄ ⬚ ⛄ P ✈ Tallinn 7km A🚌 22 "Lubja" 5km ⛴ Tallinn 8km 🚋 Tallinn Balti 8km 🚌 35,56 100m ap Mahtra ⓡ (EYHA Office)

Treppoja 40W Joa tee 10a, Laulasmaa, Harju County. **Open:** 15.5-15.9 ✉ 90 BBⁱⁿᶜ ⍾ ♦♦♦ 🔲 ⌂ P ♣ ✈ Tallinn 42km 🚢 Tallinn 40km 🚎 Kloogarand 1km 🚌 200m ap Klooga 110 **Ⓡ** (EYHA Office)

Valgerand 7NE Audru Vald, Pärnu County. **Open:** 1.6-31.8 ✉ 250 ⍾ ♦♦♦

🚲 P ♣ ♠ ✈ Tallinn 126km 🚢 Tallinn 126km 🚎 Pärnu 1km 🚌 500m **Ⓡ** (EYHA Office)

Vesiroos 1.8W Esplanaadi 42a, Pärnu. **Open:** 24hrs ✉ 34 BBⁱⁿᶜ ⍾ ♦♦♦ ⌂ P ✈ Tallinn 126km 🚢 Tallinn 126km 🚎 Pärnu 1.4km **Ⓡ** (EYHA Office)

LITHUANIA

(Associate Organization)

Lithuanian Youth Hostels, PO Box 12, Kauno 1A-407, 2000 Vilnius-C.
☎ (370) (2) 262660, **FAX** (370) (2) 725453 **E-mail:** Iyh@jnakv.vno.soros.lt

IBN Booking Centre - for outward bookings
■ Vilnius - Lithuania, *via National Office above.*

Ignalina: Mokyklos str 4, Ignalina. ☎ (370-29) 52118, 52950 **FAX** (370-29) 52293 **Open:** 09.00-23.00hrs ✉ 10 ● US$4.00 ⍾

Šiauliai: Rygos str 36, Šiauliai. ☎ (37021) 427845, 421607 **FAX** (37021) 421607 ✉ 45 ● US$4.00 ⍾(B) ☞

Kaunas: ⒾⒷ⒩ Prancūzų str 59, Kaunas. ☎ (3707) 748972, 742536 **FAX** (3707) 202761 ✉ 17 ● US$10.00 ⍾

Vilnius: YH 'Filaretai' ⒾⒷ⒩ Filaretai str 17, Vilnius. ☎ (3702) 696627, 696946 **FAX** (3702) 220149 **Open:** 06.00-24.00hrs ✉ 80 ● US$ 7.00-9.00 ⍾(B) ☞

MACEDONIA
(former Yugoslav Republic of)

(Associate Organization)

Macedonian Youth Hostel Association, PO Box 499, Prolet 25, 91000 Skopje.
☎ (389) (91) 239947 **FAX** (389) (91) 235029

Ferijalen Dom- Skopje Prolet 25, 91000 Skopje ☎ (91) 115519, 114849 **FAX** (91) 235029 **Open:** 24hrs ✉ 46 ● 18-26 DM BBⁱⁿᶜ ⍾ ♦♦♦ P ✈ Petrovec 17km A🚌 Direction Skopje 500m 🚎 Skopje 500m **Ⓡ** ☎/FAX

MALTA

(Associate Organization)

NSTS, 220 St Paul Street, Valletta VLT 07. ☎ (356) 244983, 246628 **TX** 1626
NSTS **FAX** (356) 230330

IBN Booking Centre - for outward bookings
■ **Valletta** - NSTS, 220 St Paul Street

Bugibba Crystal Hotel, Triq Il-Halel ☎ (356) 573022 **FAX** (356) 571975 **Open:** 24hrs, 1.3-30.11 ⊠ 30 ● MTL 3.55 [BB]inc ⋔ ▣ ⬚ ℗ ⚲ ⚓ ✈ 14km 🚌 49 50m ap Centre ® NSTS

Lija University Residence, Robert Mifsud Bonnici St, Lija. ☎ 436168 **FAX** 434963 **Open:** 24hrs ⊠ 250 ● MTL 3.30-4.95 [BB]inc ⦿(L D) ♂ ⋔ ▣ ⬚ ℗ 🚌 43, 44, 49, 55 from Valletta ap Lija ® NSTS

Rabat YTC bungalow, Buskett, Rabat. ☎ 459445 **Open:** 24hrs ⊠ 30 ● Rent a hostel basis ♂ ⋔ ▣ 🚌 81 from

Valletta ap Verdala Castle Gate ® NSTS (Grps only)

Sliema Hibernia House, Depiro St, Sliema ☎ 333859 **FAX** 230330 **Open:** 24hrs **Shut:** for night arrivals ⊠ 100 ● MTL 2.55-8.50 [BB]inc ♂ ⋔ ▣ ⬚ ℗ 🚌 62, 67, 68 from Valletta ap Plaza Hotel ® NSTS

St Julian's Pinto Guest House, Sacred Heart Ave, St Julians. ☎ 313897 **FAX** 319852 **Open:** 24hrs, 15.3-31.10 ⊠ 30 ● MTL 3.00-4.50 [BB]inc ⋔ ▣ ⬚ ℗ 🚌 60 ap Rudolphe St ® NSTS

RUSSIA

(Accredited Agent)

Russian Youth Hostels, St Petersburg International Hostel, 3rd Sovetskaya Ulitsa 28, St Petersburg 193036, Russia.
☎ (7) (812) 3298018 **FAX** (7) (812) 3298019, ryh@ryh.spb.su

IBN Booking Centres - for outward bookings
■ **Moscow** - Blue Chip Travel Chistoprudny Blvd 12a, Suite 628, 101000 Moscow.
■ **Moscow** - STAR Travel, 50 Bolshaya Pereyaslavskaya, 10 fl., Moscow 129041.
■ **St Petersburg** - Sindbad Trv (RYH), 3rd Sovetskaya Ulitsa 28

Visas
Visa is required. IBN voucher not sufficient to receive visa. Only RYH visa support allows guest to obtain a tourist visa from the Russian Consulate. Consulate requires copy of passport, 3 passport photos and consular fees. In USA-Canada, RYHT processes visa for you. Visa Support is valid for in-transit and reserved hostel dates + 2 weeks to allow more flexibility. We can extend tourist visas for 3 days only. For more information see the Internet WWW - http://www.spb.su/ryh/

Reservations

Fax or e-mail (electronic mail) each guest's full legal name, citizenship, birth date, passport number and expiration date, hostel dates, date of entry/exit - into/from Russia, IBN voucher number OR credit card number (Visa/MC only), cardholder name and expiration date and fax number. Reservation Confirmation and/or Visa Support will be faxed to you the next working day. A non-refundable first night lodging deposit (or IBN booking) + visa support/reservation fee per person/per hostel + fax fee + 4% credit card fee is required for reservation confirmation and/or visa support. If using IBN, visa support and fax fees are payable upon arrival.

International Reservations:

Russian Youth Hostels, (to Russia via Finnish post), PO Box 8, SF-53501, Lappeenranta, Finland. ☎ (7) (812) 3298018 **FAX** (7) (812) 3298019, Bookings ryh@ryh.spb.su

Reservations inside USA and Canada only:

RYHT, 409 N Pacific Coast Hwy, 106/390 Redondo Beach, California 90277, USA. ☎ (1) (310) 3794316 **FAX** (1) (310) 3798420.

Travel Services

Sindbad Travel, 3rd Sovetskaya Ulitsa, 28, St Petersburg 193036, Russia. ☎ (7) (812) 3278384 **FAX** (7) (812) 3298019, sindbad@ryh.spb.su
IBN Booking Centre for hostels in Russia and worldwide; full-service student and youth budget travel agency and discounted air, rail, bus and sea tickets.

St Petersburg [IBN] [CC] St Petersburg International Hostel, 3rd Sovetskaya Ulitsa 28, St Petersburg. ☎ (812) 3298018 **FAX** (812) 3298019 e-mail: ryh@ryh.spb.su 🛏 65 ● US$15.00 [BB]inc ♂♂ 🏠 📠 ⛲ P ✈ Pulkovo II International 20km A🚐 13 to Moskovskaya Metro Station 15km ⛴ Gavan Sea Terminal 10km 🚊 Moscow 300m, Finland 5km 🚃 5,7 100m ap Ploschad Vosstaniya Metro U Line 1 Ploschad Vostaniya 300m

ST. PETERSBURG

OTHER ORGANIZATIONS

International Student Travel Confederation (ISTC)

The ISTC is made up of 5 distinct member Associations, each specializing in aspects of travel-related services for students - air travel, rail passes, travel insurance, work and educational exchange programmes and the International Student Identity Card.

UNESCO - the United Nations Educational Scientific and Cultural Organization - has endorsed the aims and objectives of the ISTC and is a patron of the ISIC.

- The ISIC Association administers the distribution and development of the International Student Identity Card (ISIC) throughout 93 countries worldwide.

- The ISIC provides the only internationally accepted proof of student status; travel and other benefits including thousands of discounts and special prices on a variety of goods and services around the world and gives you access to the ISIC Helpline - a free 24 hour International Travel & Emergency Service. The ISIC is distributed by student travel centres, student unions and many national YHAs.

- The International Student Rail Association (ISRA) is a worldwide Association which meets the challenges arising from ongoing changes in world rail travel. New technology, increased investments by rail authorities and other sociopolitical developments, such as the creation of the European single market, have made rail travel, once again, an attractive option for youth and students.

- The Student Air Travel Association (SATA) is made up of travel organizations that negotiate special fares for students with more than 70 major airlines. The airline tickets, which are only issued by the various SATA organizations, as specially-priced fares for students which have very few restrictions.

- ISIS Travel Insurance is a specially-priced form of travel insurance which is associated with the International Association of Student Insurance Services (IASIS). ISIS is the world's leading low cost insurance for young people and provides direct refund in case of accidents in many countries.

- The International Association for Educational and Work Exchange Programmes (IAEWEP), is a group of organizations that facilitate work exchange programmes between youth, student and educational institutions worldwide.

If you would like to find out more about ISTC and its services please contact: ISTC, Box 9048, DK1000 Copenhagen, Denmark. ☎ (+45) 33939303 FAX (+45) 33937377 *Internet:*http://www.istc.org *E-Mail:*istcinfo@istc.org

FIYTO - Youth Services

The Federation of International Youth Travel Organisations (FIYTO) is an international organization. Since its inception in 1951, the aim of FIYTO has been to promote educational, cultural and social travel among young people. FIYTO Membership is open to many types of organizations, active in the field of youth travel and tourism. Youth travel is widely interpreted to include not only the provision of transportation or accommodation, but also educational, social, cultural and recreational opportunities which include a travel element. Our Members include non-profit and for-profit companies, public and private, retailers, wholesalers, buyers, sellers and suppliers. FIYTO is an open, worldwide, non-political and non-sectarian organization.

The Members include: language schools, travel agencies, accommodation centres, tour operators, adventure travel companies, au pair agencies, transportation providers, hotel groups, homestay organizations, educational travel groups, theme parks, national tourism administrations, student travel bureaux, Youth Hostel Associations and many others.

We have an Annual FIYTO Conference, an integral part of the World Youth and Student Travel Conference (WYSTC). This is the world's largest annual trade fair for bonafide buyers, sellers and suppliers in the youth and student travel industry. The Annual Conference week is seen as a cost effective opportunity to do business and to exchange professional information on youth tourism. Qualified non-Members can participate fully and are entitled to trade at the Conference.

The 1996 WYSTC will be held on Australia's Gold Coast from 29 September to 5 October 1996.

The **GO25 CARD** created by FIYTO in 1975 as the International Youth Travel Card, has become a universally accepted travel document for people of 25 years or younger. It entitles the holder to discounts on travel and accommodation, reduced rates on admission to museums, theatres, sports facilities and cultural events. Particularly the discounts on air and surface transportation and those on accommodation are regarded as key to promoting youth mobility. UNESCO, the United Nations Educational, Scientific and Cultural Organisation, officially endorses and supports the GO25 Card and recognises it as the unique, global document for the advancement of youth mobility.

The **GO25 Card** is sold at Youth and Student Travel Offices and via some Youth Hostel Associations. Information on the issuing office closest to you is available from:

FIYTO, Bredgade 25H, 1260 Copenhagen K, Denmark.

JOURNEY NOTES

TELL US WHAT YOU THINK!

DITES-NOUS CE QUE VOUS EN PENSEZ!
SAGEN SIE UNS IHRE MEINUNG!
¡DIGANOS LO QUE OPINA!

Hostel Name-Address/
Auberge Nom-Adresse/
Jugendherberge
Name-Anschrift/
Albergue Nombre-Dirección

City/Ville/Stadt/Ciudad

Country/*Pays*/Land/*País*

Date(s) stayed/*Dates du séjour/*
Daten des Aufenthaltes/
Fechas de la Estancia

Welcome/*Accueil/*
Aufnahme/*Recibimiento*

Comfort/*Confort/*
Komfort/*Comodidad*

Cleanliness/*Propreté/*
Sauberkeit/*Limpieza*

Security/*Sécurité/*
Sicherheit/*Seguridad*

Privacy/*Intimité, Vie Privée/*
Privatsphäre/*Intimidad, Vida Privada*

COMMENTS/*COMMENTAIRES*/BEMERKUNGEN/*OBSERVACIONES*

Name/*Nom/*
Name/*Nombre*

Address/*Adresse/*
Anschrift/*Dirección*

TELL US WHAT YOU THINK!

DITES-NOUS CE QUE VOUS EN PENSEZ!
SAGEN SIE UNS IHRE MEINUNG!
¡DIGANOS LO QUE OPINA!

Hostel Name-Address/
Auberge Nom-Adresse/
Jugendherberge
Name-Anschrift/
Albergue Nombre-Dirección

City/Ville/Stadt/Ciudad

Country/*Pays*/Land/*País*

Date(s) stayed/*Dates du séjour/*
Daten des Aufenthaltes/
Fechas de la Estancia

Welcome/*Accueil/*
Aufnahme/*Recibimiento*

Comfort/*Confort/*
Komfort/*Comodidad*

Cleanliness/*Propreté/*
Sauberkeit/*Limpieza*

Security/*Sécurité/*
Sicherheit/*Seguridad*

Privacy/*Intimité, Vie Privée/*
Privatsphäre/*Intimidad, Vida Privada*

COMMENTS/*COMMENTAIRES*/BEMERKUNGEN/*OBSERVACIONES*

Name/*Nom/*
Name/*Nombre*

Address/*Adresse/*
Anschrift/*Dirección*

TELL US WHAT YOU THINK!

DITES-NOUS CE QUE VOUS EN PENSEZ!
SAGEN SIE UNS IHRE MEINUNG!
¡DIGANOS LO QUE OPINA!

Hostel Name-Address/
Auberge Nom-Adresse/
Jugendherberge
Name-Anschrift/
Albergue Nombre-Dirección

City/Ville/Stadt/Ciudad

Country/*Pays*/Land/*País*

Date(s) stayed/*Dates du séjour/*
Daten des Aufenthaltes/
Fechas de la Estancia

Welcome/*Accueil/*
Aufnahme/*Recibimiento*

Comfort/*Confort/*
Komfort/*Comodidad*

Cleanliness/*Propreté/*
Sauberkeit/*Limpieza*

Security/*Sécurité/*
Sicherheit/*Seguridad*

Privacy/*Intimité, Vie Privée/*
Privatsphäre/*Intimidad, Vida Privada*

COMMENTS/*COMMENTAIRES*/BEMERKUNGEN/*OBSERVACIONES*

Name/*Nom/*
Name/*Nombre*

Address/*Adresse/*
Anschrift/*Dirección*

We want to hear from YOU....

......help us to implement our assurance of standards at hostels by writing to us or by using the card opposite to tell us what you think of our hostels.

Just tick the boxes to indicate how well the hostel did in the five areas (see page six for more details) and remember to let us have your comments on how you found your stay.

There are additional sheets if you need them which simply need to be put in an envelope and posted to us at the address shown at the foot of this page

NOUS VOUDRIONS CONNAITRE VOTRE OPINION.....

Aidez-nous à mettre en place la garantie de normes dans nos auberges en nous écrivant ou en utilisant la carte ci-contre pour nous faire part de votre opinion sur nos auberges.

Il vous suffira de cocher les cases pour évaluer la performance de l'auberge dans les cinq domaines (reportez-vous à la page 15 pour plus de renseignements) sans oublier de nous faire part de vos commentaires sur votre séjour.

Vous trouverez des coupons supplémentaires si vous en avez besoin qu'il vous suffira de placer dans une enveloppe et de nous envoyer à l'adresse indiquée au bas de cette page.

WIR MÖCHTEN IHRE MEINUNG HÖREN...

Helfen Sie uns unser Asssured Standards Scheme umzusetzen, indem Sie uns schreiben oder die beigelegte Karte ausfüllen, um Ihre Meinung über unsere Jugendherbergen zu erfahren.

Bitte an zutreffender Stelle ankreuzen, um Ihr Urteil über die Jugendhergergen in den fünf verschiedenen Bereichen abzugeben (s. Seite 24 für eine ausführliche Erklärung) und teilen Sie uns mit, wie Ihnen Ihr Aufenthalt gefallen hat.

Wenn nötig sind Ergänzungsblätter vorhanden, die in einem Umschlag an die untenstehende Anschrift zu schicken sind.

QUEREMOS SABER LO QUE USTED OPINA...

...ayúdenos a implementar nuestras normas garantizadas en los albergues. Escríbanos o sírvase de la tarjeta en la página de al lado para decirnos lo que piensa de nuestros albergues.

Marque simplemente las casillas según su opinión del albergue en lo que respecta a los cinco sectores mencionados (véase la página 33 para más información) y no se olvide de decirnos qué le pareció su estancia en el recuadro de las observaciones.

También encontrará un formulario y hoja en blanco adicionales por si los necesita. Introdúzcalos simplemente en un sobre y mándenoslos a la dirección a pie de página.

INTERNATIONAL YOUTH HOSTEL FEDERATION
9 Guessens Road,
WELWYN GARDEN CITY
Hertfordshire AL8 6QW
ENGLAND

TELL US WHAT YOU THINK!

DITES-NOUS CE QUE VOUS EN PENSEZ!
SAGEN SIE UNS IHRE MEINUNG!
¡DIGANOS LO QUE OPINA!

Hostel Name-Address/ *Auberge Nom-Adresse/* Jugendherberge Name-Anschrift/ *Albergue Nombre-Dirección*	
City/Ville/Stadt/Ciudad	
Country/*Pays*/Land/*País*	
Date(s) stayed/*Dates du séjour/* Daten des Aufenthaltes/ *Fechas de la Estancia*	

	😊	🙂	😐	🙁	😞
Welcome/*Accueil/* Aufnahme/*Recibimiento*					
Comfort/*Confort/* Komfort/*Comodidad*					
Cleanliness/*Propreté/* Sauberkeit/*Limpieza*					
Security/*Sécurité/* Sicherheit/*Seguridad*					
Privacy/*Intimité, Vie Privée/* Privatsphäre/*Intimidad, Vida Privada*					

COMMENTS/*COMMENTAIRES*/BEMERKUNGEN/*OBSERVACIONES*

Name/*Nom/* Name/*Nombre*	
Address/*Adresse/* Anschrift/*Dirección*	

INTERNATIONAL YOUTH HOSTEL FEDERATION
9 GUESSENS ROAD
WELWYN GARDEN CITY
HERTFORDSHIRE
AL8 6QW
ENGLAND

STAMP

EXPLANATION OF SIGNS

EXPLICACION DE LOS SIMBOLOS

⛊	Categoría Superior ⎫ Albergues que participan
▲	Categoría Estándar ⎬ en el Plan de Normas
△	Categoría Sencilla ⎭ Garantizadas
2SE	Dirección y distancia aproximada en km. en línea recta desde el centro de la ciudad hasta el albergue.
IBN	Se pueden hacer reservas a través de IBN (véase la introducción principal para más información)
CC	Se aceptan tarjetas de crédito
☎	Número de teléfono
FAX	Número de fax
Open:	Albergue abierto (fechas y horas)
Shut:	Albergue cerrado (fechas y horas)
⇌	Número de camas
●	Precio por noche
BBinc	Desayuno incluido en el precio por noche
⦿|	Se sirven comidas (a menos que se indique lo contrario):
B	Desayuno
L	Comida
D	Cena
♨	Hay cocina para huéspedes/Se cobra por el uso de la cocina
♦♦♦	Hay habitaciones familiares
♿	Instalaciones adecuadas para usuarios con sillas de ruedas
♀ ♠	Sólo para hombres Sólo para mujeres
⌂	Albergue en edificio histórico
①	Albergue situado en una isla
▣	Servicio de lavandería en el Albergue o cerca de él
⛪	Pequeña tienda en el Albergue o cerca de él
P	Aparcamiento en el Albergue o cerca de él
🎿	Albergue para esquiadores
🚲	Alquiler de bicicletas en el Albergue o cerca de él
⚓	Deportes acuáticos en el Albergue o cerca de él
✈	Aeropuerto más cercano
A🚌	Autobús al aeropuerto
🚃	Tren: Estación más cercana y distancia hasta el albergue
🚌	Autobús (desde el centro de la ciudad) Nº, parada y distancia al albergue
🚋	Tranvía o trolebús (desde el centro de la ciudad) Nº, parada y distancia hasta el albergue
⛴	Puerto: Nombre y distancia desde el centro de la ciudad
U	Metro: Nombre de la línea, nombre de la estación y distancia hasta el albergue
● ◇	Parada de autobús o de tranvía
ap	Parada
R	Reserva necesaria o recomendada, o información sobre reservas
Grps	Grupos
Mon Tues	Lunes Martes
Wed Thurs	Miércoles Jueves
Fri Sat Sun	Viernes Sábado Domingo
Ave Hwy Rd St	Avenida Autopista Camino Calle
Su Wi	Verano Invierno